Quantitative analysis for business decisions

IRWIN SERIES IN QUANTITATIVE ANALYSIS FOR BUSINESS

CONSULTING EDITOR   ROBERT B. FETTER   *Yale University*

Quantitative analysis for business decisions

HAROLD BIERMAN, JR.
Nicholas H. Noyes Professor of Business Administration
Graduate School of Business and Public Administration
Cornell University

CHARLES P. BONINI
Associate Professor of Management Science
Graduate School of Business
Stanford University

WARREN H. HAUSMAN
Associate Professor of Management
Graduate School of Management
University of Rochester

 Fourth Edition · 1973

RICHARD D. IRWIN, INC. *Homewood, Illinois 60430*
IRWIN-DORSEY INTERNATIONAL *London, England WC2H 9NJ*
IRWIN-DORSEY LIMITED *Georgetown, Ontario L7G 4B3*

© RICHARD D. IRWIN, INC., 1961, 1965, 1969, and 1973

Fourth Edition

First Printing, April 1973
Second Printing, July 1973
Third Printing, December 1973

ISBN 0-256-00068-9
Library of Congress Catalog Card No. 72–92421
Printed in the United States of America

Preface

The fourth edition of *Quantitative Analysis for Business Decisions* is considerably different from its predecessor. A new chapter dealing with branch and bound has been added. The material covering formulation of linear programming problems has been grouped into a separate chapter. Material on waiting lines and simulation (previously combined in one chapter) is now treated separately, with the simulation chapter expanded to cover risk analysis. The material on inventory control has been simplified, coverage of utility theory and game theory has been revamped, and the chapter on dynamic programming has been expanded. Two previous chapters dealing with optimal sampling with a Bernoulli process have been dropped, as has the appendix dealing with linear algebra and linear programming. Finally, many new problems have been added.

We have attempted to make changes which are consistent with the objectives described in the preface of the first edition. A prime continuing objective has been to make the material understandable to a reader who does not have an extensive mathematical background.

The list of persons who have offered us assistance continues to grow. We want especially to thank the many users of previous editions who bothered to point out errors that we had made and offered suggestions for improving this edition. This assistance is greatly appreciated. Moreover, we particularly want to thank Professor Mildred Massey of the California State College (Los Angeles) and Professor Zeb Vancura of the University of Santa Clara for their comprehensive reviews which were of major help in this revision.

While Lawrence Fouraker and Robert Jaedicke are no longer considered to be authors, we acknowledge that a large percentage of the book carries forward their words and their ideas.

March 1973

HAROLD BIERMAN, JR.
CHARLES P. BONINI
WARREN H. HAUSMAN

Extracts from the preface
to the first edition

The administration of a modern business enterprise has become an enormously complex undertaking. There has been an increasing tendency to turn to quantitative techniques and models as a potential means for solving many of the problems that arise in such an enterprise. The purpose of this book is to describe a representative sample of the models and their related quantitative techniques. It is hoped that this book will serve as a basis for a course which will not encroach upon the established subject matter of functional areas, and that it may act as a connecting force between the mathematical courses on the one hand and the applied business courses on the other.

This is an introductory work in the application of mathematics to problems of business. It is not an introductory work to the mathematics which are being applied. We have summarized—in a rather rough and ready manner by a mathematician's standards—some of the mathematical tools employed. Our purpose is to get our notation and a few basic relationships before the reader rather than to teach him mathematics.

We have attempted to minimize the amount of mathematical training required to read this book. . . . Some previous exposure to probability and statistics would certainly facilitate the reading of many of the chapters, but a reader who does not have formal training in these areas should not think that this book is beyond his ability.

The book is an attempt to consider techniques which treat quite sophisticated and difficult problems; so, even though we tried to choose the simplest means of exposition—avoiding proofs and much of the characteristic rigor of such treatments—the essential subtlety of the techniques remains. These attributes can be understood only by patient application of effort over a protracted period of time. In this connection, we commend the exercises to the reader.

HAROLD BIERMAN, JR.
LAWRENCE E. FOURAKER
ROBERT K. JAEDICKE

Contents

1

Introduction to quantitative analysis

This is a book about business decision making. We consider business decision making to be a process whereby management, when confronted by a problem, selects a specific course of action, or "solution," from a set of possible courses of action. Since there is generally some uncertainty about the future, we cannot be sure of the consequences of the decision that is chosen. The process of making decisions in a business context has the same essential characteristics as problem-solving behavior in general.

BUSINESS DECISIONS

The business manager wants to choose that course of action which is most effective in attaining the goals of the organization. In judging the effectiveness of different possible decisions, we must use some measuring unit. The most commonly used measure in making decisions is dollars, but we shall see in the following chapters that for many decisions the use of dollars in judging the relative merits of different courses of action would not be desirable.

The business manager is faced with a variety of different types of decision situations; but for our purposes, we shall classify decisions as follows:

A. Decisions under certainty (all the facts are known for sure); or uncertainty, where the event that will occur (the state of nature) is not known for sure but probabilities can be assigned to the possible occurrences (in this situation, we can say the process is stochastic).
B. Decisions made for one time period only; or a sequence of interrelated decisions over several time periods (called a *dynamic* decision problem).

1

C.   Decisions where the opponent is nature (drilling an oil well) or a thinking opponent (setting an advertising budget where we have to consider the actions of competitors).

The following general process of solution is common to all types of decision situations:

1.   Establish the criterion which will be used. For example, in a simple situation the criterion may be to choose the act which maximizes the expected profit. In a capital-budgeting decision involving several possible equipment choices, we may choose the equipment with the largest net present value.
2.   Select a set of alternatives for consideration.
3.   Determine the model which will be used and the values of the parameter of the process. For example, we may decide that the algebraic expression of the model of total expenses is:

$$\text{Total expenses} = a + b \text{ units sold}$$

The parameters are a and b, and their value would have to be determined in order to use the model.
4.   Determine which alternative optimizes (i.e., is consistent with) the criterion established above in item 1.

Example

We can sell 1,000 units of product to the government at a price of $50 per unit. Should the order be accepted? The firm has excess capacity.

1.   We shall use the profit maximization criterion.
2.   The alternatives are to (a) accept the order or (b) reject the order. In accordance with our profit criterion, we shall accept the order if it increases profit, reject the order if it does not increase profit.
3.   We need to know the incremental expenses of producing the 1,000 units. The relevant expense model is:

$$E = a + 1{,}000b$$

Assume that special dies costing $5,000 will have to be bought (a is equal to $5,000) and that the variable costs of producing a unit are $30 ($b$ is equal to $30). The total relevant expenses of filling the order are $35,000 (equal to $5,000 plus $30,000).
4.   A comparison of the incremental revenues, $50,000, and incremental expenses indicates we should accept the order. Profit will be greater

by \$15,000 if we "accept" compared with the alternative "refuse the order."

In the above example, we used basic knowledge and simple computational techniques. However, in dealing with more complex problems, we might need to use other tools of quantitative analysis, including calculus, probability, statistics, and programming (linear, nonlinear, and dynamic).

We shall now consider some aspects of model building.

ABSTRACTION

Real-world problems tend to be enormously complex. There are literally an uncountable number of inherent "facts" in any empirical situation. Further, every potential course of action starts a chain of cause, effect, and interaction that logically is without end.

Consider the problem of constructing a building. An endless amount of time could be devoted to gathering factual information about this situation: for example, the precise location and physical characteristics of the building; a detailed study of the climatic conditions of the potential sites and the influence these will have on construction costs; the sources of the funds used and their cost. Most importantly, the decision maker might decide that he must consider specifically and in detail all potential uses of the funds in this period and in future periods. If our decision maker adopts a strategy of collecting *all* the facts before he acts, it follows that he will never act. The human mind cannot consider every aspect of an empirical problem. Some attributes of the problem must be ignored if a decision is to be made. The decision maker must abstract from the empirical situation those factors which he considers to be most relevant to the problem he faces. Abstraction is the first and a necessary step in the solution of any human problem.

MODEL BUILDING

After the decision maker has selected the critical factors, or variables, from the empirical situation, he combines them in some logical manner so that they form a counterpart or model of the empirical problem. A model is a simplified representation of an empirical situation. Ideally, it strips a natural phenomenon of its bewildering complexity and duplicates the essential behavior of the natural phenomenon with a few variables, simply related. The simpler the model, the better for the decision maker, provided the model serves as a reasonably reliable counterpart of the empirical problem. The advantages of a simple model are:

1. It is economical of time and thought.
2. It can be understood readily by the decision maker.
3. If necessary, the model can be modified quickly and effectively.

The object of the decision maker is not to construct a model that is as close as possible to reality in every respect. Such a model would require an infinite length of time to construct, and then it might be beyond human comprehension. Rather, the decision maker wants the simplest model that predicts outcomes reasonably well and is consistent with effective action on his part.

SOLUTIONS

After the model has been constructed, certain conclusions may be derived about its behavior by means of logical analysis. The decision maker then bases his action or solution on these conclusions. If the logic in deriving the conclusions from the abstracted variables is correct, and if the relevant variables have been abstracted, then the solution to the model problem will also serve as an effective solution for the empirical problem. From our example, the decision maker may decide that an interest rate of 8 percent measures the annual opportunity cost of money for his firm. He can make his decision on construction of the building by computing the present value of the cash flows, and he would not have to consider alternative investments in detail.

ERRORS

There are two general sources of error in decision making. The first is a mistake in logic in the process of reasoning from premises to conclusions to solutions. The firm may be able to obtain funds at a cost of 8 percent, but management may have decided not to obtain new capital. The premise that one can use an interest rate to represent an opportunity cost is valid, but the conclusion that the use of this discount rate applies to all investments is in error.

Secondly, the decision maker may select the wrong variables, or not enough variables, for constructing his model. The decision maker has considered the time value of money, but he has not considered risk elements. The possibility of errors of this type cannot always be avoided, for to do so would require that all conceivably pertinent variables be included in the model, and this would preclude decisive action. Abstraction always does some violence to reality, but it is a necessary condition for problem solving. This is one reason decision making carries with it the possibility of error.

MODEL-BUILDING TECHNIQUES

Models may be represented in a variety of ways. For simple, repetitive problems the entire decision-making process may take place in the mind of the decision maker, perhaps in a quite informal, intuitive manner. We walk, eat, and open doors everyday without the aid of a formal model of the related problems our actions are resolving. If the problem is somewhat more unusual or complex, we spend more time thinking about it. We may be explicit to the extent of selecting the important elements of the problem and proceeding to examine and experiment with them.

The appropriate technique for describing and relating selected variables depends to a large extent on the nature of the variables. If the variables are subject to measurement of some form, and particularly if they can be given a quantitative representation, then there are strong reasons for selecting a mathematical representation of the model. First, there is a rigorous inherent discipline in mathematics which insures a certain orderly procedure on the part of the investigator: You must be specific about what variables you have abstracted and what relationships you are assuming to exist among them. For example, it is more difficult to make implicit assumptions in a mathematical model than in a literary model. Secondly, mathematics is a powerful technique for relating variables and for deriving logical conclusions from given premises. Mathematics makes it possible to handle problems which require models of great complexity and it facilitates the decision-making process where quantitative analysis is applicable.

In the relatively recent past (since World War II) a large number of business problems have been given a quantitative representation with some degree of success, leading to a general approach which has been designated as operations research. Of course, the quantitative representation and resolution of business problems is much older than the term *operations research*—witness the practice of accounting. However, quantitative analysis has been extended to many other areas of the business firm's operations and in some cases has become established as the most effective way of approaching certain business decision problems. Today's businessman has to be as knowledgeable about these techniques and models as he is about accounting reports.

A further word of caution may be in order. The business executive should never become the captive of a quantitative model and automatically adopt its conclusions as his business decision. The conclusion derived from the model contains some degree of error because of the abstraction process. The question of when the error becomes so large that the conclusion must be modified before it can be adopted as a solution is one of judgment. Operations research is an aid to business judgment and not a substitute for it. A certain amount of constructive skepticism is as desirable in considering quantitative analysis of business problems as it is in any other decision-making process. Further, there are many significant business problems which cannot be given a simple, appropriate quantitative representation, and the decision maker must rely upon qualitative models and solutions.

Within the constraints of these qualifications, quantitative analysis can become an extremely productive technique for managerial decision making. Problems which would confound the intuition of the most experienced executive may, on occasion, be resolved with relative ease.

DECISIONS AND PROBABILITY

Business decisions are made in one of two essentially different contexts—under conditions approaching certainty and, more generally, under conditions of uncertainty. The quantitative analysis which supports decision making under certainty usually takes the form of maximizing some objective (say profit or production) subject to constraints (say productive capacity).

In a previous example, we compared the alternatives "accept the order" and "refuse the order" on a 1,000-unit government contract. This was a decision under conditions of certainty. We compared the two alternatives; and since the profit was $15,000 greater for accepting the order, we chose that alternative.

Suppose, however, that we change the above situation slightly. We shall market our product at a price of $50 per unit. And as before, our expenses for producing X units are:

$$E = a + bX$$
$$= 5,000 + 30X$$

But now we are uncertain about the actual level of sales. Sales may be 100 units, 250 units, or 1,000 units, and we are not sure which level will actually materialize. Our alternatives are (1) to market the product and accept whatever profit or loss materializes, or (2) to reject the whole project and obtain zero profit. Assume that the $5,000 of fixed costs are incurred before we know the actual demand, but that the units can be produced after the demand is known (thus, there is no inventory problem).

Let us compute the profit for each level of sales if we market the product (see Table 1–1).

TABLE 1–1

States of nature: sales (units)	Consequences: profit
100.	–$ 3,000
250.	0
1,000.	15,000

Even though we have clearly enumerated the alternatives and their consequences, the decision is not obvious. The best alternative depends upon how "likely" each sales level may be. If we were certain that sales would be 1,000 units, we should market the product. If sales were to be only 100 units for sure, we should reject the whole project and avoid a loss of $3,000. If sales were 250 units, we would be indifferent as to which alternative is selected.

When the true state of nature is unknown, the decision maker has to act with imperfect information. There are several possible decision-making procedures, and we shall investigate some of the more interesting techniques later in this book. However, at this point, we shall introduce the Bayes decision rule. This is an orderly and consistent technique which can be extremely useful for business decision making. The decision maker performs the following calculations for each possible act (or decision) which is feasible:

1. Lists the set of possible outcomes that the state of nature may take on for the period (or periods) in question.
2. Assigns a probability weight to each of the possible states of nature. The probabilities may be subjective weights, though objective information should be incorporated if it is available.[1]
3. Computes for each state of nature the consequences of the given act. The consequences in certain cases may be in terms of dollars but are more generally in terms of a measure which is called utility, and which incorporates psychological reactions to the monetary gains or losses.
4. Multiplies for a specific act the probability of each state of nature by the consequences of that act and state, and sums these products for all the possible states. This sum is the expected value of the act.

These computations should be made for each possible act. That decision with the highest expected value is the Bayes solution; and following this

---

[1] Some persons object to saying that there is a probability p of x units of sales when there will be only one trial; in addition, not all observers would agree that the probability is p because of the lack of objective evidence.

criterion, it would be the decision which would be taken. While the Bayes decision rule can be used with objective as well as subjective probabilities, generally in business or governmental decision making, objective probabilities are not available.

Steps 1 and 3 in the above process have already been done—we have listed the states of nature (possible sales levels) and the profits associated with each.

Let us suppose that our decision maker feels that there are two chances out of five that the sales level will be 100 units (i.e., a probability of 0.40 is assigned to this state of nature); two chances out of five that sales will be 250 units (again a probability of 0.40); and one chance out of five that sales will be 1,000 units (a probability of 0.20).

With these probabilities, we can compute a weighted average or expected profit for marketing the product (see Table 1–2).

TABLE 1–2

Sales (units)	Probability (weight)	Profit	Probability X profit
100	0.40	−$ 3,000	−$1,200
250	0.40	0	0
1,000	0.20	15,000	3,000
	1.00		$1,800

The expected profit or expected monetary value for marketing the product is $1,800, compared to zero for rejecting the project. Hence, using the Bayes decision rule, we would proceed to market the product (this conclusion assumes that the consequences measured in dollars also measure utility).

Note that if sales actually amount to 100 units, the decision maker, after the fact, has incurred a loss of $3,000 that he might have avoided had he had more precise information about future sales.

In some situations, one possible course of action would be for the decision maker to gather additional information rather than make the basic decision now. The original probabilities (called prior probabilities) would then be revised in the light of that information, and the decision process would be repeated using the new probability measures, with the next step being a final decision or the gathering of additional information.

It should be noted that personal feelings and judgment come into the decision process at three levels. First, they affect the choices of the probabilities which are assigned to the possible states of nature. These may be subjective estimates. Second, personal feelings may affect the measures of the consequences which will result from a specific state of nature occurring with a given act. Last, they affect the choice of the objective or the decision criterion. The Bayes decision criterion is a valuable tool, but there is by no means unanimous opinion in the academic and business communities relative to its superiority. Its prime advantage is that it helps the decision maker to act consistently with his feelings about the likelihood of the states and the consequences associated with each state and act.

CONCLUSION

Decision making under uncertainty requires that the decision maker use his judgment and experience about future events. He must ascertain which outcomes are more "likely" than others and combine this knowledge with the consequences associated with the various decisions. Such a process lies behind the familiar willingness to "take a calculated risk."

The Bayes decision process that we have described is merely a logical way of bringing both the decision maker's judgment and the economic consequences of a given action to bear upon the decision. Implicit in any reasonable intuitive strategy that one may devise for action under uncertainty is a probability distribution about possible outcomes.

Some mathematicians do not think that "probabilities" should be based upon subjective intuition. They argue that only objective probabilities for repetitive events have any true meaning. However, in the real world, such objective probabilities are frequently not available—and decisions must be made upon the best available information. Thus even in the absence of objective probabilities the authors feel that the Bayes decision process is a logical procedure to apply to business decision making.

BIBLIOGRAPHY

BAUMOL, W. J. *Economic Theory and Operations Analysis.* 3d ed. Englewood Cliffs, N.J.: Prentice-Hall, Inc., 1972.

BROSS, I. D. J. *Design for Decision.* New York: Macmillan Co., 1953.

HERTZ, D. B. *New Power for Management.* New York: McGraw-Hill Book Co., 1969.

MILLER, D. W., and STARR, M. K. *Executive Decisions and Operations Research.* 2d ed. Englewood Cliffs, N.J.: Prentice-Hall, Inc., 1969.

PRATT, J. W.; RAIFFA, H.; and SCHLAIFER, R. "The Foundations of Decision under Uncertainty: An Elementary Exposition," *Journal of the American Statistical Association,* June 1964, pp. 353–75.

RAIFFA, H. *Decision Analysis*. Reading, Mass.: Addison-Wesley Publishing Co., 1968.

SAVAGE, L. J. *The Foundations of Statistics*. New York: John Wiley & Sons, Inc., 1954.

SCHLAIFER, R. *Analysis of Decisions under Uncertainty*. New York: Mc-Graw-Hill Book Co., 1969.

WAGNER, H. M. *Principles of Operations Research*. Englewood Cliffs, N.J.: Prentice-Hall, Inc., 1969.

QUESTIONS AND PROBLEMS

1–1. Setting the price of a product is a very important business decision. What are elements of uncertainty in the decision to change the price of a product?

1–2. In what sense are there "opponents" when a price is set for a product?

1–3. A family is planning a picnic. In what sense is nature the opponent? Is it reasonable to use probabilities to describe the likelihood of the different states of nature?

1–4. Profit maximization has sometimes been described as the prime criterion to be applied in business decision making. If you were a business manager, what additional criteria would you employ in your decision making?

1–5. A possible model of total expenses is:

$$T = a + bX$$

where

T = total costs
a = fixed costs
b = variable costs
X = number of units

Discuss the adequacy of this model as a predictor of the total costs associated with a given output.

1–6. Assume we know the fixed costs to be \$10,000 but there is a probability distribution associated with variable costs. Because of a pending labor contract the variable costs for one unit may be \$0.90, \$1.00, or \$1.10, with probabilities 0.4, 0.5, and 0.1. Compute the expected cost for 5,000 units.

1–7. Mr. Jones presently owns a common stock which is selling on the market for \$100 a share. Describe how the subjective feelings of Mr. Jones would enter into the decision to hold the stock or to sell.

1–8. You have an opportunity to engage in an "investment" which costs

$1 and which has the following cash payoffs for the possible states of nature:

State of nature	Probability of state	Cash payoffs
Rain................	0.2	-$0.50
Cloudy	0.5	1.00
Clear...............	0.3	2.50

Is the investment desirable? Following your recommendation, are you certain of the outcome?

1-9.   The Crude Oil Company is considering drilling for oil on property it leases. Is it reasonable to specify a probability of finding oil?

1-10. You are a poultry exporter. The federal government has offered you a contract to supply American military establishments abroad at a price of 31 cents per pound. The contract would absorb your total annual production. Your alternative market is Europe, where the price you can receive is 50 cents per pound, less tariff. Representatives of France and the United States are now negotiating the European tariff level for poultry. In your judgment, there are four possible levels, with the following subjective probabilities:

Possible tariff	Probability
$0.10........................	0.1
0.15........................	0.2
0.20........................	0.3
0.25........................	0.4

What decision would you make?

1-11. Consider some business or personal decision with which you are familiar. Describe this decision in terms of:
  a) The alternatives that are available.
  b) The criterion that you would use to select among the alternatives.
  c) The important variables that should go into a model to aid in making this decision. To what extent can you quantify these variables?
  d) To what extent can you quantify the relationships among the variables suggested in (c)?

1-12. Assume you are given two different job offers upon receiving your degree. What factors will affect your job decision? If you could "buy" probabilities of different future events happening, would you do so even if, after the purchase of the information, you still did not know what event was going to happen?

1-13. Many businessmen do not understand model building and decision making under uncertainty as defined in this book. However, it is not uncommon for a firm with one very important executive to insure his life. Why would a firm act in this manner?

1-14. New York City has been troubled for years with a shortage of electric power. Recently the electric company purchased one extremely large generator named "Big Allis." The primary consideration was that the expected cost per unit of power was to be less than with several smaller generators. Discuss this decision. What are the relevant considerations?

1-15. An executive is in the process of deciding on the price for a new product. He decides that his goal is to maximize profit. The alternatives are different possible prices from $2 per unit to $10 per unit. He uses the model described below:

Let
$$x = \text{number of units produced (and sold)}$$
$$C(x) = \text{total cost of producing } x \text{ units}$$
$$p = \text{price to be charged}$$
$$NP = \text{total net profit (to be maximized)}$$

Cost relationship: $C(x) = 800 + 1.25x$

Sales relationship: $x = -100 + \dfrac{2000}{p}$

Profit: $NP = p \cdot x - C(x)$

a) Comment on the model chosen by the executive in terms of the reasonableness of the relationships, the variables that were chosen (and ones left out), and the value of the model.

b) Find an approximate solution to the model by trial and error, (i.e., try several values of price between $2 and $10, and try to find a price that gives a good profit).

1-16. A salesman must catch a plane to be on time for an important sales call. The sales call is expected to produce a profit of $2,000. The salesman must choose one of three ways to reach the airport, each with a cost and a probability of being late estimated as follows:

Choice	Cost	Probability of being late
Airport bus	$ 2.00	0.20
Hotel limousine	7.00	0.05
Taxi	14.00	0.01

Compute the expected net profit (profit less cost) of each of the possible choices. Which choice produces the maximum expected net profit?

1–17. A firm needs temporary business space. It can rent the desired space for $6,000 for one year or for $10,000 for two years. If it rents for one year only and then decides to rent another year, the second year will cost $6,000 also. If it rents for two years but departs after one year, it cannot sublet. The firm estimates that there is an 80 percent chance that it will stay two years and a 20 percent chance it will depart after one year. Should it rent for one year or two? Why?

1–18. A proposed new product will cost either $10 per unit with 0.3 probability or $25 per unit (with 0.7 probability). Sales price will be determined by worldwide economic conditions and will be either $20 (0.6 probability) or $30 (0.4 probability). Should the firm market the product? Why?

2

A survey of probability concepts

If all business decisions could be made under conditions of certainty, the only valid justification for a poor decision would be failure to consider all the pertinent facts. In this context, "conditions of certainty" means an ability to make a *perfect* forecast of the future. Unfortunately, however, the businessman rarely if ever operates in a world of certainty. Usually, the businessman is forced to make decisions when he is very uncertain as to what will happen after the decisions are made. In this latter situation the mathematical theory of probability furnishes a tool which can be of great help to the decision maker.

The mathematical theory of probability is rigorous and well defined, and the reader is referred to books on mathematics treating the subject (see the end of the chapter for several references). In this chapter, we shall present some of the notation and basic relationships of probability which the reader will have to apply in later chapters. While the mathematics of probability is well defined, it will soon become obvious to the person attempting to apply the models of this book that there is a great deal of uncertainty concerning the informational inputs that are required. Also, many of the models abstract from the complexities of the real world.

OBJECTIVE AND SUBJECTIVE PROBABILITIES

Most of us are familiar with the laws of chance regarding coin flipping. If someone asks about the probability of a head on one toss of a coin, the answer will be one half, or 0.50. This answer assumes that the coin is a *fair* coin and that it is "fairly" tossed. If the coin is bent or weighted, or is two-tailed, the answer to this question will be quite different. Assume there is a large amount of common experience regarding the tossing of a specific coin and everyone agrees the coin is fair; that is, the head or tail has proven to be "equally likely" in a large number of trials. The *relative frequency* interpretation of probabilities indicates that when historical experience of fairness is available and if someone flips a coin one million times, the expected number of heads (i.e., the average number) is 500,000, or 0.50 × 1,000,000.

In this example, a 0.50 probability of heads is assumed to be an *objective* probability. Where did we obtain the 0.50 objective probability used in the above example? The relative frequency interpretation of probabilities makes use of available historical experience.

For example, assume a coin is tossed fairly 10,000 times and 4,998 heads appear. From this evidence, we may conclude that the probability of a head is close to 0.50, and we could use this information in forecasting what will happen with additional tosses. Assume the coin is now tossed twice more. The probabilities of the different possible outcomes resulting from two additional tosses are shown in Table 2–1.

TABLE 2–1

Number of heads	Probability
0	¼
1	½
2	¼
3 or more	0

Table 2–1 was prepared using the objective probability of 0.50 for the probability of a head. Although there is a 0.50 probability of one and only one head appearing in two tosses, and one head is our best guess, there is also a 0.50 probability that some other number of heads will appear. If we toss the coin in the same manner for an additional one million tosses, the probability of 500,000 heads will be very small (since the number of heads could well be 500,001 or 499,999 or 499,998, etc.), but 500,000 heads will still be the expected or average number of heads.

A *subjective* interpretation of probabilities is often useful for business decision making. In the case of objective probability, definitive historical information, common experience (objective evidence), or rigorous analysis lie behind the probability assignment. In the case of the subjective interpretation, historical information may not be available; and instead of objective evidence, personal experience becomes the basis of the probability assignment. For business decision-making purposes the subjective interpretation is frequently required, since reliable objective evidence may not be available.

Let us illustrate the contrast by an example. Suppose we have a box containing three red and seven black balls. If the balls are mixed thoroughly and if they all feel the same, we would assign an objective probability of 0.30 of drawing a red ball and 0.70 of drawing a black ball. As in the coin example, we could get general agreement on these probabilities, since they are based on reliable objective evidence.

In contrast to the above situation, assume a businessman is trying to decide whether or not to buy a new factory and the success of the factory depends largely on whether or not there is a recession in the next five years. If a probability is assigned to the occurrence of a recession, it would be a subjective weight. A long history and common experience, which can be projected into the future with confidence, are not directly available, as in the coin or ball problems. However, it may be appropriate, and indeed necessary, to consider the event "occurrence of a recession"; and after gathering evidence and using his business judgment, the businessman may be able to assign a probability to that event that he is willing to use for his decision-making purposes. There would certainly be less agreement on this probability than there would be on the probabilities of drawing a red ball, or a fair coin coming up heads, in the previous examples. Since we are primarily concerned in this book with business decisions, we shall often assign subjective probabilities to events which have a critical bearing on the business decision; this device aims to assure consistency between a decision maker's judgment about the likelihood of the possible states of nature and his actions.

One important objective of the suggested decision process is to force the decision maker to think in terms of the possible events that may occur after a decision, the consequences of these events, and the probabilities of these events and consequences, rather than having the manager jump immediately to the question of whether or not the decision is desirable.

BASIC STATEMENTS OF PROBABILITY

Two of the fundamental statements of the mathematical theory of probability are:

1. Probabilities of the various possible mutually exclusive and exhaustive states of a trial must sum to one.
2. Probabilities are always greater than or equal to zero (i.e., probabilities are never negative) and are equal to or less than one. The "equal to or less than one" requirement follows from the first property. The smaller the probability, the less likely the event.

The first statement of probability theory indicates that if A and B are the only candidates for an office, the probability that A will win plus the probability that B will win must sum to one (assuming a tie is not possible).

The second statement described above results in the following interpretations. If an event has a positive probability, it may possibly occur; the event may be impossible, in which case it has a zero probability; or the event may be certain to occur, in which case the probability is equal to one. Regardless of whether probabilities are interpreted as objective probabilities or as subjective weights, it is useful to think in terms of a weight scale running from zero to one. If someone tosses a coin 500 times to obtain an estimate of objective probabilities and the results are 225 heads and 275 tails, the range of possible results may be converted to a zero-to-one scale by dividing by 500, i.e., $\frac{0}{500} = 0$ and $\frac{500}{500} = 1$. The actual results are $\frac{225}{500} = 0.45$ heads and $\frac{275}{500} = 0.55$ tails. Hence, if we wish to derive probabilities, we shall manipulate the data so as to adhere to the zero-to-one scale. The 0.45 and the 0.55 may be used as estimators of the true probabilities of heads and tails (which are unknown).

MUTUALLY EXCLUSIVE EVENTS

If we have a set of mutually exclusive events (only one of the events can occur on any one trial), the probabilities of these events can be added to obtain the probability that at least one of a given collection of the events will occur.

Example

The probabilities shown in Table 2-2 reflect the subjective estimate of an editor regarding the relative chances of four candidates for a public office (assume a tie is not possible).

TABLE 2-2

Event: elect	Probability
Democratic candidate A	0.18
Democratic candidate B	0.12
Republican candidate C	0.56
Republican candidate D	0.14
	1.00

These events are mutually exclusive, since in one election (or in one trial) only one event may occur; therefore the probabilities are additive. The probability of a Democratic victory is 0.30; of a Republican victory, 0.70; or of either B or C winning, 0.68. The probability of both B and C winning is zero, since only one of the mutually exclusive events can occur on any one trial.

INDEPENDENT EVENTS

Events may be either independent or dependent. If two events are (statistically) independent, the occurrence of the one event will not affect the probability of the occurrence of the second event.[1]

When two (or more) events are independent, the probability of both events (or more than two events) occurring is equal to the product of the probabilities of the individual events. That is:

(2–1) $$P(AB) = P(A) \cdot P(B)$$

where

$P(A)$ = probability of event A
$P(B)$ = probability of event B
$P(AB)$ = probability of events A and B both occurring

Equation (2–1) indicates that the probability of A and B occurring is equal to the probability of A times the probability of B, if A and B are independent. If A is the probability of a head on the first toss of the coin and B is the probability of a head on the second toss of the coin, then:

$$P(A) = \tfrac{1}{2}$$
$$P(B) = \tfrac{1}{2}$$
$$P(AB) = \tfrac{1}{2} \cdot \tfrac{1}{2} = \tfrac{1}{4}$$

The probability of A and then B occurring (two heads) is one fourth. $P(AB)$ is the *joint probability* of events A and B.

Further, to define independence mathematically, we need another symbol:

$P(B|A)$—This symbol is read "the probability of event B, given that event A has occurred." $P(B|A)$ is the *conditional* probability of event B, given that event A has taken place. Note that

---

[1] Statistical independence or dependence is to be distinguished from causal independence or dependence. Simply because two events are statistically dependent upon each other does not imply that one is caused by the other. Whenever we use the terms *dependence* or *independence*, statistical dependence or independence will be meant.

$P(B|A)$ does not mean the probability of event B divided by A—the vertical line followed by A means "given that event A has occurred."

With independent events:

(2–2) $P(B|A) = P(B)$

That is, the probability of event B, given that event A has occurred, is equal to the probability of event B if the two events are independent. With two independent events, the occurrence of the one event does not affect the probability of the occurrence of the second [in like manner, $P(A|B) = P(A)$]. Equations (2–1) and (2–2) are the basic definitions of independence between two events.

DEPENDENT EVENTS

Two events are dependent if the occurrence of one of the events affects the probability of the occurrence of the second event.

Example: Dependent events

Flip a fair coin and determine whether the result is heads or tails. If heads, flip the coin again. If tails, flip an unfair coin which has a three-fourths probability of heads and a one-fourth probability of tails. Is the probability of heads on the second toss in any way affected by the result of the first toss? The answer here is yes, since the result of the first toss affects which coin (fair or unfair) is to be tossed the second time.

Another example of dependent events involves mutually exclusive events. If events A and B are mutually exclusive, they are dependent. Given that event A has occurred, the conditional probability of B occurring must be zero, since the two events are mutually exclusive.

CONDITIONAL, MARGINAL, AND JOINT PROBABILITIES

We now introduce a very important probability relationship:

(2–3) $P(B|A) = \dfrac{P(AB)}{P(A)} \; ; \qquad P(A) \neq 0$

The conditional probability of event B, given that event A has occurred, is equal to the joint probability of A and B, divided by the probability of event A.

Instead of writing $P(B|A) = \dfrac{P(AB)}{P(A)}$, we can multiply both sides of

the equation by $P(A)$ and rewrite equation (2–3) as:

(2–4) $$P(AB) = P(B|A) \cdot P(A)$$

That is, the joint probability of A and B is equal to the conditional probability of B given A times the probability of A.

Let us look at these formulas assuming independent events. By equation (2–3):

$$P(B|A) = \frac{P(AB)}{P(A)}$$

But by equation (2–1):

$$P(AB) = P(A) \cdot P(B)$$

for independent events. Substituting $P(A) \cdot P(B)$ for $P(AB)$ in equation (2–3) gives:

(2–2) $$P(B|A) = \frac{P(A) \cdot P(B)}{P(A)} = P(B)$$

This is the mathematical definition of independence given earlier.

We shall next make use of two examples to illustrate:

1. Unconditional (marginal) probabilities. The term *marginal* refers to the fact that the probabilities are found in the margins of a joint probability table (see Table 2–4); they sum to one. A marginal probability refers to the probability of the occurrence of an event not conditional on the occurrence of another event. $P(A)$ and $P(B)$ are examples of marginal probabilities.
2. Conditional probabilities such as $P(A|B)$ and $P(B|A)$.
3. Joint probabilities such as $P(AB)$.

Example 1

Assume we have three boxes which contain red and black balls as follows:

Box 1.................... 3 red and 7 black
Box 2.................... 6 red and 4 black
Box 3.................... 8 red and 2 black

Suppose we draw a ball from box 1; if it is red, we draw a ball from box 2. If the ball drawn from box 1 is black, we draw a ball from box 3. The diagram in Table 2–3 illustrates the game.

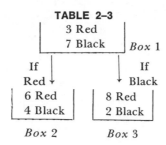

TABLE 2–3

Let us raise the following probability questions about this game:

1. What is the probability of drawing a red ball from box 1? This probability is an *unconditional* or *marginal* probability; it is 0.30 (the marginal probability of getting a black is 0.70).

2. We draw a ball from box 1 and it is red; what is the probability of another red ball when we draw from box 2 on the second draw? The answer is 0.60. This is an example of a conditional probability. That is, the probability of a red ball on the second draw if the draw from box 1 is red is a conditional probability.

3. Suppose our first draw from box 1 was black; what is the *conditional* probability of our second draw (from box 3 this time) being red? The probability is 0.80. The draw from box 1 (the conditioning event) is very important in determining the probabilities of red (or black) on the second draw.

4. Suppose, before we draw any balls, we ask the question: What is the probability of drawing two red balls? This would be a *joint* probability; the event would be a red ball on both draws. This question is a little more complicated than the above three, and some analysis will be of value. Computations are as follows:

$$(2\text{–}4) \qquad P(AB) = P(B|A) \cdot P(A)$$

Event	Marginal $P(A)$	$\cdot$	Conditional $P(B|A)$	$=$	Joint $P(AB)$
RR..........	$P(R) = 0.30$		$P(R|R) = 0.60$		$P(RR) = 0.18$
RB..........	$P(R) = 0.30$		$P(B|R) = 0.40$		$P(RB) = 0.12$
BR..........	$P(B) = 0.70$		$P(R|B) = 0.80$		$P(BR) = 0.56$
BB..........	$P(B) = 0.70$		$P(B|B) = 0.20$		$P(BB) = 0.14$

Figure 2–1 shows the joint probability of two red balls as 0.18 [i.e., $P(RR)$, the top branch of the tree].

FIGURE 2–1
Tree diagram

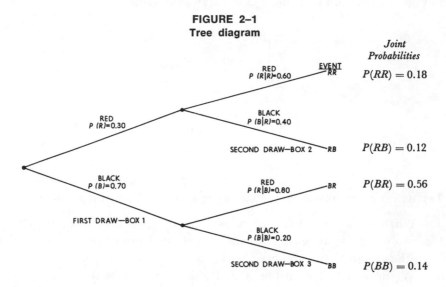

The joint probabilities may be read as follows:

Two red balls . . . . $P(RR) = 0.18$
A red ball on first draw and a black ball on second draw . . . . . . $P(RB) = 0.12$
A black ball on first draw and a red ball on second draw . . . . . . $P(BR) = 0.56$
Two black balls . . . . $P(BB) = \underline{0.14}$
                                                                                                          1.00

Figure 2–1 shows a tree diagram. This is a very useful device for illustrating uncertain situations. The first fork shows that either a red or a black may be chosen, and the probabilities of these occurrences are given. If a red is chosen, we go to box 2, where again a red or a black may be chosen, but with probabilities determined by the fact that the draw will take place in box 2. For the second forks, we have conditional probabilities (the probabilities depend on whether a red or a black ball was chosen on the first draw). At the end of each path are the joint probabilities of following that path. They are obtained by multiplying the marginal (unconditional) probabilities of the first branch by the conditional probabilities of the second branch.

In Table 2–4 the intersections of the rows and columns are *joint* probabilities: The column on the right gives the unconditional probabilities (*marginals*) of the outcome of the first draw; the bottom row gives the *unconditional* or *marginal* probabilities of the outcomes of the second

TABLE 2–4
Joint probability table

First draw \ Second draw	R	B	Marginal probability of outcome on first draw
R	P(RR) 0.18	P(RB) 0.12	0.30
B	P(BR) 0.56	P(BB) 0.14	0.70
Marginal probability of outcome on second draw	0.74	0.26	1.00

draw. Table 2–4 effectively summarizes the tree diagram. Now, let us compute some additional probabilities:

1. Probability of a red and a black ball, regardless of order $\qquad = 0.56 + 0.12 = 0.68$
2. Probability of a black ball on draw 2 $\qquad\qquad\qquad\qquad = 0.26$
    Explanatory calculation:
    Probability of red-black $\qquad\qquad = 0.12$
    Probability of black-black $\qquad\qquad = 0.14$
    Probability of black on draw 2 $\qquad = \overline{0.26}$
3. Probability of second draw being red *if* first draw is red $\qquad\qquad\qquad\qquad = 0.60$
    If first draw is red, we are in the R row, which totals 0.30. The question is, what proportion is 0.18 of 0.30? The answer is 0.60; or in terms of the appropriate formula:

$$P(R_2|R_1) = \frac{P(R_2R_1)}{P(R_1)} = \frac{0.18}{0.30} = 0.60$$

Example 2

Suppose a fair coin is flipped twice and we ask for the following probabilities:

1. Probability of two heads
2. Probability of one head and one tail in two flips

3. Probability of the second toss being a head
4. Probability of the second toss being a head, given that the first toss is a tail

Table 2–5 gives all possible outcomes for two tosses and their probabilities.

TABLE 2–5

Outcome (event)	Probability	Formula
HH	$P(HH) = ½ \cdot ½ = ¼$	$P(H) \cdot P(H)$
HT	$P(HT) = ½ \cdot ½ = ¼$	$P(H) \cdot P(T)$
TH	$P(TH) = ½ \cdot ½ = ¼$	$P(T) \cdot P(H)$
TT	$P(TT) = ½ \cdot ½ = ¼$	$P(T) \cdot P(T)$

Now, let us answer questions 1 to 4:

1. $P(HH) = ¼$
2. $P(HT + TH) = ½$
3. $P(HH + TH) = ½$

4. $P(H|T) = \dfrac{P(TH)}{P(T)} = \dfrac{¼}{½} = ½$

The important feature of the above example is that it illustrates *independence*. Note that the last two probabilities computed are the same; the probability of a head on the second toss is one half, regardless of the outcome of the first toss. The two events are said to be *independent,* since the probability of heads on the second toss is not affected by the outcome of the first toss. That was not the case in Example 1, where the probability of a red ball on the second draw was affected by the outcome of the first draw. To summarize this result:

Dependence (Example 1):

Conditional probability of red on second draw, given red on first draw $= \dfrac{\text{joint probability of } RR \ (0.18)}{\text{marginal probability of red on first draw } (0.30)} = 0.60$

General formula:

(2–3)
$$P(B|A) = \frac{P(AB)}{P(A)}$$

Independence (*Example* 2):

| Conditional probability of a head on second toss, given a tail on first toss | = | joint probability of $TH(\frac{1}{4})$ / marginal probability of tail on first toss ($\frac{1}{2}$) | = | 0.50, marginal probability of tossing a head |

General formula:

(2–2) $$P(B|A) = P(B)$$

REVISION OF PROBABILITIES

Having discussed joint and conditional probabilities, let us investigate how probabilities are revised to take account of new information.

Suppose we do not know whether a particular coin is fair or unfair. If the coin is fair, the probability of a tail is 0.50; but if the coin is unfair, the probability of a tail is 0.10. Assume we assign a prior probability to the coin being fair of 0.80 and a probability of 0.20 to the coin being unfair. The event "fair coin" will be designated A_1, and the event "unfair coin" will be designated A_2. We toss the coin once; say a tail is the result. What is the probability that the coin is fair?

Figure 2–2 shows that the conditional probability of a tail, given that the coin is fair, is 0.50; i.e., $P(\text{tail}|A_1) = 0.50$. If the coin is unfair, the probability of a tail is 0.10; i.e., $P(\text{tail}|A_2) = 0.10$.

FIGURE 2–2

$P(\text{tail}|A_1) = 0.50$ $P(\text{tail}|A_2) = 0.10$

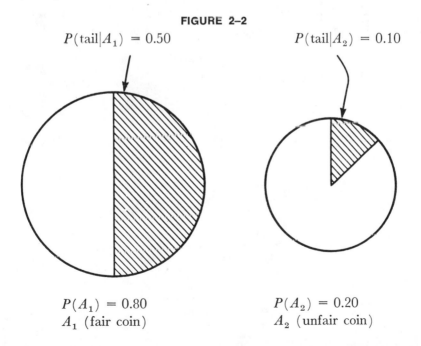

$P(A_1) = 0.80$ $P(A_2) = 0.20$
A_1 (fair coin) A_2 (unfair coin)

Let us compute $P(\text{tail and } A_1)$. There is a 0.80 probability that A_1 is the true state; and if A_1 is the true state, there is a 0.50 conditional probability that a tail will result. The joint probability of state A_1 being true and flipping a tail is $(0.80 \cdot 0.50)$, or 0.40. Thus

$$P(\text{tail and } A_1) = P(A_1) \cdot P(\text{tail}|A_1) = 0.80 \cdot 0.50 = 0.40$$

The joint probability of a tail *and* A_2 is equal to:

$$P(\text{tail and } A_2) = P(A_2) \cdot P(\text{tail}|A_2) = 0.20 \cdot 0.10 = 0.02$$

A tail can occur in combination with the state "fair coin" or in combination with the state "unfair coin." The probability of the former combination is 0.40; of the latter, 0.02. The sum of the probabilities gives the unconditional probability of a tail on the first toss; i.e., $P(\text{tail}) = 0.40 + 0.02 = 0.42$.

FIGURE 2–3

$P(\text{tail and } A_2) = 0.02$
$P(\text{tail and } A_1) = 0.40$

$$P(\text{tail}) = 0.42$$

Figure 2–3 shows that if a tail occurs, and if we do not know the true state, the probability of state A_1 being the true state is

$$\frac{P(\text{tail and } A_1)}{P(\text{tail})},$$

or $\dfrac{0.40}{0.42}$; this is the posterior probability of A_1. Thus, $\dfrac{0.40}{0.42}$ is the probability of A_1, given that a tail has occurred on the first toss. Using equation (2–3):

$$P(A_1|\text{tail}) = \frac{P(\text{tail and } A_1)}{P(\text{tail})} = \frac{0.40}{0.42} = 0.95$$

In like manner:

$$P(A_2|\text{tail}) = \frac{P(\text{tail and } A_2)}{P(\text{tail})} = \frac{0.02}{0.42} = 0.05$$

In more general symbols:

$$P(A_i|B) = \frac{P(A_iB)}{P(B)}$$

Conditional probability expressed in this form is known as *Bayes theorem*. It has many important applications in evaluating the worth of additional information (see Chapter 5).

In this example the *revised prior probabilities* for the next toss of the coin are 0.95 that it is fair and 0.05 that it is unfair (they were initially 0.80 and 0.20). These revised probabilities exist after one toss when the toss results in a tail. It is reasonable that the probability that the coin is unfair has decreased, since a tail appeared on the first toss and the unfair coin has only a 0.10 probability of a tail.

RANDOM VARIABLES

A probability function is a rule which assigns probabilities to each element of a set of events that may occur. If, in turn, we can assign a specific numerical value to each element of the set of events, a function which assigns these numerical values is termed a random variable. The value of a random variable is the general outcome of a random (or probability) experiment. It is useful to distinguish between the random variable itself and the values that it can take on. The value of a random variable is unknown until the event occurs (i.e., until the random experiment has been performed). However, the probability that the random variable will be any specific value is known in advance. The probability of each value of the random variable is equal to the sum of the probabilities of the events which are assigned that value of the random variable. Some examples of random variables are shown in Table 2–6.

TABLE 2–6

Random variable (denoted by a capital letter)	Values of the random variable	Description of the values of the random variable
U	2, 3, . . . , 12	Possible outcomes from throwing a pair of dice
X	0, 1, 2, 3, 4, 5	Possible number of heads, tossing a coin five times
Y	0, 1, 2, . . . , S	Possible daily sales of newspapers by a newsboy, where S represents his stock

For example, suppose we define the random variable Z to be the number of heads in two tosses of a fair coin. Then the possible values of Z, and the corresponding probabilities, are:

Possible values of Z	Probability of each value
0...................	¼
1...................	½
2...................	¼

THE MEAN OF A RANDOM VARIABLE

The mean of a random variable is the sum of the values of the random variable weighted by the probability that the random variable will take on that value. Consider the example of Table 2–7. In this case, 28.10 is the *mean* or *expected* demand. This is written as

$$E(X) = 28.10$$

or as $\bar{X} = 28.10$.[2] The mean of the random variable is often referred to as the expected value or the expectation of the random variable.

TABLE 2–7
Computation of the mean

Values of the random variable, X (tomorrow's demand)	Probability of X_i, $P(X_i)$	Weighted demand, $X_i P(X_i)$
$X_1 = 25$ units...........	$P(X_1) = 0.05$	1.25
$X_2 = 26$ units...........	$P(X_2) = 0.10$	2.60
$X_3 = 27$ units...........	$P(X_3) = 0.15$	4.05
$X_4 = 28$ units...........	$P(X_4) = 0.30$	8.40
$X_5 = 29$ units...........	$P(X_5) = 0.20$	5.80
$X_6 = 30$ units...........	$P(X_6) = 0.20$	6.00
	1.00	$E(X) = 28.10$

The mean is calculated, as in the above example, by weighting each value of the random variable by its probability, and summing. The mathematical definition of the mean, in symbols, is:

$$(2\text{–}5) \qquad E(X) = \sum_{i=1}^{n} X_i P(X_i) = \bar{X}$$

X_i is the ith value of the random variable; $P(X_i)$ is the probability of the ith value; and $\sum_{i=1}^{n}$ is a symbol meaning summation of all items

---

[2] Many statisticians use X only to represent the mean of a sample. In this section, we use $\bar{X}$ to be the mean of a probability distribution because it simplifies the notation.

for $i = 1$ to $i = n$, inclusive. The symbol Σ is read as "sigma." In our example, $n = 6$, since there are six possible values of the random variable. Hence:

$$E(X) = \bar{X} = \sum_{i=1}^{n} X_i P(X_i) = X_1 P(X_1) + X_2 P(X_2) + \cdots + X_6 P(X_6)$$

Substituting the specific values:

$$E(X) = \bar{X} = \sum_{i=1}^{6} X_i P(X_i) = 25(0.05) + 26(0.10) + 27(0.15)$$

$$+28(0.30) + 29(0.20) + 30(0.20)$$

$$= 28.10$$

SUMS OF RANDOM VARIABLES

The expectation of a sum of random variables is the sum of the expectations of those random variables. Thus the mean of the random variable $(X + Y + Z)$ is:

(2–6) $E(X + Y + Z) = E(X) + E(Y) + E(Z) = \bar{X} + \bar{Y} + \bar{Z}$

The expectation of a constant times a random variable is the constant times the expectation of the random variable:

(2–7) $E(cX) = cE(X) = c\bar{X}$

THE VARIANCE AND STANDARD DEVIATION OF A RANDOM VARIABLE

We might like to know something about how the values of the random variable are dispersed about the mean. The variance and the standard deviation provide measures of this dispersion.

The variance is defined as the sum of the *squared* deviations of the values of the random variable from its mean, weighted by the probability of the deviation. The mathematical statement is as follows:

(2–8) $Var(X) = \sum_{i=1}^{n} (X_i - \bar{X})^2 P(X_i)$

$\bar{X}$ is the mean; X_i, the ith value of the random variable; and $P(X_i)$, its probability. Note that the larger the dispersion of all X_i's for $i = 1$ to $i = n$, inclusive, the larger the $(X_i - \bar{X})^2$ and the larger the variance. We can also compute the variance of the random variable from equation (2–9):

(2–9) $$\text{Var}(X) = E(X^2) - (\bar{X})^2$$

where $E(X^2)$ is the expected value (i.e., mean) of the variable (X^2). This is a convenient form for calculating the variance. For example, if $X_1 = 1$, $X_2 = 4$, $X_3 = 7$, each with equal probability of $\frac{1}{3}$, the variance is:

$$\text{Var}(X) = \tfrac{1}{3}[(1)^2 + (4)^2 + (7)^2] - (4)^2$$
$$= 22 - 16 = 6$$

In the above computations:

$$\bar{X} = \tfrac{1}{3}(1 + 4 + 7) = 4, \qquad (\bar{X})^2 = 16,$$

and

$$E(X^2) = \tfrac{1}{3}(1^2) + \tfrac{1}{3}(4^2) + \tfrac{1}{3}(7^2) = \tfrac{1}{3}(1^2 + 4^2 + 7^2) = 22$$

The variance of a constant times a random variable is the constant squared times the variance of the random variable. That is:

(2–10) $$\text{Var}(cX) = c^2 \text{Var}(X)$$

The variance of a sum of *independent* random variables equals the sum of the variances. Thus:

(2–11) $$\text{Var}(X + Y + Z) = \text{Var}(X) + \text{Var}(Y) + \text{Var}(Z)$$

if X, Y, and Z are independent of each other.

If the value of the random variable X is a constant, the mean is

TABLE 2–8
Computation of the variance

Value of the random variable, X_i	Probability, $P(X_i)$	Squared deviation from the mean of 28.1—$(X_i - \bar{X})^2$	Squared deviation weighted by the probability— $(X_i - \bar{X})^2 P(X_i)$
$X_1 = 25$	0.05	$(25 - 28.1)^2 = 9.61$	0.4805
$X_2 = 26$	0.10	$(26 - 28.1)^2 = 4.41$	0.4410
$X_3 = 27$	0.15	$(27 - 28.1)^2 = 1.21$	0.1815
$X_4 = 28$	0.30	$(28 - 28.1)^2 = 0.01$	0.0030
$X_5 = 29$	0.20	$(29 - 28.1)^2 = 0.81$	0.1620
$X_6 = 30$	0.20	$(30 - 28.1)^2 = 3.61$	0.7220
	1.00		1.9900

$$\text{Var}(X) = \left[\sum_{i=1}^{6} (X_i - 28.1)^2 P(X_i) \right] = 1.9900$$

the constant value. Therefore, $(X_i - \bar{X})$ would be zero for all X_i, and the variance would be zero, indicating there is no dispersion around the mean.

In Table 2–8, we calculate the variance of the random variable, demand, of our earlier example using equation (2–8).

The *standard deviation* is the square root of the variance, and in our example the standard deviation is $\sqrt{1.99}$, or about 1.4. The standard deviation is usually designated by σ (a small sigma), and the variance is frequently written as σ^2.

THE BERNOULLI PROCESS AND THE BINOMIAL DISTRIBUTION

A Bernoulli process may be described as follows:

1. The outcomes or results of each trial in the process are characterized as one of two types of possible outcomes, such as:
   a) Success, failure
   b) Yes, no
   c) Heads, tails
   d) Zero, one
2. The probability of the outcome of any trial is "stable" and does not change throughout the process. For example, the probability of heads, given a fair coin, is 0.50 and does not change, regardless of the number of times the coin is tossed.
3. The outcome of any trial is *independent* of the outcome of any previous trial. In other words, the past history of the process would not change the probability assigned to the next trial. In our coin example, we would assign a probability of 0.50 to the next toss coming up heads, even if we had recorded heads on the last 10 trials (we assume the coin is fair).
4. The number of trials is discrete and can be represented by an integer such as 1, 2, 3, etc.

Given a certain process, we may know that it is Bernoulli, but we may or may not know the stable probability characteristic of the process. With a fair coin, we may know the process is Bernoulli, with probability 0.50 of a success (say heads) and probability 0.50 of a failure (tails). However, if we are given a coin and told it is not fair, the process (flipping the coin) may still be Bernoulli, but we do not know the probability characteristic. Hence, we may have a Bernoulli process with a known or unknown probability characteristic.

Many business processes can be characterized as Bernoulli for analytical purposes, even though they are not true Bernoulli in every respect. If the "fit" is close enough, we may assume that the Bernoulli process is a reasonable characterization. Let us discuss some examples.

Example 1

Suppose we are concerned with a production process where a certain part (or product) is being turned out on a machine. We may be interested in classifying the parts as "good" or "defective," in which case the process may be Bernoulli. If the machine is not subject to fast wear, i.e., if a setting will last for a long run of parts, the probability of good parts may be sufficiently stable for the process to qualify as Bernoulli. If, on the other hand, more defectives occur as the end of the run approaches, the process is not Bernoulli. In many such processes the occurrence of good and defective parts is sufficiently randomized (no pattern over time is observable) to call the process Bernoulli. The probability of good and defective parts may remain stable through a production run, but it may vary from run to run (because of machine setting, for example). Here, the process could still be considered Bernoulli, but the probability of a success (or failure) will change from run to run.

Example 2

A different example of a Bernoulli process is a survey to determine whether or not consumers prefer liquid to powdered soaps. The outcome of a survey interview could be characterized as "yes" (success) or "no" (failure) answers to the question. If the sample of consumers was sufficiently randomized (no pattern to the way in which the yes or no answers occur), Bernoulli (with an unknown probability) may be a useful description of the process.

Note that *if* the probability of a success in a Bernoulli process is 0.50, the probability of a failure is also 0.50 (since the probabilities of the event happening and the event not happening add to one). If the probability of a success is p, the probability of a failure is $(1 - p)$.

THE BINOMIAL PROBABILITY DISTRIBUTION

In order to answer probability questions about a Bernoulli process, we need to know what the probability parameter of the process is, such as the 0.50 in the coin example. In addition, we need to know the number of trials we are going to use. Hence, to analyze a Bernoulli process, we need to know (1) the process probability characteristic, p; and (2) the number of trials, n.

The following probability equality and inequality symbols and relationships are useful:

Relationship or symbol	Interpretation
$P(R = r \mid p, n)$	The probability that the unknown number of successes, R (the random variable), is *equal to* some specific number, r (say 10), given a specific number of trials, n (say 20), and some specific probability, p, of a success.
$P(R \geq r \mid p, n)$	The probability that the number of successes is *greater than or equal to* a specific number, r, given values for p and n.
$P(R > r \mid p, n)$	The probability that the number of successes is *greater* than a specific number. This inequality is exclusive; i.e.,

$$P(R > 10)$$

excludes 10, and includes 11 and up.

$P(R \leq r \mid p, n)$	The probability that the number of successes is less than or equal to a specific number (say 10).
$P(R < r \mid p, n)$	The probability that the number of successes is less than a specific number.
$P(R = 10) = P(R \geq 10) - P(R \geq 11)$	The probability of exactly 10 successes can be read from Table C (in the Appendix at the end of the text) by subtracting two cumulative probabilities. If

$$P(R \geq 11)$$

is subtracted from $P(R \geq 10)$, the result is the probability of *exactly* 10.

$P(R < 10) = 1 - P(R \geq 10)$	Since the probabilities add to one, if the probability of 10 or more successes is subtracted from one, the result is the probability of less than 10 successes.
$P(R \leq 10) = 1 - P(R \geq 11)$	Since *less than or equal to* 10 includes 10, subtract the probability of 11 or more successes from one.
$P(R > 10) = P(R \geq 11)$	To read a strict inequality from Table C (in the Appendix at the end of the text), add one to the number desired. The

$$P(R > 10)$$

excludes 10, so this probability is the same as $P(R \geq 11)$, which includes 11 but excludes 10.

THE BINOMIAL PROBABILITY FUNCTION

If the assumptions of the Bernoulli process are satisfied, then the probability distribution of the number of successes, R, is a *binomial* distribution. The binomial distribution function is:

$$(2\text{–}12) \qquad P(R \mid n, p) = \frac{n!}{R!(n-R)!} p^R (1-p)^{n-R}$$

where $n!$ (called n-factorial) equals $n(n-1)(n-2) \cdots (2)(1)$ and $0! = 1$.

Performing computations using equation $(2-12)$ can be tedious if the number of trials is not small. For this reason, tables of the cumulative binomial distribution have been provided at the end of the book (see Table C in the Appendix).

Example 1

Suppose we are to toss a fair coin three times and would like to compute the following probabilities:

a)   The probability of three heads in three tosses
b)   The probability of two or more heads in three tosses
c)   The probability of less than two heads in three tosses

In this example the Bernoulli process p is 0.50, and a head constitutes a success. The number of trials (n) is three.

The first probability is the probability of three heads (successes) in three tosses (three trials), given that the probability of a head on any one toss is 0.50. This probability can be abbreviated as follows:

$$P(R = 3 | p = 0.50, n = 3) = ?$$

where P = probability, R = number of successes, n = number of trials, and p = probability of a success on any one trial. The left side of the equation should be read "the probability of three successes, given a process probability of 0.50 and three trials."

In answering the probability questions, let us list all the possible outcomes of the three trials and compute the probabilities (see Table 2–9).

TABLE 2–9

Possible outcomes	Probabilities of each outcome
HHH	$\frac{1}{8}$
HHT	$\frac{1}{8}$
HTH	$\frac{1}{8}$
THH	$\frac{1}{8}$
TTH	$\frac{1}{8}$
THT	$\frac{1}{8}$
HTT	$\frac{1}{8}$
TTT	$\frac{1}{8}$
	$\overline{1}$

Questions and probabilities	Interpretation
a) $P(R = 3 \mid p = 0.50, n = 3) = \frac{1}{8}$	The probability of three heads in three trials is one eighth. This is the probability of *HHH*.
b) $P(R \geq 2 \mid p = 0.50, n = 3) = \frac{4}{8}$	The probability of two or more heads is four eighths. This is the probability of two heads plus the probability of three heads and is calculated by summing the probabilities of the following combinations: *HHH, HHT, HTH, THH*.
c) $P(R < 2 \mid p = 0.50, n = 3) = \frac{4}{8}$	The probability of less than two heads is the probability of either zero or one head and is calculated by summing the probabilities of the following combinations: *TTH, THT, HTT, TTT*.

The above probabilities can also be calculated using equation (2–12). This is illustrated for problem (*a*).

$$P(R = 3 \mid n = 3, p = 0.5) = \frac{3!}{3!(0!)}(0.5)^3(0.5)^0 = 0.1250$$

Finally, the probabilities can be calculated from Table C in the Appendix at the end of the text.

Calculations	Explanation
a) $P(R = 3 \mid p = 0.50, n = 3) = 0.1250$	Look in Table C (in the Appendix at the end of the text), under $n = 3$, $p = 0.50$; read down the column to
	$$P(R \geq 3) = 0.1250$$
	and subtract from this
	$$p(R \geq 4) = 0$$
	(four successes in three trials is impossible). The answer is 0.1250, or one eighth.
b) $P(R \geq 2 \mid p = 0.50, n = 3) = 0.5000$	Look in Table C under $n = 3$, $p = 0.50$, and read $R \geq 2$; the answer is 0.50. If we wanted $P(R = 2)$, we would compute this as follows:
	$P(R \geq 2 \mid 0.50, 10) = 0.5000$
	less: $P(R \geq 3 \mid 0.50, 10) = 0.1250$
	$P(R = 2 \mid 0.50, 10) = \overline{0.3750}$
c) $P(R < 2 \mid p = 0.50, n = 3) = 0.5000$	This probability is equal to
	$$1 - P(R \geq 2) = 1 - 0.50 = 0.50$$

Example 2

A large lot of manufactured goods is to be sampled as a check on its quality.[3] Suppose that 10 percent of the items are defective and that a sample of 20 items is drawn from the lot. What are the following probabilities:

a)   Probability of exactly zero defectives in the sample
b)   Probability of more than one defective in the sample
c)   Probability of less than two defectives in the sample

We can answer as follows. Let $p = 0.10$ and $n = 20$. Then:

a) $P(R = 0 | p = 0.10, n = 20) = P(R \geq 0) - P(R \geq 1)$
$$= 1.0 - 0.8784 = 0.1216$$

The probability of zero or more defectives is 1.0, and $P(R \geq 1)$ is read directly from Table C.

b) $P(R > 1) = P(R \geq 2) = 0.6083$ from Table C.
c) $P(R < 2) = 1.0 - P(R \geq 2) = 1.0 - 0.6083 = 0.3917$

BIBLIOGRAPHY

DRAKE, A. W. *Fundamentals of Applied Probability Theory.* New York: McGraw-Hill Book Co., 1967.

FELLER, W. *An Introduction to Probability Theory and Its Applications,* Vol I. 3d ed. New York: John Wiley & Sons, Inc., 1968.

GOLDBERG, SAMUEL. *Probability: An Introduction.* Englewood Cliffs, N.J.: Prentice-Hall, Inc., 1960.

HODGES, J. L. JR., and LEHMANN, E. L. *Elements of Finite Probability.* 2d ed. San Francisco: Holden-Day, Inc., 1970.

KEMENY, J. G.; SCHLEIFER, A., JR.; SNELL, J. L.; and THOMPSON, G. L. *Finite Mathematics with Business Applications.* 2d ed. Englewood Cliffs, N.J.: Prentice-Hall, Inc., 1972.

MOSTELLER, F.; ROURKE, R. E. K.; and THOMAS, G. B., JR. *Probability with Statistical Applications.* 2d ed. Reading, Mass.: Addison-Wesley Publishing Co., 1970.

NATIONAL BUREAU OF STANDARDS. *The Tables of the Binomial Probability Distribution.* Applied Mathematics Series 6. New York, 1950.

PARZEN, E. *Modern Probability Theory and Its Applications.* New York: John Wiley & Sons, Inc., 1960.

---

[3] Strictly speaking, if the lot is of finite size, the Bernoulli assumptions are not exactly satisfied, and the hypergeometric distribution should be employed. However, if the lot size is large relative to the sample, the use of the Bernoulli assumption introduces little error.

SAVAGE, L. J. *The Foundations of Statistics.* New York: John Wiley & Sons, Inc., 1954.

SCHLAIFER, R. *Probability and Statistics for Business Decisions.* New York: McGraw-Hill Book Co., 1959.

SPURR, W. A., and BONINI, C. P. *Statistical Analysis for Business Decisions.* Rev. ed. Homewood, Ill.: Richard D. Irwin, Inc., 1973.

PROBLEMS

2–1. Which of the following frequency distributions would be "objective" and which "subjective"?
a) Number of heads in 100,000 tosses of a fair coin
b) Number of heads in the next 100,000 tosses of an untested coin
c) Number of "prosperous" years in the next 10 years
d) The earnings of the Ford Motor Company in the next five years (number of "profitable" and number of "loss" years)
e) The probability of drawing the name of a male randomly from the student directory of Cornell University

2–2. Discuss the following statements:
a) "There is a 1.5 probability that the next president will be _____."
b) "The probability of the sun not rising tomorrow is −1.0."
c) "There is a 0.40 probability that I'll pass and a 0.70 probability that I'll flunk the examination."

2–3. Discuss whether the following events are dependent or independent:
a) (1) The Giants winning the World Series
(2) The Giants winning the pennant of the National League
b) (1) The savings from using a machine in year 2
(2) The savings from using the same machine in year 1
c) (1) The successful marketing of a high-priced car following
(2) The successful marketing of a low-priced clothing line

2–4. Consider the following two urns:

	Urn 1	Urn 2
Red balls	7	4
Black balls	3	6

$P(R_1) = P$ of red on first draw
$P(R_2) = P$ of red on second draw
$P(B_1) = P$ of black on first draw
$P(B_2) = P$ of black on second draw

a) Take a ball from urn 1, replace it, and take a second ball. What is the probability of:

(1) Two reds being drawn?

(2) A red on the second draw if a red is drawn on the first draw?

(3) A red on the second draw if a black is drawn on the first draw?

b) Take a ball from urn 1; replace it. Take a ball from urn 2 if the first ball was black; otherwise, draw a ball from urn 1. What is the probability of:

(1) Two reds being drawn?

(2) A red on the second draw if a red is drawn on the first draw?

(3) A red on the second draw if a black is drawn on the first draw?

2–5. Draw a tree diagram for Problem 2–4(a).

2–6. Draw a tree diagram for Problem 2–4(b).

2–7. Prepare a joint probability table for Problem 2–4(a).

2–8. Prepare a joint probability table for Problem 2–4(b).

2–9. Compute the following probabilities which pertain to flipping a fair coin three times:

a) P (three heads)

b) P (two or more heads in three tosses)

c) P (one or more tails in three tosses)

d) P (the last toss being a head)

2–10. a) What is the probability of eight heads in eight tosses of a fair coin?

b) Suppose a fair coin is flipped seven times and all the tosses are heads. What is the probability of the eighth toss being a head? Explain.

2–11. Assume three urns:

6R	8R	4R
4B	2B	1B
No. 1	No. 2	No. 3

Draw a ball from No. 1: if red, go to No. 2; if black, go to No. 3.

a) What is P (red on second draw, given red on draw 1)?

b) What is P (black on second draw, given red on draw 1)?

c) What is P (red on second draw, given black on draw 1)?

d) What is P (black on second draw, given black on draw 1)?

e) How would the answers to (a)–(d) change if urn No. 3 was as follows:

$$7R$$

$$3B$$

No. 3

Explain why there is a difference in the probabilities of (e) compared to (c) and (d).

2–12. The following probabilities are assigned to the possible values of the fraction defective in a manufacturing process. Compute the mean, the variance, and the standard deviation of the random variable, fraction defective.

Event	Probability of event
0.01 defective.	0.10
0.02 defective.	0.15
0.03 defective.	0.20
0.04 defective.	0.30
0.05 defective.	0.20
0.10 defective.	0.03
0.15 defective.	0.02
	1.00

2–13. Assume that we have a box containing six red balls and four black balls. We draw two balls, one at a time, without replacing the first ball. For this experiment:
a) Draw a tree diagram showing the process.
b) Prepare a joint probability table.
c) Compute the following probabilities:

$$P(B_2|B_1)$$
$$P(R_2|B_1)$$
$$P(R_2|R_1)$$

2–14. Assume there are two urns:

$$6R$$

$$4B$$

No. 1

$$8R$$

$$2B$$

No. 2

There is equal probability of choosing each urn. You take an urn, draw one ball, and find it is red. You want to know which urn you have.

a) What is the probability that you drew the ball from urn 1? From urn 2?

b) If the ball is black, what is the probability that the ball is from urn 1?

2–15. Specify which of the following are Bernoulli processes:

a) A house-to-house salesman making sales calls

b) Placing coins in a slot machine which has two payoffs—zero or jackpot

c) Purchase of shares of common stock

d) Inspection of a wire coil for defects as it is being manufactured

e) Inspection of castings as they come off the production line

Give brief explanations for your answers.

2–16. Assume an unfair coin has a 0.60 probability of a tail and a 0.40 probability of a head. Determine the following:

a) In two tosses the probability of:
  (1) Two heads
  (2) Two tails
  (3) One head
  (4) One or more heads
  (5) One or more tails
  (6) One tail or less

b) In three tosses, the probability of:
  (1) Three heads
  (2) Two heads
  (3) One head
  (4) One or more heads

2–17. Using the binomial tables, look up the following probabilities:

a) $P(R = 4|0.50, 10)$

b) $P(R > 4|0.50, 10)$

c) $P(R \geq 4|0.40, \ 8)$

d) $P(R < 4|0.20, 10)$

e) $P(R = 0|0.30, 10)$

2–18. A sales manager lists the following probabilities for various sales levels for a new product:

Probability	Sales (in units)
0.10	50
0.30	100
0.30	150
0.15	200
0.10	250
0.05	300

Calculate the mean, the variance, and the standard deviation for the random variable sales. (*Hint:* One way to make the computations easier is to treat blocks of 50 as one unit. Thus, 200 is four, 250 is five, etc.)

2–19. Assume that the probability of a salesman making a sale at a randomly selected house is 0.1. If a salesman makes 20 calls a day, determine the following:
a) The probability of no sales
b) The probability of one sale
c) The probability of four or more sales
d) The probability of more than four sales
e) The probability of four sales

2–20. A corporate president, in response to a question at lunch, said there was about one chance in a million that his firm would fail as a result of a depression in the next 10 years. Later, you read that the same man informed the stockholders of the firm that "even if there is a depression, the probability is 999/1,000 that we shall survive." The firm's monthly newsletter contains a signed article by this man in which he says the chances of a depression in the next ten years are 1 in 100. Is he consistent in his probability assessments?

2–21. A safety commissioner for a certain city performed a study of the pedestrian fatalities at intersections. He noted that only 6 of the 19 fatalities were pedestrians who were crossing the intersection against the light (i.e., in disregard of the proper signal), whereas the remaining 13 were crossing *with* the light. He was puzzled because the figures seemed to show that it was roughly twice as safe for a pedestrian to cross against the light as with it. Can you explain this apparent contradiction to the commissioner?

2–22. An accountant is about to audit 24 accounts of a firm. Sixteen of these accounts are high-volume customers. If the accountant selects 4 of the accounts at random, what is the probability that at least one is a high-volume account?
Hint: First, find the probability that none of the accounts are high volume.

2–23. You are in charge of the long-range planning department for a large English construction company. There is a possibility of two major construction projects during the period under consideration: a tunnel under the Channel to France, and an expanded English missile base system for the United States Air Force. The two projects will to some extent require different engineering skills and equipment. The company that has acquired part of such specialized factors will have a decided advantage in contract negotiation. It is beyond your firm's resources to staff for both projects, and the president has instructed you to choose between them. Upon inquiry among members of Parliament, you conclude that the most critical circumstance affecting the tunnel project is the fate of England's application for admission to the Common Market. If England is admitted to the Common Market, most experts seem to think that the probability is 0.8 that the tunnel will be built. If England is not admitted, the probability is reduced to 0.1, in their view. It is your estimate that the probability is about 0.3 for England to be admitted to the Common Market during the period under consideration.

You proceed to Washington to make a comparable analysis of the chances of the missile base system. To your surprise, you find that the American military planners are disturbed by the news stories regarding the tunnel. Should the tunnel be built, there is only one chance in 10 that the Air Force would authorize the missile system. The chances are about 50–50 if the tunnel is not constructed. If you accept the subjective probability assessments of your informants, what course of action would you suggest to your firm to maximize the probability of success?

2–24. The Acme Company has two warehouses located in different cities. Demand for the product is independent in each warehouse district. However both warehouses have identical probability distributions for demand as follows:

Demand (units)	Probability
0.	0.10
1.	0.50
2.	0.30
3.	0.10
	1.00

Assume that each warehouse normally stocks two units.

a) What is the probability that one or the other of the warehouses (not both) will have more demand than stock?

b) What is the probability that both warehouses will be out of stock?

2–25. Refer to Problem 2–24 above. Suppose the Acme Company consolidated the two warehouses into a single one serving both cities. The consolidated warehouse would carry a stock of four units.

a) Determine the probability distribution of demand at the consolidated warehouse.

b) What is the probability that the consolidated warehouse would be out of stock by one unit? by two units? Compare these to the answers obtained in Problem 2–24.

2–26. The president of a large electric utility has to decide whether to purchase one large generator (Big Jim) or four smaller generators (Little Alices) to attain a given amount of electric generating capacity. On any given summer day the probability of a generator being in service is 0.95 (the generators are equally reliable). Equivalently there is 0.05 probability of a failure.

a) What is the probability of Big Jim being out of service on a given day?

b) What is the probability of either zero or one of the four Alices being out?

c) If five Little Alices are purchased, what is the probability of at least four operating?

d) If six Little Alices are purchased, what is the probability of at least four operating?

2–27. The National Draft Lottery requires that numbers representing the order of draft call-up be randomly paired with the 365 (or 366) potential birth dates of the year. Current procedure is as follows:

(1) A set of *dates* is placed in urn 1, and one by one the capsules containing the dates are drawn at random.

(2) Simultaneously, a set of draft *numbers* (1 to 365 or 366) are placed in urn 2, and for each drawing of urn 1, a random drawing is made from urn 2. Then the date drawn (e.g., October 18) is paired with the draft number drawn (e.g., 12).

Are all the above steps necessary to create conditions of random pairing? What steps could be omitted? Why?

2–28. Newspaper articles frequently cite the fact that in any one year, a small percentage (say 10 percent) of all drivers are responsible for all automobile accidents. The conclusion is often reached that if only we could single out these "accident-prone" drivers and either retrain them or remove them from the roads, we could drastically reduce auto accidents. You are told that of 100,000 drivers who were involved in one or more accidents in one year, 11,000 of them were involved in one or more accidents in the next year.

a) Given the above information, complete the entries in the following joint probability table:

First year \ Second year	Accident	No accident	Marginal probability of event in first year
Accident			0.10
No accident			0.90
Marginal probability of event in second year.........	0.10	0.90	1.00

      b) Do you think searching for "accident-prone" drivers would be an effective way to reduce auto accidents? Why?

2–29. Suppose a new test is available to test for drug addiction. The test is 95 percent accurate "each way"; i.e., if a man *is* an addict, then there is a 95 percent chance the test will indicate "yes," while if a man is *not* an addict, then 95 percent of the time the test will indicate "no." It is known that the incidence of drug addiction in urban populations is about one out of 10,000.

      Given a positive (yes) test result, what are the chances that the man being tested is addicted?

3

Conditional and expected
value

In this chapter, we continue our consideration of the application of probability concepts to business decisions which must be made under conditions of uncertainty. We shall attempt to develop a means for making consistent decisions and for estimating the cost of uncertainty. We shall develop expected monetary value as the appropriate criterion for decision making. In subsequent chapters we will describe the limitations of expected monetary value and suggest modifications.

Example

Suppose a grocer is faced with a problem of how many cases of milk to stock to meet tomorrow's demand. Assume that any milk that remains unsold at the end of the day will represent a complete loss to the grocer. Also, any unsatisfied demand bears no cost except the cost of the lost sale; the disappointed customer will come back in the future. This example is highly simplified but illustrates the basic principles of conditional and expected value.

In our analysis of the grocer's problem, it would be helpful if we knew something about past sales, on the assumption that this experience may serve as a guide to what may be expected in the future. Suppose the grocer has maintained records such as those shown in Table 3–1.

With a purchase price (variable cost) of $8 per case and a selling price of $10 per case, the table of conditional values (Table 3–2) is a description of the problem facing the grocer.

The possible actions (number to buy) facing the grocer are listed across the top of the table. It is, of course, possible to buy 24 or 29 cases, etc.; but if in the last 200 days, sales were in the range of 25–28 cases,

TABLE 3–1
Historical demand

Total demand per day	Number of days each demand level was recorded	Probability of each event
25 cases........	20	0.10
26 cases........	60	0.30
27 cases........	100	0.50
28 cases........	20	0.10
	200	1.00

TABLE 3–2
Conditional values

Event: demand	Possible actions			
	Stock 25	Stock 26	Stock 27	Stock 28
25 cases...........	$50	$42	$34	$26
26 cases...........	50	52	44	36
27 cases...........	50	52	54	46
28 cases...........	50	52	54	56

the grocer might view a stock of greater than 28 or less than 25 as not worthy of consideration. We shall make this assumption. The possible (conceivable) events—in this example the possible sales—are listed in the far left column. If the grocer is willing to assign probabilities in accordance with the historical data, then events (sales) other than those listed will carry zero probabilities; they are considered impossible events and are not listed.

CONDITIONAL VALUE

Table 3–2 can be thought of as a "conditional value" or "conditional profit" table. Corresponding to each action the grocer takes, and each event that happens, there is a certain conditional profit. These profits are conditional in the sense that a certain profit results from following a specific course of action (act) and having a specific demand (event) occur. All the possible combinations are shown in Table 3–2.

Looking at the act column, "stock 27," let us trace through the calculation of each dollar amount. This is done in Table 3–3. Similar computations have to be made for acts "stock 25," "stock 26," and "stock 28."

The calculations of Table 3–3 show that if 27 cases are stocked, only 27 can be sold, even if the demand turns out to be 28 cases. Hence the profit reaches a maximum of $54 for the sale of 27 units, and levels off at that figure despite the demand for 28 units.

TABLE 3–3
Conditional profits of act "stock 27"

Event: demand	Selling price	Total revenue	Cost of 27 units (27 · $8)	Conditional profit of act "stock 27"
25 cases.	$10	$250	$216	$34
26 cases.	10	260	216	44
27 cases.	10	270	216	54
28 cases.	10	270	216	54

THE LOSS TABLE

In addition to making a table showing conditional profits (Table 3–2), it is possible to construct a table showing conditional *opportunity losses* (Table 3–4). Consider the act "stock 28." If the demand turns out to

TABLE 3–4
Conditional opportunity losses

Event: demand	Act			
	Stock 25	Stock 26	Stock 27	Stock 28
25 cases.	0	8	16	24
26 cases.	2	0	8	16
27 cases.	4	2	0	8
28 cases.	6	4	2	0

Computations of conditional opportunity losses for Table 3–4

Event: demand	Optimum act for each event	Profit of optimum act	Difference between profit of optimum act and the act of stocking:			
			25	26	27	28
25.	25	$50	50 − 50 = 0	50 − 42 = 8	50 − 34 = 16	50 − 26 = 24
26.	26	52	52 − 50 = 2	52 − 52 = 0	52 − 44 = 8	52 − 36 = 16
27.	27	54	54 − 50 = 4	54 − 52 = 2	54 − 54 = 0	54 − 46 = 8
28.	28	56	56 − 50 = 6	56 − 52 = 4	56 − 54 = 2	56 − 56 = 0

be 28, the grocer will make a profit of $56. This is the best he can do with a demand of 28. With a demand of 28, and if he had stocked only 27, he would have made $54; this act would entail a $2 *opportunity loss* over the *best* action with a demand of 28. If the demand was 28 and the grocer stocked 26, he would suffer a $4 conditional opportunity loss ($56 — $52). Opportunity loss can be defined in general as the *amount of profit foregone by not choosing the best act for each event.* With this definition, the conditional opportunity loss table shown in Table 3–4 can be constructed.

It should be emphasized that a conditional profit (or loss) relates to a profit conditional on:

1. An event happening and
2. A given action

We do not know which event is going to occur; there is uncertainty. Therefore the conditional profit for a decision is not one number but a table of profits (or losses) associated with possible events. Profit is $44 only on condition of both stocking 27 units and an actual demand of 26 units. If the demand is different than 26 units, the actual profit will be different than $44.

EXPECTED MONETARY VALUE

Even though the conditional values and losses help characterize the problem facing the grocer, it is not yet possible to offer an optimum solution. The grocer could choose the best act if he knew the event (if he had advance knowledge of tomorrow's demand), but this information is not available in our example. The problem facing the grocer is to make some forecast of the event and then choose an act that is consistent with the forecast. Suppose he makes this forecast by assigning probabilities to the possible events and then analyzes his action alternatives. If he assigns probabilities based on historical information (see Table 3–1), they would be as shown in Table 3–5. If the grocer believes that for some reason tomorrow's demand will vary somewhat from the observed

TABLE 3–5

Event: demand	Probability of event
25 cases.	0.10
26 cases.	0.30
27 cases.	0.50
28 cases.	0.10
	1.00

pattern, he should modify his probability assignment. The next step is to bring the assigned probabilities into the analysis. We accomplish this by *weighting the conditional values of each event in the conditional value table by the probability of the event occurring, and adding the products.* The resulting number is the *expected monetary value* for the act; the optimum act is the one with the highest expected monetary value. The calculations are given in Table 3–6 for the acts of stocking 26 and 27 units. The calculations for 25 and 28 units would be similar.

TABLE 3–6
Calculations of expected monetary values

Event: demand	Probability of event	Act: stock 26		Act: stock 27	
		Conditional value	Expected value: *CV* weighted by probability of event	Conditional value	Expected value: *CV* weighted by probability of event
25 cases.	0.10	$42	$ 4.20	$34	$ 3.40
26 cases.	0.30	52	15.60	44	13.20
27 cases.	0.50	52	26.00	54	27.00
28 cases.	0.10	52	5.20	54	5.40
	1.00				
Expected monetary value.			$51.00		$49.00

In Table 3–6 the expected monetary value (*EMV*) is calculated by multiplying each conditional value by its probability and then adding the weighted conditional values. Table 3–7 shows the expected monetary

TABLE 3–7
Summary of expected monetary values

Act	Expected monetary value
Stock 25.	$50
Stock 26.	51 (optimum act)
Stock 27.	49
Stock 28.	42

values for all acts. The grocer calculates for act "stock 26" an expected monetary value of $51, the highest *EMV*. Therefore, based on expected monetary value, he should stock 26 cases. To summarize, our plan for solving the grocer's problem is as follows:

1. Construct a payoff (conditional value) table listing the acts and events that are considered to be possibilities. In listing the events, be sure that each event is mutually exclusive (i.e., make sure that no two or more events can occur simultaneously) and that all events considered together are exhaustive (i.e., that the events listed cover all the possibilities). This table considers the economics of the problem (costs and revenues) by calculating a conditional value (or loss) for each act and event combination.
2. Assign probabilities to the events.
3. Calculate an *EMV* for each act by weighting (multiplying) the conditional values by the assigned probabilities and adding the weighted conditional values to obtain the *EMV* of the act.
4. Choose the act with the largest *EMV*.

EXPECTED OPPORTUNITY LOSS

The grocer can also choose the best act by minimizing expected opportunity loss (*EOL*). The procedure is the same as just outlined except that instead of using the payoff table (conditional value table, Table 3–2) and conditional profits, we shall use the conditional opportunity loss table (Table 3–4) and conditional opportunity losses. The calculations for act "stock 26" and act "stock 27" are as given in Table 3–8.

TABLE 3–8
Calculation of expected opportunity losses

Event: demand	Probability of event	Act: stock 26		Act: stock 27	
		Conditional losses	Expected opportunity loss: *CL* weighted by probability of event	Conditional losses	Expected opportunity loss: *CL* weighted by probability by event
25 cases.	0.10	$8	$0.80	$16	$1.60
26 cases.	0.30	0	0.00	8	2.40
27 cases.	0.50	2	1.00	0	0.00
28 cases.	0.10	4	0.40	2	0.20
	1.00				
Expected opportunity loss.			$2.20		$4.20

From Table 3–9, we find that the grocer should choose act "stock 26," which has an expected loss of $2.20, the lowest of the four expected opportunity losses.

TABLE 3–9
Summary of expected opportunity losses

Act	Expected opportunity losses	Comparison of expected opportunity losses with optimum
Stock 25.	$ 3.20	$1
Stock 26.	2.20 (optimum act)	0
Stock 27.	4.20	2
Stock 28.	11.20	9

Let us summarize the various measures of profitability which have been introduced:

Conditional value. The actual profit which would result following a given action, conditional upon a given event occurring.

Conditional opportunity loss. The relative loss (i.e., the profit not earned) following a given action, conditional upon a given event occurring.

Expected monetary value. The conditional values weighted by the probability of the events occurring, and summed for each act.

Expected opportunity loss. The conditional opportunity losses weighted by the probability of the events occurring, and summed for each act.

The optimum act is the act with the greatest expected monetary value, and thus the smallest expected opportunity loss.

EXPECTED UTILITY

Although expected monetary value may be a good guide to action in many cases, it may not be in others. This does not destroy our model; it means we must modify the analysis when the situation warrants it. Let us consider a major difficulty with expected monetary value.

Suppose a businessman has a chance to invest a large sum of money in a very speculative new product. Assume that if the product is successful, he will earn (in present value terms) profits of $1 million. However, he must risk a loss of $500,000 to develop, produce, and sell the new product. Our businessman's conditional value table is given in Table 3–10.

If, after gathering evidence, the businessman assigns a subjective probability of 0.90 of success, the *EMV* of the act "invest" would be $850,000, i.e., ($1,000,000 · 0.90 − $500,000 · 0.10 = $850,000), as compared with an *EMV* of zero for the act "do not invest." Suppose,

TABLE 3–10*
Conditional value

| | Act | |
Event	Invest	Do not invest
Product successful............	$1,000,000	0
Product not successful.........	(500,000)	0

* Losses are shown in parentheses.

however, that the businessman is in a very difficult financial position and a $500,000 loss would result in certain bankruptcy. In such a case, *EMV* may be a poor guide to action. The businessman may be unwilling to take the chance of losing $500,000 regardless of the size of the conditional profits or the *EMV*, because of the undesirable consequences of the loss. If so, the businessman has a large disutility for such a loss, and this should be brought into the analysis.

If utility considerations are to be ignored, or in problems where utility for money is approximately linear (see Chapter 17), *EMV* is a reasonable guide to action. For example, when the potential losses are not too great and the prospective profit range is narrow, utility considerations usually are not significant. Such is the case in our grocer's problem, and *EMV* is adequate.

However, where actions are contemplated that involve large potential losses, it may be desirable to make the analysis more appropriate by bringing in utility considerations. This can be done by calculating the *expected utility value* of possible actions rather than the *expected monetary value*. This modification of the analysis will be discussed in Chapter 17. For purposes of the initial chapters, we shall assume that the situation is such that utility considerations are unimportant (i.e., the expected monetary value is a reasonable measure of the expected utility).

EXPECTED PROFIT WITH PERFECT PREDICTIONS

Returning to our example of the grocer, let us raise the following question: "What profit could the grocer *expect* to make in the future if each day's demand could be *predicted with certainty* the day before the particular demand occurred?" To answer this question, let us construct a conditional value table which will show the conditional profit for the *best* act, given each event. Table 3–11 is constructed by choosing the best act and recording the highest profit figures for each event (this

TABLE 3–11
Conditional value table for optimal decisions

	Act			
Event: demand	Stock 25	Stock 26	Stock 27	Stock 28
25 cases.	$50			
26 cases.		$52		
27 cases.			$54	
28 cases.				$56

information can be obtained from Table 3–2). For example, if we knew tomorrow's demand would be 27, we would stock 27 cases, for a profit of $54. If we stocked 26, we would forgo the $2 profit on one unit; and if we stocked 28, we would have to scrap one unit at a loss of $8. Table 3–11 shows the grocer what the best action is for each possible event.

Let us convert these conditional optimal profit figures to an expectation. This can be done by weighting each profit item by its probability of occurring. The resulting amount, $53.20, is called the *expected profit under certainty*. The calculation is shown in Table 3–12, where the ex-

TABLE 3–12
Expected profit under certainty

Event: demand	Probability of event	Conditional profit under certainty	Expected profit under certainty
25 cases.	0.10	$50	$ 5.00
26 cases.	0.30	52	15.60
27 cases.	0.50	54	27.00
28 cases.	0.10	56	5.60
			$53.20

pected profit under certainty ($53.20) is the profit the grocer could make on the average if he had available a *perfect* predictor whereby each day's demand could be predicted in advance. Thus the optimum amount would be ordered each day.

Before the perfect predictor is used, the grocer is still uncertain as to what the prediction will be, since any one of the four events may occur. Before the prediction, the profit under certainty is an *expectation*, since we do not know which event will occur. To decide whether or not to use the predictor, our grocer must assign a value to the perfect prediction and compare this value with the cost of the predictor. Remember that we do not know what the prediction will be.

EXPECTED VALUE OF PERFECT INFORMATION

In many decision problems the businessman faces the question of whether to act now or delay action and seek more information. The important thing to the businessman is to balance the *cost* of additional information against the *value* (additional profit) of the information. The cost part of this decision (cost of obtaining information) is usually easier to calculate than the value of the information. However, using the expected value model, we have a way of quantifying the value of additional information.

Referring again to our grocer example, we showed in Table 3–12 that the expected profit under certainty is $53.20. This amount, an expectation, is a measure of the best the grocer could do with a *perfect* predictor. Previously, in Table 3–7, we showed that the *EMV* of the best act under uncertainty, "stock 26," is $51. The difference,

$$\$53.20 - \$51 = \$2.20,$$

is the maximum amount by which the grocer could increase his expected profit if he had available a free, perfect predictive device. Hence, $2.20 is the *expected value of perfect information* (*EVPI*). Note from Table 3–9 that $2.20 is also the *expected opportunity loss* of the optimum act. We might expect this result, since the perfect predictor should reduce the opportunity loss that exists under uncertainty to zero. Hence the expected opportunity loss of the optimum act measures the *EVPI*. A useful check on computations is provided by the identity:

$$EMV + EOL \text{ of any act } = \text{expected profit under certainty}$$

This calculation is shown in Table 3–13.

TABLE 3–13

	Act			
	Stock 25	Stock 26	Stock 27	Stock 28
EMV (uncertainty).	$50.00	$51.00	$49.00	$42.00
EOL	3.20	2.20	4.20	11.20
Expected profit (certainty)	$53.20	$53.20	$53.20	$53.20

It is important to note that it is the *EOL* of the *optimal* act which is equal to the *EVPI*. If the grocer chooses the act "stock 28," he will have an *EMV* of $42 and an *EOL* of $11.20. The *EVPI* is *not* $11.20, because the grocer can increase his *EMV* to $51 by choosing a different act ("stock 26"), and this requires *no* additional information. The value of additional information is measured starting from the assumption that the optimal action would be chosen, given the information already available.

SENSITIVITY ANALYSIS OF SUBJECTIVE PROBABILITIES

Estimating probabilities is one of the most difficult steps in applying the expected monetary value decision criterion. Sometimes it is possible to avoid this step, at least partially, by leaving the estimation of probabilities to the last. For each act, a range of probabilities can be found over which the given act is optimal. The decision maker then determines in which interval his probabilities lie.

An example will help to clarify this. In Table 3–10, the conditional values for a new product decision were given ($1,000,000 if the product is successful; − $500,000 if it fails; and zero if it is not introduced). Let p be the probability of success, and hence $(1 − p)$ is the probability of failure for the new product. Assuming the decision maker wishes to use the *EMV* criterion, the expected value of introducing the product is:

$$EMV = p(1,000,000) + (1 − p)(−500,000)$$
$$= −500,000 + 1,500,000p$$

For the product to be introduced, *EMV* must be greater than zero. That is,

$$−500,000 + 1,500,000p > 0$$

or

$$p > \frac{500,000}{1,500,000} = \frac{1}{3}$$

Hence, if the decision maker feels that the chances are greater than one third for success, he should introduce the product. Note that he does not have to specify an exact value for p in order to make his decision.

Example

To further clarify this concept, consider again the example of the grocer deciding how many cases of milk to stock. From Table 3–7 we determined that the optimum act was to stock 26 cases. This result was obtained using the probabilities in the first column in Table 3–14 below. You can easily check that the action "stock 26" remains optimal for all the various sets of probabilities shown in Table 3–14.[1] Hence, the

TABLE 3–14
Alternative possible sets of probabilities

Event: demand	Sets of probabilities			
	1	2	3	4
25 cases	0.1	0.2	0.05	0.1
26 cases	0.3	0.3	0.15	0.1
27 cases	0.5	0.4	0.40	0.3
28 cases	0.1	0.1	0.40	0.5

decision maker can see that his decision is not *sensitive* to the variations in the probabilities that are given in Table 3–14. Other variations would cause a change in decision. For example, if the probability attached to the event "demand of 25 cases" is greater than 0.20, then the optimal decision changes to ordering 25 cases.

The general approach suggested by this example is called *sensitivity analysis*. The decision maker makes a preliminary set of estimates (for probabilities or for payoffs). He then makes variations in these estimates. If the variations do not change the optimal decision, he need go no further. If, on the other hand, the decision is sensitive to the changes, he must think carefully and refine his preliminary estimates in order to arrive at a decision.

DECISION TREES

When the decision maker must select one act from a set of possible actions, the analysis presented above using conditional value tables is appropriate. However, when the decision maker must make a *sequence* of decisions rather than only a single one, the use of a *decision tree* usually helps to simplify the analysis. A decision tree is a graphic device for showing the sequence of decisions to be made and the possible events that may occur.

An example will make this clear. Suppose that the marketing manager of a firm is trying to decide whether or not to market a new product. The cost of developing and marketing the product is $35,000. The profit to be made depends upon whether a competitive firm will market a

---

[1] The act "stock 26" remains optimal as long as $P(\text{demand} = 25) \leq 0.20$ and $P(\text{demand} \geq 27) \leq 0.80$. This model is developed in detail in Chapter 10.

similar product and upon what price can be charged. If no competitive product is introduced, the firm can set price to maximize profit. However, with a competitive product, the profit will depend upon the price the firm sets and the price set by the competitor. All this is diagrammed in the decision tree in Figure 3–1.

FIGURE 3–1

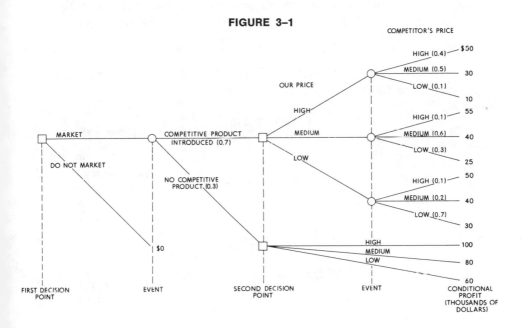

Note that this is a sequential decision problem. The firm must make a decision now about whether or not to market the product, and at a later date it must set a price.

The conditional profits are shown at the ends of the decision tree. These do not include the $35,000 market introduction cost. Note that the probabilities of the various events are also shown.[2] From the tree, we see, for example, that if there is a competitor in the market, and if our firm sets a high price, then there is a 0.4 chance that the competitor will also set a high price, a 0.5 chance that he will set a medium price, and a 0.1 chance that he will set a low price. The resulting conditional profits for these three cases are shown to be $50,000, $30,000, and $10,000, respectively. If we subtract the $35,000 market introduction cost, our firm will make a net profit of $15,000 in the first case, and losses of $5,000 and $25,000, respectively, in the second and third cases.

---

[2] We are simplifying the problem by using a set of probabilities for the competitor's reaction. In reality, this is a game decision problem in which we should consider the competitor's strategies and payoffs as well as ours. Problems of this sort are treated in Chapter 18.

To analyze a decision problem of this sort, we start at the end of the decision tree and work backward. For each possible set of decisions and events, we compute an expected value, exactly as we have done above. Thus, when we are in the upper right-hand part of Figure 3–1 (we are marketing the product, a competitive product is introduced, and we set a high price), we calculate an expected value over the high, medium, and low competitor price possibilities. This value is $36,000;

$$(\$50,000 \times 0.4) + (\$30,000 \times 0.5) + (\$10,000 \times 0.1) = \$36,000$$

and is shown in a small circle in Figure 3–2. Similar expected values are calculated for other points.

FIGURE 3–2

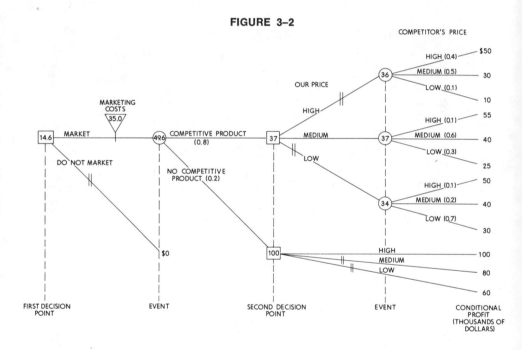

Now if we move back on the decision tree to the second decision point, we are faced with two decision situations. The first—when a competitive product has been introduced—involves setting a high, medium, or low price with expected profits of $36,000, $37,000, and $34,000, respectively. Assume the choice is the one with highest expected profit—the medium price. A mark (‖) is placed on the lines related to the other alternatives, indicating that they are nonoptimal, and the expected profit of $37,000 is attached to the upper box of the second decision point.

When no competitive product is introduced, the choice is a high price, with profit of $100,000.

At the event point to the left, an expected value of $49,600 is computed by multiplying the expected profit given a competitive product ($37,000) by its probability, 0.8, and adding the profit given no competitive product ($100,000) times its probability of 0.2.

Finally, the decision to market the product is made since the net profit of $14,600—the $49,600 expected profit less the marketing costs of $35,000—is greater than the zero profit from not marketing the product.

CONCLUSION

We have developed a method for using probabilities in making business decisions under conditions of uncertainty; the procedure may also be used for establishing the value of additional information. Future chapters will use many of the concepts introduced in this chapter. In this chapter the events were few and discontinuous (discrete events). Later, we shall discuss continuous probability distributions. Instead of a few possible events, the number of possible events will become very large.

BIBLIOGRAPHY

CHERNOFF, H., and MOSES, L. E. *Elementary Decision Theory.* New York: John Wiley & Sons, Inc., 1959.

DYCKMAN, T. R.; SMIDT, S.; and McADAMS, A. K. *Managerial Decision Making under Uncertainty.* New York: The Macmillan Co., 1969.

IEEE Transactions on Systems Science and Cybernetics (Special Issue on Decision Analysis), Vol SSC-4, No. 3 (September 1968).

MAGEE, J. F. "Decision Trees for Decision-Making," *Harvard Business Review,* July-August, 1964; and "How to Use Decision Trees in Capital Investment," *Harvard Business Review,* September-October 1964.

PRATT, J. W.; RAIFFA, H.; and SCHLAIFER, R. *Introduction to Statistical Decision Theory.* New York: McGraw-Hill Book Co., 1965.

RAIFFA, H. *Decision Analysis.* Reading, Mass.: Addison-Wesley Publishing Co., Inc., 1968.

SCHLAIFER, R. *Analysis of Decisions under Uncertainty.* New York: Mc-Graw-Hill Book Co., 1969.

————. *Probability and Statistics for Business Decisions.* New York: Mc-Graw-Hill Book Co., 1959.

SPURR, W. A., and BONINI, C. P. *Statistical Analysis for Business Decisions.* Rev. ed. Homewood, Ill.: Richard D. Irwin, Inc., 1973.

THRALL, R. M.; COOMBS, C. H.; and DAVIS, R. L. (eds.). *Decision Processes.* New York: John Wiley & Sons, Inc., 1954.

WINKLER, R. L. *Introduction to Bayesian Inference and Decision.* New York: Holt, Rinehart & Winston, Inc., 1972.

PROBLEMS

3–1. An analysis and forecast of next month's sales results in the following probability distribution:

Total demand	Probability
10 units...................	0.10
11 units...................	0.70
12 units...................	0.20
	1.00

The profit per unit is $5. The cost of the product sold is $6. If the product is not sold during the month, it is worthless (leftover units are of no value).

a) Compute the expected (mean) sales for the month.

b) Prepare a table of conditional values for the different possible acts.

c) Prepare a table of expected monetary values and indicate the optimum act.

3–2. Continuation of Problem 3–1:

a) Prepare a table of conditional opportunity losses.

b) Prepare a table of expected opportunity losses.

c) Indicate the optimum act.

d) Rank the acts. Show the differences between the expected opportunity losses of each act and the *EOL* of the optimum act.

e) Rank the acts, using expected values. Show the differences between the *EMV* of each act and the *EMV* of the optimum act. Compare these results with those of part *(d)*.

3–3. Refer to Problem 3–1.

a) Present the conditional value table, assuming a perfect predicting device.

b) Present the expected value table, assuming a perfect predicting device.

c) Compute the expected value of perfect information.

3–4. Assume the following conditional value table applies to a decision:

Event	Probability of event	Act 1	Act 2	Act 3
		Conditional monetary value of—		
A.........	0.35	4	3	2
B.........	0.45	4	6	5
C.........	0.20	4	6	8

a) Present a table of expected monetary values and determine the optimum act.
b) Present a table of expected opportunity losses.
c) Compute the conditional value table, assuming a perfect predicting device.
d) Compute the expected value table, assuming a perfect predicting device.
e) Compute the expected value of perfect information.

3–5. A newsstand operator assigns probabilities to the demand for *Fine* magazine as follows:

Event: demand	Probability of event
10 copies.	0.10
11 copies.	0.15
12 copies.	0.20
13 copies.	0.25
14 copies.	0.30
	1.00

An issue sells for 50 cents and costs 30 cents.
a) If the operator *can* return free of charge any unsold copies, how many should he order?
b) If the operator *cannot* return unsold copies, how many copies should he order?
c) Explain why the number of copies ordered decreases as the salvage value of unsold copies decreases.

3–6. A manufacturer of sporting goods has the following demand and probability schedule for a yearly fishing guide magazine:

Event: demand	Probability of event
100,000.	0.20
200,000	0.20
300,000.	0.20
400,000.	0.20
500,000.	0.20
	1.00

The incremental costs of production are $4 per thousand, the selling price is $5 per thousand, and the salvage value of unsold magazines is zero.
a) The manufacturer reasons as follows: "Since there is equal chance of demand being less or greater than 300,000, I shall produce the most likely amount, 300,000." Do you agree? If not, why not?

    b) What is the expected value of a perfect prediction?

    c) Show that the *EMV* of each act plus the *EOL* of each act equals the expected profit under certainty.

3–7. A real estate investor owns a gasoline station which he has leased to a major oil company for a rental fee based on a share of profits. If the station is successful, the present value of future rentals is estimated at $1 million. If the station is not successful, the present value of the rentals will be $200,000. The oil company has offered the investor $600,000 to buy the property outright. On an expected monetary value basis, what probability would need to be assigned to "success" for the investor to be indifferent between selling and not selling?

3–8. A wholesaler of sporting goods has an opportunity to buy 5,000 pairs of skis that have been declared surplus by the government. The wholesaler will pay $5 a pair, and he can obtain $10 a pair by selling the skis to retailers. The price is well established, but the wholesaler is in doubt as to just how many pairs he will be able to sell. Any skis left over he can sell to discount outlets at $2 a pair. After a careful consideration of the historical data, the wholesaler assigns probabilities to demand as follows:

Retailer's demand	Probability
1,000 pairs.	0.60
3,000 pairs.	0.30
5,000 pairs.	0.10
	1.00

    a) Compute the conditional monetary value of the different possible levels of demand.

    b) Compute the expected monetary values.

    c) Compute the expected profit with a perfect predicting device.

    d) Compute the expected value of perfect information.

3–9. A bookstore owner can purchase 20,000 of a publisher's leftovers for 50 cents a copy. By making use of advertising in a nationally distributed newspaper, he hopes to be able to sell the books for $2 a copy. Leftover books can be sold at 20 cents a copy to other retailers. His estimate of demand is:

Estimated demand	Probability of demand
5,000.	0.10
10,000.	0.50
20,000.	0.40
	1.00

The cost of advertising is $12,000, and incremental costs of shipping the books which are sold are 25 cents per copy.

a)   Should the bookstore owner purchase the books?

b)   What is the expected profit with a perfect predicting device?

c)   What is the expected cost of uncertainty?

d)   What is the maximum amount the owner should pay for perfect information?

3–10.   A manufacturer of hair tonic is considering production of a new hair dressing which he hopes will increase sales. The incremental profit is $10 per unit (on a present-value basis), and the necessary investment in equipment is $500,000. The estimate of demand is as follows:

Units of demand	Probability
30,000.	0.05
40,000.	0.10
50,000.	0.20
60,000.	0.30
70,000.	0.35
	1.00

a)   Should the new product be produced?

b)   What is the expected value of perfect information?

c)   How would the expected value of perfect information change if the probability of 30,000 units was 0.10 and the probability of 70,000 units was 0.30? What causes this change?

3–11.   When a new shopping center is built, the electric company must assign a transformer to the location. Since this is done before the occupants of the shopping center are known, there is uncertainty about the amount of electricity to be used (for example, beauty salons use much more electricity than toy stores) and hence uncertainty about the size of transformer needed. A too small transformer would have to be replaced, and one too large would result in more expense than necessary. A table giving these costs is shown below:

Amount of electricity ultimately needed	Size of transformer originally installed		
	Small	Medium	Large
Little.	50	100	150
Medium	140	100	150
Much.	190	190	150

Suppose, for a given shopping center, the following probabilities are assigned to the amount of electricity ultimately needed:

Need	Probability
Little	0.2
Medium.	0.7
Much	0.1
	1.0

a)   Draw up an opportunity loss table.

b)   What decision should be made? Why?

c)   What is the expected value of perfect information?

3–12.   The Wheeling Steel Corporation for several years had a PTO (price at the time of order) policy. A firm could order steel for future delivery and pay the price in effect at the time of order rather than at the time of delivery. Comment on this pricing policy.

3–13.   Football Concessions had the franchise to sell ice cream, soft drinks, hot dogs, etc., at Siwash University home football games. This was a profitable operation since crowds could be estimated reasonably accurately and the right amount of food purchased.

However, Saturday, November 11, 1972, posed a problem for the concessionnaire. Siwash was due to play its arch rival, Carbunkle U., on that day. Both teams were undefeated, and the winner was sure to get a Bowl bid. Advance sales of tickets indicated that if the weather was nice, a crowd of over 80,000 people could be expected. On the other hand, it was raining on Friday, and the weather prediction called for possible showers or rain on Saturday. If the rain was heavy, it was possible that a crowd of only 20,000 would show up for the game.

The concessionnaire had to order his food on Friday. He generally ordered on the basis of $0.50 per person, and this had proven reasonably accurate in the past. He had a markup of 50 percent (i.e., selling price was double cost). He could generally save about 20 percent of the value (cost) of anything that he had left over.

The concessionnaire assigned the following probabilities to the various possible crowd sizes. He generally felt that it would either clear up and a large crowd result, or rain and a small crowd be present. The possibility of a medium-sized crowd, he felt, was less likely.

Crowd size	Probability
20,000.	0.30
40,000.	0.20
60,000.	0.10
80,000.	0.40
	1.00

How much food should the concessionnaire order?

3–14. A company is trying to decide about the size of a new plant currently planned for Atlanta. At present, the company has only a minimal sales effort in the southern states. However, when the Atlanta plant is completed, a major promotion effort will be undertaken. Management is somewhat uncertain about how successful this effort will be. It is estimated that there is a 0.4 chance that the company will capture a *significant* share of the market and a 0.6 chance that only a *moderate* market share will result.

A *large* plant will be needed if a significant market share is realized. A *small* plant would suffice for the moderate case. The cost of the large plant is $8 million; the cost of the small plant, $5 million.

If a significant market share materializes, the estimated present value of resulting profits (excluding cost of the plant) is $13 million; if a moderate share materializes, the present value of the resulting profits (again excluding cost of the plant) is $8 million.

Management has one other alternative. This is to build a small plant, wait to see the result of the promotion effort, and then expand plant if the situation warrants. It would cost an additional $4.5 million to expand the small plant to the capacity of a large one.

a) Draw a decision tree for this problem.

b) What decision should the company make, and what is the expected value?

3–15. In early January of 1973, Etta Laboratories received an order for 10,000 ounces of its new product, Calbonite, an ingredient used to manufacture a new variety of drugs. This was by far the largest order ever received for Calbonite—total production in 1972 had been only 1,200 ounces. The order called for 5,000 ounces to be delivered in June and the remainder in November.

The process now used to synthesize Calbonite was a long one, involving processing small batches of raw material through several stages. The company would have to invest $50,000 in new equipment to bring the production capacity up to the 1,000 ounces per month level needed to meet the order. (It would take the month of January to order and set up the equipment.) The variable manufacturing cost per ounce using this process was known to be $15.

One of the research chemists at Etta had just discovered a new process for synthesizing Calbonite. If the process could be made to work on a large scale, it would greatly simplify the production process, with potentially great savings in cost. Ordinarily, a discovery of this sort would be tested thoroughly in the laboratory and in a small pilot plant to be sure it worked and to estimate production costs. This would take about a year. However, because of the potential savings, management wondered if it should shorten this test period. The engineering department suggested a crash testing program lasting five months. At the end of this period, it would be known whether or not the process would work, and estimated production costs would be determined. This test would cost $20,000 more than the more extended test.

It was estimated that there was a 0.9 chance the new process would work. Further, given that the new process worked, the chances were 4 out of 10 that the production cost would be $2 per ounce, 4 out of 10 that it would be $10 per ounce, and 2 out of 10 that it would be $18 per ounce.

If a decision was made at this stage to use the new process, the month of June would be used to set up the new manufacturing process. Thus, if this testing program were utilized, the company would have to set up and run the first 5,000 ounces using the old process.

Also, note that only the incremental testing costs associated with crashing the test program need be charged against that alternative. Since this company would test and buy the equipment for the new process if the tests were successful independent of this decision, the costs associated with these activities need not be considered in this decision.

a) Draw a decision tree for this problem.
b) What decisions should be made? What is the expected cost of filling this order?

3–16. A camera manufacturer produces two models (standard and deluxe). In preparation for the heavy Christmas selling season, he must decide how many of each model to produce. Variable cost of the standard camera is $10, and selling price is $20; variable cost of the deluxe model is $20, and selling price is $35. He estimates demand as follows:

Standard model		Deluxe model	
Demand	Probability	Demand	Probability
6,000	0.30	2,000	0.20
8,000	0.70	4,000	0.80

Any cameras not sold during the Christmas season are sold at salvage prices of $5 for the standard and $10 for the deluxe model. The manufacturer feels that different segments of the market purchase the two different models; thus the probabilities of sales given above are independent.

Suppose production capacity is not limited. Then the two decisions can be made independently. What are the optimal quantities of each model to produce? What are the two optimal *EMV*'s?

3–17. (Continuation of Problem 3–16)

Now suppose that due to capacity constraints, total production is limited to 10,000 cameras. Construct a *decision tree* for this situation and analyze it to obtain optimal production quantities in this case. What is the *EMV* of the optimal action?

3–18. (Continuation of Problem 3–16)

Now suppose that production is limited to a total of 10,000 cameras but that the manufacturer now feels that the probabilities of demands are *no longer independent* for the two models. Specifically, he now agrees that the following joint probability table is the appropriate way to describe probabilities of demands:

Joint probability table

Standard demand	Deluxe demand	2,000	4,000	Marginal probability of demand for standard
6,000		0.20	0.10	0.30
8,000		0	0.70	0.70
Marginal probability of demand for deluxe		0.20	0.80	1.00

Construct a decision tree for this situation and find the optimal act and its *EMV*.

3–19. A company owns a lease granting it the right to explore for oil on certain property. They may sell the lease for $15,000, or they may drill for oil. The four possible drilling outcomes are listed below, together with probabilities of occurrence and dollar consequences:

Possible outcome	Probability	Consequences
Dry well	0.16	−$100,000
Gas well only	0.40	50,000
Oil and gas combination	0.24	100,000
Oil well	0.20	200,000

Draw a decision tree for this problem and compute the expected monetary value for the act "drill." Should the company drill or sell the lease?

4

Decision theory

We shall define decision theory as being primarily concerned with how to assist people (or organizations) in making decisions, and improving the decision process under conditions of uncertainty. Decision theory enables the decision maker to analyze a set of complex situations with many alternatives and many different possible consequences. The major objective is to identify a course of action which is consistent with the basic psychological desires of the decision maker. Chapter 3 also dealt with decision theory but did not consider different decision criteria.

Business managers frequently deal with complicated decisions by assuming certainty. That is, the data which go into the computations are assumed to be known without question; or at most, a disclaiming statement is made, such as "Of course, the facts are not known with certainty." This approach is reasonable for many decisions. Decision making, even under certainty, can be complex. It may be desirable to start with the situation where the facts are assumed to be known. Many conventional solutions offered to such problems as inventory control, "make or buy," capital budgeting, and pricing assume certainty.

In this chapter, we shall continue to discuss the art of decision making under uncertainty. The inventory decision is used as an illustration. It will become obvious that absolutely correct answers are difficult to find when the future is uncertain, but that there are some reasonable approaches to this class of decision problems that should be understood by the businessman.

THE DECISION PROBLEM

We shall consider in this chapter a relatively common type of decision. There will be several possible acts and several possible states of nature. For example, the possible acts may be:

1. To decide the number of units of inventory to order
2. To buy or not to buy fire insurance
3. To make or to buy a product
4. To invest or not to invest in a piece of equipment
5. To add or not to add a new product line
6. To change the price or not to change the price of a product (and if so, the amount of the change)

By states of nature, we mean the actual possible events which may occur. One of the possible states of nature is the true state, but we do not know which one. Possible states of nature or events for each of the above acts are:

1. Demand for the product may be 0, 1, 2, 3, . . . , 50.
2. A fire may occur, or a fire may not occur.
3. If we make the product, the cost of making it may be 10 cents, 11 cents, . . . , 50 cents.
4. If we invest in the equipment, its cost saving per hour may be $1, $1.01, $1.02, . . . , $2.50.
5. If we add a new product line, the sales may be one million, two million, etc.
6. If we change the price, the unit sales may be 0, 1, 2, 3, . . . , 10,000.

Not knowing which of the states of nature is the true state, we place a *probability distribution* on the possible occurrence of each event (we can have as fine a breakdown as we wish of the possible states). The probability distribution could be based on objective evidence of the past if the decision maker feels the same forces will continue to operate in the future. However, we are not restricted to objective probabilities. It may be reasonable to assign the probabilities that the decision maker thinks appropriate to the possible states of nature, so that he may act consistently with his beliefs about the possible events and the economic consequences of those events. To the extent possible, objective evidence should be supplied to help the decision maker improve his assignment of probabilities.

An example

To illustrate the discussion, we shall develop an example. This is a simple inventory decision problem, similar to the type already introduced in Chapter 3. The problem is to determine how many units to order. The price of the product is $5, the cost is $3, and profit per unit is

$2. Unsold units have no salvage value. The possible states of nature (possible demands) and their probabilities are as shown in Table 4–1.

TABLE 4–1

Demand	$p(q_i)$
$q_1 = 0$....................	0.05
$q_2 = 1$....................	0.60
$q_3 = 2$....................	0.35
	1.00

The possible acts are to buy zero, one, or two units (it would be unreasonable to buy three if the probability of selling three units is zero). The possible states of nature are that demand will be zero, one, or two units requested. The first step in obtaining a solution is to prepare a table (see Table 4–2) showing the profits which will result from each combination of act and state of nature. We have called this a conditional profit or payoff table. The profits are conditional on choosing a specific act and having a given state of nature come true; the symbolic representation of an entry is $R(q_i, d_j)$. Thus $R(q_2, d_3)$ would be the profit of decision d_3 if the state of nature is q_2.

TABLE 4–2*
Conditional profit table

State of nature— demand is:	Act		
	d_1 Buy 0	d_2 Buy 1	d_3 Buy 2
$q_1 = 0$	0	(3)	(6)
$q_2 = 1$	0	2	(1)
$q_3 = 2$	0	2	4

* Losses (negative profits) are shown in parentheses.

The decision to be made is whether zero, one, or two units should be ordered. It is not obvious how many units should be ordered. The solution to even this relatively simple problem is complex; in fact, it is not clear what the answer "should" be. We shall consider several possible decision criteria.

DECISION CRITERIA

In considering some of the possible decision criteria, we shall list them in reverse order of our preference. Thus, we shall start out with the least desirable criterion and work our way toward those which the authors prefer. The possible criteria include:

1. Maximizing the *maximum possible* profit (maximax criterion);[1] i.e., choose the d_j with the maximum $R(q_i, d_j)$.
2. Assuming *equally likely* events. Choose the d_j which maximizes $\dfrac{1}{n} \sum_i R(q_i, d_j)$, where n is the number of possible events (states of nature).
3. Maximizing the *minimum possible* profit, the maximin procedure (or minimizing the maximum possible cost, the minimax procedure).
4. Basing the decision on the profits of the event with the *maximum likelihood* of occurring.
5. Using the *Bayes decision rule:* Multiply the consequences of each act by the probabilities of the several occurrences, and sum the products. The act with the largest expected value is the most desirable decision [maximize $\bar{R}(d_j)$, where $\bar{R}(d_j) = \sum_i p(q_i)R(q_i, d_j)$ and where $p(q_i)$ represents the probability of event q_i].

The type of decision being studied here may be described as a game against nature. It has been suggested that decision theory is a branch of game theory; however, it should be remembered that nature does not think and plot against its opponent. Criteria which may be completely reasonable in game theory (such as minimax) are less reasonable in a game against nature. This distinction is important, since the criticism which follows applies only in decisions involving nature, not in decisions involving a thinking opponent.

There will be one major assumption in the discussion which follows. We shall assume that the decision maker has a utility function which is linear with respect to money. That is, $2 is twice as desirable as $1, $4 twice as desirable as $2, $8 twice as desirable as $4, and so on. Most people act in a manner which indicates that this assumption is not valid. Thus, it would be appropriate to introduce a new measure (call it utility) instead of dollars. This would be useful, but it would distract one from the primary discussion. Therefore the assumption is made here that it is appropriate to use the dollar measure of rewards. A more detailed discussion of this assumption is given in Chapter 17.

MAXIMAX

Maximax chooses the act which maximizes the maximum possible profit. It is not a procedure which is generally followed, and for good

---

[1] A weighted average of minimum and maximum payoffs of each procedure has been suggested but will not be discussed here.

reason. It ignores possible losses and the probabilities of making or not making a profit. It might appeal to a highly adventurous person, but he would probably not prosper for long, since he would be attempting projects with very little chance of being successful. It would seem desirable systematically to incorporate into the decision the probabilities of success and failure.

In the example of this chapter the maximax criterion would result in an order of two units, since that act results in a profit of \$4 if the demand is two units. $R(q = 2, d = 2)$ is the maximum $R(q_i, d_j)$. In the present problem, this decision may not seem unreasonable, but suppose the probability of demand being two was 0.0001. Would an order size of two still be reasonable?

EQUALLY LIKELY

This procedure suggests that we add the possible consequences of each act and divide by the number of possible events. The act with the highest $\dfrac{1}{n} \sum\limits_{i} R(q_i, d_j)$ is the most desirable act. If we know little about the probability of the possible events, some would argue that we should then assume that each event is equally likely. However, it is rare that we do not have *some* idea about the probability of possible events. These probabilities, which may or may not be based on objective evidence, should be used in the analysis if our action is to be consistent with our judgment. Automatically assuming the events are equally likely will not insure such consistency if we feel one event is more likely to occur than another. For example, in the present problem a specific probability distribution is given. There is no reason to assume that there is equal probability that each event will occur.

As long as it is thought appropriate to use probabilities, and where there is no reason to assume the probabilities of the states of nature are equally likely, then the best estimate of the probabilities should be used, rather than the "equally likely" assumption.

MINIMAX

Minimax suggests that we choose the act with the minimum maximum loss or, alternatively, with the maximum minimum profit. That is, we should make sure that we can earn at least R dollars, and search for the act which gives the largest R (or the smallest loss, if we are discussing losses).

In the example the minimax act would be to order zero units. The maximum possible loss with zero units is zero dollars; with the other two acts the maximum losses are $3 and $6.

Unless there is zero probability of loss, minimax tends to lead to a decision to do nothing. It is a very conservative decision criterion. Ultimately, a minimaxer would be faced with the threat of starving to death (by doing nothing) and would be forced into action. In terms of business activity, the corporation would become stagnant and would be overcome by competition willing to innovate and to take reasonable chances of suffering losses.

In some situations, minimax may lead to a totally unreasonable decision. For example, assume Table 4–3 shows the conditional costs asso-

TABLE 4–3
Conditional cost table

| | Act | |
States of nature	Buy insurance	Do not buy
q_1	$100	$101
q_2	100	1

ciated with the only two possible acts. "Buy insurance" is the best act according to minimax, since the maximum cost is $100 (the maximum cost of "do not buy insurance" is $101). However, if the two given states of nature are equally likely, or if state q_2 is more likely than state q_1, then most individuals would label "do not buy" as being the most desirable act.

MAXIMUM LIKELIHOOD

Using the maximum-likelihood decision criterion procedure, we only consider the consequences of the state of nature which is most likely to occur and choose the best act for that state of nature. In the example being considered, this is state "demand is one," leading to a decision to order one unit. This is a reasonable decision in the present context, but it might not always be so. For example, assume the probability of demand being one is 0.51 and demand being two is 0.49. Now it is not clear that to order one is the best decision. To add further evidence that the maximum-likelihood decision may be faulty, reduce the loss on a leftover unit (increase the salvage value) until there is practically no penalty connected with leftovers. With the 0.49 probability of selling the second unit, ordering two is a better decision.

Since the maximum-likelihood criterion ignores the consequences of all states except the state with the highest probability, it fails to make use of much of the information which is available to the decision maker. By failing to make use of this information, it can arrive at decisions which may not be reasonable.

BAYES DECISION RULE

The Bayes decision rule, already introduced in earlier chapters, says to compute the expected value of each act (multiply the conditional profit by the probability of the state of nature, and sum the products for each state) and take the act with the largest expected value; i.e., maximize $\bar{R}(d_j)$.

The expected values of the three acts are computed as shown in Table 4–4. The act with the highest expected value is "buy 1"; thus, we should

TABLE 4–4*

Buy 0	Buy 1	Buy 2
0 X 0.05 = 0	(3) X 0.05 = (0.15)	(6) X 0.05 = (0.30)
0 X 0.60 = 0	2 X 0.60 = 1.20	(1) X 0.60 = (0.60)
0 X 0.35 = 0	2 X 0.35 = 0.70	4 X 0.35 = 1.40
$\bar{R}(d_1) = 0$	$\bar{R}(d_2) = 1.75$	$\bar{R}(d_3) = 0.50$

* The parentheses indicate a loss.

buy one unit. If the probabilities were changed, or if the conditional profits were different because of changes in price, costs, or salvage value, the expected value would be recomputed, with a possible change in decision.

In practice, the inventory problem is not solved using the payoff table and computing the expected value of each possible act. However, the procedures which are used are based on the above analysis. That is, conventional inventory procedure assumes it is appropriate to use the Bayes decision rule, with money measures representing the utilities.

In the chapters of this book, not all the problems are approached from the point of view of decision making under uncertainty. However, when uncertainty is present, it is assumed that it is reasonable to use the expected value of the act and to choose the act with the highest expected value. To be generally valid, the value should be measured in terms of utility, though there will be many situations where it is appropriate to use expected monetary value.

LINEAR FUNCTIONS

If the cost or profit function is linear, i.e., of the form $P = \sum_i a_i X_i$, then the Bayes decision computations may be simplified. Instead of computing the conditional profit for each act and each state of nature, we can compute the average state of nature and insert it in the profit or cost equation.

Example

Assume profit, P, is equal to an unknown constant, b, times the number of units sold, Q, but we are not sure of the value of b (i.e., there are several possible states of nature). However, we do have the information shown in Table 4–5.

TABLE 4–5

Values of b	Probability
$1.50	0.20
1.60	0.70
1.70	0.10

The basic profit equation is:

$$P = bQ$$

Assume the number of units to be sold the next period is known to be 10. The average or expected profit is:

$$E(P) = E(bQ) = QE(b)$$

The above equation results because Q is a constant, and the expectation of a constant times a random variable is equal to the constant times the mean of the variable. Thus the expected profit is equal to Q times the expectation of b:

$$E(b) = 1.50(0.20) + 1.60(0.70) + 1.70(0.10) = 1.59$$

The expected profit is:

$$E(P) = 10 \times 1.59 = \$15.90$$

Assume that instead of knowing Q with certainty, we know that b is $1.50 per unit, and we have the probability distribution for Q (the values of Q are now the states of nature) shown in Table 4–6.

TABLE 4–6

Values of Q	Probability
9.	0.4
10.	0.5
11.	0.1

The basic profit equation remains:

$$P = bQ$$

Since b is now a constant:

$$E(P) = E(bQ) = bE(Q)$$

The value of $E(Q)$ is:

$$E(Q) = 9(0.4) + 10(0.5) + 11(0.1) = 9.7$$

The expected profit is:

$$E(P) = 1.50 \times 9.7 = \$14.55$$

Now, let us assume that neither b nor Q is known with certainty (both are random variables with the probability distributions given above). We shall make the important assumption that b and Q are independent. If any two random variables, X and Y, are independent, then the expectation of their product is equal to the product of their expectations:

$$E(XY) = E(X)E(Y)$$

In our example:

$$P = bQ$$

and

$$E(P) = E(bQ) = E(b)E(Q)$$

Substituting the values for the expectations of b and Q:

$$E(P) = 1.59 \times 9.7 = \$15.42$$

Thus, if we assume uncertainty for both b and Q, we have an expected profit of \$15.42 and can make our plans accordingly. However, it should be noted that \$15.42 is an expectation. The profit may be as low as \$13.50 (if $Q = 9$ and $b = \$1.50$) or as high as \$18.70 (if $Q = 11$ and $b = \$1.70$).

The use of the relatively simple mathematical techniques presented here greatly simplifies the computations of the expected profit, with no loss of information (if we accept the Bayes decision rule as our decision criterion).

CONCLUSION

Decision theory concerns itself with choosing the best act from a set of possible acts, given uncertainty as to the state of nature which exists. By the use of the Bayes decision rule, this can be accomplished in a manner which is consistent with the decision maker's beliefs, even if there are no objective probabilities which can be applied to the states of nature.

A prime contribution of this procedure is that it focuses attention on all possible events and requires a calculation of the consequences of each act and each possible state of nature. Even if the analysis stopped with the conditional value table, this would be a contribution to the art of decision making. But by the use of the Bayes decision rule, it is possible to go further. For a decision maker to stop with the one computation using the most likely event is not justified in view of the techniques which are available for incorporating uncertainty into the analysis.

The advocacy of the Bayes decision rule implies measurable utility relationships. In the real world the input data for decisions is generally in the form of dollars, not measures of utility, and it will not always be appropriate to base a decision on expected monetary value.

BIBLIOGRAPHY

BAUMOL, W. J. *Economic Theory and Operations Analysis.* 3d ed. Englewood Cliffs, N.J.: Prentice-Hall, Inc., 1972.

BROSS, I. D. J. *Design for Decision.* New York: Macmillan Co., 1953.

CHERNOFF, H., and MOSES, L. E. *Elementary Decision Theory.* New York: John Wiley & Sons, Inc., 1959.

LUCE, R. D., and RAIFFA, H. *Games and Decisions.* New York: John Wiley & Sons, Inc., 1957.

WEISS, L. *Statistical Decision Theory.* New York: McGraw-Hill Book Co., 1961.

QUESTIONS AND PROBLEMS

4–1. A businessman is presented with a conditional profit table. What criterion should he use in making his decision as to which act is most desirable? Discuss the relative merits of maximax, assuming equally likely events, minimax, maximum likelihood, and the Bayes decision rule in the context of a business decision.

4–2. It has been stated in the text that decisions cannot always be based on computations involving only the monetary expressions of the consequences. Describe some business situations where factors other than money are important.

4–3. In the presence of decision making under uncertainty, can the expert evolve a procedure which will guarantee the correct decision? Explain.

4–4. Is it correct to say that $E(XY)$ is equal to $E(X)E(Y)$? Is it correct to say that $E(X + Y)$ is equal to $E(X) + E(Y)$?

4–5. Total cost of a product is equal to:

$$T = 10,000 + bX$$

The total revenue is $R = 20X$. The variable cost per unit for the next period is a random variable with the following probability distribution:

b	$p(b)$
$5	0.10
6	0.50
7	0.40

a) Compute the expected profit for the coming period, assuming that 1,000 units are expected to be sold.

b) Compute the expected profit for the coming period, assuming that there is a 0.5 probability of selling 1,000 units and a 0.5 probability of zero units (assume X and b are independent).

4–6. The following probabilities are assigned to the possible values of fraction defective in a manufacturing process:

Event	Probability of event
0.01 defective.	0.10
0.02 defective.	0.15
0.03 defective.	0.20
0.04 defective.	0.30
0.05 defective.	0.20
0.10 defective.	0.03
0.15 defective.	0.02
	1.00

Suppose we have a lot of 50,000 parts and each defective costs 25 cents in rework costs. What is the expected rework cost? Would it be cheaper to inspect 100 percent of the lot if it costs 3 cents per item to inspect (assuming that all defectives are removed by inspection)?

4–7. A sales manager lists the following probabilities for various demand levels for a new product:

Probability	Demand (in units)
0.10	50
0.30	100
0.30	150
0.15	200
0.10	250
0.05	300

Suppose that the cost of introducing the product is $500 and profit per unit sold is $5. What is the expected profit from the new product?

4–8. You are president of an American corporation which manufactures aircraft. There has been some talk in Washington about (a) going to Mars, (b) not going to Mars, and (c) going to Mars with the Russians. In your judgment the probability of these states is 0.5, 0.4, and 0.1, respectively. You must make plans in the light of these possible states. Your alternatives are (a) to continue to make airplanes only, which would provide you with an expected $10-million profit, regardless of the Mars decision; or (b) to design a payload system for the Mars shot (if the program falls through, you would lose $30 million; if it does not fall through, you will make a profit of $40 million, regardless of Russian participation or not); or (c) to design a payload booster system. If the program falls through, you will lose $100 million. If we go, but with Russian participation, it is likely that we shall use Russia's booster system, and your profits will be $20 million. If we go alone, your profits would be $80 million.

Assume you base your decision on dollar profits.

a) What is the maximax act?
b) What is the act on the assumption of equally likely states?
c) What is the minimax act?
d) What is the maximum-likelihood act?
e) What is the Bayesian act?
f) Which decision do you prefer?

4–9. A company is considering an advertising campaign to increase the sales of the Gadgeto, the company's major product. An advertising budget of $300,000 has been proposed for the next year.

The sales manager and president agree on the following probability distribution for the effect of the advertising campaign on Gadgeto sales:

Sales increase (units)	Probability
150,000	0.05
200,000	0.25
250,000	0.30
300,000	0.20
350,000	0.10
400,000	0.05
450,000	0.05
	1.00

The company makes a profit of $1.20 on each Gadgeto sold. What is the expected incremental profit if the advertising campaign is adopted?

4–10. Two students are trying to use the equally likely criterion in connection with the possible outcomes of two tosses of a coin. Student A says that each of the three following possible outcomes is considered equally likely to him:

Zero heads in two tosses
One head in two tosses
Two heads in two tosses

Student B argues that each of the following possible outcomes is considered equally likely to him: HH, HT, TH, TT.
If the coin were a fair coin, which assessment would you prefer? Why?

4–11. Refer to Problem 3–19.
a) Prepare a conditional value table for the two acts (sell lease or drill) and the four possible outcomes.
b) What is the best maximax act?
c) What is the best act under the equally likely criterion?
d) What is the best minimax act?
e) What is the best maximum likelihood act?
d) What is the best Bayes act?

4–12. A businessman needs a piece of equipment. He can buy either a new or used piece of equipment; the new piece costs more than the used piece, but it is much more likely to provide trouble-free service which is of crucial importance. Of the five decision criteria suggested in this chapter, which one(s) would seem most suitable here? Why?

4–13.   The following is a letter to the editor in *The New York Times*[2] of February 28, 1971.

Yalta: Lack of Communication on Bomb

To the Editor:

Under the title "The Truth About Yalta," C. L. Sulzberger (column Feb. 14) discussed the assessment by Ambassador Charles Bohlen of the chief problems which faced President Roosevelt and the U.S. delegation at the time of the Yalta Conference, February 1945. The third point of this assessment reads in part as follows:

"While Roosevelt and a handful of advisers knew about the Manhattan Project, no one could be certain the atomic bomb would in fact explode or how effective a weapon it would be."

This problem looked different as seen from the Los Alamos Scientific Laboratory charged with the development of the bomb. By February 1945 it appeared to me and to other fully informed scientists that there was a better than 90 percent probability that the atomic bomb would in fact explode; that it would be an extremely effective weapon, and that there would be enough material to build several bombs in the course of a few months.

Thus even if the first bomb should have failed, the project was bound to succeed in a relatively short time. Few things in war and even fewer in politics have as good a chance as 90 percent.

That the full flavor of this conviction of the scientists was not transmitted to the decision-makers was a failure of communication—excessive secrecy and the absence of direct channels between scientists and high Government officials were responsible. Because of this failure of direct communication, the U.S. at Yalta urged Russia to participate in the assault on Japan, with grave consequences for the future of the political situation in the Far East. Suppose there had been good communication. Should the U.S. Government have acted on a 90 percent probability of technical success? In my opinion, definitely yes.

Again, in 1958 we had a chance to arrange a ban on the testing of nuclear weapons at a time when the U.S. had a clear advantage over the Soviet Union in weapon design. However, we were afraid of the possibility of clandestine underground Russian tests of small nuclear weapons and insisted therefore on ironclad safeguards. These were unacceptable to the U.S.S.R., and no agreement was reached by 1961.

In 1961 the Russians conducted a series of nuclear weapons tests in which they managed to equal, in most of the important aspects, the performance of U.S. thermonuclear weapons. Thus here again, by insisting on certainty, the U.S. lost a clear advantage.

This letter is not meant to imply that our foreign policy should center on advantage over the U.S.S.R. I merely wish to argue that if and when the seeking of such an advantage is part of our policy, we should act on high technical probability rather than requiring certainty and should have easy communication between the knowledgeable persons and the decision-makers.

Hans Bethe
Ithaca, N.Y., Feb. 16, 1971

The writer, 1967 Nobel laureate in physics, headed the theoretical division of the Los Alamos Scientific Laboratory from April 1943 to January 1946.

Comment upon the above letter noting particularly the following:

a)   The decision criterion that appears to have been used at the top levels of government.

b)   The decision criterion that is suggested by the author of the letter.

[2] © 1972 by The New York Times Company. Reprinted by permission.

5

Decisions and
revision of probabilities

In this chapter, we introduce the opportunity to experiment, i.e., to gather additional information and revise probabilities before making the decision.

We will deal with the simplest of possible situations where there is only one unknown. For example, the decision may hinge on the demand for the product in the next year. The only unknown, subject to a probability distribution, is demand. In this situation (which could be an inventory problem) the decision process is as follows:

1. Choose the decision criterion; we suggest the Bayes decision rule.
2. Describe the set of possible outcomes and possible decisions.
3. Assign probabilities to the possible outcomes (states of nature).
4. Determine a profit function.
5. Conduct an experiment.
6. Revise the assigned probabilities.
7. Compute the expected profit for each decision.
8. The optimum decision is the act with the highest expected profit.

The above process assumes that it has previously been determined that experimentation is desirable. We now investigate that question.

THE VALUE OF IMPERFECT INFORMATION

In this section, we shall introduce a general method for evaluating the possibility of obtaining more information. Later chapters will expand this analysis.

The expected value of perfect information ($EVPI$) introduced in Chapter 3 sets an upper limit on the value of additional information in a decision situation. Most information that we can obtain is *imperfect* in the sense that it will *not* tell us exactly which event will occur. Such information may have value if it will improve the chances of making a correct decision, that is, if it will improve the expected profit.

The term *experiment* is intended here to be very broad. An experiment may be a study by economists to predict national economic activity, a consumer survey by a market research firm, an opinion poll conducted on behalf of a political candidate, a sample of production line items taken by an engineer to check on quality, or a seismic test to give an oil-well-drilling firm some indications of the presence of oil.

In general, we can evaluate the worth of a given experiment only if we can estimate the reliability of the resulting information. A market research study may be helpful in deciding upon whether or not to introduce a new product. However, only if the decision maker can say beforehand how closely the market research study can estimate the potential sales can he put a specific economic value on the experiment.

An example will make this clear. Let us suppose that the sales of a new product will be either at a high level or quite low (the product will be either a success or a flop). The conditional value table for this decision is shown in Table 5–1. The conditional value of $4 million

TABLE 5–1
Conditional value table for decision on introduction of new product (millions of dollars)

| Outcome | Probabilities | Actions | |
		Introduce product	Do not introduce
High sales.	0.3	4.0	0
Low sales.	0.7	–2.0	0
Expected monetary values.		–0.2	0

is the net profit, over a period of time, if the potential sales level is high. The −$2 million is the cost of an abortive introduction.

Based on expected monetary values the indicated action is to abandon (i.e., not introduce) the product. However, the decision maker, being reluctant to give up a chance to make $4 million, may wonder if he should gather more information before action. As a first step, the *EVPI* can be obtained from the opportunity losses associated with the "do not introduce" action ($4 million for high sales and zero for low sales).[1]

---

[1] "Do not introduce" is the best act. But if high sales occur, there is an opportunity loss of $4 million; if low sales occur, there is no opportunity loss.

The *EVPI* is equal to the expected opportunity loss of the optimal act. If these opportunity losses are multiplied by the respective probabilities, *EVPI* is determined as \$1.2 million $[(0.3 \times 4) + (0.7 \times 0) = 1.2]$. Thus, there is, potentially at least, considerable value that can be obtained through additional information.

The decision maker can perform an experiment in this situation. Let us suppose the experiment takes the form of a market survey conducted in two representative cities. Although, in the past, such a survey often predicted accurately the success or failure of a new product, occasionally success was predicted for a product that later failed, and vice versa. In addition, the results were often inconclusive. The survey will cost \$0.2 million.

If the marketing manager takes the survey before acting, he can base his decision upon the survey predictions. This problem can be expressed

FIGURE 5–1
Decision tree for problem on introduction of new product

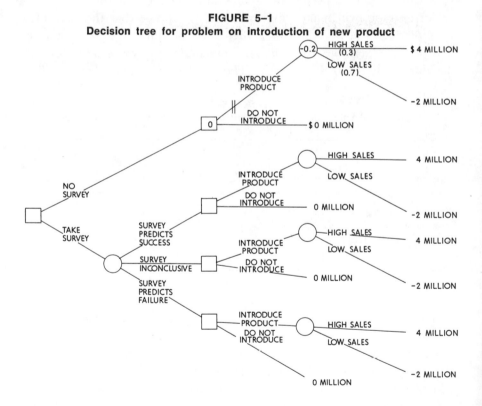

in terms of a decision tree, as shown in Figure 5–1. The upper part of the tree shows the decision process if no survey is taken. This is the same as Table 5–1, with probabilities of 0.3 and 0.7 for high and low sales, expected profit of $-\$0.2$ million for introduction, and an indicated decision of no introduction.

The marketing manager attaches conditional probabilities to the possible survey predictions as a function of the actual sales level, as specified in Table 5–2. That is, he attaches probabilities to "success," "inconclu-

TABLE 5–2
Conditional probabilities of survey predictions, given actual sales

Experimental results (survey prediction)	Actual level of sales	
	High sales (H)	Low sales (L)
Survey predicts success (S) (i.e., high sales)...............	0.4	0.1
Survey inconclusive (I)...............	0.4	0.5
Survey predicts failure (F)............	0.2	0.4
	1.0	1.0

sive," and "failure" predictions conditional on the event "high sales" and different probabilities conditional on the "low sales" event. Such probabilities would reflect past experience with surveys of this type, modified perhaps by the judgment of the marketing manager.

The probabilities shown in Table 5–2 express the reliability or accuracy of the experiment. With these estimates, the marketing manager can evaluate the economic worth of the survey. Without these reliability estimates, no specific value can be attached to taking the survey.

The decision probabilities

In order to complete the analysis of Figure 5–1, we need the *unconditional* probabilities of the various survey outcomes (all we have available are the probabilities of the high and low sales level). Similarly, we need the conditional probabilities of a high and low sales level, given a prediction of success, etc.; whereas Table 5–2 gives the conditional probabilities in the reverse order, namely, the conditional probabilities of the various predictions, given a high sales level, etc. To remedy this, the probabilities must be put in a different form.

We next construct a joint probability table, similar to those used in Chapter 2. In Table 5–3, the joint probability of both a successful prediction (S) and a high sales level (H) is obtained by multiplying the conditional probability of a successful prediction, given a high sales level (which is 0.4 from Table 5–2), by the probability of a high sales level:

$$P(SH) = P(S|H)P(H) = (0.4)(0.3) = 0.12$$

TABLE 5–3
Joint probability table

Level of sales	Survey prediction			Marginal probabilities of sales level
	Success (S)	Inconclusive (I)	Failure (F)	
High (H)	0.12	0.12	0.06	0.30
Low (L)	0.07	0.35	0.28	0.70
Marginal probabilities of survey prediction	0.19	0.47	0.34	1.00

Similarly:

$$P(SL) = P(S|L)P(L) = (0.1)(0.7) = 0.07$$

$$P(IH) = P(I|H)P(H) = (0.4)(0.3) = 0.12$$

and so on. Note that the marginal probabilities for "success," "inconclusive," and "failure" predictions are 0.19, 0.47, and 0.34, respectively. These are needed for our decision problem and are inserted in the proper places in Figure 5–2.

The decision tree also requires the conditional probabilities for the various levels of sales, given the survey prediction. These are called *posterior* probabilities and can be computed directly from the definition of Bayes theorem. For example, the probability of high sales, given a prediction of success, is:

$$P(H|S) = \frac{P(HS)}{P(S)} = \frac{0.12}{0.19} = 0.632$$

And the probability of low sales, given a prediction of success, is:

$$P(L|S) = \frac{P(LS)}{P(S)} = \frac{0.07}{0.19} = 0.368$$

Similarly:

$$P(H|I) = \frac{0.12}{0.47} = 0.255$$

$$P(L|I) = \frac{0.35}{0.47} = 0.745$$

and

$$P(H|F) = \frac{0.06}{0.34} = 0.176$$

$$P(L|F) = \frac{0.28}{0.34} = 0.824$$

These values are also listed in the appropriate places in Figure 5–2.

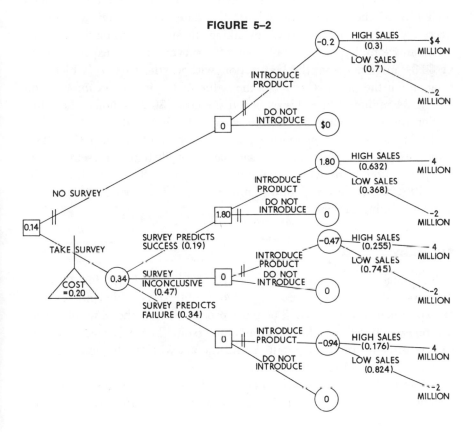

FIGURE 5–2

All the necessary information is now available, and Figure 5–2 can be analyzed—starting from the right and working backward. The expected values are shown in the circles. Expected profit is positive for introducing the product only if a successful prediction is obtained from the market survey. Hence the product should not be introduced if an "inconclusive" or "failure" prediction is obtained. The expected profit with the survey is shown as $0.34 million. This is the expected profit associated with acting on the basis of the survey outcome. It does not include the cost of the survey, which is $0.2 million. When this is included, the net expected profit is $0.14 million. Since this is preferable to the zero profit from acting without obtaining the additional information, the survey should be taken.

Discussion. Taking a survey, in the above illustration, would be a means of obtaining additional information. The information would not be perfect since the survey could not tell exactly whether the sales would be high or low. The probabilities shown in Table 5–2 give the estimated reliability of the survey predictions. Estimates of this sort are always necessary if the economic worth of taking the survey is to be determined.

In our example, the action of taking the survey gave an expected profit of $0.34 million above the best action without the survey (which was to abandon the product). Hence the value of the imperfect information was $0.34 million. Since this exceeded the cost ($0.2 million), the information was worth obtaining, and the survey should be taken.

Taking a sample represents a means of obtaining information. This information is imperfect since the sample is not likely to represent exactly the population from which it is taken. Chapters 8 and 9 discuss the reliability of samples and how sampling can be incorporated into the decision-making process.

SUMMARY

Statistical decision theory involves the choice of a decision criterion (i.e., a goal)—say, maximize expected profit. If possible and feasible, an experiment is conducted. The prior probabilities of the states of nature are revised, based on the experimental result. The expected profit of each possible decision is computed, and the act with the highest expected profit is chosen as the optimum act.

Before undertaking an experiment, the decision maker must determine whether the expected profit associated with acting after receiving the result of the experiment is sufficiently large to offset the cost of the experiment. The analysis involves finding the optimum rule (which tells what decision to make as a function of the experimental result) and evaluating the expected profit using that rule.

Chapter 8 will expand upon the material presented in this chapter. The purpose of this chapter is to introduce the concepts of experimenting in a decision framework.

BIBLIOGRAPHY

See the Bibliographies at the end of Chapters 3 and 4.

QUESTIONS AND PROBLEMS

5-1. The example of the chapter used a situation which is typical of those encountered by businessmen. What difficulties are encountered in applying the model described in a normal business situation?

5-2. You must bet on a toss of a coin of unknown physical characteristics. The coin is tossed mechanistically by a machine. The decision you have to make is to bet heads or tails.

Assume that the payoffs are described by the table below:

Actual result	You bet:	
	Heads	Tails
Heads	+100	−100
Tails	−400	+100

Your prior judgment indicates that you believe that there is a one-half chance that the coin to be tossed is fair (i.e., has a 0.5 probability of heads and a 0.5 probability of tails); further, you believe that there is a one-fourth chance that the coin is two-headed (no chance of tail); and finally you believe that there is a one-fourth chance that the coin is two-tailed (no chance of head).

You are given the opportunity to experiment before you bet. The coin will be tossed twice. After observing the results, you will be required to bet either heads or tails on the next toss.

a) Suppose both experimental tosses came up heads. What decision would you make (i.e., what would you bet on the next toss)? What is the expected payoff?

b) Suppose the experimental tosses came out with one head and one tail? What would be your decision? What is the expected payoff?

c) Suppose two tails resulted? What would be your decision? What is the expected payoff?

d) Suppose you had a choice of playing or not playing in this game (before the experimental tosses are flipped). Would you play? What is the expected payoff of playing?

5-3. You are charged with the inventory control job in the Volant Manufacturing Company. You think there is about a 0.4 chance of a recession next year. If there is a recession next year, you should sell the AE4 model now for the last-offer price of $1 million because you could get only $800,000 for it in a recession year. These amounts would be received in one year. However, you have a promise from the purchasing agent of a leading company to buy the AE4 for $1.3

million if there is no recession (amount payable one year hence). After some preliminary calculations, you are still undecided about selling and determine to gather evidence about the chances of a recession next year. You discover that bad debts have been rising recently. A little investigation indicates that for the last 10 recessions, bad debts started to increase approximately a year early in eight instances. You are willing to accept 0.8 as an estimate of the probability of bad debts rising, given that a recession will occur a year later. In the same sense, you find that for 10 randomly selected normal years, the economy experienced rising bad debts the previous year in three instances. Thus, you take 0.3 as an estimate of:

$$P \text{ (rising bad debts|no recession next year)}$$

If you revise your prior probabilities according to Bayes theorem, what would you do about the AE4?

5–4. The probability of two dice, if they are fair dice, giving either a 7 or an 11, is 2/9. If the dice are loaded in a certain fashion, the probability of a 7 or an 11 is 4/9. An acquaintance asks you to play a game with him. If he throws a 7 or an 11, he will collect $3 from you; if not, he will pay you $1. Since the game would give you an advantage if the dice were fair, you have suspicions about your acquaintance. In particular, you feel that there is a 0.7 chance that he is using loaded dice with probability 4/9 for 7 or 11. To allay your fears, your opponent offers to let you roll the dice twice. You do, and roll a four and a six. Should you play the game with your acquaintance? Show your calculations.

5–5. Refer to the example in the chapter. Suppose the reliability of the market survey was described by the following conditional probabilities:

Conditional probability of survey outcomes, given sales level

| | Actual level of sales | |
Survey prediction	High	Low
Success	0.3	0.2
Inconclusive	0.5	0.5
Failure.	0.2	0.3
	1.0	1.0

Assuming all the other information in the example is the same, should the survey be taken?

5–6. Artex Computers is going to purchase 10,000 units of a certain part that is to be assembled into the Artex products. The order is to be placed with the lowest bidder, with the 10,000 units to be delivered at a rate of 1,000 per month over the next 10 months.

The Frank Machine Shop (FMS) is considering bidding on this order. Two factors are puzzling Mr. Frank in his attempts to fix a bid price. The first factor deals with FMS's chances of winning the bid. Mr. Frank finally decides to consider only two bids—either $12 per unit or $13 per unit. He estimates that the chances are two thirds of winning at the former price and one third of winning at the latter price.

The second factor involved in the decision is the FMS unit manufacturing cost. Two production processes are available. The first, process A, is known to cost $10 per unit. The second, process B, is one that FMS has not used before. The chief foreman says that there is a one-fourth chance that the per unit cost will be $9; a one-half chance that the cost will be $10; and a one-fourth chance that the cost will be $11, if the process B is used.

The chief foreman has suggested that he conduct an experiment with the new process (B). He could produce 10 or 15 units; and from the experience gained, he believes he could estimate unit cost "pretty well." The cost of this test would be $500. When asked to be more specific about how accurate his estimate of cost would be, the chief foreman provided the following table:

Chances of various estimated costs

Foreman's estimated cost	Actual per unit cost		
	$9	$10	$11
$ 9	0.8	0.1	0.1
10	0.1	0.8	0.1
11	0.1	0.1	0.8
	1.0	1.0	1.0

Mr. Frank is not sure that this information is at all relevant to his problem. The controller has argued that the test suggested by the foreman may be valuable but should be performed after the bid is awarded. Otherwise, he argues, the firm may spend $500 and then not win the contract. The foreman feels that the test should be done before the bid, since it may influence FMS's bid price.

What action should FMS take? What is the expected profit?

5–7.   The UVW Music Company makes music boxes for a variety of toys and miscellaneous products. UVW has a guarantee on its music boxes against breakage for a one-year period.

The sales manager was concerned with the number of music boxes that were being returned under the guarantee. He thought an excessive number of music boxes that fail to last one year would damage the image of a quality product that UVW was trying to achieve. On checking, he found that approximately 5 percent of the music boxes were returned for repair within one year.

The production manager said that the trouble in almost every case was a break in a crucial spring mechanism within the music box. UVW was having trouble obtaining a spring that was entirely satisfactory. There was a special alloy that could be used in the spring and would guarantee virtually no breakage. A spring made of special alloy would cost $2 each as opposed to the cost of 20 cents for the spring currently used. The production manager did not feel the incidence of 1 failure out of 20 warranted using a part 10 times as expensive.

The production manager added that in the music boxes that were returned with a broken spring, the special-alloy spring was used, so that a second breakage was extremely unlikely. In addition, the cost of handling and repairing a box with a broken spring was $13 plus the $2 for the special-alloy spring.

The sales manager argued that the special-alloy spring should be used in each music box. He felt that in addition to the direct cost of repairing a broken music box, there was a goodwill cost of roughly $5 every time a customer's music box broke.

The decision was not a trivial one, since UVW had estimated sales of 20,000 music boxes over the next year.

a) Which alternative should UVW take?

b) What is the *EVPI*?

5-8. Refer to Problem 5–7. An alternative action is suggested by the UVW chief engineer. He has been approached by an instrument manufacturer with a test device that could measure the strength of the springs currently used and tell whether each was "strong" or "weak." An experimental program was introduced in which 100 springs were classified as either strong or weak and then put in UVW music boxes. The boxes were then put through a process designed to simulate about one year's wear. The results are shown below:

Results of test of 100 springs

Test-device prediction	Actual behavior		
	Good	Defective	Total
Strong	79	1	80
Weak	16	4	20
Total	95	5	100

The production manager did not think the test would be useful. He noted that four good springs were rejected for every bad one that was detected. Further, the test did not eliminate all defective springs.

The chief engineer thought the test would be economically feasible. He noted that the cost of the equipment and other costs associated with the test device would amount to about $4,000 for the next year.

The sales manager still preferred using all special-alloy springs but would accept using the test since, as he noted, it would reduce the number of defectives to about 1 percent.

Should UVW obtain the test device and use it to screen springs?

5-9. Refer to Problem 3-19. Suppose a test can be made at a cost of $5,000 to determine the type of underground formation (types I, II, or III). The underground formation is related to the type of well, but the relation is imperfect; of 25 wells selected at random from sites near our well, the following table illustrates historical occurrences of well type and underground formation.

Historical occurrences (25 wells)

Type of well \ Formation	I	II	III	Total
Dry	4	0	0	4
Gas	1	9	0	10
Gas, oil comb.	0	6	0	6
Oil	0	0	5	5
Total	5	15	5	25

If the test is made and you subsequently decide not to drill, you can no longer sell the lease for $15,000; your prospective purchasers will conclude that since you decided not to drill, they should not also, so the lease will have zero value after a "test without drill" outcome.

Construct a decision tree for this problem. Should you sell the lease without testing, drill without testing, or test? If you decide to test, under what circumstances will you subsequently drill? What is the maximum *EMV*?

5-10.   A large company may satisfy its fuel-oil requirements either by one annual contract or a series of separate monthly contracts throughout the winter. The cost for the annual contract is $0.10/gallon. If the year is "normal," the cost for the monthly contracts will average $0.09/gallon, while if the year is a "scarce" year with respect to fuel oil, the average cost of the monthly contracts will be $0.15/gallon. The company will use 100,000 gallons during the year, and the manager estimates a 1/10 chance of a scarce year.

The manager may spend $100 to obtain a professional economic forecast of whether the year will be a normal or scarce one. Data on previous forecasts and actual occurrences for the past 20 years is as follows:

Last 20 years

Actual \ Forecast	Normal	Scarce	Total
Normal	15	3	18
Scarce	0	2	2
Total	15	5	20

Construct a decision tree for this problem. Should the manager purchase the forecast? What is his minimum expected monetary cost?

5-11.   The credit card manager of a commercial bank must approve or reject applications for the bank's credit card. He currently uses a "scoring" procedure whereby a series of characteristics stated on an individual's credit card application are weighted by predetermined numerical weights. Based on the total weighted score, an applicant is classified either "good" or "bad" according to whether his score exceeds or falls below the predetermined cutoff score.

Recently the manager has been considering an alternative procedure whereby an applicant would be rejected if his score fell below a new "low cutoff" score, accepted if his score fell above a new "high cutoff" score, and investigated further if his score fell in between. "Further investigation" involves an extensive credit investigation at a cost of $50 each. Available data are as follows.

Current system (results for 1,000 applicants)

Current classification by scoring only \ Actual	Pays	Does not pay	Total
Good	400	100	500
Bad	*	*	500
Total	*	*	1,000

* Cannot determine payment performance of those applicants whose applications were rejected.

Proposed system (estimated results for 1,000 applicants)

Proposed classification by scoring and credit check when indicated \ Actual	Pays	Does not pay	Total
Very good (scoring alone)	350	50	400
Good (scoring + check)	150	100	250
Bad (scoring + check)	*	*	50
Very bad (scoring alone)	*	*	300
Total	*	*	1,000

* Cannot determine payment performance of those applicants whose applications were rejected.

(The "very good" and "very bad" groups are determined by scoring alone; the other two groups are determined after the credit bureau check.)

The bank has determined that the present value of future *profit* for an applicant who "pays" is $400, while the present value of the *losses* incurred by an applicant who "does not pay" is ($200).

a) Based on the above information, is the proposed system to be preferred to the current system? Why? For 1,000 applicants, what is the maximum *EMV* in present value terms?

b) In order to improve upon the current system above, what additional information would you like to have? How might this information be obtained in actual practice?

6

Decision theory and
classical statistics

Modern statistical decision theory aims at choosing the optimum course of action. Classical statistics has the same objective, but a somewhat different approach, and may arrive at a less useful answer for purposes of business decision making.

CLASSICAL STATISTICS

The following explanation somewhat simplifies the scope of classical statistics; but hopefully, it conveys the main stream of the concepts. We shall illustrate classical statistics using a decision problem.

To determine whether or not to market a new product, we are interested in estimating the extent of the demand for the product. A statistician using the classical approach might do any or all of the following:

1. Make a point estimate of demand. He could estimate p, the proportion of people who, when approached, will buy the product.
2. Make an interval estimation; e.g., p, the proportion who will buy the product, will be larger than 0.04 and less than 0.16, with 0.95 certainty.
3. Test two hypotheses. The hypotheses may be:
   a) That p is equal to or less than 0.09.
   b) That p is greater than 0.09.

The statistician has various tests he applies in performing the above operations. If he is making a point estimate, he may want the estimator to be unbiased; i.e., the expected value of the estimate would be equal to the true value of the parameter being estimated, as well as satisfying other requirements.

In this chapter the different values of p represent different states of nature.

Assume a random sample of 100 persons is contacted out of a population of 10 million and 10 persons purchase the product. The unbiased estimate of the proportion of people who will buy the product is:

$$p = \frac{10}{100} = 0.10$$

An unbiased estimate of the number who will buy is $10,000,000 \times 0.10$, or one million. This is a *point estimate* of demand (a single number). This estimate is made without reference to the economic considerations of cost or revenues, and a decision made using just the estimate of one million customers would be an intuitive decision. It should also be noted that because of the small size of the sample, the one million estimate would not necessarily be a very reliable predictor of demand.

Instead of making a point estimate, we can make an interval estimate. Let us assume the standard deviation of the proportion of purchasers, σ_p, is 0.03.[1] We can estimate with 0.95 probability that the true proportion who will buy will be included within a range of ± 1.96 standard deviations from the estimate, assuming the distribution of sample proportions is normal.[2] (See Figure 6–1.)

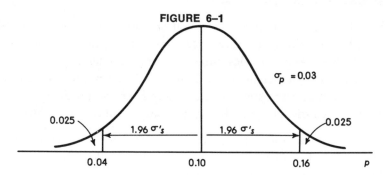

FIGURE 6–1

$\sigma_p = 0.03$

0.025

1.96 σ's   1.96 σ's

0.025

0.04   0.10   0.16 p

Why were the 1.96 σ's and the 0.95 probability chosen, rather than 0.90 or 0.99? It is a matter of arbitrary convention, and other choices of the number of standard deviations and the probabilities may be just as reasonable. The advantage of an interval estimate is that it takes some pressure off the statistician. He no longer has to be exactly correct. It also removes the implication that the statistician knows the exact, correct answer.

Neither of the two procedures described were concerned with the basic

---

[1] The source of σ_p could be past experience or an estimate from the sample.

[2] Chapter 7 discusses this and other properties of the normal distribution.

decision that is being made. They merely estimated values of the parameter of a process. The third procedure, hypothesis testing, is concerned with comparing two hypotheses and arriving at a decision rule for choosing one of them, based on sample evidence. The analysis is assumed to take place prior to the taking of a sample.

We shall assume that an analysis of the economic considerations indicates that with a 0.09 fraction of persons in the market purchasing the product, the firm will break even, and the firm would be indifferent as to whether or not the product is sold if 0.09 of those contacted purchase the product. The hypotheses are:

1. The proportion of persons who will buy is equal to or less than 0.09; thus the product should not be sold.
2. The proportion of persons who will buy is greater than 0.09; thus the product should be sold.

Which hypothesis is valid? If we knew with certainty that the true proportion (i.e., the proportion of persons who would buy) is equal to 0.10, the decision would be easy—we would market the product. However, the actual proportion buying could easily be less than the breakeven proportion of 0.09. In like manner, if we knew the true proportion was less than 0.09, we could make a "reject" decision, but there is a probability that the true proportion is larger than 0.09. The classical approach is to investigate the probabilities of success and error of a decision rule with the true proportion being given different values.

We can define hypothesis 1 as the null hypothesis (if this hypothesis is true, we want to avoid making an error) and hypothesis 2 as the alternative hypothesis.[3] There are two types of errors which may be made:

Type 1:   When the null hypothesis is true, arrive at the conclusion that the proportion who will buy is greater than 0.09.

Type 2:   When the alternative hypothesis is true, arrive at the conclusion that the proportion who will buy is less than 0.09.

What is the probability of making the first type of error, assuming the proportion of the population who will buy takes on different values? For illustration we shall use the following decision rule in our computations: Accept the null hypothesis if the sample indicates 0.11 or less will buy, i.e., if $\frac{r}{n} \leq 0.11$, where r is the number buying and n is the sample size.

---

[3] The labeling of one hypothesis as being the null hypothesis is conventional procedure, but this may be an arbitrary process, and too much importance should not be placed on the labeling.

Table 6–1 (column 3) shows the probability of accepting the null hypothesis (which, in the context of this example, means rejecting the product) for selected values of p. We are limiting the number of values of p in order to simplify the computations.

TABLE 6–1

1 Assumed true value of p	2 $P(r \geq 12 \mid p, n = 100)$	3 $P(r \leq 11) = 1 - P(r \geq 12)$
0.00	0.0000	1.0000
0.07	0.0469	0.9531
0.09	0.1876	0.8124
0.11	0.4206	0.5794
0.13	0.6611	0.3389

Explanation of Table 6–1

Column 1 gives the assumed true value of p.

Column 2 gives the probability of the sample of 100 having 12 or more purchasers, given different values of p. These probabilities may be obtained from binomial probability tables (Table C in the Appendix at the end of the text).

Column 3 is equal to one minus column 2 and gives the probability of the sample having 11 or fewer purchasers. These values are based on the decision rule "Choose the null hypothesis if $\dfrac{r}{n} \leq 0.11$." With a sample size of 100, this rule is equivalent to requiring that $r \leq 11$.

FIGURE 6–2

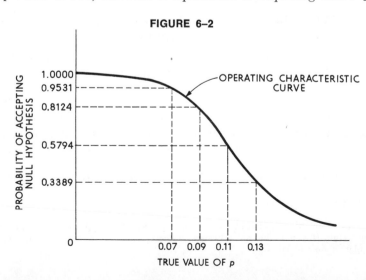

Column 3 gives the probability of being *correct* for true values of $p \leq 0.09$; i.e., if the true p is less than or equal to the break-even proportion, then the probabilities shown in column 3 are the probabilities of correctly accepting the null hypothesis. Column 3 gives the probabilities of being in *error* for the values of $p > 0.09$; i.e., the probabilities of accepting the null hypothesis when it is not valid. The graph of column 3 of Table 6–1 (see Figure 6–2) is called the *operating characteristic* curve.

PROBABILITY OF ERROR

If the true p is less than 0.09 (the break-even proportion), then the null hypothesis is correct, and the operating characteristic curve shows the conditional probability of making the correct decision (using the decision rule that if $\frac{r}{n}$ is less than 0.11, reject the product). If $p > 0.09$, then the operating characteristic curve shows the probability of making an error (the error arises because $\frac{r}{n}$ is less than 0.11, despite the fact that the true p is greater than the break-even proportion of 0.09).

If the true p is 0.07, there is a 0.9531 probability of making the correct decision (i.e., rejecting the product and assuming the null hypothesis is correct). It follows that there is a 0.0469 probability of error. For values of p less than 0.09, we find the probability of error by subtracting the operating characteristic curve from one. For values of p greater than 0.09, the operating characteristic curve measures the probability of error. Figure 6–3 shows the probabilities of error for all values of p, assuming the decision rule "Accept the null hypothesis if $\frac{r}{n} \leq 0.11$" is used.

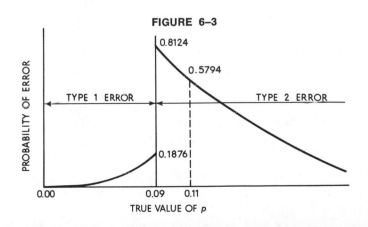

FIGURE 6–3

One important question has been deferred to this point. How did we arrive at the decision rule "Reject the product unless the sample proportion is greater than 0.11"? We wanted to avoid the type 1 error; thus, we made it less probable to declare the null hypothesis false if it was actually true. Economically, we wanted to be reasonably certain to reject the product if the true p was less than 0.09. One way of accomplishing this objective is to make the barrier to acceptance relatively high.

In practice, the statistician sets the "level of significance." This is the maximum probability of a type 1 error. In the example the maximum probability of a type 1 error is equal to 0.1876, and this arises when the true p is equal to 0.09. In addition, the probability of a type 2 error is set for some value of p—say, p equal to 0.11. Assume that this probability is set at 0.58. With these two probabilities established, we would find that the decision rule as described in this example satisfies the probabilities of error which are required.[4]

The so-called "level of significance" can be decreased below 0.1876 by changing the decision rule; but in doing so, we would increase the probabilities of type 2 errors. We could also decide to decrease the type 2 errors, but this would increase the level of significance, unless the reduction was accomplished by an increase in sample size.

The question may be asked as to how we arrived at a desired level of significance of 0.1876 and a desired probability of error of 0.58 for p equal to 0.11. There is no completely satisfactory answer to this question, and this is one of the weaknesses of the classical hypothesis-testing procedure. We want to bring into the analysis the economic consequences arising from the two types of errors, but it is not clear how to accomplish this systematically within the classical framework, and the classical statistical model generally stops at this point.

In theory, one could set the type 1 and type 2 errors so as to minimize the economic consequences of these errors times the probability of the errors occurring. There are two difficulties with this approach, however. First, it is usually unrealistic to attach all economic consequences to two values (those points at which the type 1 and type 2 errors are measured, $p = 0.09$ and $p = 0.11$ in the above example). Secondly, no account is taken of the *likelihood* of different states of nature (in the example, different values of p). Implicit in this omission is the assumption that all states are equally likely to occur (i.e., $p = 0.09$ is as likely as $p = 0.11$). This may be a very unrealistic assumption.

---

[4] With a given n, we can solve for the critical value of r. Also, by changing $\frac{r}{n}$ we can change the probabilities of error.

INCORPORATING CONSEQUENCES

In the example being discussed, we can make two types of errors, with the following consequences:

1. We can accept the product when marketing the product is not desirable. The loss will be a function of the true p (the lower the true p, the larger is the loss arising from leftover units). Assume this type of loss is equal to:

$$W = 100(0.09 - p) \text{ if } p \leq 0.09$$

2. We can reject the product when marketing the product is desirable. The profits lost will be a function of the true p. Assume this loss is equal to:

$$W = 60(p - 0.09) \text{ if } p > 0.09$$

We can plot these two loss functions[5] for different values of p.

Figure 6–4 shows the losses which are associated with an error as a function of the different possible states of nature, i.e., the different values of p, the proportion of people who will buy. The Bayes decision rule

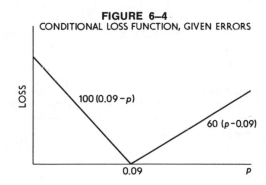

FIGURE 6–4
CONDITIONAL LOSS FUNCTION, GIVEN ERRORS

says we should compute the expected loss or risk function of each possible decision rule and choose the rule with the lowest expected risk. Figure 6–3 gives the probability of the error for the different values of p and the specific decision rule stated above. If we multiply the conditional probabilities of error from Figure 6–3 by the conditional losses of Figure 6–4, we obtain the conditional risk or expected loss curves of Figure 6–5. These are called butterfly curves (they are still conditional on the true value of p). Since the loss with p equal to 0.09 is zero, the curves

---

[5] In Chapters 4 and 5, we spoke of profit functions. A loss function may be obtained from a profit function by multiplying by -1.

take on the zero value at p equal to 0.09. This is interesting because in classical statistics the level of significance (the probability of a type 1 error at $p = 0.09$) generally receives considerable attention. Since the loss at the break-even p is zero, and near to zero for values of p close to the break-even, the probability of making an error at that point, or close to that point, is not of significant interest.

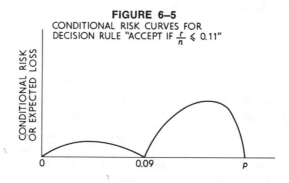

FIGURE 6–5
CONDITIONAL RISK CURVES FOR
DECISION RULE "ACCEPT IF $\frac{r}{n} \leqslant 0.11$"

The computation of the values shown in Figure 6–5 is illustrated by Table 6–2.

TABLE 6–2

1	2	3		4
		Loss: W		Conditional risk or expected loss
Possible values of p	Probability of error*	$100(0.09 - p)$	$60(p - 0.09)$	(col. 2 × col. 3)
0.00........	0.0000	9		0.0000
0.07........	0.0469	2		0.0938
0.09........	0.1876	0	0.0	0.0000
0.11........	0.5794		1.2	0.6953
0.13........	0.3389		2.4	0.8134

* For the break-even case $p = 0.09$ the probability of error is ambiguous; it is either 0.1876 or 0.8124, depending on whether the borderline point $p = 0.09$ is included in the null or the alternative hypothesis. However, since the loss at that point is zero by definition, the probability of making an *error with undesirable economic consequences* is zero.

The next step in the Bayes procedure is to assign probabilities to the possible states of nature, the values of p, and compute the unconditional expected risk (we are taking an expectation of the conditional expected loss). Assume the probabilities shown in Table 6–3 are assigned (only selected values of p are allowed, to simplify the computations). Table 6–3 shows the computations of the expected risk.

TABLE 6–3

1 Possible values of p	2 Proba- bilities of p	3 Conditional risk or expected loss (from Table 6–2)	4 Product of prob- ability and risk (col. 2 × col. 3)
0.00	0.1	0.0000	0.00000
0.07	0.2	0.0938	0.01876
0.09	0.4	0.0000	0.00000
0.11	0.2	0.6953	0.13906
0.13	0.1	0.8134	0.08134
	1.0		Unconditional expected risk = 0.23916

The expected risk of the 0.11 decision rule is 0.239. This computation of expected risk would be repeated for other possible decision rules; the rule with the lowest expected risk is the Bayes decision rule.

The classical statistician might stop with the computation of the operating characteristic curve (or one minus this amount), or with the resulting probability-of-error curves. He might add the loss functions to the analysis and even multiply the error curves by the loss functions to obtain the butterfly or risk curves, though this step is frequently omitted. He is not likely to be sympathetic to the computation of the expected risk using subjective probabilities assigned to the different possible values of p. If objective evidence is available, then he might incorporate this into the analysis, though not necessarily systematically by computing the expected risk.

The differences between statistical decision theory using the Bayes decision rule and classical statistics are not exactly defined, but one important difference is the explicit computation of expected risk by the Bayes decision maker. The failure of some statisticians to include some loss function in the decision process would be another difference, though a large number of modern statisticians would agree to the necessity of including a loss function in the analysis.

It is not uncommon for statisticians to speak of hypothesis testing or interval estimation without reference to the losses resulting from incorrect decisions. This is an undesirable omission. The consequences of incorrect decisions are a necessary part of the decision process.

Of course, there is a large class of decision problems where economic consequences cannot be accurately measured or are of meaningless importance compared to noneconomic consequences. Such, for example, would be the decision problem of the scientist investigating a new drug. He must decide if the new drug is effective or not. The consequences of an incorrect decision may possibly affect the suffering of many people and the reputation of the scientist. One would like to be very sure about the correct decision in such situations. The classical statistics decision framework is designed for such problems as this. It tells the scientist how confident he can be about his results (with, for example, only a $1/1,000$ chance of being wrong) and when he must find more evidence before making his decision.

Thus, classical statistics was designed, and is useful, for scientific or experimental work where the probability of error is more accurately measured than the consequences of a decision. The business decision maker frequently has a situation where objective probabilities are lacking, but the consequences are subject to measurement. In all decisions the consequences of the decision should be incorporated into the decision process.

BIBLIOGRAPHY

See the Bibliography at end of Chapter 4.

QUESTIONS AND PROBLEMS

6–1. Discuss the following statement: "Statistics is a science and an objective discipline. As such, it has no place for subjective probabilities. The use of subjective probabilities may be fine for psychology —but not statistics."

6–2. Using the example in the chapter, compute the expected risk of the decision rule "Accept the null hypothesis if $\frac{r}{n} \leq 0.10$" for $n = 20$.

6–3. Using the example in the chapter, compute the expected risk of the decision rule "Accept the null hypothesis if $\frac{r}{n} \leq 0.05$" for $n = 20$.

6–4. Using the example in the chapter, compute the expected risk of the decision rule "Accept the null hypothesis if $\frac{r}{n} \leq 0$" for $n = 20$.

6–5. Compare the values of expected risk in Problems 6–2 through 6–4. Explain why one has less expected risk than the others.

6–6. A manufacturer has just received a large shipment of gears to be used in the assembly of motors. In the past, the quality (i.e., percentage defective) of gears has varied from lot to lot. It costs $10 to replace a gear once assembled in the motor. The manufacturer may either accept the lot as is and pay $10 for removing each defective gear, or he may have the lot 100 percent inspected on special test equipment for $1 for each gear. This inspection process will pick out all defectives before they are put in the assembly and thus save the $10 cost.

The quality control manager plans to take a sample of 10 items from the lot. If there are two or more defectives in this sample, he plans to have the lot 100 percent inspected. If there are zero or one defective items, he plans to accept the lot and incur the cost of $10 for each defective.

a) At what value of p is the expected cost of accepting the lot equal to that of 100 percent inspection? Set up the null hypothesis that p is less than or equal to this value and the alternative hypothesis that p is greater than this value.

b) Consider the possible values of p as: $p = 0.04$; $p = 0.08$; $p = 0.10$; $p = 0.12$; $p = 0.16$. Prepare a table (such as Table 6–1) showing the probabilities of accepting the null hypothesis and rejecting the hypothesis for the manager's sampling plan. Then prepare a chart (such as Figure 6–3) plotting the probabilities of a type 1 and a type 2 error.

c) Determine the cost functions for both alternatives and loss functions as in Figure 6–4. Note that in this case the cost of rejecting the hypothesis (and of 100 percent inspection) is constant and does not depend on p.

d) Compute the risk or expected loss for each of the values of p given in part (b) above. Plot the values and graph risk curves, such as Figure 6–5.

e) Compute the expected risk using the following probabilities for the possible values of p:

Possible values of p	Probability
0.04	0.20
0.08	0.30
0.10	0.30
0.12	0.10
0.16	0.10

6–7. Repeat (a) through (e) of Problem 6–6 on the assumption that the manager will accept the lot if 0, 1, or 2 defectives are found out of 10, and will reject if 3 or more are found.

6–8. Repeat (a) through (e) of Problem 6–6 on the assumption that the manager will accept the lot only if there are no defectives out of 10. He will reject the lot if there are one or more defectives.

6–9. Compare the values of expected risk in Problems 6–6, 6–7, and 6–8. Which sampling plan is best? Why?

6–10. An appliance manufacturer currently purchases motors from a supplier who guarantees that no more than one out of one hundred motors will be defective. The manufacturer has recently been approached by a new potential supplier who has motors available at a lower cost. However, the new supplier will not guarantee a minimum percentage of defectives; he simply says he will replace any defective motor with a new one, but the appliance manufacturer must perform the installation of the new motor when required. After careful study of the various costs involved, the manufacturer has reached the following conclusions: If the true fraction defective of the new supplier is $p = 0.03$, he will break even; i.e., at that level of fraction defective, the increased costs of replacing defectives (including ill will) will just balance the lower per unit cost of the motors. If he switches to the new supplier and the p is greater than 0.03, the loss is

$$W = 500(p - 0.03) \text{ if } p > 0.03 \,,$$

while if the true p is less than or equal to 0.03 and he does *not* switch to the new supplier, the opportunity loss is

$$W = 200(0.03 - p) \text{ if } p \leq 0.03$$

The manufacturer has assessed the following subjective probability distribution over the possible values of p:

Possible values of p	Probabilities
0.00	0.20
0.02	0.20
0.03	0.20
0.04	0.20
0.05	0.20
	1.00

Suppose no sample information is available (i.e., the decision must be made prior to any testing of a sample). Compute the expected loss of switching to the new supplier. Which supplier should be selected?

6–11. Refer to Problem 6–10. Now suppose that the new supplier has agreed to let the manufacturer sample 20 motors. The manufacturer plans to use the following decision rule: If there are no defective motors in the sample, select the new supplier; if there are one or more defectives, keep the old supplier.

a) Using the binomial tables (Table C in the Appendix at the end of the text), compute the probability of error for the five possible values of p (i.e., compute the probability that given the true value of p, the decision rule above will result in choosing the wrong supplier).

b) Compute the conditional risk or expected loss of this decision rule for each possible value of p (as in Table 6–2).

c) Compute the unconditional expected risk for this decision rule (as in Table 6–3). Is this number smaller than the loss for the optimal answer to Problem 6–10? Will it always be so? Why?

6–12. Refer to Problems 6–10 and 6–11. Now suppose that the new supplier is willing to provide the manufacturer with an analysis of an extremely large sample of his motors; this sample information will pinpoint precisely the true value of p (one of the five values indicated).

a) Under these circumstances, what is the probability of error for each possible value of p (*after* viewing the extremely large sample results)?

b) As compared to the situation in Problem 6–10, how much would the manufacturer be willing to pay for this completely reliable information? Why?

c) Suppose the $n = 20$ sample of Problem 6–11 were now available for free. As compared with that information (and the decision rule specified therein), how much would the manufacturer be willing to pay for the perfect information mentioned above? Why? Given that the only "small" sample size available was $n = 20$, what else should he investigate before choosing between sample information and perfect information?

7

The normal probability distribution and the value of information

There are discrete and continuous probability distributions. A discrete distribution is called a probability *mass* function (p.m.f.), and a continuous probability function is called a probability *density* function (p.d.f.). In a probability mass function (discrete distribution), the random variable is allowed to take on only selected values (for example, 0.1, 0.2, or 0.3, but perhaps not 0.11, 0.21, or 0.31).

We could indicate the proportion of families which have X members. A family may have 4 members, but it cannot have 4.2 members; thus, X must be an integer. Sometimes, we classify the data so that we may use a discrete probability distribution, where we could use a continuous distribution. For example, it is possible that any amount of product may be demanded, but we may classify the demand for a day as falling into classifications of 10ths of a ton (i.e., 0.1, 0.2, etc.).

The binomial distribution, which is described in Chapter 2, is another example of a discrete probability distribution. The random variable, number of successes, can only take on zero and positive integer values from one to n (the number of trials).

A continuous probability density function is a distribution where the value of the random variable may be any number within some given range of values—say between zero and infinity. For example, assuming a probability density function of the height of the members of a population, there would be a value of the density function for 5.3 feet, 5.324 feet, 5.32431 feet, etc., but the height cannot be negative. The density function has a value for all possible values of the random variable.

The concept of probability is defined differently for discrete and continuous variables. For a continuous variable, the density function measures the height of the graph for the value of the random variable; it is *not* the probability of the event. The area under the curve over any interval on the horizontal axis represents the probability of the random variable taking on a value in that interval.

Graphs of the two types of distributions are shown in Figures 7–1 and 7–2.

FIGURE 7–1
Discrete probability distribution (probability mass function or p.m.f.)

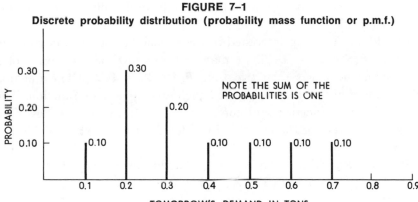

FIGURE 7–2
Continuous probability distribution (probability density function or p.d.f.)

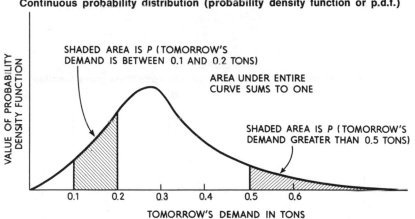

CUMULATIVE MASS FUNCTIONS

Associated with probability mass functions are cumulative mass functions. A cumulative mass function shows cumulative probability. Let us

TABLE 7–1

S	P(S)
0	0.00
1	0.20
2	0.40
3	0.30
4	0.10
	1.00

consider random variables with the discrete probability mass function shown in Table 7–1.

In addition to being interested in the probability of S being equal to two [i.e., $P(S = 2) = 0.40$], we may wish to know the probability of S being equal to or less than two [i.e., $P(S \leq 2) = 0.60$]. The function giving values of this nature is called the *cumulative* mass function. The probability mass function and cumulative mass function of a "less than or equal to" type for the example in Table 7–1 are shown in Table 7–2 and Figure 7–3.

We may also wish to know the probability of S being greater than two: $P(S > 2) = 1 - P(S \leq 2) = 1 - 0.60 = 0.40$.

TABLE 7–2

S	$P(S = s)$	$P(S \leq s)$
0	0.00	0.00
1	0.20	0.20
2	0.40	0.60
3	0.30	0.90
4	0.10	1.00

FIGURE 7–3
Example of probability mass function and cumulative mass function

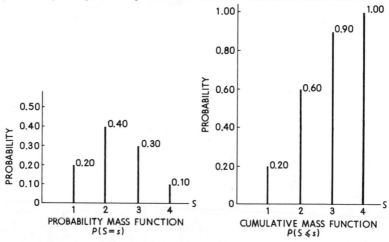

Given the probability mass function, we can obtain the cumulative mass function and such variations as $P(S \geq 2)$ or $P(2 \leq S \leq 4)$.

CUMULATIVE DISTRIBUTION FUNCTIONS

Cumulative distribution functions are associated with probability density functions just as cumulative mass functions are associated with probability mass functions.

FIGURE 7–4

Probability density function $f(S) = \dfrac{1}{b-a}$, $a \leq S \leq b$;
$= 0$ otherwise

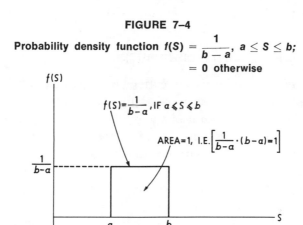

We shall illustrate the cumulative distribution function using a rectangular probability distribution (see Figure 7–4). If S is between a and b ($a \leq S \leq b$), then the value of the probability density function is $\dfrac{1}{b-a}$, and zero otherwise.

FIGURE 7–5

$F(S)$, cumulative distribution function for $f(S) = \dfrac{1}{b-a}$

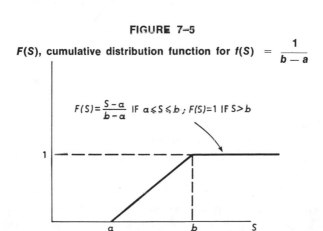

If we sum the area under the probability density function

$$f(S) = \frac{1}{b - a}$$

over the range from a to S for each value of S, we obtain the cumulative distribution, $F(S)$. We use $f(\cdot)$ to represent the probability density function and $F(\cdot)$ to represent the cumulative distribution function of the "less than or equal to" type (see Figure 7–5).

THE NORMAL PROBABILITY DISTRIBUTION

The *normal* distribution is an extremely important one. It is easier to manipulate mathematically than many other distributions, and is a good approximation for several of the others. In many cases the normal distribution is a reasonable approximation for a prior probability distribution for business decision purposes; and in the following chapters, we shall use the normal distribution in many of the applications. Despite its general application, it should not be assumed that every process can be described as having a normal distribution.

The normal distribution has a probability density function which is a smooth, symmetric, continuous, bell-shaped curve, as pictured in Figure 7–6. The area under the curve over any interval on the horizontal axis

FIGURE 7–6

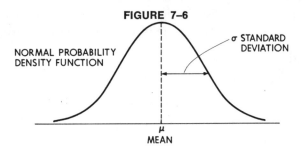

represents the probability of the random variable, X, taking on a value in that interval. The area under the curve sums to one.

A normal distribution is completely determined by its mean (denoted by μ) and standard deviation (σ); i.e., once we know the mean and standard deviation the shape and location of the distribution is set. The curve reaches a maximum at the mean of the distribution. One half of the area lies on either side of the mean. The greater the value of

σ, the standard deviation, the more spread-out the curve.[1] This is illustrated in Figure 7–7.

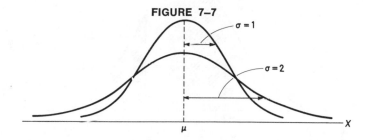

FIGURE 7–7

With any normal distribution, approximately 0.50 of the area lies within ±0.67 standard deviations from the mean; about 0.68 of the area lies within ±1.0 standard deviations; and 0.95 of the area lies within ±1.96 standard deviations. See Figure 7–8.

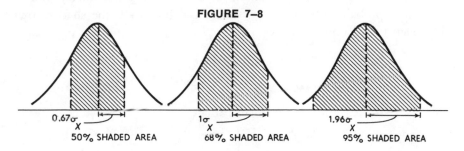

FIGURE 7–8

Since the normal probability function is continuous (a probability density function), probability cannot be read directly from the graphs. We must consider the probability of the value of a random variable being in an interval (see Figure 7–9).

In Figure 7–9:

$P(-2 \leq X \leq 0)$ = shaded area A

$P(X \geq 2)$ = shaded area B

$P(0 \leq X \leq 2)$ = area between A and B (also equal to the shaded area A because of the symmetry of the normal curve)

---

[1] The normal probability density function with parameters μ and σ is:

$$f_N(x) = \frac{1}{\sigma(2\pi)^{1/2}} e^{-(x-\mu)^2/2\sigma^2}, \quad -\infty < x < \infty$$

The normal cumulative distribution function is:

$$F_N(x) = \int_{-\infty}^{x} f_N(y)dy$$

FIGURE 7–9

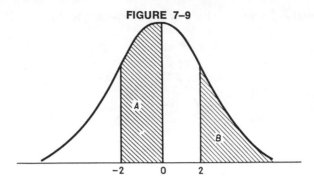

RIGHT AND LEFT TAILS

We are now ready to discuss the right and left tails of normal probability distributions.

The symbol F_N is used to represent a cumulative distribution function of a normal probability distribution. It is the area under the *left* tail of a normal probability density function. In Figure 7–10 the shaded area is the left tail of a normal curve, i.e., $F_N(b)$.

FIGURE 7–10

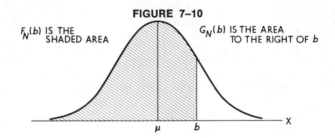

$F_N(b)$ is the probability of X being equal to or less than b; i.e., $F_N(b) = P(X \le b)$.

We now introduce a new symbol, G, which we define as the area under the *right* tail of a probability density function. In Figure 7–10 the unshaded area is the right tail of a normal curve, i.e., $G_N(b)$.

$G_N(b)$ is the probability of X being greater than b, i.e.:

$$G_N(b) = P(X > b)$$

From Figure 7–10, it can be seen that $F_N(b)$ and $G_N(b)$ are related:[2]

(7–1) $G_N(b) = 1 - F_N(b)$

---

[2] The basic mathematical relationships may be stated as:

$$F_N(b) = \int_{-\infty}^{b} f_N(X)dX$$

and

$$G_N(b) = \int_{b}^{\infty} f_N(X)dX$$

NORMAL PROBABILITY TABLES

A normal distribution with $\mu = 0$ (mean of zero) and $\sigma = 1$ (standard deviation of one) is said to be a *standard* normal distribution. If a normal distribution has a mean other than zero or a standard deviation other than one, we may standardize the distribution. The ability to standardize normal distributions is one of the useful features of the distribution and allows us to look up normal probabilities in a relatively short table.

To standardize a normal random variable, we shall define a new *standardized normal variable Z* as follows:

$$(7\text{–}2) \qquad\qquad Z = \frac{X - \mu}{\sigma}$$

where X is the nonstandardized normal random variable we are concerned with, μ is the mean of this random variable, and σ is the standard deviation. In the above expression, Z is the distance of X from its mean, μ, measured in units of standard deviations. For example, if $Z = 4$, then:

$$4 = \frac{X - \mu}{\sigma}$$

$$4\sigma = X - \mu$$

Thus, $Z = 4$ corresponds to a value of X which is four standard deviations larger than its mean. As a result of this operation, Z is a standardized, normally distributed random variable and has a mean of zero and a standard deviation of one. Since we look up the probabilities in terms of Z, and all Z's have a mean of zero and a standard deviation of one, we need only one table of probabilities. Table A (in the Appendix at the end of the text) is a table of cumulative normal probabilities. It should be noted that in equation $(7\text{–}2)$ we are transforming a value from one normal distribution into a value of a standard normal distribution. The value being transformed must come from a normal distribution.

Assume we are concerned with a normally distributed random variable, X, with mean $\mu = 8$ and standard deviation $\sigma = 3$. Let us find the following probabilities:

1. $P(X \le 10)$
2. $P(X > 10)$
3. $P(10 < X \le 15)$

Example 1

We first standardize the random variable X:

$$Z = \frac{X - \mu}{\sigma} = \frac{10 - 8}{3} = \frac{2}{3} = 0.67$$

We then look up the probability $P(Z \leq 0.67)$ in Table A and find it to equal 0.7486. The probability of X being less than 10 is 0.7486. (Note that $P(X \leq 10)$ is the same as $P(X < 10)$ since the probability of being exactly 10 is zero.)

Example 2

From Example 1 we know that for $X = 10$, $Z = 0.67$, and

$$P(X \leq 10) = P(Z \leq 0.67) = 0.7486$$

Then

$$P(X > 10) = 1 - P(X \leq 10) = 0.2514$$

If the probability of X being less than 10 is 0.75, the probability of its being greater than 10 is 0.25. In terms of areas, if the area to the left of 10 is 0.75 and the total area under the density function is one, then the area to the right of 10 is $(1 - 0.75)$, or 0.25.

Example 3

We know $P(X > 10) = 0.2514$ from Example 2. To calculate $P(X \leq 15)$, we must compute Z for a value of 15:

$$Z = \frac{15 - 8}{3} = \frac{7}{3} = 2.33$$

In Table A (in the Appendix at the end of the text), we find:

$$P(Z > 2.33) = 0.00990$$

Note that:

$$P(Z > 2.33) = 1 - P(Z \leq 2.33) = 1 - 0.99010 = 0.00990$$

The probability of X being larger than 10 and less than 15 (or equivalently, Z being larger than 0.67 and less than 2.33) is:

$$
\begin{aligned}
P(10 < X \leq 15) &= P(0.67 < Z \leq 2.33) \\
&= P(Z > 0.67) - P(Z > 2.33) \\
&= 0.2514 - 0.0099 = 0.2415
\end{aligned}
$$

An alternative computation is:

$$
\begin{aligned}
P(10 < X \leq 15) &= P(Z \leq 2.33) - P(Z \leq 0.67) \\
&= 0.9901 - 0.7486 = 0.2415
\end{aligned}
$$

NORMAL PRIOR PROBABILITIES AND THE VALUE OF INFORMATION

In the preceding sections, we described the general characteristics of the normal probability distribution. We shall now show the use of the normal distribution as a prior probability distribution. Our discussion here will follow closely the explanation of expected value contained in Chapter 3. The difference will be the use of continuous, rather than discrete, prior probabilities.

Suppose a company has an opportunity to buy for $8,600 a machine which, if successful, will save labor hours in a certain production process which now uses a large amount of hand labor. The physical life of this machine is one year. Assume the incremental cost of a labor hour to the company is $4; thus, if the machine will save more than 2,150 labor hours $\left(\dfrac{\$8,600}{\$4} = 2,150 \right)$, the company would benefit from owning the machine.

Let us assume that the production engineer feels that the mean number of hours saved will be 2,300. He also feels that there is a 50–50 chance that the actual hours saved could be less than 2,100 or more than 2,500 hours for the year.

With this description of the engineer's feelings, it is possible to assume that a specific normal distribution will fit his prior expectations. The mean of the distribution is 2,300. If we can determine the standard deviation, we have described the normal prior probability distribution.

In the normal distribution, roughly one half the area (hence, one half the probability) lies within ±0.67 standard deviations of the mean. Figure 7–11 approximates the fit of a normal distribution to the engineer's estimates. The engineer has estimated a mean of 2,300 hours, and he has judged that the true value lies between 2,100 and 2,500 hours, with

FIGURE 7–11

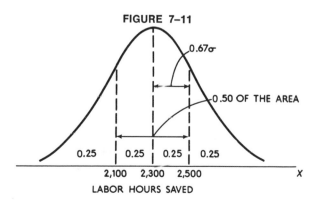

LABOR HOURS SAVED

probability 0.50. Hence, one half the area must lie outside these limits, 0.25 on the left side and 0.25 on the right side. We can see that if we move in a positive direction of 200 units, we move out 0.67σ; that is:

$$0.67\sigma = 200 \text{ hours}$$

$$\sigma = \frac{200}{0.67} = 300 \text{ hours}$$

The normal prior distribution has a standard deviation of approximately 300 hours.

Note also that the normal distribution assigns probabilities to both large and small hour savings. This will be in accordance with the engineer's judgment if he feels the probabilities are symmetrically distributed around the mean.

To summarize, we have taken the engineer's narrative description and converted it to a normal prior distribution with mean $\mu = 2,300$ hours and standard deviation $\sigma = 300$ hours. We also know that in order to break even, the machine must save at least 2,150 hours; and for every hour that actual savings differ from 2,150, the profit changes at a rate of $4 per hour.

Profits can be represented as a linear function of hours saved, with zero profit at 2,150 hours. Thus:

$$\text{Profits} = \pi = -8,600 + 4X$$

where X is the actual number of hours saved. Since this is a linear function, expected profits can be determined by replacing X by its expected value.[3]

$$E(\pi) = -8,600 + 4\mu$$
$$= -8,600 + 4(2,300) = 600$$

Whenever the estimate of mean savings $E(\pi)$ is above the break-even point, expected profits are positive, and we should buy the machine (assume we are willing to buy the machine on a break-even basis; i.e., in this chapter, we shall ignore utility considerations and the interest return required for acceptable investments). Even though the engineer's prior probability distribution is fairly tight (the standard deviation, $\sigma = 300$, is relatively small compared to the size of the mean, so that the engineer is fairly certain of his estimate of the mean), perhaps it would pay us to gather more information before we act. Hence, we are interested in the expected value of perfect information (*EVPI*).

Let us first define the conditional opportunity loss. The optimal action on an expected-value basis is to buy the machine. Suppose we buy the

---
[3] See Chapter 4.

machine and it turns out that the actual savings are less than 2,150 hours. In such a case, how much do we lose? If we use X_b to stand for the break-even amount of 2,150 hours, the conditional loss will increase by $4 for every hour we fall short of the break-even point. Thus the conditional opportunity loss (assuming we buy the equipment) will be:

$$\begin{cases} \$4(X_b - X) \text{ if } X \le X_b \\ \qquad\quad 0 \text{ if } X > X_b \end{cases}$$

where X = the actual hours that are saved and X_b = 2,150, the hours required to break even. The conditional opportunity loss is graphed in Figure 7–12.

FIGURE 7–12

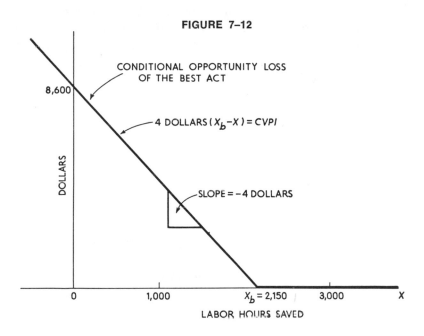

The reader will recall that the *EVPI* is a measure of the value of a perfect predictor or of perfect information. It is the expectation of the conditional value of perfect information.

We have decided that our best act, based on present information and using the mean savings, is to buy the machine. If a perfect prediction device were to tell us the actual hour savings would be 2,852, or any number greater than 2,150, we would choose the same act as we would have chosen without this information, and the predictor would be of no value. However, if our predictor were to tell us the true hour savings would actually be 2,029, or any number less than 2,150, then we would not buy the machine, and we would avoid a loss. Hence the predictor has value *only* if we change our decision when given the new information. The computation of conditional value of perfect information $(CVPI)$ may be summarized as follows:

$$CVPI = \begin{cases} 0 \text{ if } X > X_b \\ \$4(X_b - X) \text{ if } X \leq X_b \end{cases}$$

This functional relationship is graphed in Figure 7–12, which shows that perfect information is worth nothing if the forecast of hours saved is greater than X_b and increases linearly to the left of the break-even point (the hours saved are less than 2,150 and are decreasing). The $CVPI$ is identical to the conditional opportunity loss of the best act.

The expected value of perfect information $(EVPI)$ is calculated by weighting the conditional value of perfect information $(CVPI)$ by the probability distribution. It is equal to the expected opportunity loss of the best act.

Figure 7–13 shows the prior normal probability distribution superim-

FIGURE 7–13

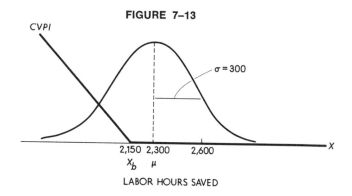

LABOR HOURS SAVED

posed on the conditional value graph. The $EVPI$ is the sum of the product of the normal curve and the $CVPI$ line to the left of the breakeven point. This results because $CVPI = 0$ for values of X greater than X_b (2,150 hours).

It can also be seen that the larger the standard deviation, σ, the higher the $EVPI$. This is because the larger the σ, the more spread-out the normal curve, and the greater the probability weight given the larger losses (i.e., the higher values of the $CVPI$ line). If the engineer was very close to being certain that the value of the mean was 2,300, there would be little or no expected value of perfect information. Figure 7–14 shows a situation where the value of information is very low. A σ of 50 hours would result in a situation of this nature.

FIGURE 7–14

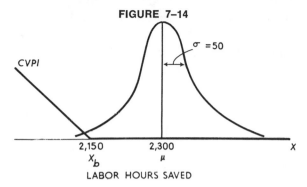

LABOR HOURS SAVED

The reason for perfect information being almost valueless in this latter situation is because the σ of the prior distribution is quite small compared to the mean and to the distance from the mean to the break-even point. Note that the closer X_b is to μ (with a given σ), the higher will be the $EVPI$. This is shown graphically in Figure 7–15, where we

FIGURE 7–15

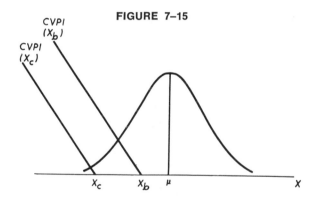

first assume X_b is the break-even point and then assume X_c is the break-even point. If μ, the prior mean, is close to X_b, perfect information is more likely to change the decision as to which is the best act than if μ is relatively far from X_b. Remember that for perfect information to have any value, it is necesary for there to be a possibility that the optimum act will change in the light of the new information.

Summarizing, assuming a normal prior distribution, the $EVPI$ depends on the following three factors:

1. The standard deviation, σ. This is a measure of how "uncertain" the estimator is about the prior mean.
2. The distance of the prior mean from the break-even point $(X_b - \mu)$.

This is important because it helps determine how likely the decision maker is to change his decision because of new evidence.

3. The absolute value of the slope of the *CVPI* line, *C*. The slope of the line is a measure of how rapidly the loss increases as the hours saved decrease below the break-even point.

It is at this point that we employ one of the more useful features of the normal distribution. The computation of the *EVPI* can be reduced to a straightforward formula calculation where the components of the formula are those listed above. This formula is:[4]

$$(7\text{--}3) \qquad EVPI = C \cdot \sigma \cdot N(D)$$

C is the absolute value of the slope of the *CVPI* line or the loss constant; σ is the standard deviation of the normal prior distribution; *D* of $N(D)$ is defined as follows:

$$D = \frac{|X_b - \mu|}{\sigma}$$

Thus, *D* is a measure of the distance of the mean from the break-even point, measured in units of standard deviations. The vertical bars in the formula for *D* should be read as "absolute value." The quantity $N(D)$ may be obtained from Table B (in the Appendix at the end of the text). It may be interpreted as a loss function for the standard normal curve, valued for the quantity *D*.

It should be noted that the higher the value of *D*, the lower the value of $N(D)$, and all other things being equal, the lower the *EVPI*.[5] The lower $N(D)$ results from the fact that the larger the distance $(X_b - \mu)$, the less likely it is that perfect information will change the optimum decision.

In the example of this chapter, *EVPI* is calculated as follows:

$$C = \$4$$
$$\sigma = 300$$
$$D = \frac{|2{,}150 - 2{,}300|}{300} = \frac{|-150|}{300} = \frac{1}{2} = 0.50$$
$$N(D) = N(0.50) = 0.1978$$
$$EVPI = C \cdot \sigma \cdot N(D)$$
$$EVPI = \$4 \cdot 300 \cdot 0.1978 = \$237.36$$

---

[4] See R. Schlaifer, *Probability and Statistics for Business Decisions* (New York: McGraw-Hill Book Co., 1959), pp. 452–55.

[5] $N(D)$ is defined as follows:

$$N(D) = \int_{-\infty}^{-D} (-D - X)f^*(X)dX = \int_{D}^{\infty} (X - D)f^*(X)dX$$

where $f^*(X)$ is the standardized normal density function.

The reader may recall from Chapter 3 the difficulty of computing the *EVPI* for the discrete case. The use of the normal distribution simplifies computations substantially in most business applications. In the above example, we have computed the expected value of perfect information, $237 (which is also the opportunity loss of the best act), and the expected profit of the best act, $600. The sum of these two values, $837, may be defined as the *expected profit under certainty*.

If we had a perfect predictor available, we would be willing to pay up to $237 to use it. It is not likely that we have a *perfect* predictor; but in some instances, we shall be able to obtain helpful though imperfect information. The problems of determining optimum sample size and revising the prior normal distribution in the light of this additional information are introduced in the following chapters. For a more advanced discussion the reader is referred to R. Schlaifer, *Probability and Statistics for Business Decisions* (see Bibliography).

BIBLIOGRAPHY

NATIONAL BUREAU OF STANDARDS. *Tables of the Normal Probability Functions.* Applied Mathematics Series 23. New York, 1953.

SCHLAIFER, R. *Probability and Statistics for Business Decisions.* New York: McGraw-Hill Book Co., 1959.

Also see the Bibliographies of Chapters 2, 3, and 8.

PROBLEMS

7–1. For the probability distribution of sales given below, write out the required probability functions:

Sales (S)	Probability
1 unit	0.10
2 units	0.15
3 units	0.20
4 units	0.30
5 units	0.20
10 units	0.03
15 units	0.02
	1.00

Required probability functions:

$$P(S \geq s)$$
$$P(S > s)$$
$$P(S < s)$$
$$P(S \leq s)$$

7–2. Find the following probabilities for a normally distributed random variable, X:

a) Mean of zero, standard deviation of one:

$$P(X > 0.8)$$
$$P(X \leq 0.8)$$
$$P(X \geq -0.8)$$
$$P(-0.8 \leq X \leq 1.2)$$

b) Mean of six, standard deviation of two:

$$P(X > 8)$$
$$P(X \leq 8)$$
$$P(X \geq -8)$$
$$P(-8 \leq X \leq 12)$$

c) Mean of six, standard deviation of one:

$$P(X > 8)$$
$$P(X \leq 8)$$
$$P(X \geq 4)$$
$$P(4 \leq X \leq 12)$$

7–3. Find the value of the following normally distributed random variables, given each set of conditions:

a) X is normal; mean, zero; standard deviation, one.

$$P(X > x) = 0.02068$$

What is x?

b) X is normal; mean, eight; standard deviation, three.

$$P(Z > z) = 0.1587$$

What is x? (Z and z are the standardized values of X and x.)

c) X is normal; mean, eight; standard deviation, three.

$$P(Z \leq z) = 0.7224$$

What is x?

d) X is normal; mean, ten; standard deviation, two.

$$P(Z > z) = 0.2327$$

What is x?

7–4. Daily sales of a certain product are known to have a normal distribution of 20 per day, with a standard deviation of 6 per day.

a) What is the probability of selling fewer than 16 on a given day?

b) What is the probability of selling between 15 and 25 units on a given day?

c) How many units would have to be on hand at the start of a day in order to have less than a 10 percent chance of running out?

7–5.   A manufacturer is considering a modification in his product which will require a capital investment of $100,000. The product contributes an incremental profit of $5 per unit on a present-value basis. Increased sales will result from the product modification by making the product attractive to 5,000 new retail stores. Without the modification, these retail stores would not handle the product. The sales manager feels that the mean sales per new store will be about six units. However, he thinks there is a 50–50 chance that the mean sales could be less than five or more than seven units.

    a)   Fit a normal distribution to the above situation.

    b)   Calculate the expected profit of the best act. Should the investment be made?

    c)   Calculate the *EVPI*.

7–6.   In the situation of Problem 7–5, suppose the sales manager feels that the mean sales per store will be six units but that there is a 50–50 chance that the actual mean sales could be less than four or greater than eight units. Calculate the *EVPI*, and explain why it is greater than in Problem 7–5.

7–7.   In each of the following situations a normal distribution is considered to be a good prior probability distribution. However, in each case, different characteristics of the distribution are assumed.

    a)   Calculate the *EVPI*.

    b)   Explain the difference in *EVPI* between each situation and situation 1.

       (1) Mean—10 units:

           Break-even value—7 units

           Standard deviation—2 units

           C, the loss constant—$5,000 per unit

       (2) Mean—10 units:

           Break-even value—7 units

           Standard deviation—5 units

           C, the loss constant—$5,000 per unit

       (3) Mean—10 units:

           Break-even value—9 units

           Standard deviation—2 units

           C, the loss constant—$5,000 per unit

       (4) Mean—10 units:

           Break-even value—7 units

           Standard deviation—2 units

           C, the loss constant—$10,000 per unit

7–8.   A manufacturer is considering a capital investment necessary to enter a new market territory. The required investment is $100,000, and he feels that the mean present value of the cash flow is $150,000. However, he thinks there is a 50–50 chance that the mean present value could be less than $80,000 or more than $220,000. The $150,000,

$80,000, and $220,000 figures are before subtracting the $100,000 investment.

a) Should the investment be made?

b) Calculate the *EVPI*, using a normal prior distribution.

7–9. A mail-order firm is considering inserting color advertising in its catalog, which is mailed to 100,000 customers. Current purchases of those receiving black-and-white catalogs are $6 per customer. With the color catalog, management thinks that most probably sales would be increased to $7 per customer, but the probability distribution of sales per customer has a standard deviation equal to one dollar.

The company makes an average profit of 20 percent on a sale. It costs 25 cents more to print a color catalog than a black-and-white one.

a) Should the company use the color catalog?

b) What is the *EVPI*?

7–10. The ABC Company is considering the sale of a new product. There are $1,750 of fixed costs associated with undertaking the project. The product will sell for $4 a unit, and the variable costs are $1.50. It is expected that 1,000 units will be sold, but the demand has a normal probability distribution with a σ of 150.

a) How many units have to be sold to break even?

b) What is the expected profit if the product is handled?

c) What is the expected opportunity loss if the product is handled?

d) What is the expected gross profit?

7–11. The ABC Company is currently selling a product for $3 per unit. The incremental fixed costs associated with the product are $50,000 per unit time. The variable costs are $2 per unit. There is excess capacity, and up to 250,000 units can be produced with no additional fixed costs or changes in marginal costs.

The following schedule has been prepared for the purpose of analyzing a possible price change:

	Information for:		
	Current price	Price after decrease	Price after increase
Price..................	$3	$2.50	$4
Expected sales	100,000 units	250,000 units	60,000 units
Standard deviation of sales distribution......	10,000 units	75,000 units	35,000 units

a) Compute the expected profit for each price.

b) Compute the break-even number of units for each price.

c) Compute the expected opportunity loss for each price.

d) Compute the expected gross profit for each price.

7–12. A construction company has a contract to complete a job in 180 days. It will have to pay a penalty of $10,000 per day for each day beyond 180 that it takes to complete the project. There is some uncertainty about how long it will take due to weather conditions, possible strikes, etc. Management has assigned a normal probability distribution to the number of days necessary to complete the project. This distribution has a mean of 170 days and a standard deviation of 12 days.

a) What is the probability that the job will be completed on time?

b) What is the expected penalty cost?

7–13. A contractor is considering the possibility of bidding on the construction of a new state highway. He has already decided that if he were to bid, he would do so at a price of $8.4 million. For the job to be worth his while, he would need a profit of at least $0.4 million. Hence, he would not bid at all if his estimated costs were above $8 million.

Based upon some preliminary calculations, the contractor has estimated his cost of building the highway at $7.8 million. However, he knows that these preliminary calculations are often considerably in error. In a study of past jobs, it was found that the average of the preliminary estimates was close to the average actual cost. Furthermore, about two thirds of the preliminary estimates were within 10 percent of actual cost.

Assuming that the contractor is willing to base his decision on expected monetary value, which decision should he make? What is the *EVPI?*

7–14. An electronics manufacturer is faced with a problem of deciding how to inspect integrated circuits as they come off the assembly line. A large percentage of the circuits are defective, and the manufacturer must choose between two inspection systems. Both inspection systems will give perfect performance on good circuits; that is, a good circuit will never be classified as defective. The two systems differ on classifying defectives. The first device, which is mechanical will misclassify at an average rate of 10 percent, but the actual misclassification rate will be normally distributed about 0.10 with a standard deviation of 0.03 (this randomness is due to imperfect adjustment of the inspection machine at the beginning of each production run). A misclassification rate of 0.10 means that 0.10 of the *total lot* remains defective after inspection, and so on. Because of the nature of the production run, once the inspection machine is adjusted, it cannot be readjusted until the next run.

The alternative inspection system is to place a workman on the assembly line, and the experience in the past has been that this system produces only 0.01 misclassifications. If the workman is used, the incremental cost over the machine will be $25 per production run (a run is 1,000 circuits). When a defective is classified as good, there is a cost of reworking the subassembly when the circuit is used. This cost is 50 cents per circuit misclassified.

Calculate the following (per production run):

a) The *EMV* of the best act

b) The *EVPI* (concerning perfect information about the machine's rate of misclassification)

c) The expected cost under certainty

7–15. Solve Problem 7–14 assuming the mean machine misclassification rate is still 0.10 but the standard deviation is 0.05.

7–16. Solve Problem 7–14 assuming the mean machine misclassification rate is 0.07 and the standard deviation is 0.03.

8

Revision of normal probabilities

In Chapters 2 and 5, we discussed the idea of revising subjective probabilities in the light of new or experimental evidence. Chapter 2 introduced the Bayes theorem for probabilities, and in Chapter 5 the general framework for including experimental or sample evidence was considered. It is the purpose of this chapter and the next to extend this analysis and apply it in a specific decision situation.

We shall use a problem to illustrate the concepts that are involved. Suppose a manufacturer is considering introducing a new product. He will market this product through a chain of 5,000 stores. The manufacturer is uncertain about the level of sales for the product and has not been able to decide whether or not to market it.

The first source of information the manufacturer can tap in making this decision is his judgment and experience (including analysis of similar product introductions in the past). This experience may be represented by a subjective probability distribution for the mean sales per store of the new product. Suppose the manufacturer states that his subjective probability distribution for average sales per store is normal with a mean of 400 units and a standard deviation of 30.

With no other evidence the manufacturer would make his decision using the above information. However, he may be able to experiment and obtain additional information. Experimentation could take the form, in this example, of a market research study in which a random sample is taken from the 5,000 stores. The new product could be introduced into these selected stores and sales of the product measured. The results could then be used as estimates for all 5,000 stores.

The sample evidence itself is subject to some uncertainty. There may be a bias in the evidence.[1] In addition, there is random or sampling error, due to the fact that we have experimented with a sample and not with the entire group of stores. Hence, we should not use sample evidence as the only basis for making this decision.

Using the Bayes theorem, we can combine the subjective probabilities of the manufacturer with the sample evidence to give a revised or posterior subjective distribution. This posterior distribution is then the basis for decision making.

In this chapter we are concerned with the revision of the mean and the standard deviation of a normal prior distribution in the light of sample evidence. In the next chapter we shall discuss whether or not it is desirable to obtain the sample evidence, assuming the sampling process has a cost.

We will first describe the several distributions which are encountered in the revision of the prior normal probability distribution.

THE PROBABILITY DISTRIBUTIONS

We shall use five probability distributions in the analysis:

1. *The population distribution, where* σ_p = *standard deviation and* μ = *mean.* This distribution reflects the characteristics of the individual components of the population from which the sample is to be drawn.

For example, we might be interested in the probability distribution of actual sales per store for the population of all 5,000 stores. If all the data were available, we could array the number of stores making sales of different amounts and divide these numbers by the total number of stores, so that the sum of the proportions is equal to one. A possible empirical distribution of the sales of stores in the population is presented in Figure 8–1.

There would be a small proportion of stores with large sales, but most stores are expected to sell less than 800 units. This distribution, as is typical of many distributions of economic data, is skewed to the right (i.e., has a long right tail), and a normal distribution would be a poor approximation to the curve in Figure 8–1. The manufacturer is assumed to have a reasonably good estimate of σ_p, the standard deviation of the empirical distribution of store sales. It may be that studies of this type have been made in the past; and although the true mean in any particular study is unknown, the deviations of the sales per store from this true mean (whatever it is) are known.

---

[1] We shall concern ourselves in this book only with sampling error. For a discussion of how some forms of bias may be treated, see R. Schlaifer, *Probability and Statistics for Business Decisions* (New York: McGraw-Hill Book Co., 1959), chap. 31.

FIGURE 8–1
Population distribution (distribution of sales per store)

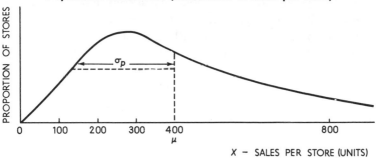

Frequently, μ and σ_p are unknown, and the mean and the standard deviation of the sample are used as estimates of μ and σ_p.

2. *The distribution in the sample.* Suppose a random sample of n stores is selected. A frequency distribution, somewhat similar to that above, could be made for the elements in the sample, i.e., a distribution of sales by store for those stores in the sample. Certain relationships exist between this distribution and the population distribution. In particular, let X_i be the sales of the ith store in the sample of n stores. Then the sample mean is

$$ X = \frac{\sum_{i=1}^{n} X_i}{n} $$

and is an unbiased estimate[2] of the population mean μ.

The sample variance[3] is:

$$ \sigma_s^2 = \frac{\sum_{i=1}^{n} (X_i - \bar{X})^2}{n - 1} $$

and is an unbiased estimate of the population variance σ_p^2. The sample standard deviation is σ_s and is an estimate of σ_p.

3. *The distribution of sample means.* There are many possible random samples that could be selected from a given population, and each

---

[2] A sample statistic is unbiased if the expected value of that statistic is equal to the corresponding population parameter. In particular, $E(\bar{X}) = \mu$ and $E(\sigma_s^2) = \sigma_p^2$. The sample mean is unbiased since, on the average, it will equal the population mean.

[3] In this book, we shall call σ_s^2, as defined above, the sample variance, although other writers may use that term to refer to the above formula with $n - 1$ replaced by n. Using n, the sample variance is not an unbiased estimate of the population variance σ_p^2.

sample will have a mean $\bar{X}$. Considering all possible samples, $\bar{X}$ itself is a random variable and has a probability distribution with mean $E(\bar{X})$ and standard deviation $\sigma_{\bar{x}}$. $E(\bar{X})$ and $\sigma_{\bar{x}}$ are unknown; however, the population distribution and the distribution of sample means are connected by the following relationships:

$$(8\text{-}1) \qquad\qquad E(\bar{X}) = \mu$$

$$\sigma_{\bar{X}} = \frac{\sigma_p}{\sqrt{n}} \quad \text{or} \quad \sigma_{\bar{X}}^2 = \frac{\sigma_p^{\,2}}{n}$$

It should be remembered that $\bar{X}$ represents the mean of a particular sample and $E(\bar{X})$ is actually an average of means of samples.

For large samples, even when the distribution of X is not normal, the distribution of sample means is approximately normal.[4] Normality of this distribution is important in subsequent analysis. We shall assume in this book that a large enough sample has been taken to assure normality of the distribution of sample means.[5]

4. The prior distribution of the population mean. Before a sample is taken, there is a prior (or betting) distribution of the mean of the population. This is a subjective probability distribution of the decision maker. In our example, the manufacturer has a subjective prior distribution for mean sales per store. The parameters of his prior distribution are mean = 400 units (denoted by $\bar{\mu}_0$) and standard deviation = 30 units (denoted by σ_0). Note that σ_0 is the standard deviation of the prior probability distribution of the estimate of the population mean (it is *not* an estimate of the population standard deviation σ_p).

The random variable in the prior distribution (and also in the posterior distribution) is μ, the population mean. Although the actual population distribution has a given mean (as in Figure 8–1), this mean is unknown to the decision maker and, to him, is a (subjective) random variable.

The subscript zero of the symbols $\bar{\mu}_0$ and σ_0 indicates a prior distribution. The subscript one will be used to indicate a posterior distribution.

5. The posterior distribution of the population mean. After the sample is taken, the betting distribution of the population mean is updated to obtain the posterior distribution with $\bar{\mu}_1$, the mean, and σ_1, the stan-

---

[4] This is the result of the central limit theorem of statistics. See any text on statistical theory, such as P. G. Hoel, *Introduction to Mathematical Statistics* (3d ed.; New York: John Wiley & Sons, Inc., 1963).

[5] The question of how large a sample is necessary to assure normality of the sampling distribution of $\bar{X}$ is not simple. If the population distribution is symmetric, very small samples are adequate. For extremely skewed distributions, very large samples are needed. For practical purposes, samples of 30 to 50 items are usually considered adequate. For more discussion of this point, see Schlaifer, *Probability and Statistics,* chap. xvii.

dard deviation. If the prior distribution is normal, and if the distribution of the sample mean is normal, then the posterior distribution will also be normal.

We now indicate how to update the prior distribution using sample information.

REVISING THE PRIOR DISTRIBUTION

Assume the prior distribution of a population mean is normal and has a mean of $\bar{\mu}_0$ and a standard deviation of σ_0. A random sample of size n, is taken; the sample mean is $\bar{X}$, and the standard deviation of the sample is σ_s (σ_s is an estimate of σ_p, the standard deviation of the population).

To simplify the formulas which we shall use, we introduce the symbol I to represent the amount of information contained in a distribution, and define I as being equal to the reciprocal of the corresponding variance; i.e.:

$$I_0 = \frac{1}{\sigma_0{}^2}$$

(8–2)
$$I_{\bar{X}} = \frac{1}{\sigma_{\bar{X}}{}^2} = \frac{n}{\sigma_p{}^2}$$

$$I_1 = \frac{1}{\sigma_1{}^2}$$

If the amount of information in a distribution is large, the amount of uncertainty is small, which is indicated by a tight distribution with small variance, and vice versa, Therefore, the variance of a distribution is inversely related to the amount of information.

The mean of the revised distribution, $\bar{\mu}_1$, is obtained by taking a weighted average of the prior mean and the sample mean, where the weights are the relative amounts of information of the distributions:

(8–3)
$$\bar{\mu}_1 = \left(\frac{I_0}{I_0 + I_{\bar{X}}}\right)\bar{\mu}_0 + \left(\frac{I_{\bar{X}}}{I_0 + I_{\bar{X}}}\right)\bar{X}$$

Equations (8–3) and (8–5) (below) are the equivalent of the Bayes theorem for normal prior and sampling distributions. They determine the mean and the standard deviation of the posterior normal distribution.

Example

Our manufacturer who is considering the introduction of a new product has a normal prior distribution of mean sales per store for the product with mean $\bar{\mu}_0 = 400$ units and a standard deviation of $\sigma_0 = 30$ units. There are 5,000 stores, and a sample of 100 stores is drawn at random. The product is introduced in the 100 stores, and sales records are kept. The average sales per store for the 100 stores is 420 units; i.e., $\bar{X}$ (the sample mean) $= 420$. The sample standard deviation is 200 units; i.e., $\sigma_s = 200$.

Using σ_s as an estimate of the standard deviation of the population σ_p, we can estimate $\sigma_{\bar{X}}$, employing equation (8-1):

$$\sigma_{\bar{X}} = \frac{\sigma_p}{\sqrt{n}} = \frac{\sigma_s}{\sqrt{n}} = \frac{200}{\sqrt{100}} = \frac{200}{10} = 20$$

The values of information are:

$$I_0 = \frac{1}{\sigma_0^2} = \frac{1}{900}$$

$$I_{\bar{X}} = \frac{1}{\sigma_{\bar{X}}^2} = \frac{1}{400}$$

The revised mean, using equation (8-3), is:

$$\bar{\mu}_1 = \left(\frac{1/900}{1/900 + 1/400}\right) \times 400 + \left(\frac{1/400}{1/900 + 1/400}\right) \times 420$$

$$= \frac{400/900 + 420/400}{1/900 + 1/400} = \frac{400 \times 400 + 420 \times 900}{400 + 900}$$

$$= \frac{538,000}{1,300} = 413.8$$

The mean of the prior distribution was 400, but since the standard deviation ($\sigma_0 = 30$) was relatively large compared to $\sigma_{\bar{X}}$, the amount of information in the prior distribution ($I_0 = 1/900$) was small. The mean of the sample was 420; and since the standard deviation of the sample mean was relatively small ($\sigma_{\bar{X}} = 20$), the amount of information in the sample ($I_{\bar{X}} = 1/400$) was relatively large. Thus the revised mean, 413.8, was closer to the sample mean of 420 than the prior mean of 400. If the prior betting distribution has a relatively large standard deviation, the prior mean will be lightly weighted and will not significantly affect the posterior (or revised) mean.

Note that $I_{\bar{X}} = \dfrac{n}{\sigma_p^2}$; therefore the amount of information in the sample is directly related to sample size. Since very large samples tend to be quite accurate. when n is large the prior distribution will tend to have little effect upon the posterior distribution and hence upon the decision.

On the other hand, for smaller samples the prior distribution can have important effects, particularly if the population standard deviation (σ_p) is large.

REVISION OF THE STANDARD DEVIATION

The information in the revised distribution is equal to the sum of the information in the prior distribution plus the information in the sample:

(8–4) $$I_1 = I_0 + I_{\bar{x}}$$

Example

In the example of the previous section the values of I_0 and $I_{\bar{x}}$ were:

$$I_0 = \frac{1}{900}$$

$$I_{\bar{x}} = \frac{1}{400}$$

The value of I_1 is:

$$I_1 = \frac{1}{900} + \frac{1}{400} = \frac{1,300}{360,000}$$

The standard deviation of the revised distribution may be computed using the definition of I_1:

$$I_1 = \frac{1}{\sigma_1{}^2}$$

$$\frac{1}{\sigma_1{}^2} = \frac{1,300}{360,000}$$

$$\sigma_1{}^2 = \frac{360,000}{1,300} = 276.9$$

$$\sigma_1 = \sqrt{276.9} = 16.6$$

The revised standard deviation ($\sigma_1 = 16.6$) is smaller than that of either the standard deviation of the prior ($\sigma_0 = 30$) or the standard deviation of the sample ($\sigma_{\bar{x}} = 20$). Thus the posterior distribution, combining estimates from both sources (judgment and sample), has more information than either source has separately.

Instead of using the above formula, which makes use of I_1, we can develop a variation of the formula which uses only the relevant standard deviations:

$$\frac{1}{\sigma_1{}^2} = \frac{1}{\sigma_0{}^2} + \frac{1}{\sigma_{\bar{x}}{}^2}$$

$$\frac{1}{\sigma_1{}^2} = \frac{\sigma_{\bar{x}}{}^2 + \sigma_0{}^2}{\sigma_0{}^2 \times \sigma_{\bar{x}}{}^2}$$

$$\sigma_1{}^2 = \frac{\sigma_0{}^2 \times \sigma_{\bar{x}}{}^2}{\sigma_{\bar{x}}{}^2 + \sigma_0{}^2}$$

The revised standard deviation is equal to:

$$(8\text{--}5) \qquad\qquad \sigma_1 = \sqrt{\frac{\sigma_{\bar{x}}{}^2 \times \sigma_0{}^2}{\sigma_0{}^2 + \sigma_{\bar{x}}{}^2}}$$

Using this equation to solve the example:

$$\sigma_1 = \sqrt{\frac{400 \times 900}{900 + 400}} = \sqrt{276.9} = 16.6$$

which agrees with the previous solution.

If σ_p, the standard deviation of the population, is known, then instead of estimating $\sigma_{\bar{x}}$ with $\dfrac{\sigma_s}{\sqrt{n}}$, we can compute $\sigma_{\bar{x}}$ using the relationship $\sigma_{\bar{x}} = \dfrac{\sigma_p}{\sqrt{n}}$.

Figure 8–2 compares the prior distribution with the posterior distribution.

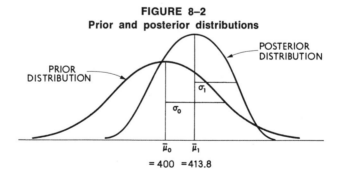

FIGURE 8–2
Prior and posterior distributions

THE POSTERIOR NORMAL DISTRIBUTION AND DECISION MAKING

The posterior distribution results from a combination of the prior subjective probabilities and sample evidence. The posterior distribution is itself a betting or decision-making distribution. Since it is normal, the techniques introduced in Chapter 7 are applicable. Let us briefly illustrate some of these points.

Suppose our manufacturer who is considering the introduction of a new product has the following economic information. The cost of machinery and promotion for the new product is $520,000. The variable profit (or contribution) per unit sold is 25 cents, and the number of stores is 5,000.

After the sample is taken, the posterior random variable is μ_1 — the mean sales per store. The profit equation, in terms of μ_1, is:

$$\text{Profit} = \pi = -520{,}000 + (0.25)(5{,}000)\mu_1$$
$$= -520{,}000 + 1{,}250\mu_1$$

The break-even value is:

$$\mu_b = \frac{520{,}000}{1{,}250} = 416$$

Since the posterior mean $\bar{\mu}_1 = 413.8$ is still less than μ_b, the manufacturer should not market the product.

We can determine the expected value of perfect information ($EVPI$) for the posterior distribution:

$$EVPI = C \cdot \sigma \cdot N(D)$$

where $\sigma = \sigma_1$; in this case:

$$C = 1{,}250$$

$$D = D_1 = \frac{|\bar{\mu}_1 - \mu_b|}{\sigma_1} = \frac{|413.8 - 416|}{16.6} = 0.13$$

$$N(D_1) = 0.3373$$
$$EVPI = (1{,}250)(16.6)(0.3373) = \$7{,}000$$

CONCLUSIONS

The procedures described in this chapter are no better than the information that is used as input (the same thing is true with the other models of this book). If a decision maker were to use a prior distribution with an extremely small standard deviation in the calculations, even though he was very uncertain, the resulting computations would not be useful. In like manner it must be realized that two persons with different prior probabilities might well arrive at different decisions after obtaining the same set of sample information (their revised probabilities would be different).

BIBLIOGRAPHY

CHERNOFF, H., and MOSES, L. E. *Elementary Decision Theory.* New York: John Wiley & Sons, Inc., 1959.

HADLEY, G. *Introduction to Probability and Statistical Decision Theory.* San Francisco: Holden-Day, Inc., 1967.

HOEL, P. G. *Introduction to Mathematical Statistics.* 3d ed. New York: John Wiley & Sons, Inc., 1963.

PRATT, J. W.; RAIFFA, H.; and SCHLAIFER, R. *Introduction to Statistical Decision Theory.* New York: McGraw-Hill Book Co., 1965.

RAIFFA, H., and SCHLAIFER, R. *Applied Statistical Decision Theory.* Boston: Graduate School of Business Administration, Harvard University, 1961.

SASAKI, K. *Statistics for Modern Business Decision Making.* Belmont, Calif.: Wadsworth Publishing Co., 1968.

SCHLAIFER, R. *Probability and Statistics for Business Decisions.* New York: McGraw-Hill Book Co., 1959.

WEISS, L. *Statistical Decision Theory.* New York: McGraw-Hill Book Co., 1961.

WINKLER, R. L. *Introduction to Bayesian Inference and Decision.* New York: Holt, Rinehart & Winston, Inc., 1972.

QUESTIONS AND PROBLEMS

8–1. Given a normal prior distribution with $\bar{\mu}_0 = 10$ and $\sigma_0 = 2$. A sample of size $n = 36$ is taken, with $\bar{X} = 12$ and $\sigma_s = 6$. Compute the mean and the standard deviation of the posterior distribution.

8–2. Given a normal prior distribution with $\bar{\mu}_0 = 500$ and $\sigma_0 = 30$. A sample of size $n = 441$ is taken, with $\bar{X} = 450$ and $\sigma_s = 210$. Compute the mean and the standard deviation of the posterior distribution.

8–3. Given a normal prior distribution with $\bar{\mu}_0 = 20$ and $\sigma_0 = 4$. A sample of size $n = 25$ is taken, with $\bar{X} = 24$ and $\sigma_s = 15$. Calculate the mean and the standard deviation of the posterior distribution.

8–4. Which sample contains the most information:
  a) A sample of 100 from a population with a standard deviation of 50, or
  b) A sample of 64 from a population with a standard deviation of 40? Explain.

8–5. Management has a normal prior distribution with a mean of 200 and a standard deviation of 10. The population from which a sample is to be taken has a standard deviation of 100. How large a sample must be taken so that the standard deviation of the posterior distribution is five?

8–6. An auditor believes the average credit card balance outstanding is probably over $10. More precisely, his feelings about the average balance can be represented by a normal distribution with a mean of 12 and a standard deviation of two. A sample of 25 accounts is drawn at random, and the average balance on these accounts is $9. The standard deviation of the balances in the sample is $5. What should be the auditor's posterior distribution? What probability would he assign to the possibility that the average balance is less than $10?

8–7. Refer to Problem 7–9. Suppose that before making the decision as to which catalog to use, 100 color catalogs were printed and mailed to a sample of 100 customers. The average sale to these customers was then $7.40, with a standard deviation of $5. Utilizing this information and the prior probabilities of Problem 7–9, what decision should be made? What is the posterior *EVPI*?

8–8. A firm was considering introducing a new product into the market. The product was to be distributed through 5,000 independent wholesale merchants. Management expressed a prior judgment about the average sales per wholesaler in terms of a normal distribution with mean $\bar{\mu}_0 = 4$ cases per month and standard deviation $\sigma_0 = 1.5$ cases per month.

An experimental run of the new product was made. Then a sample of 36 of the 5,000 wholesalers was contacted and persuaded to try the new product. The sales in the month in which the product was introduced were ignored, but the sales to each wholesaler for the second month were noted carefully. It was felt that the level of these repeat sales (i.e., second-month sales) would be a good indication of future sales.

In the sample of 36 wholesalers, the average sale per wholesaler was 3.6 cases for the second month, with a standard deviation of 2.4 cases per month.

a) After the sample, what posterior distribution should management assign to the average sales per month per wholesaler?

b) Suppose that to introduce the product to all the market would require $200,000 for purchase of new equipment and promotional effort. Because of certain financial considerations, Management did not wish to undertake the introduction of the new product unless the profits would pay back this $200,000 cost within the first year. The firm would make a profit of $1 per case sold. After the sample, what decision should be made? What is the posterior *EVPI*?

8–9. The ACME Manufacturing Company is considering a more sophisticated inventory control procedure for its inventory of 10,000 different items. Management estimates that the average percent cost saving due to the improved methods would be 20 percent: Management feels that a normal prior distribution with a mean of 20 percent and a standard deviation of 8 percent adequately describes their feelings about the cost savings which would actually be produced.

Company analysts have explored cost savings in detail for a random sample of 100 items in the inventory. In the sample, percentage cost savings had an average value of 15 percent, with a standard deviation of 12 percent.

a) After the sample, what posterior distribution should management assign to the average percent savings to be obtained?

b) Suppose the new procedure will cost approximately 5 percent of the inventory-associated costs per year. Should the new procedure be implemented?

c) What is the *EVPI* for the prior distribution?

d) What is the *EVPI* for the posterior distribution?

8–10. Refer to Problem 8–9. Suppose now that the break-even percentage cost saving was 14 percent instead of 5 percent.

a) Should the new procedure be implemented now? Why?

b) What is the *EVPI* for the prior distribution?

c) What is the *EVPI* for the posterior distribution?

8–11. The controller of the ABC Machine Shop was complaining that unprofitable orders were being quoted by the company's salesmen. Top management felt that a reasonable profit standard was 15 percent of total invoice for each job. Management was confused by the controller's complaint since they felt they were close to their 15 percent target. Specifically, they had a normal prior distribution for "average percent profit" with a mean of 15 percent and a standard deviation of 2 percent.

A sample of 50 jobs were selected at random; of these, the average profit was 10 percent and the standard deviation was 5 percent. Compute the appropriate posterior distribution after the sample.

9

Decision making with
normal probabilities

In the preceding chapter, we discussed the use of normal prior probabilities and how the normal prior distribution is changed in the light of additional sample information. Companion analytical problems discussed in this chapter are how to decide when sampling is appropriate and also how large a sample should be taken. The analysis in this chapter differs from that of the previous chapter in that it is prior to rather than posterior to the sample.

THE INITIAL SITUATION

Management is considering investing in a new product. Assume the change in profit per unit resulting from a favorable decision is C (the profit function is linear) and the break-even amount is μ_b. The mean of the prior betting distribution on average sales is $\bar{\mu}_0$.

Figure 9–1 indicates the decision is not desirable. The mean $\bar{\mu}_0$ is to the left of μ_b, the break-even point; and the investment has a negative expected value equal to $-C(\mu_b - \bar{\mu}_0)$. However, there is a possibility that the true value of μ is to the right of μ_b.

The expected value of perfect information is:

$$(9\text{--}1) \qquad\qquad EVPI = C \cdot \sigma_0 \cdot N(D_0)$$

where

$$D_0 = \frac{|\bar{\mu}_0 - \mu_b|}{\sigma_0}$$

Equation (9–1) also measures the expected opportunity loss for the decision not to invest since that is the optimum decision. Before sampling,

143

FIGURE 9–1
The prior distribution of the population mean

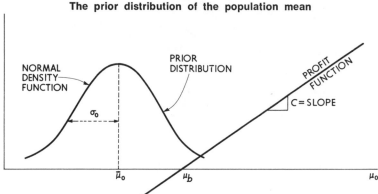

this value is based on the subjective feelings of the decision maker expressed in terms of a probability distribution for the population mean.

Example

Consider the example used in Chapter 8, in which a manufacturer is investigating the introduction of a new product. He has a normal prior distribution of mean sales per store for the product with $\bar{\mu}_0 = 400$ units and a standard deviation of $\sigma_0 = 30$ units. There are 5,000 stores. The cost of machinery and promotion for the new product is $520,000. The variable profit (or contribution) per unit sold is 25 cents. The profit per unit change in μ, the mean sales per store, is:

$$C = 0.25 \times 5,000 = 1,250$$

The break-even value is $\mu_b = 416$.

The optimum act based on the prior probabilities is to reject the new product. However, the expected opportunity loss of the act of rejecting (the expected value of perfect information) is:

$$EVPI = C \, \sigma_0 \, N(D_0)$$
$$D_0 = \frac{|\bar{\mu}_0 - \mu_b|}{\sigma_0} = \frac{|400 - 416|}{30} = 0.53$$
$$N(D_0) = N(0.53) = 0.19$$
$$EVPI = (\$1,250)(30)(0.19) = \$7,100$$

THE EXPECTED POSTERIOR DISTRIBUTION

Before taking a sample, we can estimate the change which will take place in the betting distribution. That is, we can obtain some idea of the posterior distribution before actually taking a sample and revising our prior betting distribution. We do not know beforehand the sample mean $\bar{X}$ and hence do not know exactly what the mean of the posterior distribution will be. However, if we can obtain some measure of the sample variance, we can estimate the posterior variance and the information in the posterior distribution. Recall that the sampling error (the standard deviation of the distribution of $\bar{X}$'s) is:

$$\sigma_{\bar{x}} = \frac{\sigma_p}{\sqrt{n}}$$

Hence, we need a measure of the standard deviation of the population distribution (σ_p) to estimate the variance of a sample of a given size n. Such an estimate of σ_p could come from past studies, from an educated guess, or from a pilot sample of the population.

We shall use $\sigma_*{}^2$ to indicate the amount of reduction in the variance from the prior to the posterior distribution. That is:

(9–2) $$\sigma_*{}^2 = \sigma_0{}^2 - \sigma_1{}^2$$

From equation (8–5) in Chapter 8, we have:

$$\sigma_1{}^2 = \frac{\sigma_{\bar{x}}{}^2 \cdot \sigma_0{}^2}{\sigma_0{}^2 + \sigma_{\bar{x}}{}^2}$$

and substituting in equation (9–2):

$$\sigma_*{}^2 = \sigma_0{}^2 - \frac{\sigma_{\bar{x}}{}^2 \cdot \sigma_0{}^2}{\sigma_0{}^2 + \sigma_{\bar{x}}{}^2} = \frac{\sigma_0{}^2 \cdot \sigma_0{}^2}{\sigma_0{}^2 + \sigma_{\bar{x}}{}^2}$$

and

(9–3) $$\sigma_* = \sqrt{\sigma_0{}^2 \cdot \frac{\sigma_0{}^2}{\sigma_0{}^2 + \sigma_{\bar{x}}{}^2}}$$

THE EXPECTED VALUE OF SAMPLE INFORMATION

The economic value of a sample results from the fact that it reduces the posterior expected loss. That is, the sample, by supplying additional information, reduces the probability of a wrong decision. The expected value of sample information—*EVSI*—is computed in a manner similar to the *EVPI*, with σ_* used as the standard deviation. Thus:

(9–4) $$EVSI = C\sigma_* N(D_*)$$

where

$$D_* = \frac{|\mu_b - \bar{\mu}_0|}{\sigma_*}$$

THE SAMPLING DECISION

For the example above, let us consider the possibility of taking a sample of size $n = 100$. Recall that $EVPI = \$7,100$. Even if the cost of the sample is less than this, we are not sure that the sample is worthwhile, since the sample gives only imperfect information.

Assume that $\sigma_p = 200$ (we know this from past experience). With a sample size of 100, the standard deviation of sample means is:

$$\sigma_{\bar{x}} = \frac{\sigma_p}{\sqrt{n}} = \frac{200}{10} = 20$$

The value of σ_* is:

$$\sigma_* = \sqrt{\frac{\sigma_0^2 \times \sigma_0^2}{\sigma_0^2 + \sigma_{\bar{x}}^2}}$$

$$= \sqrt{\frac{30^2 \times 30^2}{30^2 + 20^2}} = \sqrt{\frac{810,000}{1,300}}$$

$$= \sqrt{623}$$

$$= 24.9 \quad \text{(approximately)}$$

$$EVSI = C\sigma_* N(D_*)$$

$$D_* = \frac{|400 - 416|}{24.9} = 0.64$$

$$N(D_*) = 0.1580$$

$$EVSI = (\$1,250)(24.9)(0.1580) = \$4,900$$

In this situation, sampling of 100 units would not be undertaken if the cost of sampling 100 units were greater than $4,900.

Now, assume the break-even number of units is 402 (it was previously 416; it is now easier to make an incorrect decision). The expected value of perfect information is:

$$EVPI = C\sigma_0 N(D_0)$$

$$D_0 = \frac{|400 - 402|}{30} = \frac{2}{30} = 0.07$$

$$N(D_0) = N(0.07) = 0.36$$

$$EVPI = (\$1,250)(30)(0.36) = \$13,500$$

The expected value of sample information for a sample size of $n = 100$ is

$$EVSI = C\sigma_* N(D_*)$$

$$D_* = \frac{|400 - 402|}{24.9} = 0.08$$

$$N(D_*) = N(0.08) = 0.3602$$
$$EVSI = (\$1,250)(24.9)(0.3602) = \$11,200$$

If the cost of sampling 100 units is less than $\$11,200$, then sampling is desirable.

The expected value of sample information has been made much larger in this second example by reducing the difference between the expected number of units and the break-even number of units. The expected value of sample information would also have been larger if σ_0 had been larger (hence more uncertainty about the true μ), thus increasing the likelihood of making the wrong decision.

Now, assume σ_0 is 300 (it was previously 30) and σ_p is still 200. The computations would become:

$$\sigma_{\bar{x}} = \frac{\sigma_p}{\sqrt{n}} = \frac{200}{10} = 20$$

$$\sigma_* = \sqrt{\frac{\sigma_0^2 \times \sigma_0^2}{\sigma_0^2 + \sigma_{\bar{x}}^2}} = \sqrt{\frac{300^2 \times 300^2}{300^2 + 20^2}} = \sqrt{\frac{90,000 \times 90,000}{90,400}}$$

$$= \sqrt{89,600} = 299$$

Assuming the break-even number of units is still 402, the $EVSI$ is now:

$$EVSI = C\sigma_* N(D_*)$$

$$D_* = \frac{|400 - 402|}{299} = \frac{2}{299} = 0.007$$

$$N(D_*) = N(0.007) = 0.3955$$
$$EVSI = (\$1,250)(299)(0.3955) = \$148,000$$

The $EVSI$ is now higher than in either of the previous two illustrations. A value of 300 for σ_0 implied a great deal of uncertainty about our prior estimate $\bar{\mu}_0 = 400$. The sample greatly reduces this uncertainty; thus it has large value.

If σ_p were smaller than 200 units, the sample would give more information, since the items would be picked from a less spread-out population; σ_* would increase. This would tend to increase the value of the information. Moreover, the value of D_* would decrease and the term $N(D_*)$

would thus increase, also increasing the expected value of sample information.

In many situations, σ_p will not be known. An estimate of σ_p can be obtained by taking a small preliminary sample and using the relationship:

$$\sigma_s = \sigma_{p\,\text{est.}} = \sqrt{\frac{\Sigma(X - \bar{X})^2}{n - 1}}$$

We can then determine whether further sampling is desirable, using σ_s to compute $\sigma\bar{x}$:

$$\sigma\bar{x} = \frac{\sigma_s}{\sqrt{n}}$$

OPTIMUM SAMPLE SIZE

The difference between the expected value of a sample of a given size ($EVSI$) and its cost is defined to be the expected net gain from sampling (ENG). As the size of the sample increases, its value ($EVSI$) increases, but at a decreasing rate. The $EVSI$ can never be greater than the expected value of perfect information ($EVPI$). The cost of sampling is related to sample size. In general, the larger the sample, the larger its

FIGURE 9–2

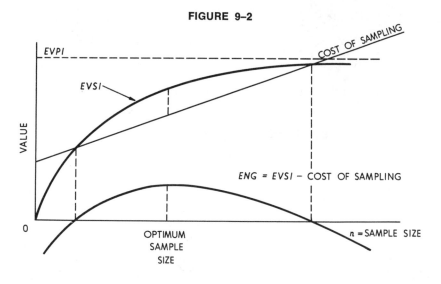

cost. These relationships are graphed in Figure 9–2 for the case in which the cost of sampling is linear.

The expected net gain (ENG) rises at first and then declines. The value of n which maximizes ENG is the optimum sample size. A sample larger than this would have less net value; a sample smaller than this optimum could profitably be increased in size.[1]

The term "optimum" is used here in a special sense. It is the result of the current informational inputs; and if additional information is obtained (say, relative to the cost of sampling), the optimum sample size would also change.

A comprehensive example

Assume a manufacturer of toys is considering the production of a new toy. The investment necessary to undertake production and distribution of the toy is $500,000 for one year. The incremental profit (selling price less variable cost) is $1 per toy. If the manufacturer is to break even, he must sell at least 500,000 units in the one year.

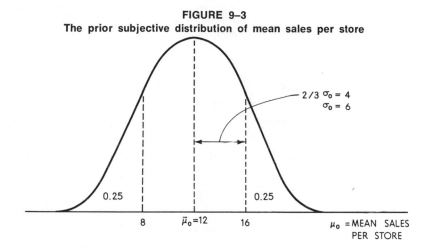

FIGURE 9–3
The prior subjective distribution of mean sales per store

The product will be sold to 50,000 retail sport stores to which the company is selling its present products. The break-even sales per store, μ_b, is 10 units per store ($500,000 \div 50,000$). After careful thought, the manufacturer feels that the mean sales per store will be 12 units (i.e., $\bar{\mu}_0 = 12$), and he assigns a 50 percent chance that mean sales per store will be less than 8 or greater than 16. If he is willing to accept a normal distribution as an indication of his prior subjective probabilities, the distribution may be roughly fitted as shown in Figure 9–3.

---

[1] Under certain circumstances, the determination of the optimum sample size can be reduced to a mathematical formula. See, for example, R. Schlaifer, *Probability and Statistics for Business Decisions* (New York: McGraw-Hill Book Co., 1959), chap. xxxvi. In this chapter, we shall determine approximate optima by trial and error.

The mean of the distribution, $\bar{\mu}_0$, is equal to 12 units, and the standard deviation, σ_0, is 6 units. This is a distribution showing the likelihood of the different possible values of mean sales per store.

Under the above conditions, the best act is to introduce the new toy. This is because the required break-even sales per store, $\mu_b = 10$, is less than the estimated mean of 12. The cost of uncertainty, or the *EVPI*, is $76,650.

$$C = \text{One Toy} \times 50,000 \text{ Stores} \\ \times \$1 \text{ per Toy}$$
$$= \$50,000$$
$$D = \frac{|\bar{\mu}_0 - \mu_b|}{\sigma_0} = \frac{|12 - 10|}{6} = 0.333$$
$$N(D) = N(0.333) = 0.2555$$

$$EVPI = C\sigma_0 N(D)$$
$$= \$50,000 \times 6 \times 0.2555$$
$$= \$76,650$$

We must determine whether sampling is worthwhile, and if it is, how large a sample should be taken.

Let us first consider whether our action will be changed after we have obtained the sample information. If we take a sample and observe its mean, we shall then revise the mean of our prior subjective distribution. If the revised mean is greater than 10 (the break-even mean), we shall still choose to market the toy, and the sample information would turn out to have had zero value. On the other hand, if the sample mean is sufficiently below 10 so that the revised mean is also lower than 10, we would choose not to market the toy, and the sample would have value. Hence the value of the sample depends to a great extent on the value of the revised mean.

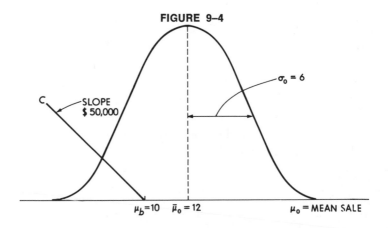

FIGURE 9-4

The above discussion is illustrated in Figures 9–4 and 9–5. If the revised mean, $\bar{\mu}_1$, falls to the right of $\mu_b = 10$, we choose the same act as we would have chosen without the sample. On the other hand, if it falls at t (see Figure 9–5), we would have avoided an expected loss of C^*

FIGURE 9–5

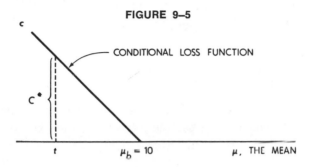

CONDITIONAL LOSS FUNCTION

by sampling. Before taking the sample we do not know what $\bar{\mu}_1$ will be, so we shall treat it as a random variable. The best estimate of the revised mean is the mean of the prior distribution, since $\bar{\mu}_0$ is an unbiased estimate of $\bar{\mu}_1$.

Assume that $\sigma_{p'} = 10$; i.e., the standard deviation of the distribution of purchases of the many individual stores is 10. The standard deviation of the population, σ_p, is an important ingredient in the sample decision. If σ_p is large, it means the purchases of individual stores are widely dispersed from the mean sales of all stores. In such a case a sample would not give as much information as if σ_p is small. To take an extreme case, if $\sigma_p = 0$, then a sample of one store will tell the manufacturer the amount of sales to each store in the population, for if $\sigma_p = 0$, then all stores in the population will purchase the same amount. On the other hand, if σ_p is very large, a small sample will give very little information, since we may be obtaining observations from the extremes of the population distribution.

We must now compute the square root of the change in the variance of the prior probability distribution. The manufacturer has estimated σ_p, the standard deviation of this population, to be 10. We first consider a sample size of 25. The standard deviation of sample means $\sigma_{\bar{x}}$ is:

$$\sigma_{\bar{x}} = \frac{\sigma_p}{\sqrt{n}} = \frac{10}{5} = 2$$

and

$$\sigma_{\bar{x}}^2 = 4$$

We need to compute σ_*:

$$\sigma_* = \sqrt{\frac{\sigma_0^2 \cdot \sigma_0^2}{\sigma_0^2 + \sigma_{\bar{x}}^2}} = \sqrt{\sigma_0^2 \frac{\sigma_0^2}{\sigma_0^2 + \sigma_{\bar{x}}^2}}$$

where σ_0^2 is the prior variance; in our example, its value is 36, and $\sigma_{\bar{x}}^2$ is the variance of the sample means. The calculations are as follows:

$$\sigma_* = \sqrt{36 \cdot \frac{36}{36 + 4}} = \sqrt{36 \cdot \frac{36}{40}} = \sqrt{32.4} = 5.69$$

The estimate of σ_* is 5.69. Remember, this estimate is made before the sample is taken. With a sample size of 25, the expected value of the sample information is calculated as follows:

$$D_* = \frac{|12 - 10|}{5.69} = 0.351$$

$$\begin{aligned} EVSI &= C \cdot \sigma_* \cdot N(D_*) \\ &= \$50,000 \times 5.69 \times 0.248 \\ &= \$70,556 \end{aligned}$$

As can be seen from the above calculation, the $EVSI$ with $n = 25$ is quite large. If the cost of sampling each store is \$100, the cost of the sample is \$2,500. The expected net gain (ENG) from sampling 25 units is the $EVSI$ less the cost of sampling. Hence:

$$\begin{aligned} ENG_{25} &= EVSI - \text{cost of sampling} \\ &= 70,556 - 2,500 = \$68,056 \end{aligned}$$

Since the ENG is positive, it is desirable to take a sample of 25. However, we may be able to increase the ENG by adjusting the sample size. We can approximate the optimal n by iterative procedures (trial and error), making calculations on either side of $n = 25$ and converging on the best n until we maximize the ENG. As we increase n, we shall increase the $EVSI$, but the sample cost will also increase. Hence, we must find the proper balance between the value of the additional information and the increased cost caused by increasing the sample size, n.

Table 9–1 shows the calculation of ENG from sampling for several sample sizes between 20 and 45. The ENG rises until the sample size reaches approximately 40 and then begins to decline. Therefore we assume the optimal size is between 35 and 45. The change in the ENG is quite small even when the sample size is doubled. In this example the ENG is not too sensitive to changes in sample size in the 20-to-45 range.

TABLE 9–1
Calculation of optimal sample size

Sample size n	$\sigma_{\bar{x}}^2$ variance of sample means $\sigma_p^2 = \dfrac{100}{n}$	σ_*	D_* $\dfrac{\lvert 12 - 10 \rvert}{\sigma_*}$	$N(D_*)$	EVSI 50,000 $\sigma_* \, N(D_*)$	Sample cost	ENG (EVSI − sample cost)
20.......	5.00	5.62	0.356	0.246	$69,126	$2,000	$67,126
25.......	4.00	5.69	0.351	0.248	70,556	2,500	68,056
35.......	2.85	5.75	0.346	0.250	72,125	3,500	68,625
40.......	2.50	5.77	0.345	0.251	72,739	4,000	68,739
45.......	2.22	5.80	0.344	0.251	73,099	4,500	68,599

CONCLUSION

The last three chapters have considered decision making with normal probabilities and linear loss functions. While these assumptions of normality and linearity imply that we have considered a special case, the applications appear widespread. Other methods have been developed for different distributions and loss functions; however, these methods are beyond the scope of this book. The normal distribution–linear loss function case illustrates well the concepts involved in Bayesian decision making under uncertainty.

BIBLIOGRAPHY

See the Bibliography at the end of Chapter 8.

QUESTIONS AND PROBLEMS

9–1. Suppose that the total cost of taking a sample of any size was a fixed amount, K. What would be the optimum sample size?

9–2. Assume a normal prior distribution with $\bar{\mu}_0 = 20$ and $\sigma_0 = 10$. Also, $\sigma_p = 20$. The cost of sampling $= 10 + 2n$, $\mu_b = 15$, and $C = \$100$.
  a) Compute the *EVPI* before the sample.
  b) Compute the *EVSI* for $n = 10$, $n = 25$, and $n = 50$.
  c) What is the optimum sample size (of the three items above), and what is its *ENG*?

9–3. Refer to Problem 7–9. Suppose that the mail-order firm can print a few color catalogs and mail them to a sample of customers. The purchases of these customers could be measured and some information about the effect of the color catalog obtained. From past experience the standard deviation of customer purchases is known to be about

$5. Suppose that the cost of sampling is $500 plus $5 per item sampled. What is the optimum sample size? (To simplify the problem, consider only the following values of n: $n = 0$ [no sample], $n = 64$, $n = 100$, and $n = 225$.)

9–4. Refer to Problems 7–9, 8–7, and 9–3. Consider only a sample of size $n = 100$. Does the difference between the *EVPI* prior to the sample (Problem 7–9) and the *EVPI* posterior to the sample (Problem 8–7) equal the expected value of sample information (*EVSI* in Problem 9–3)? Should it? Explain.

9–5. Refer to Problem 8–8. Suppose the firm had not yet taken the sample. However, based upon judgment and experience, the standard devia. tion of sales per wholesaler per month was estimated to be 2.5 cases per month.

a) Compute the *EVSI* for a sample of 36 wholesalers.

b) Suppose it costs $2,500 to make up, by special means, the product to be used in the sample test and an additional $1,000 in other fixed costs. The variable cost is $100 per wholesaler in the sample. Should the sample be taken? What is the *ENG?*

c) What is the *ENG* for a sample of 50 wholesalers?

d) What is the *ENG* for a sample of 75 wholesalers?

e) Based upon (*b*), (*c*), and (*d*) above, what is the approximate optimum sample size?

9–6. Refer to Problem 7–13. Suppose the contractor could made a detailed cost estimate before submitting his bid. The cost of making this detailed estimate is $18,000. Based upon past experience with these detailed estimates, there is a two-thirds chance that a given estimate will be within 3 percent of the actual cost.

Should the contractor make the detailed estimate? What is the *ENG?*

Hint: Treat $(0.03)(7.80) = 0.234$ as $\sigma_{\bar{x}}$. Then proceed to calculate the *EVSI*.

9–7. A major magazine publisher was considering publishing a hard-cover volume of pictorial selections from its magazine. The pictorial volume would be sold largely by mail solicitation of the persons on the magazine's large mailing list. This list included not only subscribers but persons considered potential subscribers. Management felt that the volume would sell a considerable number of copies because of the reputation of the magazine and because the pictorial essays had received wide acclaim when they appeared in the magazine. In fact, many persons wrote in suggesting that a volume of this type be considered.

Some of the cost of publishing the volume had already been incurred when the photographs and text were prepared for the magazine. However, it was estimated that additional costs of $10,000 would be incurred. In addition, it was estimated that the costs of designing and printing the advertising material and the costs of the repeated mailings would amount to about $250,000. (The mailing list contained 2 million names—some, of course, were duplicates. Two mailings were contemplated, with a cost per individual name of 5 cents per mailing. In addition, there was about $50,000 involved in the development of the advertising material.)

The variable manufacturing cost of the proposed book was estimated to be $2 per volume. The selling price was fixed at $3.

Because of the high initial costs, management was undecided about the publishing venture. The best guesses centered at about 250,000 sold. Management felt (two chances out of three) that the sales would be somewhere between 200,000 and 300,000.

Management was somewhat reluctant to abandon the project completely because of the possible prestige value of such a volume. Therefore the possibility of doing some market survey work prior to making the final decision was considered. It was a fairly simple task to select a sample of individuals from the mailing list and test the salability of the volume on these persons. The mailing costs and other variable costs for each of the individuals in the sample amounted to 25 cents per person. However, it was necessary to design and print some special advertising literature, and this would cost about $13,000, regardless of the number of persons sampled. A sample of 2,000 persons was considered an appropriate sample size. The company statistician estimated that the standard error for the sample of 2,000 persons would be 10,000 books (that is $\sigma_{\bar{x}} = 10,000$).

a) Based upon the prior information only, what is the expected profit from publishing the volume? Disregarding any possibility of fringe benefits, such as prestige value, should it be published? What is the expected value of perfect information (*EVPI*)?

b) What is the expected value of sample information (*EVSI*)? What is the expected net gain from sampling (*EVSI*—cost of sample)? Should the sample be taken?

c) Suppose that spending the $13,000 on advertising literature would reduce the estimated development cost of $50,000 to $40,000 if the complete mailing is undertaken (i.e., $10,000 of the $13,000 is recoverable if the book is published). The break-even point is now 250,000 books. What is the *EVSI* in this case? What is the net gain from sampling? *Hint:* Note that if the sample is taken, the posterior profit function and hence the posterior break-even point are changed.

9–8. The Massachusetts Bay Transit Authority (MBTA) has been authorized by the state legislature to construct a rapid transit line from Route 128 to downtown Boston via Cambridge. The legislature has offered to subsidize the construction and operating costs of the line, but state law requires that the line not incur a loss (taking the subsidy into account). The MBTA has calculated that if 10,000 riders rode the line each weekday (round trip), they would just break even, given the subsidy. For each rider above or below the break-even point the present value of the change in revenue is $150.

MBTA officials estimate that out of the 100,000 daily commuters currently commuting into Boston from the relevant area, approximately 12 percent (or 12,000) would ride the new line; however, they are not overly confident about their estimate of percent of ridership and feel that a prior distribution with $\bar{\mu}_0 = 0.12$ and $\sigma_0 = 0.04$ adequately describes their knowledge.

They plan to sample the appropriate commuter population to obtain better information. Samples are taken in groups of 100, and the standard deviation of sample proportions has been estimated as $\sigma_p = 0.08$ for each group of 100; e.g., if 16 groups of 100 are sampled, the appropriate $\sigma_{\bar{x}} = 0.08/\sqrt{16} = 0.08/4 = 0.02$. The cost of interviewing each group of 100 commuters is $900.

a) Ignoring the state law against losses and assuming an immediate decision is required (sampling is not possible), should the MBTA construct the line or not? What is the expected opportunity loss of the best action?

b) Consider a sample of 16 groups (of 100 each). Prior to the sample actually being taken, what is the *EVSI*?

c) For part (b), compute the *ENG*.

d) Now consider the following sample sizes (all referring to the number of groups of 100): 1, 9, 16. Compute the *EVSI* and the *ENG*. Which of those is the optimum sample size?

e) Will use of the optimal sample size *ensure* that if the line is constructed, it will not run at a loss? Comment on the effect of the state law on this type of decision.

9–9. Refer to Problem 9–8. Suppose the sample interviews are conducted in separate groups of 100, one after the other, and also suppose that the *MBTA* can stop interviewing at any time. For concreteness, suppose that the first four groups have been interviewed and the average percent ridership over the four groups is indicated to be 20 percent (0.20).

a) What are the parameters of the posterior distribution of fraction of ridership?

b) Given the posterior distribution, what is the *EVPI*?

c) Compare the current *EVPI* (from [b] above) to the cost of interviewing the next 100 commuters. Without performing the *EVSI* calculation, can you guess whether it would be economic for the *MBTA* to cancel subsequent interviewing and make their decision now?

d) As of now, calculate the *EVSI* for the next single group (of 100 commuters). Is it larger or smaller than the sampling cost?

10

Inventory control and
uncertainty: No reordering

Chapter 3 suggested a method of solving inventory problems making use of conditional and expected value tables. In many situations, that method of analysis requires an excessive amount of clerical effort. An alternative procedure is to make use of marginal analysis and find the last unit worthy of being ordered.

It should be noted that this chapter deals with inventory control problems where the problems of order size, in conjunction with frequency and timing of order, are *not* present. We are concerned only with the problem of how much should be ordered if we are faced with a demand with known probabilities and *reordering is not possible*.

We shall divide the problem to be analyzed into three classifications:

1. Fixed demand under certainty—i.e., the exact number of units to be sold is known and is always one amount.
2. Uncertain demand with perfect information (there can be changing demand)—i.e., the exact number of units to be sold may change, but the number is known in advance. The probability of selling different numbers of units is known, and we know which event has occurred before we make a decision. This is analogous to knowing that a coin will come up either a tail or a head, the rewards being different for a head and a tail, and knowing which has come up on the most recent toss of the coin before making our bet. We have perfect information about the outcome.
3. Uncertain demand with a probability distribution as to the demand of the next period. This is analogous to knowing that a fair coin has a tail and a head, but not knowing which will come up on the next toss.

FIXED DEMAND UNDER CERTAINTY

With fixed demand under conditions of certainty, the number of units to be used in each period is known in advance and the same number of units is used in each period. In terms of probabilities, the probability of the demand occurring is one. Examples of reasonably fixed known demand would be the number of meals served during a weekday at the United States Naval Academy once the academic year has started. Another example is the demand for a text required for a course after it has been assigned by an instructor (assuming no used copies are available). Under a fixed demand the order size will be made equal to the number of units required. This classification of the situation will occur very infrequently in practice. The profit in any time period will be equal to the sales price minus the incremental costs times the fixed number of sales.

UNCERTAINTY WITH PERFECT INFORMATION

In most situations, sales will not be fixed but will vary from period to period. Thus the sales of a product may vary in successive weeks from 1,000 to 400 to 2,000. If the amount of sales is not fixed, but if we know prior to placing our order the total amount of the sale for the next time period, then we may speak of inventory decision making under uncertainty with perfect information.

Let us assume that the demand for the product is known to have the distribution shown in Table 10–1 (the net profit earned on each unit sold is $3).

TABLE 10–1

Demand	Probability	Conditional profit assuming demand is known ($3 · demand)
0	0.10	$0
1	0.30	3
2	0.40	6
3	0.20	9
	1.00	

The profit may be zero, $3, $6, or $9, depending on the number of units demanded. Before we obtain the perfect prediction of the demand for the next period, we do not know what the profit will be.

The decision policy would be to order the number of units to be demanded. The number demanded will be known, but it could vary from zero to three units. Thus, demand is known with certainty before the purchase decision, but the resulting profits will vary from period to period. Before we receive this information, the uncertainty is with respect to the number of units to be sold, since the number demanded in each period will not always be the same. Imagine two dice being thrown where the rewards will be equal to the sum of the numbers appearing on the dice (2, 3, . . . , 12). Assume that the price of playing the game is $4 and you do not have to play or pay until after the dice are rolled and you have been informed of the result. You can play only once. There is certainty, in a sense, for you know the results before you have to take action; but before the dice are rolled, there is no assurance of the amount you will win, and you can be sure the amount appearing will change with a known probability distribution. This is what is meant by our description of "uncertainty with perfect information."

The amount of profit which we expect to make is not known with certainty before the perfect information is received. The expected value of the profit may be found by multiplying the conditional profit for each demand by the probability of the event taking place (see Table 10–2).

TABLE 10–2

1 Demand	2 Probability	3 Conditional profit for each demand	4 Expected profit (col. 2 · col. 3)
0	0.10	$0	$0.00
1	0.30	3	0.90
2	0.40	6	2.40
3	0.20	9	1.80
	1.00		$5.10

The expected profit, assuming that the demand is known before ordering, is $5.10 for any period. But the profit for that period may be zero, $3, $6, or $9. Thus, if we know that zero units will be demanded, we shall order no units and sell none, making zero profits. If we know that three units will be demanded (as they will be 0.20 of the time), we shall order and sell three units, making $9 profit. The weighted average of these and other events is such that we expect, on the average, a profit of $5.10.

UNCERTAIN DEMAND

The third case being discussed is where there is a probability distribution of demand and we do not have perfect information. For example, we know that two dice may appear with some number between 2 and 12, and we know the probabilities of each number occurring, but we have to make our bet *before* the dice are rolled. In like manner, we know the probability distribution of demand for our product, but we do not know before the period begins how much will be demanded in this period. In this situation, how many units should be ordered?

One possibility would be to compute the different expected profits which would occur with different ordering plans. This is the procedure followed in Chapter 3. Table 10–3 presents this computation. Remember

TABLE 10–3
Computation of expected profit*

Event: demand	Probability of demand	Order one unit		Order two units		Order three units	
		Conditional	Expected	Conditional	Expected	Conditional	Expected
0	0.10	$(2)	$(0.20)	$(4)	$(0.40)	$(6)	$(0.60)
1	0.30	3	0.90	1	0.30	(1)	(0.30)
2	0.40	3	1.20	6	2.40	4	1.60
3	0.20	3	0.60	6	1.20	9	1.80
	1.00						
Expected profit			$ 2.50		$ 3.50		$ 2.50

* Negative amounts are in parentheses.

that if no units are purchased, no units may be sold; if one unit is purchased, no more than one unit may be sold, even if the amount demanded is greater. Assume that units cost $2.50 each and that leftovers may be sold for salvage for 50 cents. The sales price is $5.50 per unit.

Based on expected profit, the optimum act is to order two units, since the expected profit of $3.50 is higher than the expected profit resulting from any other strategy. However, the expected profit of $3.50 following the optimum strategy is less than the $5.10 expected profit which we computed assuming *perfect information*. This decrease in expected profit occurs since at the time of ordering we no longer know with certainty how many units will be demanded. We only know the probability that different demands will occur. The expected value of perfect information (*EVPI*) is $5.10 minus $3.50, or $1.60.

A MARGINAL APPROACH

In the above analysis, we computed the different total profits which would be expected following different ordering policies. An alternative solution uses a marginal approach. We compute the effect on profit of adding one more unit to the order size.

Let the probability of selling an additional unit (or more) be designated by p; then $(1 - p)$ is the probability of not selling the additional unit (or more). The values of p in our example are shown in Table 10–4.

TABLE 10–4

Demand	Probability of demand	Cumulative probabilities (p)
0	0.10	1.00
1	0.30	0.90
2	0.40	0.60
3	0.20	0.20
	1.00	

The column headed "Cumulative probabilities" is p, since it indicates the probability of selling zero or more (1.00), one or more (0.90), two or more (0.60), or three or more (0.20) units. It is the right tail of the probability distribution.

Let k_o be defined as the unit cost of *overage*, i.e., the cost of having one unit left over. For example, if a unit costs $2.50 and leftover units can be sold for $0.50, then the cost of overage is $2 per unit.

Let k_u be defined as the unit cost of *underage,* i.e., the cost of not having any units to sell when a customer wants one. In our example, a unit costs $2.50 and sells for $5.50. Thus the firm loses $3 of profit for each unit that it is short; that is, k_u is $3.

The relationship between the costs of overage and underage and the probability of demand for the next unit is shown in Table 10–5.

Table 10–5 shows that if a unit is ordered but there is no demand, the conditional cost is k_o. Similarly, if the unit is not ordered and there is a demand for it, the conditional cost is k_u. Note that these costs are *opportunity losses* (see Chapter 3).

The expected cost for the act "do not order" is pk_u; and that for the act "order" is $(1 - p)k_o$. The decision maker will order the additional unit provided the cost of doing so is less than the cost of not

TABLE 10–5
Conditional and expected costs

Event: demand for next unit (or more)	Probability of event	Act Do not order	Act Order
No............................	$1 - p$	0	k_o
Yes...........................	p	k_u	0
Expected cost of acts................................		pk_u	$(1 - p)k_o$

ordering. That is, he will order if:

$$(1 - p)k_o < pk_u$$

Using this rule, the decision maker will keep adding additional units until the expected cost of "order" equals or exceeds the cost of "do not order." Recall that as more units are added, the probability of demand for the next unit (or more), p, will decline, and $(1 - p)$ increase. Ultimately, the expected cost from ordering will exceed that of not ordering.

Suppose we let p_c be the probability at which the cost of ordering equals the cost of not ordering. We call p_c the *critical* probability and can find it by solving the following equation:

$$(1 - p_c)k_o = p_c k_u$$

or

(10–1)
$$p_c = \frac{k_o}{k_o + k_u}$$

The ratio $k_o/(k_o + k_u)$ is called the *critical ratio*.

If the events are not continuous (for example, demand can be either 1,000 or 2,000 units, but not in between), it is not always possible to find the marginal sale with a probability of p_c. The following rule is useful in finding the optimum in the discrete case:

1. As long as the probability of selling one or more additional units is greater than p_c, the critical ratio, we should order that unit.
2. If the probability of selling the additional unit is equal to p_c, we are indifferent to including it in our order or leaving it out.
3. If the probability is less than p_c, do not order that unit.

In our example, k_o equals \$2 and k_u is \$3; thus:

$$p_c = \frac{k_o}{k_o + k_u} = \frac{2}{2 + 3} = \frac{2}{5} = 0.40$$

Referring to Table 10–4, we see that the decision maker would order two units (since $p = 0.60$ for two units and this is greater than $p_c = 0.40$) but would not order the third unit (since $p = 0.20$ and this is less than 0.40).

Table 10–6 shows the expected costs of different ordering policies for the different possible demands, where p measures the probability of selling the additional unit ordered.

TABLE 10–6

1 Policy: go from ordering	p	2 Expected cost of ordering the next unit: $(1 - p)k_o$	3 Expected cost of not ordering the next unit: pk_u	4 Net incremental cost of ordering (col. 2 − col. 3)
0 to 1......	0.90	$0.10 \times 2 = 0.20$	$0.90 \times 3 = 2.70$	−2.50
1 to 2......	0.60	$0.40 \times 2 = 0.80$	$0.60 \times 3 = 1.80$	−1.00
2 to 3......	0.20	$0.80 \times 2 = 1.60$	$0.20 \times 3 = 0.60$	1.00

A negative cost in column 4 of Table 10–6 is a net profit. Ordering the first unit increases profit by $2.50, ordering the second unit increases profit by $1 (to $3.50), and ordering the third unit decreases profit by $1 (to $2.50). It would not be desirable to stock three units, since there is an expected marginal loss of $1 associated with the third unit.

Note that the inventory model that we have developed assumed linearity in the costs of overage and underage. That is, it has assumed that the per unit costs are the same for all units. Frequently these assumptions are not realistic; and more appropriate, but more complex, functions for the marginal costs are available. Let the cost of underage $k_u = f(Q)$ and the cost of overage $k_o = g(Q)$, where f and g are the marginal cost functions for underage and overage respectively, and Q is the number ordered. Then the optimum order can be obtained by solving the equation

$$p \cdot f(Q) = (1 - p) \cdot g(Q)$$

for the number of units (Q) for which the equality holds.

VALUE OF ADDITIONAL INFORMATION

In the example of the inventory decision under uncertainty with perfect information, we found that the expected profit was $5.10. This means that we could expect, on the average, to make \$5.10 a period if we knew the demand before ordering (eliminating the possibility of a stock-out or a leftover unit). We found that the best decision under uncertainty (stock two units) resulted in an expected profit of \$3.50. The difference between the two (\$5.10 — \$3.50 = \$1.60) is the expected value of perfect information (*EVPI*). While perfect information may not be attainable, it may be possible to obtain additional information that would increase the expected profit. The techniques presented in Chapters 5 and 9 may be used in determining the value of additional information and incorporating such information into the decision.

COST OF ILL WILL

Thus far we have assumed that the only cost of an underage (i.e., of being out of stock) was the profit that was lost. But it is possible to modify the model to include customer ill will that might result from not finding the goods on hand. It is necessary that an estimate of this factor be made in terms of the present value of future profits lost because of a unit underage. This amount can then be included in determining the critical ratio, and hence in setting the optimal ordering policy.

Continuing the example of this chapter, let us assume there is an additional "ill will" cost of 75 cents associated with every unit of demand not filled because of an inventory shortage. Consider these definitions and data:

k_o = unit cost of overage = \$2. The \$2 is the difference between the cost per unit (\$2.50) and the distress price (\$0.50).

k_u = unit cost of underage = \$3.75. The \$3.75 is equal to the sum of the gross profit lost by underordering a unit (\$5.50 — 2.50 = \$3.00) and the cost of ill will (\$0.75) for each unit of underage, i.e., when there is demand and there are no units to sell.

The inventory decision of whether to increase the order by a marginal unit may again be considered in terms of the additional expected cost of underage (pk_u) and the additional expected cost of overage $[(1 - p)k_o]$. As before, the optimum is obtained by adding additional units until

$$(1 - p)k_o = pk_u$$

The critical ratio is obtained as above [equation (10–1)]:

$$p_c = \frac{k_o}{k_o + k_u}$$

In our modified example:

$$p_c = \frac{k_o}{k_o + k_u} = \frac{2}{2 + 3.75} = 0.35$$

The increased penalty for not filling an order has had the same effect as an increase in the profit margin (i.e., an increase in the regret of not having a unit on hand when a unit is demanded), and it will tend to increase the size of the order by decreasing p_c.

USING A CONTINUOUS PROBABILITY DISTRIBUTION

Instead of assuming that sales can take on only a few discrete values, we can make use of a continuous probability distribution. Such a distribution will make it possible to consider all feasible values of the random variable, demand. For illustrative purposes, assume that the random variable, tomorrow's demand, is normally distributed.

As in the previous section on the discrete case, we begin by computing p_c, where p_c is the critical ratio. This critical ratio is the probability of selling the last unit which is advantageous to the company and which should result in an increase in order size. In terms of the normal distribution, p_c can be represented by the shaded area as shown in Figure 10–1. It should be noted that p_c is the right tail of the distribution.

Figure 10–1 shows an optimum order size of 50 units. If less than 50 units are ordered, p, the probability of selling an additional unit or

FIGURE 10–1

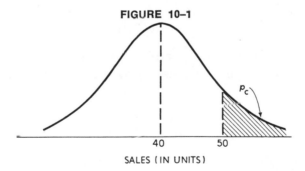

40   50

SALES (IN UNITS)

more, will be greater than p_c; the same arguments presented for the discrete case hold in the continuous case.

In the computation of optimum order size, the first step is to find Z, the number of standard deviations from the mean, that will equate the right tail of the normal density function and p_c. It is then necessary to convert Z to units by multiplying Z by the standard deviation of the sales distribution. This number of units is then added to mean sales, if $p_c < 0.50$ (as shown in Figure 10–1), or subtracted, if $p_c > 0.50$. If $p_c = 0.50$, then $Z = 0$. This is the same process of standardizing a normal probability distribution as was introduced in Chapter 7.

Example 1

Assume that the distribution of demand is normal, k_o is equal to 64 cents, and k_u is equal to \$3.36. The critical ratio is:

$$p_c = \frac{k_o}{k_o + k_u} = \frac{0.64}{0.64 + 3.36} = 0.16$$

The 0.16 probability corresponds to the right tail of a normal distribution. Referring to Table A (in the Appendix at the end of the text), we find that the left tails are given. The left-tail complement of a 0.16 right tail is 0.84, and this is approximately one standard deviation from the mean (with one standard deviation, the value in the table is 0.8413). If we move out one standard deviation to the right of the mean, the probability of making an additional sale will be equal to 0.16.

Assume mean sales for the coming period are 40 units and the standard deviation of the prior distribution is 10. We want to increase the order size until the probability of making an additional sale is equal to 0.16. We have to move one standard deviation to the right of the mean ($Z = 1$). In order to convert Z to units, we multiply by the standard deviation:

$$Z\sigma = 1 \cdot 10 = 10 \text{ units}$$

Since $p_c < 0.50$, we have to add the 10 units to the mean sales to obtain Q, the optimum order size of 50. We can write the following equation:

$$Q = \text{mean sales} \pm Z\sigma$$
$$= 40 + 10 = 50$$

The sign is plus if $p_c < 0.50$ and minus if $p_c > 0.50$.

Example 2

Assume that demand has the same normal distribution as above. Suppose we have now computed p_c and found it to be 0.25. Figure 10–2 shows this situation.

The left-tail complement of a 0.25 right tail is 0.75; Table A shows that the Z value corresponding to $F(Z) = 0.75$ is approximately

$Z = 0.67$. Then the optimal order size is:

$$Q = \text{mean sales} + Z\sigma$$
$$= 40 + 0.67(10) = 46.7 \doteq 47$$

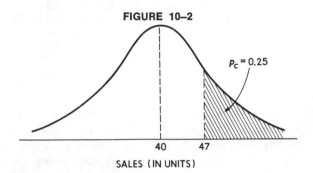

FIGURE 10–2

$P_c = 0.25$

40   47

SALES (IN UNITS)

CONCLUSION

We have developed an example of the application of probability concepts to business decision making under uncertainty. The following chapters will treat related problems, but where more factors are considered. In this chapter the possibility of reordering was excluded from consideration; inventory decision models with reordering will be introduced in the next two chapters.

BIBLIOGRAPHY

Buffa, E. S., and Taubert, W. H. *Production-Inventory Systems: Planning and Control*. Rev. ed. Homewood, Ill.: Richard D. Irwin, Inc., 1972.

Hadley, G., and Whitin, T. M. *Analysis of Inventory Systems*. Englewood Cliffs, N.J.: Prentice-Hall, Inc., 1963.

Hillier, F., and Lieberman, G. J. *Introduction to Operations Research*. San Francisco: Holden-Day, Inc., 1967.

Magee, J. F., and Boodman, D. M. *Production Planning and Inventory Control*. 2d. ed. New York: McGraw-Hill Book Co., 1967.

Starr, M. K., and Miller, D. W. *Inventory Control: Theory and Practice*. Englewood Cliffs, N.J.: Prentice-Hall, Inc., 1962.

Wagner, H. M. *Principles of Operations Research*. Englewood Cliffs, N.J.: Prentice-Hall, Inc., 1969.

PROBLEMS

10–1. The probability distribution of the demand for a product has been estimated to be:

Demand	Probability of demand
0	0.05
1	0.15
2	0.30
3	0.35
4	0.10
5	0.05
6	0.00
	1.00

Each unit sells for $100, and the total incremental costs per unit sold (including selling incentives) are $60. If the product is not sold, it is completely worthless. The purchase costs of a unit are $10.

a) Assuming no reordering is possible, how many units should be purchased?

b) If customer ill will is estimated to be $65 for every unit for which there is unfilled demand, how many units should be ordered?

c) Assume the purchase costs are $60 (i.e., equal to the total incremental costs). If the product is not sold, it is completely worthless. Assume no costs of customer ill will. How many units should be purchased?

10–2. Assume that our estimate of the demand for the next period is a normal distribution with a mean of 50 units and a standard deviation of 10 units. Reordering is not possible. Compute the optimum order sizes for the different p_c's given below:

$$p_c$$

a) 0.40
b) 0.50
c) 0.55
d) 0.60
e) 0.78
f) 0.90
g) 0.98

10–3. Given the following information, compute the optimum order size (reordering is not possible):

Sales price	$100
Incremental cost per unit sold (including purchase cost)	70
Purchase cost per unit.	50
Salvage value (if not sold)	10
Loss in goodwill for each unit of demand not satisfied	50

The probability distribution of demand is normal; mean, 140; standard deviation, 20.

10-4. Refer to Problem 10-3. Recompute the optimum order size, assuming the standard deviation of the probability distribution is 50.

10-5. Refer to Problem 10-3. Recompute the optimum order size, assuming there is *no* loss in goodwill with unfilled orders.
a) Assume a standard deviation of 20.
b) Assume a standard deviation of 50.
c) Compare the above answers with those of Problems 10-3 and 10-4.

10-6. A wholesaler of stationery is deciding how many desk calendars to stock for the coming year. It is impossible for him to reorder, and leftover units are worthless. The following table indicates the possible demand levels and the wholesaler's prior probabilities:

Demand (in thousands)	Probability of demand
100	0.10
200	0.15
300	0.50
400	0.25
	1.00

The calendars sell for $100 per thousand, and the incremental purchase cost is $70. The incremental cost of selling (commissions) is $5 per thousand.
a) Use the analysis of this chapter to find how many calendars should be ordered.
b) Check this calculation by preparing conditional and expected value tables and computing expected values for each act. Also, calculate the *EVPI*.
c) How much of an ill-will cost would have to exist to justify an order of 400,000 calendars?

10-7. Demand for a product is approximately normal with mean 40 units and standard deviation 12 units. The product costs $2 per unit and sells for $5. Unsold units have no value.
a) Assuming there is no goodwill loss due to unfilled demand, what is the optimum order size?
b) Suppose that the manager in charge of the product has usually ordered 60 units. He defends this policy on the ground that there is loss of customer goodwill associated with unfilled demand. What is the implied goodwill loss associated with the manager's policy?

10-8. List two inventory situations that you think would be reasonably represented by the model presented in this chapter. For each, describe what factors would be involved in the cost of overage, the cost of underage, and the goodwill loss.

10–9. A camera manufacturer makes most of his sales during the Christmas selling season. For each camera sold he makes a unit profit of $20; if a camera is unsold after the major selling season, it must be sold at a reduced price, which is $5 less than the variable cost of manufacturing the camera. The manufacturer estimates that demand is normally distributed with a mean of 10,000 units and a standard deviation of 1,000 units.

a) Ignoring ill-will costs of a stockout, what is the optimum order size?

b) What ill-will cost per stockout would justify an order size of 11,500 units?

10–10. The ACME Company produces air conditioners. Due to limited production capacity and the desire to maintain steady employment throughout the year, production of particular models must be determined prior to the heavy summer selling season. The junior model costs $60 to produce (incremental cost) and sells for $100, while the super model costs $120 to produce and sells for $210. Any units unsold at the end of the summer must be sold for a sacrifice price of 80 percent of the incremental production cost.

Seasonal demand for the junior model is estimated as normal with a mean of 10,000 and a standard deviation of 3,000; for the super model, estimated demand is normal with a mean of 6,000 and a standard deviation of 2,000. The company feels that since the two models sell in different price ranges, the demands are independent.

a) Ignoring ill-will costs, compute optimal production sizes for the two models.

b) Now suppose that the demands are no longer independent. As an extreme case, suppose that the number of units of the super model sold are precisely 60 percent of the number of units of the junior model sold. Also, suppose the mean sales of the junior model are estimated to be 10,000 with a standard deviation of 3,000 (ignore the other mean and standard deviation). Now compute the optimal order size. (*Hint:* Given the strict dependence assumed, consider a *composite product* which contains 1 unit of the junior and 0.6 unit of a super.)

10–11. The Fox Photo Company is a mail-order firm specializing in 24-hour service on developing of negatives and making of prints. The general policy is that orders arriving in the morning mail must be finished and in the outgoing mail before the midnight mail pickup. This has usually involved little difficulty. Six full-time technicians work an eight-hour day from 8:00 A.M. to 5:00 P.M. and are paid at a rate of $4 per hour (including fringe benefits). These technicians can process an average of five orders an hour. When on occasion more than about 240 orders arrive on a given day, one or more of the men work overtime at a rate of $6 per hour.

Fox Photo has recently bought out a competitor in the same community and plans to consolidate operations. Mr. Fox is undecided, however, on how many technicians to add to the six he now employs. By adding together the past order data of his competitor to his, Mr. Fox has the following frequency data to ponder:

Number of incoming orders	Fraction of days
Under 220	0.03
220–39	0.03
240–59	0.09
260–79	0.16
280–99	0.18
300–19	0.20
320–39	0.15
340–59	0.10
360–79	0.05
380 and above	0.01
	1.00

One of the technicians at Fox Photo was taking a night course in statistics at a local college and tried his hand at analyzing the above data. After a couple of evenings' work he told Mr. Fox that the data closely fit a normal distribution with mean 300 and standard deviation 40. But the technician was unable to answer the question of how many to employ.

a) How many technicians should Mr. Fox employ? What is his expected cost?
b) What additional factors should be included in making this decision?

11

Inventory control with reordering and certain demand

In the previous chapter, inventory control was discussed in a situation where there were only one-shot orders; and though the situation might be repetitive, within each cycle no reordering was allowed. That is, the order was placed and then the demand occurred, but there was no opportunity for reordering and the item ordered could not be stored for the next cycle. An illustration of this type of situation is production planning for highly seasonal or style goods. In the majority of business situations, we are not restricted to one-shot orders. Items may be reordered as the stock runs low.

In this chapter, we shall assume demand is known; and in the next chapter, we shall consider the uncertainty situation.

With the ability to reorder, there are two operating decisions to be made:

1. *When to place an order.* We shall assume the order point is determined by the units on hand rather than a passage of calendar time (for example, placing an order every month).
2. *The size of the order.* We shall assume there are no discontinuous quantity discounts.

The objective is to maximize the difference between revenue and cost associated with maintaining an inventory.

There are two general types of costs to be considered: (1) the cost of placing one order and (2) the cost of carrying inventory in stock. The optimum order size and optimum order point will in general be a function of these two costs plus the intensity or rate of use (quantity used during a unit time period). Note that costs of underage and overage are not included here. When demand is certain, underage will not occur unless backordering is allowed. A cost of overage is not present because unsold units are carried over into the next period, and the carrying cost therefore measures the cost of unsold units.

INVENTORY CONTROL WITH KNOWN DEMAND

In this chapter, we shall investigate inventory control when we know the demand. We assume that both the replenishment lead time and the demand rate are known and constant. With this assumption, the computation of the order point is not complicated. If the usage rate is 3 units per day and the lead time for replenishment is 40 days, we would set an order point of 40 times 3, or 120 units. This allows us no room for error, but it is consistent with the assumptions of known demand and known lead time. Figure 11–1 illustrates the inventory behavior of the system under our assumption of known and constant demand rate and lead time.

FIGURE 11–1
Reordering and known demand

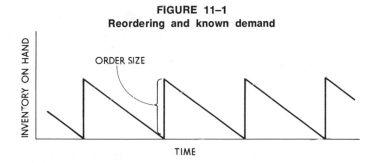

The optimum order size is determined by analyzing total costs. The total cost (TC) for a period will be equal to the sum of the ordering costs (or setup costs) plus the costs of carrying the inventory during the period. Assume that the units ordered will be received all at once.

Let:

K = incremental cost of placing an order (or setting up production)
k_c = annual cost of carrying one unit of inventory
D = annual total usage (demand) in units
Q = optimum order size in units (the unknown)

Note that:

$\dfrac{D}{Q}$ = annual number of orders

and

$$\frac{Q}{2} = \text{average inventory (assuming linear usage)}$$

Then:

$\frac{Q}{2} k_c = $ annual cost of carrying inventory (average inventory times

k_c, the annual holding cost per unit)

$\frac{D}{Q} K = $ annual cost of placing orders (annual number of orders,

$\frac{D}{Q}$, times the cost of placing an order, K)

Total annual cost is:

(11–1) $$TC = \frac{Q}{2} k_c + \frac{D}{Q} K$$

These costs are plotted as a function of order size in Figure 11–2. The minimum total cost of Figure 11–2 occurs when the slopes of the two cost components (ordering and carrying cost) are equal and opposite

FIGURE 11–2
Inventory costs

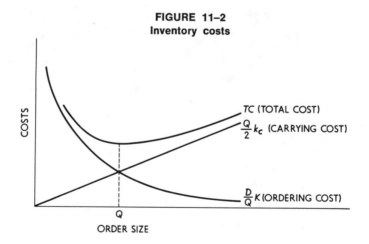

in sign. In this case, this occurs where the two cost components are equal (where the lines cross). We may use this fact to obtain a formula[1] for the optimal order quantity Q by setting the two costs equal and solving

---

[1] This formula may also be obtained by using the calculus to minimize total cost with respect to Q. Take the first derivative of equation (11–1) with respect to Q, set it equal to zero, and solve for Q:

for Q. At the optimum,

$$\frac{Q}{2} k_c = \frac{D}{Q} K$$

or

$$Q^2 = \frac{2KD}{k_c}$$

so that

(11–2)
$$Q = \sqrt{\frac{2KD}{k_c}}$$

An example follows:

$D = 3,000$ units (expected annual demand)
$k_c = \$3$ per unit per year
$K = \$5$ per order

$$Q = \sqrt{\frac{2KD}{k_c}} = \sqrt{\frac{2 \cdot 5 \cdot 3000}{3}} = \sqrt{10,000} = 100 \text{ units}$$

The optimum order size is 100 units. The total cost of using the optimal order size can be computed by substituting $Q = 100$ into the total cost equation (11–1):

$$TC(Q = 100) = \frac{100}{2}(3) + \frac{3,000}{100}(5) = 150 + 150 = 300$$

If D is measured in dollars instead of units and if k_c is measured per dollar instead of per unit, then Q will also be in terms of dollars.

Even when the demand is not known with certainty, the above model may be helpful in approximating a solution for the problem of optimum order size.

SENSITIVITY OF COSTS TO ERRORS IN Q

It is possible to use the cost model of equation (11–1) above to demonstrate that total costs in this model are not very sensitive to errors in

---

$$TC = \frac{Q}{2} k_o + \frac{DK}{Q}$$

$$\frac{dTC}{dQ} = \frac{1}{2} k_c - \frac{DK}{Q^2} = 0$$

$$Q = \sqrt{\frac{2KD}{k_c}}$$

Since $\dfrac{d^2TC}{dQ^2} = \dfrac{2DK}{Q^3} > 0$, this solution does produce a minimum TC.

determining Q. For example, suppose in the example just considered, the expected annual demand was incorrectly stated as 4,500 units instead of 3,000 units (a 50 percent overstatement). Then, using the optimal formula for Q, we would obtain the following (incorrect) order quantity:

$$Q = \sqrt{\frac{2 \cdot 5 \cdot 4,500}{3}} = \sqrt{15,000} = 123 \text{ units}$$

Note that because of the square root formula, a 50 percent error in estimating demand produces only a 23 percent error in the order size as compared to the optimal $Q = 100$. However, the true test of an error is how much it costs. Substituting $Q = 123$ into the total cost equation (11–1) produces:

$$TC(Q = 123) = \frac{123}{2} (3) + \frac{3,000}{123} (5)$$
$$= 184.5 + 122 = 306.5$$

Comparing this total cost with the total cost of the optimal order size derived above ($TC = 300$), we see that the percentage increase in cost, or penalty for our error, is only $6.5/300 = 2.2$ percent. Thus as long as the order quantity is somewhere close to the optimum, very little will be gained by making it more precise.

ASSUMING A CONTINUOUS FLOW OF PRODUCT

Instead of receiving the ordered units all at once, the firm may receive the product continuously over a period of time. For example, the units being produced may be sent into inventory one at a time instead of in a batch of size Q. Assume units are used at a rate D, that they are produced at a rate p, and that Q units are to be produced on each production run. Figure 11–3 shows the situation being considered.

FIGURE 11–3

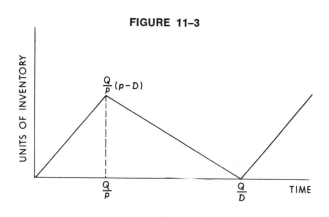

It takes time $\frac{Q}{p}$ for the entire Q to be produced. During this time, $\frac{Q}{p} D$ has been used. Hence the amount available at the highest point in Figure 11–3 is $Q - \frac{Q}{p} D = \frac{Q}{p} (p - D)$ at the point in time $\frac{Q}{p}$.

The optimum production run size is:[2]

$$Q = \sqrt{\frac{2KD}{k_c} \times \frac{p}{p - D}}$$

Example

It costs \$50 to set up the production line for a product that is used at the rate of 100,000 units per year. The carrying cost per unit is \$5 per year. The rate of production is 200,000 units per year. What should be the size of the production run?

$$
\begin{aligned}
Q &= \sqrt{\frac{2KD}{k_c} \times \frac{p}{p - D}} \\
&= \sqrt{\frac{2 \times 50 \times 100,000}{5} \times \frac{200,000}{100,000}} \\
&= \sqrt{4,000,000} = 2,000 \text{ units}
\end{aligned}
$$

In doing calculations of the type illustrated, one must be careful that the units are compatible. For example, if we were told that production *per day* was 800 units, we could not let p be equal to 800 and still use the demand rate of 100,000 units *per year* and the carrying cost of \$5 *per year*. In this situation, we might convert the 800 units *per day* to an annual equivalent by multiplying by the number of workdays in a year (say there are 250 workdays in a year; this would give us the equivalent annual rate of 200,000 units per year).

DEMAND IS KNOWN: BACKORDERING IS ALLOWED

In this situation the firm can run out of inventory without losing the sale; however, there is now a third cost representing a penalty for backordering. We want to determine the optimum order size and the amount we shall backorder before ordering (see Figure 11–4). We will assume

---

[2] See Appendix 1 to this chapter for the derivation.

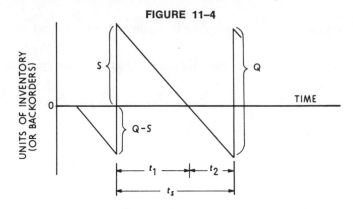

FIGURE 11–4

orders are filled instantaneously. Let:

Q = order size

D = annual demand rate

K = annual incremental fixed cost of ordering

k_c = annual cost of carrying one unit in inventory

k_s = penalty cost of backordering one unit of demand for one year

t_1 = time from stock replenishment to having zero inventory, in fraction of a year

t_2 = time from running out to next stock replenishment (it is the backlog time) (in fraction of a year)

t_s = time of the order cycle (fraction of a year)

S = amount we have remaining from order after backlog is satisfied

During time t_1, the average inventory is $\dfrac{S}{2}$ units, and the carrying cost for one order cycle is $\dfrac{S}{2} k_c t_1$.

During time t_2 the average shortage is $\dfrac{Q - S}{2}$, and the shortage cost for one order cycle is $\dfrac{Q - S}{2} k_s t_2$.

The total cost for one order cycle is:

$$\frac{S}{2} k_c t_1 + \frac{Q - S}{2} k_s t_2 + K$$

The number of cycles per year is $\dfrac{D}{Q}$, and the total cost for a year is:

$$TC = \left(\frac{S}{2} k_c t_1 + \frac{Q - S}{2} k_s t_2 + K \right) \frac{D}{Q}$$

We next find the values of Q and S which minimize the total cost:[3]

$$Q = \sqrt{\frac{2KD}{k_c}} \times \frac{k_c + k_s}{k_s}$$

$$S = \sqrt{\frac{2KD}{k_c}} \times \frac{k_s}{k_c + k_s}$$

or equivalently:

$$S = Q \times \frac{k_s}{k_s + k_c}$$

Example

Let us assume a situation where a firm, if out of stock, can backorder the demands of its customers. The facts are:

$$D = 10,000 \text{ units per year}$$
$$K = \$10 \text{ per order}$$
$$k_c = \$4 \text{ per unit per year}$$
$$k_s = \$5 \text{ per unit per year}$$

Determine the order quantity and amount backordered for each cycle.

$$Q = \sqrt{\frac{2 \times 10 \times 10,000}{4}} \times \frac{4 + 5}{5} = \sqrt{90,000} = 300$$

$$S = \sqrt{\frac{2 \times 10 \times 10,000}{4}} \times \frac{5}{9} = \sqrt{\frac{10^6}{36}} = \frac{1,000}{6} = 167$$

or

$$S = 300 \times \frac{5}{9} = \frac{1,500}{9} = 167$$

$Q - S = 300 - 167 = 133$ is the amount backordered.

Even though the annual cost of backordering a unit demanded is greater than the annual cost of carrying a unit, the model indicates that we should allow a backorder of 133 units before we order 300 units. This solution suggests that in some situations it may pay to offer discounts to customers if they will allow later delivery. The backordering of some orders (for a short period of time) will result in decreased costs unless k_s is very large compared to k_c.

In this model, we assumed that the cost of the backordered orders

---
[3] See Appendix 2 in this chapter for the derivation.

was a function of the average shortage of $\dfrac{Q-S}{2}$, and the time of shortage. We could modify the model to reflect a situation where the cost of shortage was a function of the maximum number of units backordered. This would be the case if backorders were met by borrowed stock and the total number of units to be borrowed had to be borrowed in one group.

APPENDIX 1. PRODUCTION LOT SIZE

How many units should be produced on one production run? This model assumes units are produced at a rate p and used at a rate D (see Figure 11–5).

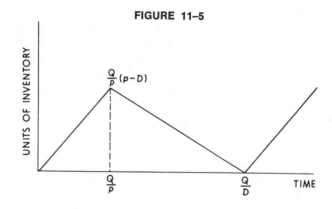

FIGURE 11–5

Q = units of production (the unknown)
p = annual production rate
D = annual rate of demand
$p - D$ = net inventory increase rate (production less demand)
$\dfrac{Q}{p}$ = duration of production run

$\dfrac{Q}{D}$ = cycle time

$\dfrac{Q}{p}(p - D)$ = maximum inventory; $\dfrac{Q}{p}$ is duration of production

run and $(p - D)$ is inventory increase rate during production

$\dfrac{Q}{2p}(p - D)$ = average inventory

The total annual cost of having a run size of Q units is:

$$TC = k_c \left[\frac{Q}{2p} (p - D) \right] + K \frac{D}{Q}$$

Taking the derivative of total cost with respect to Q:

$$\frac{dTC}{dQ} = k_c \left(\frac{p - D}{2p} \right) - \frac{KD}{Q_2}$$

Setting the first derivative equal to zero and solving for Q:

$$Q^2 = \frac{2KD}{k_c} \times \frac{p}{p - D}$$

$$Q = \sqrt{\frac{2KD}{k_c} \times \frac{p}{p - D}}$$

APPENDIX 2. INVENTORY MODEL WITH BACK ORDERS

Assume a firm, when it runs out of units, can backorder units at a cost of k_s per unit per unit time. Figure 11–6 shows the situation where Q units are ordered at time t_0 and $Q - S$ units are backordered.

FIGURE 11–6

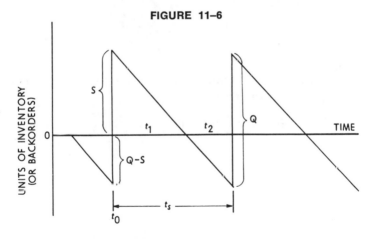

By simple geometry, we have:

$$\frac{t_1}{S} = \frac{t_s}{S + (Q - S)} = \frac{t_s}{Q}$$

$$t_1 = \frac{S}{Q} t_s$$

$$t_2 = \frac{Q - S}{Q} t_s$$

During time period t_1, there are on the average $\dfrac{S}{2}$ units in inventory.

The carrying cost per inventory cycle is $\dfrac{S}{2} k_c t_1$.

During time period t_2 the average inventory shortage is $\dfrac{Q - S}{2}$. The

shortage cost per inventory cycle is $\dfrac{Q - S}{2} k_s t_2$.

There are $\dfrac{D}{Q}$ cycles per year. The total cost is:

$$TC = \left(\frac{S}{2} k_c t_1 + \frac{Q - S}{2} k_s t_2 + K \right) \frac{D}{Q}$$

Substituting for t_1 and t_2:

$$TC = \left(\frac{S^2}{2Q} k_c t_s + \frac{(Q - S)^2}{2Q} k_s t_s + K \right) \frac{D}{Q}$$

Note that $t_s \dfrac{D}{Q} = 1$ year or $t_s = \dfrac{Q}{D}$, and simplify:

$$TC = \frac{S^2}{2Q} k_c + \frac{(Q - S)^2}{2Q} k_s + K \frac{D}{Q}$$

Taking the partial derivative of the total cost equation with respect to S and setting it equal to zero:

$$\frac{\partial TC}{\partial S} = \frac{S}{Q} k_c - \frac{(Q - S)}{Q} k_s = 0$$

$$S k_c = (Q - S) k_s$$

$$S = Q \frac{k_s}{k_c + k_s}$$

Taking the partial derivative with respect to Q and setting it equal to zero:

$$\frac{\partial TC}{\partial Q} = -\frac{S^2 k_c}{2Q^2} + \frac{4Q(Q - S) - 2(Q - S)^2}{4Q^2} k_s - \frac{KD}{Q^2} = 0$$

$$- 2S^2 k_c + [4Q(Q - S) - 2(Q - S)^2] k_s - 4KD = 0$$

$$- 2S^2 k_c + [(Q - S)(4Q - 2Q + 2S)] k_s = 4KD$$

$$- 2S^2 k_c + [2(Q^2 - S^2)] k_s = 4KD$$

$$Q^2 k_s - S^2(k_s + k_c) = 2KD$$

Substituting for S^2:

$$Q^2 k_s - Q^2 \frac{k_s^2}{(k_c + k_s)^2} \times (k_c + k_s) = 2KD$$

$$Q^2 \left(\frac{k_s k_c + k_s^2 - k_s^2}{k_c + k_s} \right) = 2KD$$

so that

$$Q = \sqrt{\frac{2KD}{k_c}} \times \frac{k_c + k_s}{k_s} = \sqrt{\frac{2KD}{k_c}} \times \sqrt{\frac{k_c + k_s}{k_s}}$$

and

$$S = Q \times \frac{k_s}{k_s + k_c}$$

BIBLIOGRAPHY

See the Bibliography of Chapter 10.

PROBLEMS

11–1. The costs of placing an order are $6. It is estimated that 1,000 units will be used in the next 12 months. The carrying cost per unit per year is $30. Compute the optimum order size.

11–2. The costs of placing an order are $150. It is estimated that 1,000 units will be used in the next 12 months. The carrying cost per unit per month is $2.50. Compute the optimum order size.

11–3. The ABC Company uses 100,000 units per year of a product. The carrying cost per unit is $3 per year. The cost of ordering a batch is $60.
a) What is the optimum order size?
b) If the ordering costs were 60 cents per order, how many units should be ordered at one time?

11–4. Assume the same situation as in part (*a*) of Problem 11–3, with the added information that the firm can run short (with a cost of $1 per year per unit) and fill the shortages from the next order.
a) How many units should be ordered?
b) How many units should be backordered?
c) What will be the maximum inventory?

11–5. The ABC Company is growing rapidly. It forecasts cash needs of $40 million a year for the foreseeable future. It is currently paying 5 percent per year for long-term debt and can earn 3 percent on idle funds in short-term securities. The fixed incremental cost of a bond issue is $100,000. The variable costs of a bond issue are $10 per thousand. The company forecasts constant interest rates in the future.
a) What should be the size of the bond issue?

b)   Assume the company can borrow short-term funds at its banks as the funds are needed at an effective cost of 6 percent. What should be the size of a bond issue?[4] How much should the company borrow from the banks before issuing more long-term debt?

11–6. The XYZ Company can turn out products at the rate of 14,000 units a day. Usage is 4,000 units a day. The cost of a setup for production is $1,000. The number of units used in a year is 1,440,000. The carrying cost per unit per year is $28. Assume a year consists of 360 days. Compute the optimum lot size for a production run.

11–7. The costs of placing an order are $7.50. It is estimated that 256 units will be used in the next 12 months. The carrying cost per unit per month is $1.25. Compute the optimum order size.

11–8. The ABC Company can turn out a product at the rate of 18,000 units a day. The cost of a setup for production is $2,250. The number of units used in a year is 2,880,000. The carrying cost per unit per year is 18 cents. Assume a year consists of 360 days. Compute the optimum lot size for a production run.

11–9. A company uses a certain part in the assembly of sets of electronic equipment at the rate of 8,000 per year. Each part has a value of $18. The company estimates that the cost of holding inventory is 20 percent of the value of the item per year.

The company can produce the part on either of two machines. Machine A has a setup cost of $200; machine B has a setup cost of only $100. However, it costs 10 cents more per unit to produce using machine B than it does using machine A.

Which machine should the company use? What is the optimum lot size?

11–10. Consider equation (11–1), total annual cost, and equation (11–2), the economic order quantity formula. Suppose an error in data gathering creates an erroneous Q which is 20 percent smaller than the "true" Q^* (i.e., $Q_{error} = 0.80Q^*$). Substitute this error back into equation (11–1) and find the percentage cost penalty which results from the 20 percent error in Q. (*Hint:*   Use the fact that with the optimum Q^*, the two terms of equation (11–1) are equal and each is one half of optimal (minimum) total annual cost.)

11–11. Refer to Problem 11–1. Suppose the unit annual carrying cost of $30 is caused by a 20 percent holding cost rate per dollar tied up in inventory per year, multiplied by a unit variable cost of $150. Now suppose that the company can purchase units at a price of $148 each if they order in lots of 100 units each. Compute the total annual variable costs associated with both the original and the recently suggested purchase quantity (be sure to include the effect of the lower price). Should they buy in lots of 20 or 100 units?

---

[4] This problem assumes the equivalent of an overdraft system is in effect.

12

Inventory control with reordering and uncertain demand

Instead of assuming that the demand rate is known, let us hypothesize that we know only the probability distribution of demand during the lead time, but not the actual demand during that period. When we set the order point, there is some probability that we shall run out of inventory and encounter a cost of underage.

FIGURE 12–1
Illustration of inventory pattern

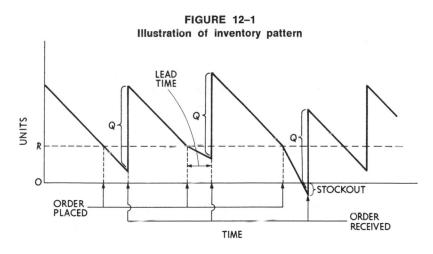

Figure 12–1 illustrates the behavior of inventory under this assumption. Note that an order of size Q is placed when inventory reaches a level R. Because of the uncertainty of demand during the lead time, a stockout sometimes occurs (such as during the third cycle in Figure 12–1). The

expected cost of underage will be affected by the choice of both the order point (R) and the order size (Q). It is interesting to look at the interaction between the various costs and the two variables (order point and order size):

Action	Result
Decrease order point (i.e., place order when fewer units on hand), *or* decrease order size.	Decrease carrying costs of inventory, and increase expected cost of underage.
Increase order point *or* increase order size.	Increase carrying costs of inventory, and decrease expected cost of underage.

A change in order size affects the annual frequency of reaching the ordering point (thus the frequency of encountering a chance of underage). A change in the order point affects the likelihood of underages and affects the optimum number of times the order point should be encountered. Thus the total cost is affected by both the order point and the order size, and the optimum order point and the optimum order size are related.

Again, we want to minimize the total cost incurred during a given time period. There are now three costs to consider:

K = cost of placing one order

k_c = cost of carrying one unit in inventory for one year

k_u = cost of being out of stock one unit (cost of underage)

The optimum order size and optimum order point will in general be a function of these three costs plus the average rate of demand over the lead time and the variability of demand over the lead time.

THE ASSUMPTIONS

We shall first assume that the lead time is known and constant. Secondly, the cost of underage is assumed to be a cost per unit, independent of the duration of the out-of-stock position.[1] The third assumption is that M, the demand during the lead time, is normally distributed. This is the least essential of the assumptions and may be changed; it is chosen to simplify the computations. Next, we assume that the optimal order point R is larger than average lead time demand $\bar{M}$, so that the corresponding safety stock $(R - \bar{M})$ is positive. Finally, we assume safety

---

[1] This measurement of underage is most appropriate where sales are lost if inventory is not available. In this case the cost of underage would represent the opportunity cost of foregone profit plus any cost of ill will.

stock, on the average, is always carried in inventory. We want to determine how much to order (Q) and when to order (R).

THE MODEL

Let:

R = order point (the number of units on hand that triggers the reorder)

Q = order quantity (the number of units ordered at one time)

D = average demand per year

K = cost of placing one order

k_c = cost of carrying one unit in inventory for one year

k_u = penalty cost of being out of stock one unit (cost of underage)

M = number of units of demand over the lead time (a random variable)

$\overline{M}$ = average number of units demanded during the lead time

σ_M = standard deviation of demand over the lead time (demand is stochastic)

We want to determine the optimum order quantity (Q) and the optimum order point (R). We will assume that as a reasonable approximation, the optimal order quantity for this situation (random demand) is the same as the optimal order quantity for the case of known demand covered in Chapter 11. That is, we will recommend use of the same square root optimal order quantity derived there:

$$(12\text{–}1) \qquad\qquad Q = \sqrt{\frac{2KD}{k_c}}$$

This recommendation is made for two reasons. First, as shown in Chapter 11, the sum of annual order-processing costs plus annual inventory holding costs is not very sensitive to moderate errors in Q; as long as the order quantity is reasonably close to the optimal value, extreme precision is not required. Secondly, a number of studies have indicated that while theoretically, Q and R should be determined *simultaneously,* in most practical situations no serious cost penalty is created if Q is *independently* determined by the square root formula of equation (12–1) above. Thus we will advocate (12–1) as the basic formula for Q even when demand is probabilistic.

Once Q is chosen, however, it is important to take its value into account in determining R, since the size of Q directly influences the number of times per year that we will be exposed to a possible stockout position.

OPTIMAL ORDER POINT—A MARGINAL APPROACH

It is possible to obtain a formula for the optimal order point by applying marginal analysis as follows. We start with some value of the order point R; for example, $R = \bar{M}$. We then ask if it is worthwhile to increase R by one unit. That is, we compare the expected annual cost of adding another unit to R, versus the expected annual cost of *not* adding the additional unit.

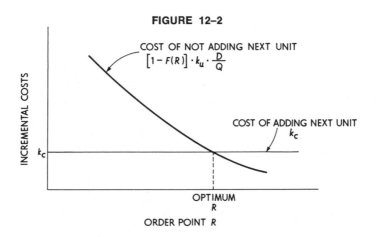

FIGURE 12–2

The annual incremental cost of *adding* an additional unit to R is approximately equal to k_c, since the additional unit will be added to safety stock $(R - \bar{M})$ and therefore held in inventory almost all of the time.[2]

The annual incremental expected cost of *not adding* the additional unit to R will equal the probability that the additional unit (or more) will be demanded during the lead time, multiplied by the unit stockout cost k_u, all multiplied by the number of inventory cycles per year (D/Q):

$$\begin{array}{c} \text{Incremental cost} \\ \text{of not adding} \\ \text{incremental unit} \end{array} = \text{Prob}\begin{bmatrix} \text{next unit} \\ \text{(or more)} \\ \text{demanded} \end{bmatrix} \cdot k_u \cdot \begin{bmatrix} \dfrac{D}{Q} \end{bmatrix}$$

Suppose we define $F(R)$ to be the probability that the demand (M) during the lead time will be less than or equal to our current value of R:

$$F(R) = \text{Prob}(M \leq R)$$

Then the probability that the next unit (or more) will be demanded

<hr>

[2] This is a reasonable approximation, since the additional unit will always be in inventory except during stockout (which is a small part of the time).

is $1 - F(R)$. The costs of adding and not adding the incremental unit are graphed in Figure 12–2.

Note that as R increases, the probability of the additional unit (or more) being demanded falls, and eventually the two lines cross in Figure 12–2. At this point we stop adding units to R, since the cost of adding a unit exceeds the cost of not adding the unit. At this point, the two costs are equal:

$$k_c = [1 - F(R)] \cdot k_u \cdot \frac{D}{Q}$$

or

$$[1 - F(R)] = \frac{k_c Q}{k_u D}$$

so that

(12–2) $$F(R) = 1 - \frac{k_c Q}{k_u D}$$

Equation (12–2) may be used as follows to obtain the optimal value for R:

1. Compute Q from the square root formula (12–1).
2. Compute the right-hand side of (12–2); this is the desired probability of lead time demand being less than or equal to R.
3. From normal tables, find the value of R for which the stated probability applies.

Expanding on step 3,

The term $F(R)$ is read: "Set R so that there is $1 - \dfrac{k_c Q}{k_u D}$ probability of M being equal to or less than R."[3]

FIGURE 12–3

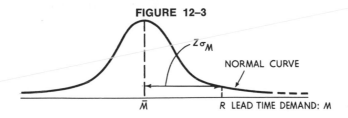

Let Z be the number of standard deviations[4] we must go from the

---

[3] $F(R)$ is the *left* tail of a probability distribution, i.e., the $P(M \leq R)$. In most business situations the underage cost will be substantially higher than the carrying cost, so the ratio will usually be greater than 0.50, and expected safety stock $(R - \overline{M})$ will be positive.

[4] See Chapter 7 for a discussion of this type of calculation.

mean sales, $\overline{M}$, before the probability is $F(R)$ that the demand, M, is equal to or less than R. We can obtain R, the optimum order point, as follows (see Figure 12–3):

(12–3) $$R = \overline{M} + Z\sigma_M$$

Example 1

We assume that the order quantity Q has been determined, and our task is to find the optimum order point.

Let:

$$D = 100 \text{ units per year}$$
$$Q = 50 \text{ units}$$
$$k_c = \$40 \text{ per unit per year}$$
$$k_u = \$80 \text{ for each unit short}$$
$$\overline{M} = 20$$
$$\sigma_M = 5$$

$$1 - \frac{k_c Q}{k_u D} = 1 - \frac{40 \times 50}{80 \times 100} = 1 - 0.25 = 0.75$$

$$F(R) = 0.75$$

Referring to a table of cumulative probabilities for the standard normal distribution (Table A in the Appendix at the end of the text), we find $Z = 0.67$.

The optimum order point is:

$$R = \overline{M} + Z\sigma_M = 20 + (0.67)(5)$$
$$R = 20 + 3.35 = 23.35 \doteq 23$$

With an order point of 23 units, we shall not run out of stock approximately 75 percent of the time (remember the mean demand is 20 units) during the ordering period.

Example 2

The following example illustrates the computation of the optimum order size and order point.

The amount expected to be used (D) is 1,800 units per year.

The cost of making one order (K) is $10.

The cost of carrying one unit for one year is 60 cents (this is k_c).

The replenishment lead time is 20 days; and the mean usage, $\overline{M}$, during the lead time is 100 units, with a standard deviation of 30 units, and is normally distributed.

The cost of underage is $5 per unit out of stock (this is k_u).

Using equation (12–1), we can determine Q:

$$Q = \sqrt{\frac{2KD}{k_c}} = \sqrt{\frac{2 \times 10 \times 1,800}{0.60}} = \sqrt{60,000} = 245 \text{ units}$$

From equation (12–2), we obtain:

$$F(R) = 1 - \frac{k_c Q}{k_u D} = 1 - \frac{0.6(245)}{5(1,800)} = 0.98367$$

Referring to a table of cumulative probabilities for the normal distribution (Table A in the Appendix at the end of the text), $F(R) = 0.98367$ is equivalent to:

$$Z = 2.14 \text{ standard deviations}$$
$$R = 100 + 2.14 \times 30 = 164 \text{ units}$$

TOTAL EXPECTED COST

The total cost for an inventory policy of (R, Q) is:[5]

$$(12\text{–}4) \quad \text{Total cost } (R, Q) = [K + k_u \sigma_M N(Z)] \frac{D}{Q}$$
$$+ \left[\frac{Q}{2} + (R - \bar{M}) \right] k_c$$

where $N(Z)$ refers to the unit loss function for the standard normal distribution (Table B in the Appendix at the end of the text), and Z is equal to R converted into standard deviation units from the mean demand over the lead time:

$$Z = \frac{R - \bar{M}}{\sigma_M}$$

Continuing with our example, the total cost of a policy of ordering 245 units at an order point of 164 units is:

$$TC(R, Q) = [K + k_u \times \sigma_M \times N(2.14)] \frac{D}{Q} + \left[\frac{Q}{2} + (R - \bar{M}) \right] k_c$$

$$TC(R, Q) = [10 + 5 \times 30 \times 0.0058] \frac{1,800}{245}$$

$$+ \left[\frac{245}{2} + 164 - 100 \right] (0.6)$$

$$= (10.87)7.35 + (186.5)0.6$$
$$= 79.89 + 111.90 = 191.79$$

Recall that the above values for Q and R were determined using the simplified square root formula [equation (12–1)] for Q. Let us now

---

[5] See Appendix at the end of the text for a derivation of this formula.

explore what the total cost is without this approximation. By trial and error it is possible to find the pair of values for Q and R which minimize the total cost: $Q = 255$ and $R = 164$. The (minimum) total cost of these optimal values is:

$$TC(R, Q) = [10 + 5 \times 30 \times 0.0058] \frac{1,800}{255}$$

$$+ \left[\frac{255}{2} + 164 - 100 \right] (0.6)$$

$$= (10.87)7.06 + (191.5)0.6 = 76.74 + 114.90 = 191.64$$

The more exact values result in an expected cost which is approximately 15 cents less than the decision rule which assumes the order quantity is not affected by the order point.

For our example, the total cost is not very sensitive to the order quantity if an amount in the general magnitude of 250 units is ordered. Thus, we suggest using equation (12–1) to obtain an approximate order quantity Q, and then using equation (12–2) to solve for the corresponding order point R. Usually the effect of these approximations on total cost is minor, as in our example above.

SUMMARY

Assuming known demand and known lead time of supply, the solution for optimum order size and order point is relatively easily obtained using $Q = \sqrt{\dfrac{2KD}{k_c}}$ and equation (12–2).

Instead of knowing demand during the lead time (i.e., knowing the exact number of units which will be demanded), we may only know the probability distribution of demand, where demand is treated as a random variable. We have assumed that sales during the lead time were normally distributed. For this type of situation, we have computed a formula for obtaining the optimum order point. In most situations, it is sufficient to use the square root formula for the optimal order quantity without affecting total costs significantly.

APPENDIX. THE DETERMINATION OF THE OPTIMUM ORDER POINT AND ORDER SIZE

Let:

Q = order size
R = order point

D = average demand per year

M = amount demanded during lead time ($\overline{M}$ = mean amount); a random variable

$f(M)$ = probability density function for M

$R - \overline{M}$ = safety stock

σ_M = standard deviation of demand over lead time

$R - M$ = units unsold when new units are received (if $M < R$)

$M - R$ = amount by which demand during lead time exceeds order point (if $M > R$)

K = cost of placing one order

k_c = carrying cost per unit per year

k_u = penalty cost for being out of stock one unit (cost of underage)

THE TOTAL ANNUAL EXPECTED COST

The total cost of a policy involving a specific order size, R, and a specific order quantity, Q, is equal to the sum of the costs of ordering, the costs of being out of stock, and the costs of carrying inventory:

(12–5)
$$\text{Total cost } (R, Q) = K\left(\frac{D}{Q}\right) + \left[k_u \int_R^\infty (M - R)f(M)dM\right]\frac{D}{Q}$$
$$+ \left[\frac{Q}{2} + (R - \overline{M})\right]k_c$$

where $K\left(\dfrac{D}{Q}\right)$ is the cost of ordering; K is the cost per order; $\dfrac{D}{Q}$ is the

annual number of orders; $\left[k_u \displaystyle\int_R^\infty (M - R)f(M)dM\right]\dfrac{D}{Q}$ is the cost of

being out of stock; k_u is the cost per unit; the integral is the ex-

pected number of units out of stock per cycle; $\dfrac{D}{Q}$ is the annual num-

ber of replenishment cycles, i.e., the annual number of orders;

$\left[\dfrac{Q}{2} + (R - \overline{M})\right]k_c$ is the cost of carrying inventory; and k_c is the

cost of carrying one unit for one year. The remainder of the term is

the average inventory; $\dfrac{Q}{2}$, the average inventory of working stock,

plus the average safety stock $(R - \overline{M})$. The term $(R - \overline{M})$ only approximates the average level of safety stock, but the approximation is valid in most practical instances (see footnote 2 in this chapter).

The equations for Q and $F(R)$ are obtained from equation (12–5), the equation for the total cost, by taking the partial derivatives with respect to R and with respect to Q and setting them equal to zero.[6]

$$\text{Total cost } (R, Q) = K\frac{D}{Q} + \left[\frac{Q}{2} + (R - \overline{M})\right] k_c$$

$$+ \left[k_u \int_R^\infty (M - R)f(M)dM \right] \frac{D}{Q}$$

$$= K\frac{D}{Q} + k_c\left[\frac{Q}{2} + R - \overline{M}\right]$$

$$+ \frac{D}{Q} k_u \left[\overline{M} - \overset{R}{\underset{-\infty}{E}} (M) - R[1 - F(R)] \right]$$

Differentiating with respect to R:

$$\frac{\partial \text{ Total cost}}{\partial R} = k_c - \frac{D}{Q} k_u Rf(R)$$

$$+ \frac{D}{Q} k_u[F(R) + Rf(R) - 1]$$

$$= k_c - \frac{D}{Q} k_u + \frac{D}{Q} k_u F(R)$$

Setting the derivative equal to zero and solving for $F(R)$:[7]

(12–2) $$F(R) = 1 - \frac{k_c Q}{k_u D}$$

Differentiating total cost with respect to Q:

$$\frac{\partial \text{ Total cost } (Q, R)}{\partial Q} = -\frac{KD}{Q^2} + \frac{k_c}{2} - \frac{D}{Q^2} k_u \int_R^\infty (M - R)f(M)dM$$

Setting the derivative equal to zero and solving for Q:

(12–6) $$Q = \sqrt{\frac{2D\left[K + k_u \int_R^\infty (M - R)f(M)dM \right]}{k_c}}$$

Equation (12–6) can be converted into a form which is more susceptible to computation. We make use of the fact that if M is normally distributed and if R is larger than the expected sales ($\overline{M}$) during the reorder period, then:

(12–7) $$\int_R^\infty (M - R)f(M)dM = \sigma_M N(Z)$$

---

[6] The symbol $\overset{R}{\underset{-\infty}{E}}$ in the equations is the partial expectation. It equals $\int_{-\infty}^R Mf(M)dM$.

[7] Second-order conditions must also be checked.

where $N(Z)$ is the unit normal loss integral valued for Z (R converted to standard deviations from the mean). The σ_M is the standard deviation of the distribution of demand during the lead time.

Equation (12–6) now becomes:

(12–8)
$$Q = \sqrt{\frac{2D[K + k_u\sigma_M N(Z)]}{k_c}}$$

Note that R is in the above formula (12–6) for Q, and Q is in the equation (12–2) for R. Theoretically, the two equations must be solved simultaneously. This can be done by the use of an iterative procedure which starts with an estimate of Q, solves for R, then solves for a new Q, and repeats this process until a Q and an R are found to satisfy both equations. However, for practical purposes it is sufficient to determine the value of Q by using the formula in the last chapter, where certain demand was assumed:

(12–1)
$$Q = \sqrt{\frac{2KD}{k_c}}$$

The equation for total cost can be simplified (assuming $R > \overline{M}$) by making use of equation (12–6). Substituting into equation (12–5), we obtain:

(12–9)   Total cost $(R, Q) = [K + k_u\sigma_M N(Z)]\dfrac{D}{Q}$

$$+ \left[\frac{Q}{2} + (R - \overline{M})\right] k_c$$

BIBLIOGRAPHY

See Bibliography of Chapter 10.

PROBLEMS

12–1.   The following information relates to an item in inventory:

k_u = \$2 cost per unit for sales lost
$\overline{M}$ = 50 mean sales during lead time
σ_M = 10 units
D = 1,000 units per year (estimated demand)
K = \$6 per order (ordering costs)
k_c = \$30 (cost of carrying a unit in inventory for one year)

The distribution of M is assumed to be normal.

a) Compute the approximate optimum order size.

b) Compute the approximate optimum order point.

12-2. A retailer feels that the mean demand for a unit of inventory for the coming year is 1,800 units. The lead time on orders is 20 days, and the mean demand during the lead time is 100 units. The lead time demand is assumed to be normally distributed, with $\sigma = 30$ (there is a 50–50 chance that the lead time demand could be less than 80 units or more than 120 units). The cost per unit of lost sales is $5, the cost of placing an order is $10, and the cost of carrying a unit in inventory for one year is $50.

a) Compute the approximate optimum order size (round to nearest whole unit).

b) Compute the approximate optimum order point.

12-3. The mean demand for a unit of inventory for the coming year is 40,000 units. The lead time is 36 days, and the mean demand during the lead time is 4,000 units. The lead time demand is assumed to be normally distributed with $\sigma = 500$. The cost per unit of shortages is $10, the cost of placing an order is $64, and the cost of carrying a unit in inventory for one year is $2.

a) Compute the approximate optimum order size (round to the nearest whole unit).

b) Compute the approximate optimum order point.

c) Compute the total cost of the approximate order size and reorder point.

12-4. The mean demand for a unit of inventory for the next year is 4,000 units. The lead time on orders is 10 days. The demand for the product during the lead time is normally distributed and has a standard deviation of 30 units. The cost per unit of lost sales is $5. The cost of placing an order is $10, and the cost of carrying a unit in inventory for one year is 50 cents.

a) Compute the square root estimate of Q.

b) Compute the order point.

c) Compute the optimum order size after iterating (see Appendix at end of the chapter).

d) Compute the total cost of the initial order size and reorder point.

e) Compute the total cost of the optimum order size and reorder point.

12-5. A firm has a choice of manufacturing a part internally or purchasing it from an outside supplier. The variable cost per unit is the same in either case. However, if the part is made internally, there is a setup cost of $100. If the part is purchased, there is a fixed order cost of $20. If the part is made internally, there is zero lead time; if purchased from outside, the lead time is 25 days (usage during the lead time is normally distributed with mean 100 units and standard deviation 20 units). The cost of carrying one unit in inventory is $2 per year. The cost of being short one unit is $18 (this is k_u). Annual requirements for this part are 1,000 units.

Should the firm make this part internally or purchase it on the outside? What other considerations besides inventory costs would actually go into a decision of this type?

12–6. The ABC Company has a machine which requires replacement of a certain part at random intervals when the part breaks. The lead time for ordering spares from the manufacturer is one month. The average number of breakdowns is one per month, and management accepts the premise that the breakdown of the part is consistent with the characteristics of a Poisson process.[8]

a) The current policy is to order five units of the part whenever a replenishment order is placed. If the management requires at least a 0.99 probability of the part being in stock during a replenishment lead time, what should the reorder point be to insure this level of service?

b) If ordering costs are $10 and carrying costs are $2.40 per unit per year, what should the optimal order quantity be?

c) If the order quantity is changed, should management's goal of at least 0.99 probability of service during a lead time be revised? How should this goal be set? What information would you need in order to make this decision?

12–7. An item is replenished 10 times per year, on the average. The annual unit holding cost is one half the unit cost of being short. Weekly demand is normally distributed with a mean of 100 and a standard deviation of 20.

a) Compute the desired probability of not running out of stock during a lead time.

b) Suppose the replenishment lead time is *four* weeks. Compute the optimum order point. (*Hint:* Recall from Chapter 2 that the variance of a sum of independent random variables equals the sum of the variances.)

12–8. Refer to Problem 12–7. Suppose that an error is made in estimating one of the values used to compute the order point. Specifically, suppose that a 50 percent error is made in estimating the shortage cost, with the result that the ratio k_c/k_u is erroneous.

---

[8] If the process is Poisson, then the probability of k occurrences during a unit time interval is:

$$P(k) = \frac{e^{-\lambda}\lambda^k}{k!}$$

where λ is both the mean or expected number of occurrences per unit of time and the variance of the number of occurrences per unit of time.

a)   Suppose the erroneous ratio is $k_c/k_u = 1.0$ instead of the true value of one half. Compute the probability of not running out of stock during a lead time and the associated order point.

b)   Suppose the erroneous ratio is $k_c/k_u = 1/4$. Again, compute the probability of not stocking out, and the order point.

c)   Comment on the relative sensitivity of the order quantity versus the order point.

13

Introduction to linear
programming

Linear programming is a mathematical technique designed to assist an organization in allocating its scarce resources. The problem for which linear programming provides a solution may be summarized as follows: Maximize (or minimize) some dependent variable which is a function of several independent variables when the independent variables are subject to various restraints. The dependent variable is usually some economic objective, such as profits, production, costs, workweeks, or tons shipped. More profits are generally preferred to less profits, and lower costs are preferred to higher costs, etc.; therefore, it is appropriate to represent one of the organization's objectives as a maximization or minimization of the dependent variable (other things being equal). The size of the dependent variable depends upon several critical factors in most situations; these factors are designated as the independent variables. We assume a *linear* relationship between the dependent variable and its determinants; i.e., we assume that a linear equation of the form

$$f = A_1X_1 + A_2X_2 + \cdots + A_NX_N$$

may be written, where f is the dependent variable (say profits) and $X_1, X_2, \ldots, X_N$ are the independent variables that affect f. This equation is often called the *objective function*. The coefficients $A_1, A_2, \ldots, A_N$ are constants. All the X's are of the first power, which is necessary to characterize the relationship as a linear equation. The assumption of linearity has two justifications: (1) For many situations, it is a good approximation of reality, and (2) it simplifies the mathematics enormously. These reasons also explain the general practice of assuming that the restraints on the independent variables have the form of *linear inequalities*. Each of the variables $X_1, X_2, \ldots, X_N$ are subject to some restraint of the type

$$B_1X_1 + B_2X_2 + \cdots + B_NX_N \geq C_1$$

The B coefficients are constants. The constant C_1 restricts f, the objective function, as a result of restricting the independent variables, X_1, X_2, $\ldots$, X_N (instead of $\geq$, we could have $\leq$ or an equality). The solution provided by linear programming is the set of values of the independent variables which achieves the desired maximum (or minimum) within the various restraints.

The problem of maximizing the objective function subject to the various restraints is conceptually simple. When there are few independent variables, common sense and some arithmetic will yield a solution, and businessmen have solved such problems for generations. However, as is often the case, intuition is of little use when the problem is more complex; when the number of independent variables is increased from three to four, from four to five, and so on, the problem defies rule-of-thumb procedures. Linear programming has made it possible to handle a problem with any finite number of restraints in an orderly way.

This technique has exceptional power and generality. It is applicable to a variety of problems in a modern business organization and may be handled in a routine way with the aid of digital computers. It is one of the quantitative techniques which has provided management with a remarkable leverage on a set of problems that defied efficient solutions a relatively few years ago.

As a simple example, consider the following problem, which can be solved by the use of common sense or marginal analysis. Assume the incremental profit of product A is $5 per unit and the profit of product B is $2 per unit and we can sell all we make of both products; further, the products may be produced with the same equipment. We can compute which product we should produce once we find out the capacity of our facilities in terms of A and B (see Table 13–1).

TABLE 13–1

Product	Capacity	Per unit profit	Total incremental profit per day
A	100 units per day	$5	$ 500
B	600 units per day	2	1,200

In this simple example, product B is obviously a more desirable product than A. Now assume a more complicated problem where the plant is capable of making 20 different products in 15 different departments, and each product requires different production time in each department. If the difficulty of this problem is not impressive, assume that each department contains 10 processes and each product requires different production time in each process. How do we determine the optimum product mix? A problem of this type is best solved by linear programming. The term *linear* is appropriate, since all profit and production relationships are assumed to be linear; i.e., the highest degree of any variable is one, and no variables are multiplied by any other variable.

There are several methods for solving linear programming problems. In this chapter, we shall introduce a graphical solution and in the next chapter we introduce the simplex method, which is a systematic method for deriving a solution.

In some of the examples to follow, the answers will be obvious; this is because the examples were constructed to be as simple as possible. The reader should keep in mind that we are attempting to illustrate a technique that may be applied to extremely complex problems. We apply it to simple situations for expository purposes. The computations arising in most complex linear programming problems would be done on a computer; one of the important features of the simplex procedure is that it can be programmed on a computer.

FORMULATION OF LINEAR PROGRAMMING PROBLEMS

Before going into the details of learning how to solve linear programming problems, it will be beneficial to learn how to define the variables and equations—generally how to set up a business problem in the form of maximizing (or minimizing) a linear function f, subject to linear constraints. We shall use the term *formulation* to mean translating a real-world problem into a format of mathematical equations. Formulation is often the most difficult part of analyzing a business problem. For large problems, once the problem has been properly formulated, a computer is used to obtain the solution.

We shall study several different problems, offering some experience in formulation and introducing some of the wide variety of problems to which linear programming is applicable.

Example 1

A manufacturing firm produces two products, A and B. Each of these products must be processed through two different machines. One machine has 12 hours and the second machine has 8 hours of available capacity. Each unit of product A requires two hours of time on both machines. Each unit of product B requires three hours of time on the first machine and one hour on the second machine. The incremental profit is $6 per unit of product A and $7 per unit of product B, and the firm can sell as many units of each product as it can manufacture.

The objective of the firm is to maximize profits. The problem is to determine how many units of product A and product B should be produced within the limits of available machine capacities.

Formulation. Let:

$$X_1 = \text{number of units of product A to be produced}$$
$$X_2 = \text{number of units of product B to be produced}$$
$$P = \text{total incremental profit to the firm}$$

The objective function is:

$$\text{Maximize } P = 6X_1 + 7X_2$$

This states that the firm's total profit is made up of the profit from product A ($6 times the number sold) plus the profit from product B ($7 times the number sold).

The first constraint relates to the availability of time on the first machine. This can be expressed as:

$$2X_1 + 3X_2 \leq 12$$

Each unit of product A uses 2 hours of this machine, and each unit of product B uses 3 hours. Hence the total hours used is expressed by the left-hand side of the expression above. This must be equal to or less than the total hours available on the first machine (12).

For the second machine, a similar constraint is:

$$2X_1 + 1X_2 \leq 8$$

In addition, implicit in any linear programming formulation are the constraints that restrict X_1 and X_2 to be nonnegative. In terms of the problem, this means that the firm can produce only zero or positive amounts.

The total formulation is thus:

$$\text{Maximize:} \quad P = 6X_1 + 7X_2$$
$$\text{Subject to:} \quad 2X_1 + 3X_2 \leq 12$$
$$2X_1 + X_2 \leq 8$$
$$X_1, X_2 \geq 0$$

This example is simple, and one would not need linear programming to solve it. However, problems involving hundreds of products and

many different constraints cannot be solved intuitively, and linear programming has proved valuable in these cases.

Example 2

Various grades of gasoline are obtained by blending together certain
blending gasolines which are the direct output of the refinery operation.
In an actual refining operation, there are many blending gasolines, many
final-product gasolines (e.g., various grades of aviation and motor gasoline), and many characteristics that are considered important in the
chemical composition of the various grades of gasoline (including, for
example, octane rating, vapor pressure, sulphur content, and gum content). In this simplified example, we assume that a refinery has available
only two types of blending gasoline, whose characteristics are shown in
Table 13–2.

TABLE 13–2
Characteristics of blending gasolines

	Octane rating	Vapor pressure	Amount available
Blending gasoline, type 1.................	104	4	30,000 barrels
Blending gasoline, type 2.................	94	9	70,000 barrels

These blending gasolines may be mixed to produce two final products,
aviation gasoline and motor gasoline. The characteristics of these final
products are shown in Table 13–3.

TABLE 13–3
Characteristics of final-product gasolines

	Minimum octane rating	Maximum vapor pressure	Maximum sales	Selling price
Aviation gasoline........	102	5	20,000 barrels	$5.10/bbl.
Motor gasoline	96	8	Any amount	4.40/bbl.

When gasolines are mixed together, the resulting mixture has an octane
and a vapor pressure in proportion to the volume of each gasoline mixed.
For example, if 1,000 barrels of blending gasoline 1 were mixed with

1,000 barrels of blending gasoline 2, the resultant gasoline would have an octane rating of 99:

$$\left(\frac{1{,}000 \times 104 + 1{,}000 \times 94}{2{,}000} = 99\right)$$

and a vapor pressure of 6.5:

$$\left(\frac{1{,}000 \times 4 + 1{,}000 \times 9}{2{,}000} = 6.5\right)$$

The firm wishes to maximize revenue from the sale of final-product gasoline.

Formulation. Let:

X_1 = number of barrels of blending gasoline 1 used in aviation gasoline
X_2 = number of barrels of blending gasoline 2 used in aviation gasoline
X_3 = number of barrels of blending gasoline 1 used in motor gasoline
X_4 = number of barrels of blending gasoline 2 used in motor gasoline

The objective function is then to maximize P = total revenue:

$$\begin{aligned} \text{Maximize } P &= \$5.10(X_1 + X_2) + \$4.40(X_3 + X_4) \\ &= \$5.10X_1 + \$5.10X_2 + \$4.40X_3 + \$4.40X_4 \end{aligned}$$

Note that $X_1 + X_2$ is the total amount of aviation gasoline mixed (in barrels), and since it sells at $5.10 per barrel, the revenue from this product is $5.10($X_1 + X_2$)$. Similarly, the revenue from motor gasoline is $4.40($X_3 + X_4$)$, and the sum of these terms is the total revenue, P.

There are several kinds of constraints that affect how the refinery will blend its gasoline. The first is on the sales or demand side—the fact that no more than 20,000 barrels of aviation gasoline can be sold (see Table 13–3). This may be represented by the following expression:

$$X_1 + X_2 \leq 20{,}000$$

A second set of constraints relates to available amounts of blending gasolines. Thus, we have:

$$X_1 + X_3 \leq 30{,}000$$

Note that $X_1 + X_3$ represents the total amount of blending gasoline 1 (the sum of the amount used in aviation gasoline, X_1, and the amount used in motor gasoline, X_3). The equation above states that the amount of blending gasoline 1 used must not exceed the amount available—30,000 barrels. A similar constraint for blending gasoline 2 is:

$$X_2 + X_4 \leq 70{,}000$$

Another set of constraints relates to the octane ratings of the final-product gasolines. Recall that the total amount of aviation gasoline is $X_1 + X_2$. Its octane rating will be determined by the relative amounts of X_1 and X_2 according to the following formula:

$$\frac{\text{Octane rating of}}{\text{aviation gasoline}} = \frac{104 \times X_1 + 94 \times X_2}{X_1 + X_2}$$

The numbers 104 and 94 are from Table 13–2 and are the octane ratings of blending gasoline 1 and blending gasoline 2, respectively. From Table 13–3, we note that the octane rating of aviation gasoline must be at least 102. So we have the following constraint:

$$\frac{104X_1 + 94X_2}{X_1 + X_2} \geq 102$$

Rewriting this expression, we have:

$$104X_1 + 94X_2 \geq 102X_1 + 102X_2$$

or

$$2X_1 - 8X_2 \geq 0$$

Similarly, for the octane rating for motor gasoline, we have:

$$104X_3 + 94X_4 \geq 96(X_3 + X_4)$$

or

$$8X_3 - 2X_4 \geq 0$$

A final set of constraints is related to the vapor pressure requirements of the final-product gasolines. For aviation gasoline, we have:

$$4X_1 + 9X_2 \leq 5(X_1 + X_2)$$

or

$$-X_1 + 4X_2 \leq 0$$

and the vapor pressure requirement of motor gasoline is:

$$4X_3 + 9X_4 \leq 8(X_3 + X_4)$$

or

$$-4X_3 + X_4 \leq 0$$

In summary, the total formulation of the linear programming model is:

Maximize: $P = \$5.10X_1 + \$5.10X_2 + \$4.40X_3 + \$4.40X_4$

Subject to: $X_1 + X_2 \leq 20,000$ demand constraint

$\left.\begin{array}{l} X_1 + X_3 \leq 30,000 \\ X_2 + X_4 \leq 70,000 \end{array}\right\}$ availability of blending gasoline constraints

$\left.\begin{array}{l} 2X_1 - 8X_2 \geq 0 \\ 8X_3 - 2X_4 \geq 0 \end{array}\right\}$ octane rating constraints

$\left.\begin{array}{l} -X_1 + 4X_2 \leq 0 \\ -4X_3 + X_4 \leq 0 \end{array}\right\}$ vapor pressure constraints

$X_1, X_2, X_3, X_4 \geq 0$

Gasoline blending was one of the very first applications of linear programming to business problems. Our example here is, of course, very much of an oversimplification of the real problem, but it captures the essential elements.[1] The problem as formulated above is termed the *blending problem*. Blending problems turn up in many contexts. One example of such a problem is in the production of feeds for animals. A feed mix for chickens, for example, may be made up of several different kinds of grains, etc. The feed mix manufacturer would like to use the cheapest grains he can buy. However, he is constrained by the fact that the feed mix must satisfy certain nutritional requirements (similar to the constraints on vapor pressure and octane rating in our gasoline example above). In fact, it was discovered that certain aesthetic constraints also had to be added—the chickens would not eat the mixes determined solely by nutritional constraints.

Example 3

A manufacturer of soap and detergents has three plants located in Cincinnati, Denver, and Atlanta. Major warehouses are located at New York, Boston, Chicago, Los Angeles, and Dallas. Sales requirements for the next year at each warehouse are given in Table 13–4.

TABLE 13–4

Warehouse location	Annual sales (thousands of cases)
New York	50
Boston	10
Chicago	60
Los Angeles	30
Dallas	20
Total	170

There is some concern in the company about which factory should

[1] For an excellent discussion of the gasoline-blending problem in more detail, see W. W. Garvin, *Introduction to Linear Programming* (New York: McGraw-Hill Book Co., 1960), chap. 5.

supply each warehouse. Factory capacity at each location is limited. Cincinnati has an annual capacity of 100,000 cases, Denver has a capacity of 60,000 cases, and Atlanta has a capacity of 50,000 cases.

The cost of shipping soap from each warehouse to each factory is given in Table 13–5. The company wishes to determine a shipping schedule which will minimize overall company transportation costs (denoted by C).

TABLE 13–5
Cost ($) of shipping 1,000 cases of soap

From ⟍ To	New York	Boston	Chicago	Los Angeles	Dallas
Cincinnati	120	150	80	250	180
Denver	210	220	150	100	110
Atlanta	150	170	150	240	200

Formulation. Let:

X_{11} = number of cases shipped from first factory (Cincinnati) to first warehouse (New York), in thousands of cases

Similarly:

$X_{12}, X_{13}, X_{14}, X_{15}$ = number of cases shipped from first factory (Cincinnati) to second, third, etc., warehouses (Boston, Chicago, etc.)

$X_{21}, X_{22}, X_{23}, X_{24}, X_{25}$ = number of cases shipped from second factory (Denver) to first, second, etc., warehouses

$X_{31}, X_{32}, X_{33}, X_{34}, X_{35}$ = number of cases shipped from third factory to first, second, etc., warehouses

Then the objective is to:

$$\text{Minimize } C = 120X_{11} + 150X_{12} + 80X_{13} + 250X_{14} + 180X_{15}$$
$$+ 210X_{21} + 220X_{22} + 150X_{23} + 100X_{24} + 110X_{25}$$
$$+ 150X_{31} + 170X_{32} + 150X_{33} + 240X_{34} + 200X_{35}$$

The total cost is the sum of the products for each possible shipping route (from factory to warehouse) of the shipping cost from Table 13–5 times the number of thousands of cases shipped.

There are two sets of constraints for this problem. The first set guarantees that the warehouse needs will be met. Thus, for New York:

$$X_{11} + X_{21} + X_{31} = 50$$

This states that the sum of the cases shipped to New York from the first (Cincinnati), second (Denver), and third (Atlanta) factories must be 50,000 cases, the sales requirement for New York. For the other warehouses, we have:

$$\begin{aligned}
\text{Boston:} \quad & X_{12} + X_{22} + X_{32} = 10 \\
\text{Chicago:} \quad & X_{13} + X_{23} + X_{33} = 60 \\
\text{Los Angeles:} \quad & X_{14} + X_{24} + X_{34} = 30 \\
\text{Dallas:} \quad & X_{15} + X_{25} + X_{35} = 20
\end{aligned}$$

The second set of constraints guarantees that the factories do not exceed their capacities. Thus, for the Cincinnati factory:

$$X_{11} + X_{12} + X_{13} + X_{14} + X_{15} \leq 100$$

This expression indicates that the amount shipped from the first factory to the first, second, third, etc., warehouses must not exceed the factory's capacity of 100,000 cases.

Similarly, for:

$$\begin{aligned}
\text{Denver:} \quad & X_{21} + X_{22} + X_{23} + X_{24} + X_{25} \leq 60 \\
\text{Atlanta:} \quad & X_{31} + X_{32} + X_{33} + X_{34} + X_{35} \leq 50
\end{aligned}$$

Finally, all the X's must be greater than or equal to zero.

The solution of this linear programming problem will give the optimum (i.e., least-cost) shipping schedule for the company. This is an example of a special type of problem, known, naturally enough, as the *transportation problem*. Chapter 16 is devoted to a special procedure for solving this type of problem.

In summary, the formulation of this problem is:

Minimize: $C = 120X_{11} + 150X_{12} + 80X_{13} + 250X_{14} + 180X_{15}$
$+ 210X_{21} + 220X_{22} + 150X_{23} + 100X_{24}$
$+ 110X_{25} + 150X_{31} + 170X_{32} + 150X_{33}$
$+ 240X_{34} + 200X_{35}$

Subject to: $X_{11} + X_{21} + X_{31} = 50$
$X_{12} + X_{22} + X_{32} = 10$ 　warehouse
$X_{13} + X_{23} + X_{33} = 60$ 　requirement
$X_{14} + X_{24} + X_{34} = 30$ 　constraints
$X_{15} + X_{25} + X_{35} = 20$
$X_{11} + X_{12} + X_{13} + X_{14} + X_{15} \leq 100$ 　factory
$X_{21} + X_{22} + X_{23} + X_{24} + X_{25} \leq 60$ 　capacity
$X_{31} + X_{32} + X_{33} + X_{34} + X_{35} \leq 50$ 　constraints
$X_{11}, X_{12}, \ldots, X_{35} \geq 0$

The three examples so far have dealt with problems in one time period—often called *static* problems. Linear programming has also been applied to *dynamic* problems, that is, those extending over several time periods.[2] Consider the following example.

Example 4

At the beginning of each month, a firm places an order for a particular product, which is delivered at the end of the month. The firm sells some product during the month (from inventory on hand—ordered in previous months—since the amount ordered at the beginning of the current month will not arrive until the end of the month). The firm can sell any number of units in any month.

The purchase and selling prices of the product vary from month to month. Table 13–6 gives the projected prices for the next six months. The firm is limited in its operations by the size of its warehouse, which can hold a maximum of 100 units of the product.

TABLE 13–6
Purchase and selling price

Month	Purchase price (beginning of month)	Selling price (during month)
January	$50	. . .
February	50	$60
March	40	40
April	60	50
May	50	60
June	. . .	70

The problem for the firm is to determine the number of units to buy and sell each month in order to obtain the most profit. The firm has no units on hand at the beginning of January and wishes to have no units on hand at the end of June.

$X_1, X_2, X_3, X_4, X_5, X_6$ = number of units *ordered* at beginning of January (first month), February (second month), etc.

$Y_1, Y_2, Y_3, Y_4, Y_5, Y_6$ = number of units *sold* during January, February, etc.

Note that because the firm starts with no inventory, it cannot sell any units in January (that is, $Y_1 = 0$). Similarly, since it wants zero inven-

---

[2] Dynamic programming also deals with dynamic problems (see Chapter 23). It is sometimes possible to formulate a problem both as a linear programming problem and as a dynamic programming problem. See the exercises at the end of Chapter 23.

tory at the end of June, orders at the beginning of June must be zero (i.e, $X_6 = 0$).

Profit for the firm (P) is sales (in dollars) minus purchase cost. Thus the objective function is:

$$\text{Maximize profit} = P = 60Y_2 + 40Y_3 + 50Y_4 + 60Y_5 + 70Y_6$$
$$- (50X_1 + 50X_2 + 40X_3 + 60X_4 + 50X_5)$$

The first part of this expression is the sale prices (from Table 13–6) times the amounts sold each month. The second part relates to purchase cost; it is the costs from Table 13–6 times the amounts purchased.

In order to formulate the constraints, let us introduce a new set of variables, I_1, I_2, I_3, I_4, I_5, and I_6, representing the inventory at the end of a month (after all sales have been made and *after* the amount ordered at the beginning of the month has arrived).

Then:

$$\begin{array}{c} \text{Inventory at} \\ \text{end of} \\ \text{month} \end{array} = \begin{array}{c} \text{inventory at} \\ \text{end of} \\ \text{previous} \\ \text{month} \end{array} - \text{sales} + \text{purchases}$$

For January, this is $I_1 = X_1$, since there is neither previous inventory nor sales.

For February:

$$I_2 = I_1 - Y_2 + X_2$$

Similarly, for the remaining months:

$$\begin{array}{ll} \text{March:} & I_3 = I_2 - Y_3 + X_3 \\ \text{April:} & I_4 = I_3 - Y_4 + X_4 \\ \text{May:} & I_5 = I_4 - Y_5 + X_5 \\ \text{June:} & I_6 = I_5 - Y_6 \end{array}$$

The above set of equations defines the dynamic aspect of the model and connects one month to the next.

A final set of constraints is needed to guarantee that storage at the warehouse never exceeds its capacity of 100 units. This is accomplished by letting:

$$\begin{array}{l} I_1 \le 100 \\ I_2 \le 100 \\ I_3 \le 100 \\ I_4 \le 100 \\ I_5 \le 100 \end{array}$$

and $I_6 = 0$ in order to end up with zero inventory at the end of June.

Again, this example is oversimplified relative to real-world dynamic problems. In fact, one might be able to determine the solution to this example with a little trial-and-error calculation. The problem would become nontrivial, however, if we added several products instead of one, and if we added constraints on the cash the firm has available and the number of units that can be sold in any period.

Example 5

This example deals with the formulation of a large scale or system model, designed primarily for planning the integrated activities of a business firm.[3] The example is diagrammed in Figure 13–1. It is of course oversimplified and includes only two species of trees, two lumber and plywood products, and very few of the technological constraints involved in the production of lumber and plywood. The objective function is not shown in Figure 13–1. It would be obtained by taking the prices of the finished products times the output of these products and subtracting the variable operating costs throughout the whole system.

A GRAPHIC SOLUTION

It is not usually possible to solve linear programming problems graphically because of our inability to graph a space of dimension greater than three. However, it is useful to see how a simple problem may be solved graphically.

Example

Situation.   One machine has 12 hours and a second machine has 8 hours of available capacity. The firm manufactures products A and B. Each unit of product A requires two hours of time on both machines. Each unit of product B requires three hours of time on the first machine and one hour on the second machine. The incremental profit is $6 per unit of A and $7 per unit of B, and the firm can sell as many of either product as it can manufacture.

Problem.   Assuming the objective is to maximize profit, how many units of product A and product B should be produced? This is a problem discussed previously. We shall briefly repeat its formulation.

---

[3] A good illustration of the same kind of model in the oil industry is given in "A Mathematical Approach to Long Range Planning," by L. A. Rapoport and W. P. Drews, in *Harvard Business Review,* May-June, 1962.

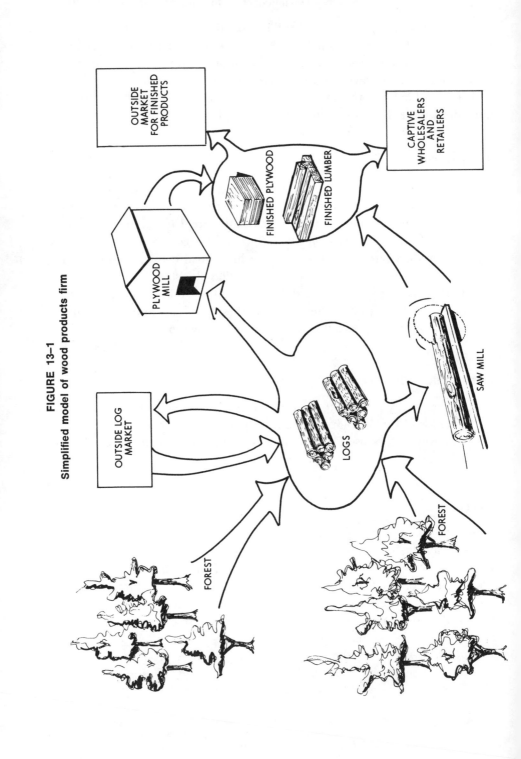

FIGURE 13-1
Simplified model of wood products firm

OUTSIDE MARKET FOR FINISHED PRODUCTS

CAPTIVE WHOLESALERS AND RETAILERS

FINISHED PLYWOOD

FINISHED LUMBER

PLYWOOD MILL

OUTSIDE LOG MARKET

LOGS

SAW MILL

FOREST

FOREST

CONSTRAINTS

Availability of lumber	Shipments of lumber	Mill constraints	Production technology	Shipments to markets	Market demand
Fir: $X_1 \leq A_1$	Fir: $X_7 + X_9 = X_1 + X_3 - X_5$	$X_7 + X_8 \leq A_3$	$X_{11} = a_5 X_7 + a_6 X_8$	$X_{11} + X_{12} = X_{15} + X_{16}$	$X_{15} \leq D_1$
Pine: $X_2 \leq A_2$	Pine: $X_8 + X_{10} = X_2 + X_4 - X_6$	$a_1 X_7 + a_2 X_8 \leq A_4$	$X_{12} = a_7 X_7 + a_8 X_8$		$X_{16} \leq D_2$
		etc.		$X_{13} + X_{14} = X_{17} + X_{18}$	$X_{17} \leq D_3$
		$X_9 + X_{10} \leq A_5$	$X_{13} = a_9 X_9 + a_{10} X_{10}$		$X_{18} \leq D_4$
		$a_2 X_9 + a_4 X_{10} \leq A_6$	$X_{14} = a_{11} X_9 + a_{12} X_{10}$		
		etc.			

SYMBOLS*

A_1 = MBF of fir available to cut
A_2 = MBF of pine available to cut
A_3 = overall sawmill capacity
A_4 = capacity of a particular part of sawmill (e.g., leadrig saw)
A_5 = overall plywood mill capacity
A_6 = capacity of some particular part of plywood mill (e.g., lathe)

$a_1, a_2, \ldots, a_{12}$ = technological coefficients

D_1, D_2, D_3, D_4 = market demand limits

X_1 = MBF of fir cut
X_2 = MBF of pine cut
X_3 = MBF of fir purchased from outside
X_4 = MBF of pine purchased from outside
X_5 = MBF of fir sold to outside
X_6 = MBF of pine sold to outside
X_7 = MBF of fir to sawmill
X_8 = MBF of pine to sawmill
X_9 = MBF of fir to plywood mill
X_{10} = MBF of pine to plywood mill
X_{11}, X_{12} = production in MBF of two types of lumber (e.g., 2 × 4's and 2 × 6's)
X_{13}, X_{14} = production in panels of two types of plywood (e.g., ½ in. and ⅜ in.)
X_{15} = lumber sold to captive distributors
X_{16} = lumber sold on outside market
X_{17} = plywood sold to captive distributors
X_{18} = plywood sold to outside markets

* MBF stands for thousands of board feet.

Formulation. Let:

X_1 = number of units of product A to be produced
X_2 = number of units of product B to be produced
P = incremental profit

We can express the situation and the objective (to maximize profit) using the equations below:

$$\text{Maximize:} \quad P = 6X_1 + 7X_2$$
$$\text{Subject to:} \quad 2X_1 + 3X_2 \leq 12$$
$$2X_1 + X_2 \leq 8$$
$$X_1, X_2 \geq 0$$

Solution. In Figure 13–2 the two constraining equations are shown. The equation

$$2X_1 + 3X_2 \leq 12$$

is the constraint imposed by limitation of hours available (12) on the first machine, and all points to the left are possible (feasible) combinations of X_1 and X_2. Similarly:

$$2X_1 + X_2 \leq 8$$

is the constraint associated with the second machine, and points to the left are feasible. We also have constraints $X_1 \geq 0$ and $X_2 \geq 0$, since we cannot have negative output. The hatched region in Figure 13–2 is the set of points that are feasible under all the constraints; it is called the *feasible region.* Clearly, not all of these points will maximize profit.

FIGURE 13–2

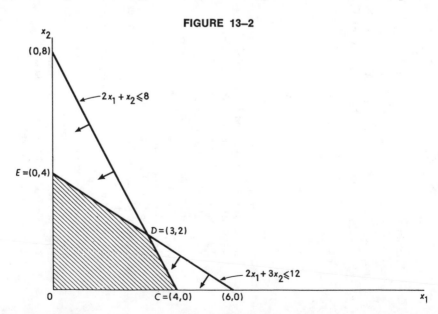

The area $OCDE$ is a convex polygon. (Because we are dealing with linear equations, the set of possible solutions [feasible points] will always be a convex polygon for solvable linear programming problems.) It can be shown mathematically that the optimum solution will always be at an extreme point (corner point) of the convex polygon.[4]

To see intuitively why the optimum solution will always be at a corner point of the feasible region, we plot the *profit function*. The profit function is a line containing all combinations of X_1 and X_2 which represent a constant amount of profit. In Figure 13–3 a series of profit functions, for different profit levels, are shown.

FIGURE 13–3

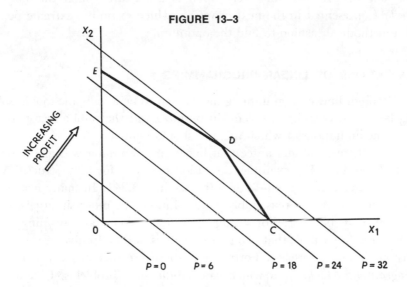

Consider the profit function for which $P = 18$. This line contains many feasible points (points within $OCDE$), all of which would give us $18 profit. But the line $P = 24$ is better than $P = 18$, since it contains feasible points with profit of $24. We continue considering lines parallel to line $P = 18$ until we reach the line $P = 32$. Here, there is only one point in the $OCDE$ polygon—namely, D itself. And D (which is $X_1 = 3$, $X_2 = 2$) is the optimal solution.

The fact that D is the optimal point is dependent upon the slope of the profit function,[5] that is, upon the relative profitability of products A

---

[4] If there is more than one optimum solution, these solutions will comprise two or more corner points and all convex combinations of these points.

[5] The slope of the objective function is $-\frac{6}{7}$:

$$P = 6X_1 + 7X_2; \quad 7X_2 = P - 6X_1; \quad X_2 = P - \frac{6}{7}X_1; \text{ and } -\frac{6}{7} \text{ is the slope.}$$

and B. Had B been considerably more profitable than A (say $8 per unit of B to $2 per unit of A), then our profit function would have much less slope, and the optimum point would be point E with $X_1 = 0$ and $X_2 = 4$ (i.e., only product B would be produced). Similarly, if product A were sufficiently more profitable than B, the optimum solution would be point C.

Since we know the optimum solution must be at an *extremum* or corner point, one method of solving a linear programming problem is simply to list all extreme points and find the one (or more) that maximizes the profit function. However, for large problems, this is an impractical method. Instead, we shall rely upon a procedure called the *simplex method* (presented in the next chapter), which examines extreme points in a methodical fashion to find the optimum.

LIMITATIONS OF LINEAR PROGRAMMING

Although linear programming has proven to be a valuable tool in solving large and complex problems in business and the public sector, there are some limitations of which the user should be aware.

First, there is no guarantee that linear programming will give integer valued solutions. For example, a solution may call for 8.241 trucks. And the manager can buy only 8 or 9 trucks—not 8.241. In many instances, rounding would give reasonably good solutions. In other situations, such answers may be poor. For example, in a decision about opening up a new plant (a variable that can take on values of 0 or 1 only), a fractional answer would be useless. Fortunately, there are methods called *integer programming techniques* which can handle such problems. Chapter 24 discusses some of these techniques.

A second major limitation of linear programming is that uncertainty is not allowed. The model assumes known values for costs, constraint requirements, etc., when in real problems such factors may be unknown. Again, there are some approaches to dealing with this problem with techniques known as *linear programming under uncertainty* or *chance constrained programming*. Some of the advanced references in the Bibliography discuss these topics.

The third limitation is the assumption of linearity. Sometimes the constraints in real business problems are not linearly related to the variables. Again, advanced techniques under the title of *nonlinear programming* are available for dealing with problems of this type.

These limitations merely point out that linear programming cannot be applied to all business problems. But for those problems where it is applicable, it has proven to be a useful and powerful tool.

CONCLUSIONS

In this chapter, we considered the solutions of one class of problems, namely, problems in which we are seeking a maximum or minimum of a linear function which is constrained by a set of linear equations. We examined the formulation of such problems and presented the graphical solution (for very simple cases). In the next chapter we introduce the simplex method as a computational device to solve large problems.

BIBLIOGRAPHY

BAUMOL, W. J. *Economic Theory and Operations Analysis.* 2nd ed. Englewood Cliffs, N.J.: Prentice-Hall, Inc., 1965.

BOWMAN, E. H., and FETTER, R. B. *Analysis for Production and Operations Management.* 3rd ed. Homewood, Ill.: Richard D. Irwin, Inc., 1967.

CHARNES, A., and COOPER, W. W. *Management Models and Industrial Applications of Linear Programming.* 2 vols. New York: John Wiley & Sons, Inc., 1963.

DANTZIG, G. B. *Linear Programming and Extensions.* Princeton, N.J.: Princeton University Press, 1963.

GARVIN, W. W. *Introduction to Linear Programming.* New York: McGraw-Hill Book Co., 1960.

HADLEY, G. *Linear Programming.* Reading, Mass.: Addison-Wesley Publishing Co., Inc., 1962.

HENDERSON, A., and SCHLAIFER, R. "Mathematical Programming: Better Information for Better Decision Making," *Harvard Business Review,* May-June, 1954.

HILLIER, F., and LIEBERMAN, G. J. *Introduction to Operations Research.* San Francisco: Holden-Day, Inc., 1967.

NAYLOR, T. H., BYRNE, E. T., and VERNON, J. M. *Introduction to Linear Programming: Methods and Cases.* Belmont, Calif.: Wadsworth Publishing Co., 1971.

SEARLE, S. R., and HAUSMAN, W. H. (with assistance from H. Bierman, Jr., J. E. Hass, L. J. Thomas). *Matrix Algebra for Business and Economics.* New York: John Wiley & Sons, Inc., 1970.

SPIVEY, W. A., and THRALL, R. M. *Linear Optimization.* New York: Holt, Rinehart & Winston, Inc., 1970.

STRUM, J. E. *Introduction to Linear Programming.* San Francisco: Holden-Day, Inc., 1972.

TEICHROEW, D. *An Introduction to Management Science: Deterministic Models.* New York: John Wiley & Sons, Inc., 1964.

WAGNER, H. *Principles of Operations Research.* Englewood Cliffs, N.J.: Prentice-Hall, Inc., 1969.

PROBLEMS

13–1. A firm produces four products: A, B, C, and D. Each unit of product A requires 2 hours of milling, one hour of assembly, and $10 worth of in-process inventory. Each unit of product B requires one hour of milling, 3 hours of assembly, and $5 worth of in-process inventory. Each unit of product C requires 2½ hours of milling, 2½ hours of assembly, and $2 worth of in-process inventory. Finally, each unit of product D requires 5 hours of milling, no assembly, and $12 of in-process inventory.

The firm has 120 hours of milling time and 160 hours of assembly time available. In addition, not more than $1,000 may be tied up in in-process inventory.

Each unit of product A returns a profit of $40; each unit of B has a profit $24; each unit of product C has a profit of $36; and each unit of product D has a profit of $23. Not more than 20 units of product A can be sold; not more than 16 units of product C can be sold; and any number of units of products B and D may be sold. However, at least 10 units of product D must be produced and sold to satisfy a contract requirement.

Formulate the above as a linear programming problem. The objective of the firm is to maximize the profit resulting from the sale of the four products. Do not attempt to solve this problem.

13–2. The U-Save Loan Company is planning its operations for the next year. The company makes five types of loans, listed below, together with the annual return (in percent) to the company.

Type of loan	Annual return (percent)
Signature loans	15
Furniture loans	12
Automobile loans	9
Second home mortgage.	10
First home mortgage	7

Legal requirements and company policy place the following limits upon the amounts of the various types of loans.

Signature loans cannot exceed 10 percent of the total amount of loans. The amount of signature and furniture loans together cannot exceed 20 percent of the total amount of loans. First mortgages must be at least 40 percent of the total mortgages, and at least 20 percent of the total amount of loans. Second mortgages may not exceed 25 percent of the total amount of loans.

The company wishes to maximize the revenue from loan interest, subject to the above restrictions. The firm can lend a maximum of $1.5 million.

Formulate the above as a linear programming problem. Do not solve it.

13–3. A company sells two different products, A and B. The selling price and incremental cost information is as follows:

	Product A	Product B
Selling price	$60	$40
Incremental cost	30	10
Incremental profit.	$30	$30

The two products are produced in a common production process and are sold in two different markets. The production process has a capacity of 30,000 man-hours. It takes three hours to produce a unit of A and one hour to produce a unit of B. The market has been surveyed, and company officials feel that the maximum number of units of A that can be sold is 8,000; the maximum for B is 12,000 units. Subject to these limitations, the products can be sold in any combination.

a) Formulate the above problem as a linear programming problem; i.e., write the appropriate equations.

b) Solve this problem by graphic methods.

13–4. The treasurer of Racy's department store is performing his financial planning for the next six months, September through February.[6] Because of the Christmas season, Racy's has need for large amounts of cash, particularly in the months of November and December; and a large cash inflow occurs in January and February when customers pay their Christmas bills. These requirements are summarized in the table below (in thousands of dollars):

	Sept.	Oct.	Nov.	Dec.	Jan.	Feb.
Accounts receivable balance (at beginning of month)	$70	$50	$ 70	$120	$100	$ 50
Planned payments of purchases (on assumption that discount is taken)	80	90	100	60	40	50
Cash needs for operations	. . .	30	60	90	. . .	. . .
Cash surplus from operations.	20	. . .	. . .	. . .	30	150

[6] This problem is based upon the article "Optimal Short Term Financing Decisions," by A. A. Robichek, D. Teichroew, and J. M. Jones, in *Management Science*, September, 1965.

The treasurer has three sources of short-term funds to meet Racy's needs. These are:

1. *Pledge accounts receivable.* A local bank will loan Racy's funds on a month-by-month basis against a pledge on the accounts receivable balance at the beginning of a given month. The maximum loan is 75 percent of the receivables in a given month. The cost of this loan is 1.5 percent per month of the amount borrowed.

2. *Stretch payment of purchases.* Payment of purchases can be delayed one month. Thus, for example, the $100,000 planned for payments for November could be delayed until December, and Racy's could use the funds to meet November needs. When purchase payments are thus stretched, Racy's loses the 3 percent discount it normally receives for prompt payment.

3. *Use short-term loan.* A bank is willing to lend Racy's any amount from $40,000 to $100,000 on a six-month basis. The loan would be taken out in full in the beginning of September for a fixed amount and paid back in full at the end of February. It would not be possible to add to the loan or to pay off part of the loan during the period. The cost of the loan would be 1 percent per month, payable each month.

In any period, if the firm has excess funds, they can be invested in short-term government securities that return 0.5 percent per month.

The objective of the treasurer is to minimize the net interest cost to Racy's, while meeting the firm's cash needs.

Formulate the above short-term financing decision as a linear programming problem. Be sure to label all variables and to explain the relationships between variables.

13–5. A manufacturer has contracted to produce 2,000 units of a particular product over the next eight months. Deliveries are scheduled as follows:

January	100
February	200
March	300
April	400
May	100
June	100
July	500
August	300
Total	2,000

The manufacturer has estimated that it costs him $1 to store one unit of product for one month. He has a warehouse capacity of 300 units.

The manufacturer can produce any number of units in a given month, since the units can be produced mostly with part-time labor, which can be easily obtained. However, there are costs of training new personnel and costs associated with laying off personnel who have been hired. The manufacturer has estimated that it costs approximately 75 cents per unit to increase the production level from one month to the next (e.g., if production in January is 200 and is increased to 300 in February, the cost is $75 for training the additional people required to produce at the 300-unit level). Similarly, it costs 50 cents per unit to reduce production from one month to the next. (At the end of eight months, all employees will be laid off, with the corresponding production-reduction costs.) Assume the production level before January is zero.

a)   Formulate the above as a linear programming problem.
b)   Suppose there was a production capacity of 300 units per month. Formulate the linear programming problem with this additional constraint.

13–6.   The director of passenger services of Ace Air Lines was trying to decide how many new stewardesses to hire and train over the next six months. He had before him the requirements in number of stewardess flight-hours needed:

Month	Hours needed
January	8,000
February	7,000
March	8,000
April	10,000
May	9,000
June	12,000

The problem was complicated by two factors. It took one month to train a stewardess before she could be used on regular flights. Hence, hiring had to be done a month before the need arose. Secondly, training of new stewardesses required the time of already trained stewardesses. It took approximately 100 hours of regular stewardess time for each trainee during the month training period. In other words, the number of hours available for flight service by regular stewardesses was cut by 100 hours for each trainee.

The director of passenger services was not worried about January, since he had 60 stewardesses available. Company rules required that a stewardess could not work more than 150 hours in any month. This meant that the director had a maximum of 9,000 hours available for January, 1,000 in excess of his need. (Stewardesses were not laid off in such cases; each merely worked fewer hours.)

Company records showed that 10 percent of the stewardesses quit their jobs each month for various reasons.

The cost to Ace Air Lines for a regular stewardess was $800 per month for salary and fringe benefits, regardless of how many hours she worked (of course, she could not work more than 150 hours). The cost of a trainee was $400 per month for salary and fringe benefits.

Formulate the above as a linear programming problem designed to solve the problem of the director of passenger services at minimum cost. Do not attempt to solve the programming problem. Be sure to identify all the symbols you use.

13–7. The land of Milkandhoney produced only three products—machinery, steel, and automobiles. All other goods were imported. The minister of the economy held the responsibility for economic planning, and he felt that the welfare of the country could best be served by maximizing the net dollar value of exports (that is, the value of the exports less the cost of the materials imported to produce those exports). Milkandhoney could sell all the steel, automobiles, or machinery it could produce on the world market at prices of $500 per unit for steel, $1,500 per unit for automobiles, and $2,500 per unit for machinery.

In order to produce one unit of steel, it took 0.05 units of machinery, 0.01 units of automobiles, 2 units of ore purchased on the world market for $100 per unit, and other imported materials costing $50. In addition, it took one-half man-year of labor to produce each unit of steel. Milkandhoney's steel mills had a rated capacity of 100,000 units.

To produce one unit of automobiles, it took one unit of steel, 0.1 units of machinery, and one man-year of labor. In addition, it took $300 worth of imported materials to produce each unit of automobiles. Automobile capacity was 700,000 units.

To produce one unit of machinery required 0.01 units of automobiles, 0.5 unit of steel, and 2 man-years of labor, in addition to $100 for items imported from outside. The capacity of the machinery plants was 50,000 units.

The total manpower available for labor in Milkandhoney was 800,000 men per year.

a) Assuming that no steel, automobiles, or machinery can be imported, formulate a linear programming model to determine the production mix that will maximize net exports (dollars). Be careful to define all variables and to state exactly all relationships among variables.

b) How would you formulate the linear programming problem if there were no restrictions on importation of any or all of automobiles, steel, or machinery at the prices given in the second paragraph of the problem? Can you see an obvious solution to the problem thus formulated?

13–8. The Stateside Electric Company is planning construction of new facilities in its area for the next 10 years.[7] It is possible to construct four types of electric power facilities—steam plants using coal for energy, hydroelectric plants with no reservoir, hydroelectric plants with small reservoirs (enough water storage capacity to meet daily fluctuations), and hydroelectric plants with large reservoirs (with enough water storage to meet seasonal fluctuations in power demand and water flow).

Consumption of electricity is based upon three characteristics. The first is the total annual usage—the requirement in the area is estimated to be 4,000 billion kilowatt-hours by the 10th year. The second characteristic is the peak usage of power—usually on a hot summer day at about 4 P.M. Any plan should provide enough peaking capacity to meet a projected peak need of 3,000 million kilowatts in the 10th year. The third characteristic is guaranteed power output—measured as the average daylight output in midwinter when the consumption is high and water levels for hydroelectric power are low. The 10-year requirement is for 2,000 million kilowatts of guaranteed power.

The various possible power plants vary in terms of how they can satisfy these characteristics. For example, hydroelectric plants with reservoirs are able to provide substantial peaking capacity, whereas steam plants and hydroelectric plants with no reservoirs are poor in this respect.

The characteristics of the various types of plants are shown in the table below. Each is measured in terms of a unit of capacity. The

Characteristics of electric plants per unit (1 billion kilowatt-hours) of annual output

Type	Guaranteed output (millions of kilowatts)	Peak output (millions of kilowatts)	Investment cost (thousands of dollars)	Discounted total cost (thousands of dollars)
Steam	0.15	0.20	$ 30	$ 65
Hydroelectric—no reservoir	0.10	0.10	40	42
Hydroelectric—small reservoir	0.10	0.40	60	64
Hydroelectric—large reservoir	0.80	0.90	100	110

unit of capacity is defined to be the capacity to produce 1 billion kilowatt-hours per year. Note that the types of plants vary substantially in their investment costs. The annual operating costs of the various types of plants also vary considerably. For example,

---

[7] This problem is based upon the article "Application of Linear Programming to Investments in the Electric Power Industry," P. Masse and R. Gibrat, in *Management Science,* January 1957.

the cost of coal makes the annual cost of the steam plants quite high, whereas the annual costs of operating the hydroelectric plants are relatively less. The final column in the table shows the discounted total costs, including both the investment cost and the discounted annual operating costs.

The company wants to develop a 10-year plan which would detail how much capacity of each type of plant to build. The objective is to minimize the total discounted cost. However, there is a restriction that no more than $350 million can be used for investment in plants over the 10 years.

Formulate this problem as a linear programming model.

13–9. Solve the following problem graphically:

Maximize: $P = 2X_1 + 5X_2$

Subject to: $X_1 + 3X_2 \leq 16$

$4X_1 + X_2 \leq 20$

$X_1 \leq 4$

$X_1, X_2 \geq 0$

13–10. Solve the following *minimization* problem graphically. (*Hint:* Graph the feasible region, and then plot the objective function to find its *minimum* feasible value.)

Minimize: $C = 4X_1 - 2X_2$

Subject to: $X_1 \geq 6$

$X_1 + X_2 \geq 10$

$X_1, X_2 \geq 0$

13–11. It is desired to select an advertising strategy[8] to reach two types of customers: housewives in families with over $10,000 annual income and housewives in families with under $10,000 income. We feel that people in the first group will purchase twice as much of our product as people in the second, and our goal is to maximize purchases. We may advertise either on TV or in a magazine; one unit of TV advertising costs $20,000 and reaches approximately 2,000 people in the first group and 8,000 in the second. One unit of advertising in the magazine costs $12,000 and reaches 6,000 people in the first group and 3,000 in the second.[9] We require that at least six units of TV advertising be used, and that no more than 12 units of magazine advertising be used, for policy reasons. The advertising budget is $180,000.

a)   Formulate this problem as a linear programming problem, defining all variables used.

b)   Solve it graphically.

---

[8] This problem is adapted from the article, "An Exploration of Linear Programming in Media Selection," by F. M. Bass and R. T. Lonsdale, in *Journal of Marketing Research,* vol. 3 (1966).

[9] In this problem it is assumed that the magazine's audience has no overlap with the TV audience.

13–12. The American Safety Council must allocate its national budget for the next fiscal year. Irrevocable decisions have already been made concerning various "program areas" and their total funding; e.g., a total of $100,000 has been allocated to prevention of automobile fatalities and reduction of property damage. However, detailed allocation decisions must be made concerning specific *projects* designed to contribute to the program missions. In the case of automobile fatality prevention and reduction of property damage, the following projects have been recommended by council analysts, together with appropriate data:

Project	Upper limit of expenditure on project (measured in dollars)	Expected fatalities prevented per $1,000 expended	Expected reduction in property damage per $1,000 expended
Seat belt advertising	$ 80,000	0.33	$ 0
Research in improved highway design	20,000	0.25	20,000
Research in improved automobile design	75,000	0.15	30,000
Dollars spent lobbying for tougher state "drunk driving" penalties. . . .	100,000	0.27	10,000

The decision makers of the council want you to help them make their budget allocation (or project choice and magnitude) decisions. In response to a question concerning which of their two specific missions is more important, they said: "That's a tough question! On the one hand, human life is sacred and cannot be purchased for any amount of money. On the other hand, if there are two competing ways to save the *same number of lives*, we would naturally prefer the project which also results in the lower amount of property damage."

When asked specifically what "trade-off" between lives saved and property damage would make them be indifferent, they said: "That's really a tough question! However, we are aware that a certain government agency has, for internal resource allocation purposes, an implicit dollar value for a human life saved of $300,000 (we think another agency also uses this number in making decisions about building additional safety into their equipment)."

Formulate an LP model whose solution would represent an optimal allocation of the budgeted $100,000, based on all the information above. Be sure to define all variables used. You need *not* solve the formulation.

13–13. The Impala Gold Company operated a gold mine in the Orange Free State, South Africa. The mining operation consisted of mining underground, at a depth of 4,000 feet, gold bearing rock. The rock was transported up the mine shafts to a mill which crushed the rock and extracted the gold.

The Impala mine had three shafts. Information on these shafts is given in the table below. Note that the rock mined in each shaft area has a different gold content as well as different costs.

	Shaft 1	Shaft 2	Shaft 3
Hoist capacity of shaft (tons per month)	85,000	90,000	95,000
Ore grade (grams of gold per ton of rock)	25	20	15
Variable cost of mining rock (Rands* per ton)	6	5	4

* The South African Rand is worth about $1.40 U.S. dollars.

Rock mined from all three shafts was sent to the mill to be crushed and refined. The mill capacity depended upon how fine the rock was ground. If the rock was ground fine, mill capacity was 240,000 tons per month and 95 percent of the gold was recovered in the operation. The cost of milling a ton of rock ground fine was 1.12 Rand per ton. If the rock was ground coarse, mill capacity was 250,000 tons per month, but gold recovery dropped to 90 percent. The cost of milling a ton of rock ground coarse was 0.85 Rand. Intermediate grinding sizes were possible with proportionate recovery rates and costs.

The mine could sell all the gold it produced at a price of 0.80 Rand per gram.

The mine manager was concerned about how much rock he should mine in each shaft area. He noted that the mill capacity was not sufficient to handle all three shafts operating at full capacity. The problem was further complicated by the legal requirements that a mine could not mine "above the average grade" of the ore reserves. In the Impala mine this average grade was 20 grams per ton. Thus there was the legal restriction that the mix of rock from the three shafts could not exceed an average of 20 grams per ton in ore grade.

Formulate a linear programming model to maximize profit from operating the mine.

13–14. The Transvaal Diamond Company mined diamonds in three locations in South Africa. The three mines differed in terms of capacities, number, and weight of stones mined and costs. These are shown below:

Mine	Capacity (cubic meter—* M^3—of earth processed)	Treatment† costs (Rand per M^3)	Grade (carats per M^3)	Stone count (number of stones per M^3)
Plant No. 1........	83,000	R0.60	0.36	0.58
Plant No. 2........	310,000	R0.36	0.22	0.26
Plant No. 3........	190,000	R0.50	0.269	0.21

* M^3 is cubic meters.
† Note mining costs are excluded from these figures. Assume that they are the same at each mine.

Due to marketing considerations, a monthly production of exactly 148,000 stones was required. A similar requirement called for at least 130,000 carats. (Thus average stone size was at least $130/148 = 0.88$ carats.)

The problem for the company manager was to meet the marketing requirements at the least cost.

Formulate a linear programming model to determine how much should be mined at each location.

13-15. The Consolidated Company has in the past contracted out the shipment of its products from its factory to its warehouses. The volume of deliveries is measured in ton-miles (the tons of product times the number of miles over which it is to be delivered). Consolidated has 400,000 ton-miles to be delivered each month.

Currently, Consolidated is paying Speedie Trucking Company $0.50 per ton-mile to deliver the product. Consolidated is considering purchasing a fleet of trucks to take over a part or all of this delivery service.

Three types of trucks are under consideration: large trailer-trucks, medium-size trucks, and pickup trucks. Details of each are given below:

Type	Purchase cost	Operating cost (per ton-mile)	Capacity (ton-miles per month)
Trailer.......	$15,000	$0.28	10,000
Medium......	8,000	0.32	8,000
Pickup.......	5,000	0.40	6,000

Speedie Trucking has indicated that it would be willing to continue to deliver any excess not delivered by Consolidated's own trucks at the rate of $0.50 per ton-mile.

Capital equipment funds are in short supply in Consolidated and only $380,000 is available to purchase the equipment.

In addition to the budget limitation, there were other restrictions on the types of trucks purchased. The first involved dock loading space. Because of parking space and dock limitations, not more than 28 truck spaces were available. A trailer or medium truck would use one space. Two pickup trucks use one space.

Also, because of the types and size of deliveries, at least two thirds of the trucks purchased would have to be either trailers or medium trucks.

a) Formulate this as a linear programming problem. Do not solve. Be careful to specify the objective and define the variables.

b) Suppose the company had no limitation on budget to purchase trucks but wanted to find the mix that gave the greatest return on investment. Outline a procedure—using the model given in (a) above—for doing this.

14

Linear programming: The simplex method

In the previous chapter we solved small linear programming problems graphically. In this chapter we demonstrate a systematic procedure, the *simplex method,* to solve large linear programming problems. Recall that the optimum solution to a linear programming problem lies at a corner point. The simplex method simply examines corner points in a systematic manner to find the optimum. Computer programs (using the simplex method or variations of it) are widely available, but it is important to gain an understanding of how the method works in order to interpret the results.

THE SIMPLEX METHOD

Example 1: Maximization of profits

Let us consider the same problem that we solved in the previous chapter by graphic methods. Recall that we had:

$$\text{Maximize:} \quad P = 6X_1 + 7X_2$$
$$\text{Subject to:} \quad 2X_1 + 3X_2 \leq 12$$
$$2X_1 + X_2 \leq 8$$
$$X_1 \geq 0$$
$$X_2 \geq 0$$

where

X_1 = number of units of product A
X_2 = number of units of product B
6 = incremental profit per unit of product A
7 = incremental profit per unit of product B

The first step in using the simplex procedure is to convert the inequality expressions in the problem to equalities. This is done by adding two new variables, X_3 and X_4, called *slack variables*. The slack variables represent the *unused capacity* in the first and second constraint respectively. It is always possible to convert the inequalities to equalities since there must be some amount—the unused capacity X_3—which, when added to $(2X_1 + 3X_2)$, will equal 12 (X_3 may be equal to or greater than zero).

The constraints of the problem are now rewritten as:

$$2X_1 + 3X_2 + X_3 = 12$$
$$2X_1 + X_2 + X_4 = 8$$

So that all variables are represented in each equation, we add slack variables with zero coefficients to the equations which are lacking some variables. For example, $0X_4$ is added to the first equation, and $0X_3$ is added to the second:

$$2X_1 + 3X_2 + X_3 + 0X_4 = 12$$
$$2X_1 + X_2 + 0X_3 + X_4 = 8$$

The profit equation becomes:

$$P = 6X_1 + 7X_2 + 0X_3 + 0X_4$$

The slack variables introduce no profit, so their coefficients in the profit equation are zero.

Note that we have two equations in four unknown variables and it is not possible to solve for unique values for the X's using algebraic methods—to do this we would need the same number of equations as unknowns. However, it is possible to let two of the variables equal zero and solve for the remaining two (we then have two equations in two unknowns). For example, if we assume $X_1 = X_2 = 0$, then $X_3 = 12$ and $X_4 = 8$ is a solution. All such solutions for this problem are given in Table 14–1.

TABLE 14–1

Variables set equal to zero	Solution	Profit	Label in Figure 14–1
X_1 and X_2	$X_3 = 12, X_4 = 8$	0	A
X_1 and X_3	$X_2 = 4, X_4 = 8$	28	E
X_1 and X_4	$X_2 = 8, X_3 = -12$	Infeasible	F
X_2 and X_3	$X_1 = 6, X_4 = -4$	Infeasible	B
X_2 and X_4	$X_1 = 4, X_3 = 4$	24	C
X_3 and X_4	$X_1 = 3, X_2 = 2$	32	D

Each solution in Table 14–1 corresponds to intersections of pairs of lines in Figure 14–1 (which is the graph of the constraints of this prob-

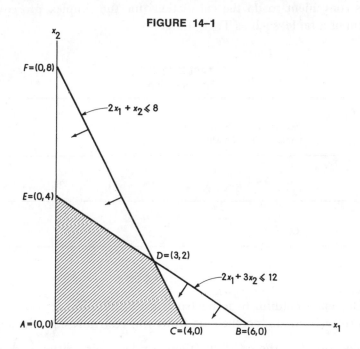

FIGURE 14–1

lem, repeated from the previous chapter). Points A, C, E, and D correspond to corner points for the feasible region. Points B and F are infeasible—and this infeasibility is easily recognized by noting that the solutions for these points contain negative values (for example, the solution at point F requires $X_3 = -12$). We can rule out infeasible solutions simply by excluding those giving negative values for any of the X's.

In this simple problem, the optimum solution can be found by enumerating all the feasible corner points, calculating the profit for each, and selecting the best, as is done in Table 14–1. However, a reasonably sized business problem may have hundreds or thousands of corner points, and this procedure is not reasonable.

The simplex method starts from an initial (corner point) solution (by setting selected variables equal to zero and solving for the rest, as above), and then proceeds step by step to subsequent solutions in a systematic fashion. At each step the procedure guarantees that:

a)   With each new solution (corner point) the profit is increased.[1]
b)   The solution remains feasible.

---

[1] In some circumstances it is possible for the profit to remain the same from one step to the next, but it cannot decrease.

The simplex table

It is convenient to do the calculations for the simplex procedure in the form of a table, such as Table 14–2.

TABLE 14–2
First solution

C_j			0	0	6	7
	Solution variables	Solution values	X_3	X_4	X_1	X_2
		12	1	0	2	3
		8	0	1	2	1
	Z_j					
	$C_j - Z_j$					

Under each column heading (such as X_3, X_4, X_1, or X_2) of Table 14–2 are written the coefficients from the restraint equations of the variables found in the heading. Thus, under X_1 is written $\begin{pmatrix} 2 \\ 2 \end{pmatrix}$; under X_2 is written $\begin{pmatrix} 3 \\ 1 \end{pmatrix}$; under X_3 is written $\begin{pmatrix} 1 \\ 0 \end{pmatrix}$; and under X_4 is written $\begin{pmatrix} 0 \\ 1 \end{pmatrix}$. Under the column headed "Solution values," the constants of the equations are listed. Each row in the table is thus associated with a given constraint. It is convenient to write the columns containing the slack variables immediately after the solution column. The first row in the heading of the table contains the C_j's, or the profit per unit (the coefficients of the variables in the profit equation) for each variable X_1 through X_4.

Before proceeding to fill in the rest of Table 14–2, we must identify the initial solution. This consists of the slack variables X_3 and X_4. That is, we are starting with the solution point labeled A in Table 14–1 and Figure 14–1. This is not a very profitable solution (profit is zero) but is easy to obtain since the slack variables simply equal the constant terms in the constraint equations (i.e., $X_3 = 12$ and $X_4 = 8$). In terms of the problem, the solution calls for no production of either product A or B. The terms X_3 and X_4 are entered in the simplex table under the "Solution variables" column, and their per unit profits (the C_j's) are entered in the first column under the C_j heading (Table 14–4).

Several characteristics of the solution should be noted. The number of solution variables is equal to the number of constraints.[2] Second, the solution variables can be identified as those having columns under them containing one element with $+1$, and the remainder of the elements zero. Thus, column X_3 is $\begin{pmatrix}1\\0\end{pmatrix}$, and column X_4 is $\begin{pmatrix}0\\1\end{pmatrix}$. Also, the one must be in a different row than the one of any other column. Thus, X_3 has a one in the first row, and X_4 has a one in the second row. Note that this is equivalent to saying that we have solved the constraint equations in terms of X_3 and X_4:

$$(14\text{--}1) \qquad \begin{aligned} X_3 &= 12 - [2X_1 + 3X_2] \\ X_4 &= 8 - [2X_1 + X_2] \end{aligned}$$

If there are n constraints in the problem, then the first n columns should appear as shown in Table 14–3.

TABLE 14–3

Solution variables	X_1	X_2	$\ldots X_n$
X_1	1	0	$\ldots 0$
X_2	0	1	$\ldots 0$
$\ldots$	.	.	$\ldots$
$\ldots$	.	.	$\ldots$
$\ldots$	.	.	$\ldots$
X_n	0	0	$\ldots 1$

Note that we have a diagonal of ones and the remainder of the numbers in the first n columns are zeros.

Substitution coefficients. The coefficients in the columns of the body of the simplex table can be considered *substitution coefficients*. That is, they are the reductions in variables in the solution which will result from introducing one unit of each variable. For example, in Table 14–4, $\begin{pmatrix}3\\1\end{pmatrix}$ is under column X_2. For every unit of product B (i.e., units of X_2) introduced into the solution, three units of slack variable X_3 and one unit of slack variable X_4 must be removed from the solution in order to stay within the required restraints. Thus the 3 and 1 are the amounts of X_3 and X_4 *substituted* for one unit of X_2. Similarly, for every unit of X_1 introduced into the solution, two units of X_3 and two units of X_4 must

---

[2] Excluding nonnegativity constraints, $X_1 \geq 0$, $X_2 \geq 0$, $X_3 \geq 0$, and $X_4 \geq 0$.

TABLE 14–4
First solution

C_j			0	0	6	7
	Solution variables	Solution values	X_3	X_4	X_1	X_2
0	→X_3	12	1	0	2	③
0	X_4	8	0	1	2	1
	Z_j	0	0	0	0	0
	$C_j - Z_j$		0	0	6	7

$$\uparrow$$

be removed. An inspection of our constraint equations (14–1) confirms the reasonableness of this interpretation.

Under each column of Table 14–4 is a Z_j total (where the j subscript refers to the specific column which is being totaled). The Z_j total of a column is the amount of profit which is given up by replacing some of the present solution mix with *one* unit of the item heading the column. It is found by multiplying the C_j of the row by the number in the row and jth column, and adding. The computations of the Z_j's of Table 14–4 are as follows:

$$Z_3 = 1(0) + 0(0) = 0$$
$$Z_4 = 0(0) + 1(0) = 0$$
$$Z_1 = 2(0) + 2(0) = 0$$
$$Z_2 = 3(0) + 1(0) = 0$$

Similarly, a Z value can be calculated for the "Solution values" column (which we shall refer to hereafter as the 0th column):

$$Z_0 = 12(0) + 8(0) = 0$$

Z_0 represents the profit of the current solution.

Under the Z_j row is a row labeled $C_j - Z_j$. Subtract the Z_j total from the C_j amount at the very top of the column to find the *net* profit which is added by one unit of the product (if $C_j - Z_j$ is positive) or the amount of profit which will be lost (if $C_j - Z_j$ is negative). Thus, if one unit B is added to the solution (replacing some amounts of X_3 and X_4), $7 of net profit will be added.

We have found 12 units of X_3 and 8 units of X_4 to be one possible solution; but since the profit resulting from this product mix is zero (Z_j

for the "Solution values" column), we attempt to find a more desirable solution. The procedure to compute the second simplex solution is as follows:

a) Determine the column (if any) of Table 14–4 which will contribute the greatest net profit per unit (the column which has the greatest positive $C_j - Z_j$). Product B contributes \$7 per unit, which is greater than the contribution of any other product. This means that we want to replace some of X_3 or X_4 with one or more units of B (column X_2, the replacing column, is marked with an arrow). The significance of the three and the one in the X_2 column is that to insert one unit of X_2 into the solution, we must remove three units of X_3 and one unit of X_4.

b) The next step is to determine which row (X_3 or X_4) is to be replaced by X_2. Divide each amount in the "Solution values" column by the amount *in the comparable row* of the X_2 column:

$$\text{For } X_3 \text{ row: } \quad 12/3 = 4$$
$$\text{For } X_4 \text{ row: } \quad 8/1 = 8$$

The smallest number obtained by this computation gives the maximum number of X_2 units, four, which may be injected into the solution (more than four units of X_2 would drive variable X_3 negative, which is not allowed). If any of the amounts are negative, they should be eliminated from consideration; otherwise, the smallest amount, as computed above, determines the row to be replaced. In this case the X_3 row should be replaced (this row is marked by an arrow in Table 14–4).

Note what we have done so far in the simplex procedure. Step (*a*) identified a variable that will increase profitability and indicated that it is to be included in the next solution. Step (*b*) guarantees that the next solution will be a feasible one by identifying a variable to be removed from the solution that will keep all variable values nonnegative. The next step is to determine the new solution.

c) The actual replacement of X_3 by X_2 is accomplished making use of two techniques.

The element in the X_2 column and the X_3 row is designated the *pivot element*. (In our example the pivot element is circled in Table 14–4 and has a value of 3.) In order to obtain a new solution containing X_2, this element must be converted to a plus one and the other elements in the X_2 column converted to zero.

To convert the pivot element to plus one requires simply that we divide every element in the present X_3 row by the value of the pivot element (i.e., by 3). Recall that each row is in reality a constraint equation, and it is perfectly legitimate to divide a whole equation by a constant.

The calculations are:

$$1\tfrac{2}{3} = 4$$
$$\tfrac{1}{3} = \tfrac{1}{3}$$
$$\tfrac{0}{3} = 0$$
$$\tfrac{2}{3} = \tfrac{2}{3}$$
$$\tfrac{3}{3} = 1$$

Thus the new top row should be $(4, \tfrac{1}{3}, 0, \tfrac{2}{3}, 1)$; and it is labeled X_2 in the second simplex solution (see Table 14–5).

TABLE 14–5
Second solution—partially complete

C_j			0	0	6	7
	Solution variables	Solution values	X_3	X_4	X_1	X_2
7	X_2 (new)	4	$\tfrac{1}{3}$	0	$\tfrac{2}{3}$	1
0	X_4 (old)	8	0	1	2	①
	Z_j $C_j - Z_j$					

The second part of the procedure is aimed at converting all the elements (except the pivot element) in the X_2 column to zero. In our example, the only other value in the X_2 column is a 1 in the X_4 row (circled in Table 14–5). This can be accomplished by multiplying the entire *new* X_2 row by the value in the X_2 column, X_4 row—i.e., the circled value, 1—and subtracting the result from the old X_4 row. This is easier to illustrate than to describe (see Table 14–6).

TABLE 14–6

Old X_4 row	−	$\left(\begin{array}{c}\text{Old } X_4 \text{ row} \\ X_2 \text{ column}\end{array}\right.$	·	$\left.\begin{array}{c}\text{New} \\ X_2 \text{ row}\end{array}\right)$	=	Values of new X_4 row
8	−	(1)	·	(4)	=	4
0	−	(1)	·	$(\tfrac{1}{3})$	=	$-\tfrac{1}{3}$
1	−	(1)	·	(0)	=	1
2	−	(1)	·	$(\tfrac{2}{3})$	=	$\tfrac{4}{3}$
1	−	(1)	·	(1)	=	0

The new values of the X_4 row are $(4, -\tfrac{1}{3}, 1, \tfrac{4}{3}, 0)$.

To understand why the procedure described above is legitimate, recall again that each row in the table is equivalent to an equation. Hence we are simply multiplying one equation by a constant (1 in this case), and subtracting it from another equation. The result is a new equation. Table 14–7 shows the new solution.

TABLE 14–7
Second solution

C_j			0	0	6	7
	Solution variables	Solution values	X_3	X_4	X_1	X_2
7	X_2	4	$\frac{1}{3}$	0	$\frac{2}{3}$	1
0	X_4	4	$-\frac{1}{3}$	1	$\frac{4}{3}$	0
	Z_j	28	$\frac{7}{3}$	0	$1\frac{4}{3}$	7
	$C_j - Z_j$		$-\frac{7}{3}$	0	$\frac{4}{3}$	0

In equation form, the new solution is:

$$X_2 = 4 - [\tfrac{1}{3}X_3 + \tfrac{2}{3}X_1]$$
$$X_4 = 4 - [-\tfrac{1}{3}X_3 + \tfrac{4}{3}X_1]$$

With X_3 and X_1 equal to zero, the new solution has four units of product B ($X_2 = 4$) and four units of slack in the second constraint ($X_4 = 4$).

Calculating the Z_j's. We first illustrate the calculation of the Z_j values for Table 14–7 by considering the X_1 column and Z_1. Recall that the coefficients $\frac{2}{3}$ and $\frac{4}{3}$ in the X_1 column are substitution coefficients indicating that one unit of X_1 would now replace $\frac{2}{3}$ of a unit of X_2 and $\frac{4}{3}$ of a unit of X_4. Since we are making a profit of $7 and $0 per unit of X_2 and X_4 respectively, the *opportunity cost* of introducing a unit of X_1 is:

$$Z_1 = \tfrac{2}{3} \times 7 + \tfrac{4}{3} \times 0 = 1\tfrac{4}{3}$$

In other words, it would cost us $1\frac{4}{3}$ dollars to inject one unit of X_1 into the solution. But since X_1 has a profit of $6, the *net* profit from one unit of X_1 is $C_1 - Z_1 = 6 - 1\frac{4}{3} = \frac{4}{3}$.

The Z_j's for the other columns are calculated similarly:

$$Z_3 = 7 \cdot \tfrac{1}{3} + 0(-\tfrac{1}{3}) = \tfrac{7}{3}$$
$$Z_4 = 7 \cdot 0 + 0(1) = 0$$
$$Z_2 = 7 \cdot 1 + 0(0) = 7$$

Finally, $Z_0 = 7 \cdot 4 + 0(4) = 28$. This is the profit associated with the current (second) solution. It is an improvement over the previous solution. However, our calculations above indicated that we can yet improve our solution by adding product A (i.e., X_1), increasing our profit by $1.33 for each unit added.

The Third Solution. This is computed as follows:

a)   The new replacing product or column is X_1 (it has the largest net profit per replacing unit; see Table 14–8).

b)   The row which is replaced by X_1 is X_4, determined as follows:

$$\text{For } X_2 \text{ row: } \quad \frac{4}{\frac{2}{3}} = 6$$

$$\text{For } X_4 \text{ row: } \quad \frac{4}{\frac{4}{3}} = 3$$

Each amount in the "Solution value" column is divided by the amount in the comparable row of the X_1 column. The three is the smaller amount and is from the X_4 row; thus, X_4 should be replaced by X_1.

The replacing variable (X_1) and the variable to be replaced (X_4) are indicated by arrows in Table 14–8.

TABLE 14–8
Second solution

C_j			0	0	6	7
	Solution variables	Solution values	X_3	X_4	X_1	X_2
7	X_2	4	$\frac{1}{3}$	0	$\frac{2}{3}$	1
0	→X_4	4	$-\frac{1}{3}$	1	$\textcircled{$\frac{4}{3}$}$	0
	Z_j	28	$\frac{7}{3}$	0	$14\frac{2}{3}$	7
	$C_j - Z_j$		$-\frac{7}{3}$	0	$\frac{4}{3}$	0
					↑	

c)   The pivot element in the X_1 column, X_4 row (circled in Table 14–8) has a value of $\frac{4}{3}$. To convert this to 1, the old X_4 row is divided by $\frac{4}{3}$:

$$\frac{4}{\frac{4}{3}} = 3$$

$$\frac{-\frac{1}{3}}{\frac{4}{3}} = -\frac{1}{4}$$

$$\frac{1}{\frac{4}{3}} = \frac{3}{4}$$

$$\frac{\frac{4}{3}}{\frac{4}{3}} = 1$$

$$\frac{0}{\frac{4}{3}} = 0$$

The new X_1 row is $(3, -\frac{1}{4}, \frac{3}{4}, 1, 0)$ and is shown in Table 14–9.

TABLE 14–9
Third solution—partially complete

C_j	Solution variables	Solution values	0 X_3	0 X_4	6 X_1	7 X_2
7	X_2 (old)	4	$\frac{1}{3}$	0	②⁄₃	1
6	X_1 (new)	3	$-\frac{1}{4}$	$\frac{3}{4}$	1	0
	Z_j $C_j - Z_j$					

d) The next step is to convert the circled value in Table 14–9 to zero. To do this, the new X_1 row is multiplied by $\frac{2}{3}$ and subtracted from the old X_2 row as shown in Table 14–10. The new X_2 row is $(2, \frac{1}{2}, -\frac{1}{2}, 0, 1)$, inserted in Table 14–11.

TABLE 14–10

Old X_2 row	$-$	$\left(\begin{array}{c}\text{Old } X_2 \text{ row,} \\ X_1 \text{ column}\end{array}\right.$	$\cdot$	$\left.\begin{array}{c}\text{New} \\ X_1 \text{ row}\end{array}\right)$	$=$	Values of new X_2 row
4	$-$	$(\frac{2}{3})$	$\cdot$	(3)	$=$	2
$\frac{1}{3}$	$-$	$(\frac{2}{3})$	$\cdot$	$(-\frac{1}{4})$	$=$	$\frac{1}{2}$
0	$-$	$(\frac{2}{3})$	$\cdot$	$(\frac{3}{4})$	$=$	$-\frac{1}{2}$
$\frac{2}{3}$	$-$	$(\frac{2}{3})$	$\cdot$	(1)	$=$	0
1	$-$	$(\frac{2}{3})$	$\cdot$	(0)	$=$	1

TABLE 14–11
Third solution

C_j	Solution variables	Solution values	0 X_3	0 X_4	6 X_1	7 X_2
7	X_2	2	$\frac{1}{2}$	$-\frac{1}{2}$	0	1
6	X_1	3	$-\frac{1}{4}$	$\frac{3}{4}$	1	0
	Z_j $C_j - Z_j$	32	2 -2	1 -1	6 0	7 0

The computation of the Z_j's of Table 14–11 is as follows:

$$
\begin{aligned}
Z_0 &= 7 \cdot \quad 2 + 6 \cdot \quad 3 = 32 \\
Z_3 &= 7 \cdot \quad \tfrac{1}{2} + 6 \cdot (-\tfrac{1}{4}) = 2 \\
Z_4 &= 7 \cdot (-\tfrac{1}{2}) + 6 \cdot \quad \tfrac{3}{4} = 1 \\
Z_1 &= 7 \cdot \quad 0 + 6 \cdot \quad 1 = 6 \\
Z_2 &= 7 \cdot \quad 1 + 6 \cdot \quad 0 = 7
\end{aligned}
$$

All $C_j - Z_j$ values are negative or zero, indicating that any further substitution will not result in an increase in profit; thus an optimum solution has been obtained. The optimum strategy is to produce two units of B and three units of A (that is, $X_1 = 3$, $X_2 = 2$); this will result in \$32 of profit. From the profit equation, we also obtain:

$$ P = \$6X_1 + \$7X_2 + 0X_3 + 0X_4 = (\$6 \cdot 3) + (\$7 \cdot 2) = \$32 $$

The restraint equations are satisfied:

$$
\begin{aligned}
2X_1 + 3X_2 &\leq 12 \\
6 \quad + 6 \quad &\leq 12 \\
2X_1 + \quad X_2 &\leq 8 \\
6 \quad + 2 \quad &\leq 8
\end{aligned}
$$

It should be noted that in this problem we were maximizing an amount (profit) subject to restraints, all of which were in the form of a sum of variables equal to or less than a constant. This is important, since certain steps in the solution process will be modified as we change the description of the problem.

Example 2: Minimization of costs

This example will differ from the previous example in several respects:

a) An amount is being minimized (rather than maximized).

b) There are three restraints—one equality and two inequalities.

Note that one of the inequalities is in the form of the variable being equal to *or greater than* a constant.

Situation. The final product has a requirement that it must weigh exactly 150 pounds. The two raw materials used are A, with a cost of \$2 per unit, and B, with a cost of \$8 per unit. At least 14 units of B and no more than 20 units of A must be used. Each unit of A weighs 5 pounds; each unit of B weighs 10 pounds.

Problem. How much of each type of raw material should be used for each unit of final product if we wish to minimize cost?

Solution. The first step is to define variables and establish the cost equation, i.e., the objective function. In Example 1 the objective function was the profit equation. In this example, it is the cost equation

$$C = 2X_1 + 8X_2$$

where

$$X_1 = \text{number of units of product A}$$
$$X_2 = \text{number of units of product B}$$
$$2 = \text{cost of a unit of product A}$$
$$8 = \text{cost of a unit of product B}$$

Instead of finding the combination of X_1 and X_2 which minimizes the function $2X_1 + 8X_2$, we could solve the problem of maximizing $P = -2X_1 - 8X_2$. Both solutions would be the same, but to illustrate the procedure, we shall solve the minimization problem.

We must set up the equations which establish the restraints. There are three (not counting nonnegativity restraints):

Interpretation

$5X_1 + 10X_2 = 150$	The total weight must be equal to 150 pounds.
$X_1 \le 20$	No more than 20 units of A may be used.
$X_2 \ge 14$	At least 14 units of B must be used.
$X_1 \ge 0$	The amount of A used cannot be negative.

Graphic analysis. To strengthen our understanding of the problem, we shall briefly illustrate again the graphic approach (see Figure 14–2).

Since the equation $5X_1 + 10X_2 = 150$ must be satisfied exactly, the solution must lie on the line *DEF*. And since the solution must

FIGURE 14–2

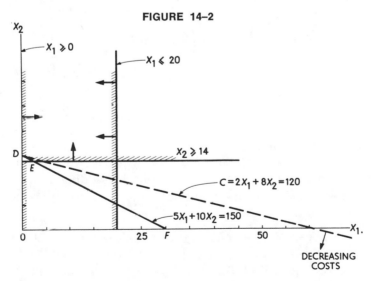

satisfy the constraints $X_1 \geq 0$ and $X_2 \geq 14$, we can eliminate all but the line segment DE. Actually, we need examine only the points D and E, since the optimum must be a corner point. Note that the constraint $X_1 \leq 20$ is not binding; i.e., it in no way influences our set of feasible solutions. The restrictions of the other constraints make the $X_1 \leq 20$ constraint unnecessary.

The objective function $C = 2X_1 + 8X_2 = 120$ is also shown in Figure 14–2. This is not the optimum, since we can move the $C = 120$ line down to the left and decrease cost. The least cost will be reached at $C = 116$, which goes through the optimum point $E(X_1 = 2, X_2 = 14)$.

We shall now solve the same problem with the simplex procedure.

The simplex method. In the previous example, we introduced slack variables to establish equalities. To solve the present problem, we introduce "artificial" variables in the equalities, or where there is an inequality with the symbol $\geq$, indicating the sum of the variables is equal to or greater than a constant. In the equality an artificial variable, X_3, is introduced; but in the cost function (speaking more generally, the objective function) the coefficient of this variable will be made *large,* so that the X_3 will be driven out of the final solution through the minimizing process. This is necessary, since there can be no X_3 in the final solution (X_3 must equal zero, so that $5X_1 + 10X_2 = 150$).

In a "greater than" inequality, two variables are introduced. One, a slack variable with a negative sign, here X_5, is used to convert the inequality to an equality (this will have a zero coefficient in the cost function). The second, here X_6, is an artificial variable which will be driven out of the final solution by a large coefficient in the cost function. The restraints may now be expressed in the following equations:

$$
\begin{aligned}
5X_1 + 10X_2 + X_3 \quad\quad\quad\quad\quad &= 150 \\
X_1 \quad\quad\quad\quad\quad + X_4 \quad\quad\quad &= 20 \\
X_2 \quad\quad\quad - X_5 + X_6 &= 14
\end{aligned}
$$

The new cost function is:

$$
C = 2X_1 + 8X_2 + MX_3 + 0X_4 + 0X_5 + MX_6
$$

where M is a very large number.

To understand better the simplex table which follows (Table 14–12), we shall expand the restraint equations by adding X's with zero coefficients to each restraint equation so that each equation has all the variables X_1 through X_6:

$$
\begin{aligned}
5X_1 + 10X_2 + 1X_3 + 0X_4 + 0X_5 + 0X_6 &= 150 \\
1X_1 + 0X_2 + 0X_3 + 1X_4 + 0X_5 + 0X_6 &= 20 \\
0X_1 + 1X_2 + 0X_3 + 0X_4 - 1X_5 + 1X_6 &= 14
\end{aligned}
$$

TABLE 14–12
First solution

C_j			M	0	M	2	8	0
	Solution variables	Solution values	X_3	X_4	X_6	X_1	X_2	X_5
M	X_3	150	1	0	0	5	10	0
0	X_4	20	0	1	0	1	0	0
M	$\rightarrow X_6$	14	0	0	1	0	1	-1
	Z_j	$164M$	M	0	M	$5M$	$11M$	$-M$
	$C_j - Z_j$		0	0	0	$2-5M$	$8-11M$	M

The first simplex table in this example (Table 14–12) is constructed from the coefficients of the variables of the restraint equations, the constant restraints (150, 20, 14 in the "Solution values" column), and the cost coefficients of the cost equation.

Note that the first solution consists of the slack variables or artificial variables which have *coefficients of one* in one row and zero in the other rows (check the X_3, X_4, and X_6 columns).

Since we are attempting to minimize costs, the column with the *most negative* $(C_j - Z_j)$ total will be chosen as the replacing column. Column X_2 wins this contest, since $8 - 11M$ (M is very large) is the most negative total.

The row to be replaced is the X_6 row, since $^{14}\!/_1$ is less than $^{150}\!/_{10}$, and $^{20}\!/_0$ is not mathematically defined. Since there is already a 1 in the X_2 column of the old X_6 row, nothing further has to be done to this row (except change its name to X_2).

Table 14–13 is the second simplex table of this example. A computation of the X_3 row and the X_4 row follows:

X_3 row

$$150 - 14 \cdot (10) = 10$$
$$1 - 0 \cdot (10) = 1$$
$$0 - 0 \cdot (10) = 0$$
$$0 - 1 \cdot (10) = -10$$
$$5 - 0 \cdot (10) = 5$$
$$10 - 1 \cdot (10) = 0$$
$$0 - (-1) \cdot (10) = 10$$

X_4 row

$$20 - 14 \cdot (0) = 20$$
$$0 - 0 \cdot (0) = 0$$
$$1 - 0 \cdot (0) = 1$$
$$0 - 1 \cdot (0) = 0$$
$$1 - 0 \cdot (0) = 1$$
$$0 - 1 \cdot (0) = 0$$
$$0 - (-1) \cdot (0) = 0$$

The largest negative $(C_j - Z_j)$ column of Table 14–13 is X_5 (the $-10M$ is very large), and the row to be replaced is X_3 ($^{10}\!/_{10}$ is chosen,

TABLE 14–13
Second solution

C_j	Solution variables	Solution values	M X_3	0 X_4	M X_6	2 X_1	8 X_2	0 X_5
M	$\rightarrow X_3$	10	1	0	-10	5	0	10
0	X_4	20	0	1	0	1	0	0
8	X_2	14	0	0	1	0	1	-1
	Z_j	$112 + 10M$	M	0	$8 - 10M$	$5M$	8	$-8 + 10M$
	$C_j - Z_j$		0	0	$11M - 8$	$2 - 5M$	0	$8 - 10M$

↑

since $2/\!\!/0$ is not mathematically defined, and $14/\!\!-1$ is not eligible, since the ratio is negative).[3]

Table 14–14 is the third simplex table of this example. The new X_5 row is computed by dividing the old X_3 row by 10, the value in the X_5 column and X_3 row of Table 14–13. A computation of the X_4 row and the X_2 row follows:

X_4 row

$$
\begin{aligned}
20 - \quad 1 \cdot (0) &= 20 \\
0 - \tfrac{1}{10} \cdot (0) &= 0 \\
1 - \quad 0 \cdot (0) &= 1 \\
0 - (-1) \cdot (0) &= 0 \\
1 - \tfrac{1}{2} \cdot (0) &= 1 \\
0 - \quad 0 \cdot (0) &= 0 \\
0 - \quad 1 \cdot (0) &= 0
\end{aligned}
$$

X_2 row

$$
\begin{aligned}
14 - \quad 1 \cdot (-1) &= 15 \\
0 - \tfrac{1}{10} \cdot (-1) &= \tfrac{1}{10} \\
0 - \quad 0 \cdot (-1) &= 0 \\
1 - (-1) \cdot (-1) &= 0 \\
0 - \tfrac{1}{2} \cdot (-1) &= \tfrac{1}{2} \\
1 - \quad 0 \cdot (-1) &= 1 \\
-1 - \quad 1 \cdot (-1) &= 0
\end{aligned}
$$

The largest negative $(C_j - Z_j)$ column of Table 14–14 is X_1 (X_3 is not negative, since M is very large). The row to be replaced is X_5.

Table 14–15 is the fourth simplex table of this example. The new X_1 row is $(2, \tfrac{2}{10}, 0, -2, 1, 0, 2)$; that is, 2 times the old X_5 row. A computation of the X_4 row and the X_2 row follows:

X_4 row

$$
\begin{aligned}
20 - \quad 2 \cdot (1) &= 18 \\
0 - \tfrac{2}{10} \cdot (1) &= -\tfrac{1}{5} \\
1 - \quad 0 \cdot (1) &= 1 \\
0 - (-2) \cdot (1) &= 2 \\
1 - \quad 1 \cdot (1) &= 0 \\
0 - \quad 0 \cdot (1) &= 0 \\
0 - \quad 2 \cdot (1) &= -2
\end{aligned}
$$

X_2 row

$$
\begin{aligned}
15 - \quad 2 \cdot (\tfrac{1}{2}) &= 14 \\
\tfrac{1}{10} - \tfrac{2}{10} \cdot (\tfrac{1}{2}) &= 0 \\
0 - \quad 0 \cdot (\tfrac{1}{2}) &= 0 \\
0 - (-2) \cdot (\tfrac{1}{2}) &= 1 \\
\tfrac{1}{2} - \quad 1 \cdot (\tfrac{1}{2}) &= 0 \\
1 - \quad 0 \cdot (\tfrac{1}{2}) &= 1 \\
0 - \quad 2 \cdot (\tfrac{1}{2}) &= -1
\end{aligned}
$$

---

[3] At this point, it would save several steps if we replaced row X_3 with column X_1. The total saving from using X_1 is greater than the total saving from using X_5, but the simplex method bases its choice of replacing column on unit costs. Without working the problem, we do not know that X_1 is a better choice; thus the use of the simplex method always leads to the correct solution, but not always via the shortest route.

TABLE 14–14
Third solution*

C_j			M	0	M	2	8	0
	Solution variables	Solution values	X_3	X_4	X_6	X_1	X_2	X_5
0	→X_5	1	$\frac{1}{10}$	0	−1	$\frac{1}{2}$	0	1
0	X_4	20	0	1	0	1	0	0
8	X_2	15	$\frac{1}{10}$	0	0	$\frac{1}{2}$	1	0
	Z_j	120	$\frac{8}{10}$	0	0	4	8	0
	$C_j - Z_j$		$M - \frac{8}{10}$	0	M	−2	0	0

* Note that at this point, the artificial variables X_3 and X_6 are no longer in the solution. They could be eliminated in future tables.

With Table 14–15, we have reached an optimum solution. Exactly the same solution could have been reached by maximizing the objective function $P = -2X_1 - 8X_2$ (finding the smallest negative amount).

TABLE 14–15
Fourth solution

C_j			M	0	M	2	8	0
	Solution variables	Solution values	X_3	X_4	X_6	X_1	X_2	X_5
2	X_1	2	$\frac{2}{10}$	0	−2	1	0	2
0	X_4	18	$-\frac{1}{5}$	1	2	0	0	−2
8	X_2	14	0	0	1	0	1	−1
	Z_j	116	$\frac{4}{10}$	0	4	2	8	−4
	$C_j - Z_j$		$M - \frac{4}{10}$	0	$M - 4$	0	0	4

The optimum solution is to use 2 units (or 10 pounds) of A and 14 units (or 140 pounds) of B. This combination leads to a cost of $116, which is the least-cost combination of raw material consistent with the restraints. The end product weighs 150 pounds; there are two units of $X_1 \leq 20$, 14 units of $X_2 \geq 14$; thus the restraints are satisfied. Although we easily solved this problem earlier by graphic analysis, with a more complicated version of the problem (for example, 30 raw materials and 20 restraints), we would find the computerized simplex method more efficient for obtaining an optimum solution.

Example 3: A problem with an unbounded solution

In certain situations, it is possible that the linear programming problem does not have a finite solution. For example, assume that the third simplex table (Table 14–14), when developed in Example 2, appeared as shown in Table 14–16.

TABLE 14–16
Table 14–14 modified

C_j			M	0	M	-16	8	0
	Solution variables	Solution values	X_3	X_4	X_6	X_1	X_2	X_5
0	X_5	1	$\frac{1}{10}$	0	-1	$-\frac{1}{2}$	0	1
0	X_4	20	0	1	0	-1	0	0
8	X_2	15	$\frac{1}{10}$	0	0	$-\frac{1}{2}$	1	0
	Z_j	120	$\frac{8}{10}$	0	0	-4	8	0
	$C_j - Z_j$		$M - \frac{8}{10}$	0	M	-12	0	0

Column X_1 has been changed so that not only is $(C_j - Z_j)$ negative (as it was in Table 14–14) but all coefficients in the X_1 column are negative. In this situation, there is no one optimum solution. If profit was being maximized, an analogous situation would occur if the $(C_j - Z_j)$ total were positive and all coefficients in the column were negative.

In modified Table 14–14 (Table 14–16) the negative $(C_j - Z_j)$ indicates that \$12 of costs are saved for every unit of X_1 injected into the solution. However, the negative coefficients of $-\frac{1}{2}$, -1, and $-\frac{1}{2}$ indicate that for every unit of X_1 injected into the solution, say as a substitute for X_5, the ability to inject additional units will be increased. Thus the desirable action would be to keep adding units of X_1. The more X_1 we use, the higher the profits; the problem does not have a finite optimum solution, since it contains no restriction on X_1.

If the above situation develops, the cause will frequently be a misstated restraint. Business situations properly described will not usually result in an unbounded solution as illustrated above.

Example 4: Multiple solutions

There may be more than one optimal solution to a linear programming problem. In this case, two (or more) corner points[4] have the same optimum profit (or cost).

---

[4] Also, any convex combination of these corner points is also an optimum solution.

Let us again modify the problem in Example 2 to illustrate this. Suppose that the cost of raw material A is $4 per unit rather than $2. Then Table 14-14 (with this modification and leaving out the artificial variables X_3 and X_6) would appear as Table 14-17.

TABLE 14-17
Second modification of Table 14-14

C_j			0	4	8	0
	Solution variables	Solution values	X_4	X_1	X_2	X_5
0	X_5	1	0	½	0	1
0	X_4	20	1	1	0	0
8	X_2	15	0	½	1	0
	Z_j	120	0	4	8	0
	$C_j - Z_j$		0	0	0	0

No $C_j - Z_j$ value is negative, indicating an optimum has been reached. Note, however, that variable X_1 is not a solution variable but $C_1 - Z_1 = 0$. This indicates that variable X_1 can be brought into the solution without increasing or decreasing the cost. If variable X_1 is brought into the solution, the result is the same as that shown in Table 14-15 (except that total cost is $120, since X_1 costs $4 per unit). The two solutions are:

	Solution 1	Solution 2
Raw material A	0	2
Raw material B	15	14
Total cost	$120	$120

Example 5: Degeneracy

A solution known as a degenerate solution may develop when one of the restraints is redundant, i.e., when one of the restraints is not necessary for a solution. For example, if there are two restraints, $X_1 \geq 16$ and $X_1 \geq 30$, the former restraint is not necessary. The restraint stating that X_1 must be equal to or greater than 30 eliminates the need for the restraint that X_1 must be equal to or greater than 16. If X_1 is greater than or equal to 30, it will also be greater than or equal to 16. Most redundant restraints will not be so easily recognized as the above.

Only certain redundant restraints will lead to degeneracy; it is not always a simple matter to predict a degenerate situation. The following illustration shows how to recognize degeneracy and suggests a method of solution which will generally be effective.

Maximize profits, given the profit equation $P = 4X_1 + 3X_2$, and subject to the restraints:

$$4X_1 + 2X_2 \leq 10.0$$
$$2X_1 + \tfrac{8}{3}X_2 \leq 8.0$$
$$X_1 \geq 0.0$$
$$X_2 \geq 1.8$$

This can be interpreted as a problem of assigning two machines to two products, X_1 and X_2 (one machine has 10 hours and the other 8 hours of free time). At least 1.8 units of X_2 must be manufactured.

Written out in full and converted to equalities, the inequalities become:

$$4X_1 + 2X_2 + 1X_3 + 0X_4 + 0X_5 + 0X_6 = 10.0$$
$$2X_1 + \tfrac{8}{3}X_2 + 0X_3 + 1X_4 + 0X_5 + 0X_6 = 8.0$$
$$0X_1 + 1X_2 + 0X_3 + 0X_4 + 1X_5 - 1X_6 = 1.8$$

X_3, X_4, and X_6 are slack variables. X_5 is an artificial variable.

The complete profit function becomes:

$$P = 4X_1 + 3X_2 + 0X_3 + 0X_4 - MX_5 + 0X_6$$

Note that the artificial variable X_5 has a profit factor coefficient of $-M$, where M is a very large number. This insures that X_5 will not appear in the final solution.

The first two simplex tables of this illustration are Tables 14–18 and 14–19.

TABLE 14–18

C_j	Solution variables	Solution values	0 X_3	0 X_4	$-M$ X_5	0 X_6	4 X_1	3 X_2
0	X_3	10	1	0	0	0	4	2
0	X_4	8	0	1	0	0	2	$\tfrac{8}{3}$
$-M$	$\rightarrow X_5$	1.8	0	0	1	-1	0	1
	Z_j	$-1.8M$	0	0	$-M$	M	0	$-M$
	$C_j - Z_j$		0	0	0	$-M$	4	$3 + M$

$\uparrow$

In Table 14–18, column X_2 replaces row X_5.
In Table 14–19, column X_1 is the next replacing column. What row

TABLE 14–19

C_j			0	0	$-M$	0	4	3
	Solution variables	Solution values	X_3	X_4	X_5	X_6	X_1	X_2
0	X_3	6.4	1	0	-2	2	4	0
0	$\rightarrow X_4$	3.2	0	1	$-8/3$	$8/3$	2	0
3	X_2	1.8	0	0	1	-1	0	1
	Z_j	5.4	0	0	3	-3	0	3
	$C_j - Z_j$		0	0	$-M-3$	3	4	0

↑

should be replaced? Dividing the components of the "Solution values" column by the corresponding components of X_1, we obtain:

$$\text{For row } X_3: \quad \frac{6.4}{4} = 1.6$$

$$\text{For row } X_4: \quad \frac{3.2}{2} = 1.6$$

$$\text{For row } X_2: \quad \frac{1.8}{0} = \text{undefined}$$

The choice of row to be replaced is complicated by the fact that both row X_3 and row X_4 are equally acceptable according to the criterion we have established. This is the signal that degeneracy exists. Fortunately, the simplex procedure will generally give the correct answer if we choose *either* of the two rows and later choose the other row if the first choice does not give a solution. Let us replace row X_4 with X_1.

In Table 14–20, all $C_j - Z_j$'s are zero or negative; thus the solution is $X_1 = 1.6$ and $X_2 = 1.8$.

TABLE 14–20

C_j			0	0	$-M$	0	4	3
	Solution variables	Solution values	X_3	X_4	X_5	X_6	X_1	X_2
0	X_3	0	1	-2	$10/3$	$-10/3$	0	0
4	X_1	1.6	0	$1/2$	$-4/3$	$4/3$	1	0
3	X_2	1.8	0	0	1	-1	0	1
	Z_j	11.8	0	2	$-7/3$	$7/3$	4	3
	$C_j - Z_j$		0	-2	$-M+7/3$	$-7/3$	0	0

If we had substituted column X_1 for row X_3, we would obtain the simplex table shown in Table 14–21.

TABLE 14–21

C_j			0	0	$-M$	0	4	3
	Solution variables	Solution values	X_3	X_4	X_5	X_6	X_1	X_2
4	X_1	1.6	$\frac{1}{4}$	0	$-\frac{1}{2}$	$\frac{1}{2}$	1	0
0	$\rightarrow X_4$	0	$-\frac{1}{2}$	1	$-\frac{5}{3}$	$\frac{5}{3}$	0	0
3	X_2	1.8	0	0	1	-1	0	1
	Z_j	11.8	1	0	1	-1	4	3
	$C_j - Z_j$		-1	0	$-M-1$	1	0	0
						$\uparrow$		

The column X_6 has a positive $C_j - Z_j$; thus, X_6 is the next replacing column. The row to be replaced is X_4 (zero divided by $\frac{5}{3}$ is the smallest nonnegative amount, i.e., smaller than 1.6 divided by $\frac{1}{2}$). The new simplex table is shown in Table 14–22. All the $(C_j - Z_j)$'s are negative, and a solution has been reached.

TABLE 14–22

C_j			0	0	$-M$	0	4	3
	Solution variables	Solution values	X_3	X_4	X_5	X_6	X_1	X_2
4	X_1	1.6	$\frac{4}{10}$	$-\frac{3}{10}$	0	0	1	0
0	X_6	0.0	$-\frac{3}{10}$	$\frac{3}{5}$	-1	1	0	0
3	X_2	1.8	$-\frac{3}{10}$	$\frac{6}{10}$	0	0	0	1
	Z_j	11.8	$\frac{7}{10}$	$\frac{6}{10}$	0	0	4	3
	$C_j - Z_j$		$-\frac{7}{10}$	$-\frac{6}{10}$	$-M$	0	0	0

Thus, replacing either row X_4 or row X_3 leads to the same amount of X_1 and X_2, and a profit of 11.8.

To summarize, redundant restraints may lead to degeneracy. A situation of degeneracy will show up through the simplex procedure when two or more rows can equally well be replaced according to the simplex criterion. The solution is to replace either row arbitrarily. This leads to two of the rows being eliminated from the solution. Note that the amount of X_3 becomes zero in the first solution, and the amount of

X_4 becomes zero in the second solution; thus, both X_3 and X_4 are eliminated from the solution by the substitution of X_1 for either X_3 or X_4.

If the choice of the row does not lead to a solution (the simplex tables begin to repeat themselves), then choose the other row at the point where the degeneracy was discovered.

The degeneracy situation can also be identified by examining the graph of this problem, shown in Figure 14–3. Note that the optimum point

FIGURE 14–3

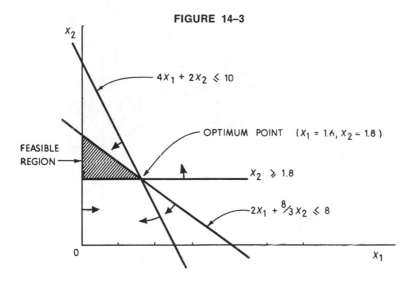

occurs at the intersection of the three constraint equations. Since all the constraints are satisfied exactly, there is no slack in any constraint (i.e., X_3, X_4, and X_6 all equal zero). In a nondegenerate case, at least one of these slack variables would be nonzero.[5]

Example 6: Extension to many dimensions

The previous five examples have involved only two dimensions. To illustrate the formulation and simplex solution of a linear programming problem in many dimensions, the following example is given.

A manufacturing firm makes equipment which utilizes many components. The assembly and testing of the complete unit are done by the firm; but it does not have enough capacity, technical personnel, or funds to produce all the components in its own plants. It therefore must purchase many components from outside suppliers. Seven such components and their requirements are shown in Table 14–23.

---

[5] In general, the number of nonzero variables in the solution equals the number of constraints (other than the $X_j \geq 0$ constraints). Degeneracy results when a solution contains a smaller number of nonzero variables than the number of constraints.

TABLE 14–23

Part number	Variable designation	Hours of machining required	Hours of assembly required	Hours of test required	Engineering supervision required	Working capital funds required	Total number of units needed	Price quoted by outside manufacturer	Variable cost of materials, direct labor, etc.
182...	X_1	5	1	0	1	3	10	$100	$ 50
184...	X_2	2	1	0	1	5	5	150	50
193...	X_3	1	4	2	3	1	50	200	100
197...	X_4	3	0	3	2	1	25	100	50
284...	X_5	1	5	2	2	2	10	250	100
629...	X_6	0	2	2	3	2	5	200	100
845...	X_7	2	1	1	1	4	20	100	40

From Table 14–23, it can be seen that different parts require different amounts of resources and have different outside purchase costs. The question is: Which, if any, of these parts (and how many of each part) should be manufactured internally, and which should be purchased from outside?

We can express this as a linear programming problem in which we maximize savings from internal manufacture, subject to constraints on capacity, personnel, and funds. Let us suppose we have available the amounts of resources shown in Table 14–24.

TABLE 14–24

Hours of machining	90
Hours of assembly	97
Hours of testing	200
Engineering supervisor hours	150
Discretionary cash	$250

We can formulate the linear programming problem as follows:

Maximize:

$$P = 50X_1 + 100X_2 + 100X_3 + 50X_4 + 150X_5 + 100X_6 + 60X_7$$

where X_i is the amount of the ith part manufactured internally and the coefficients are the incremental per unit savings (purchase cost minus variable cost)

Subject to:
$$5X_1 + 2X_2 + X_3 + 3X_4 + X_5 + 0X_6 + 2X_7 \leq 90$$
$$X_1 + X_2 + 4X_3 + 0X_4 + 5X_5 + 2X_6 + X_7 \leq 97$$
$$0X_1 + 0X_2 + 2X_3 + 3X_4 + 2X_5 + 2X_6 + X_7 \leq 200$$
$$X_1 + X_2 + 3X_3 + 2X_4 + 2X_5 + 3X_6 + X_7 \leq 150$$
$$3X_1 + 5X_2 + X_3 + X_4 + 2X_5 + 2X_6 + 4X_7 \leq 250$$

and

$$X_1 \leq 10$$
$$X_2 \leq 5$$
$$X_3 \leq 50$$
$$X_4 \leq 25$$
$$X_5 \leq 10$$
$$X_6 \leq 5$$
$$X_7 \leq 20$$
$$\text{and all } X_j \geq 0, (j = 1, 2, \ldots, 7)$$

The initial tableau is given in Table 14–25, including the slack variables X_8 through X_{19}.

Note that there are 12 constraint equations, and so the main part of Table 14–25 has 12 rows. The initial solution is given by using the slack

TABLE 14–25
Initial solution

C_j	Solution variables	Solution values	0 X_8	0 X_9	0 X_{10}	0 X_{11}	0 X_{12}	0 X_{13}	0 X_{14}	0 X_{15}	0 X_{16}	0 X_{17}	0 X_{18}	0 X_{19}	50 X_1	100 X_2	100 X_3	50 X_4	150 X_5	100 X_6	60 X_7
0	X_8	90	1												5	2	1	3	1		2
0	X_9	97		1											1	1	4		5	2	1
0	X_{10}	200			1												2	3	2	2	1
0	X_{11}	150				1									1	1	3	2	2	3	1
0	X_{12}	250					1								3	5	1	1	2	2	4
0	X_{13}	10						1							1						
0	X_{14}	5							1							1					
0	X_{15}	50								1									1		
0	X_{16}	25									1						1				
0	→X_{17}	10										1						1			
0	X_{18}	5											1							1	
0	X_{19}	20												1							1
	Z_j	0	0	0	0	0	0	0	0	0	0	0	0	0	0	0	0	0	0	0	0
	$C_j - Z_j$		0	0	0	0	0	0	0	0	0	0	0	0	50	100	100	50	150	100	60

↑ (under X_5)

TABLE 14–26
Final solution

C_i	Solution variables	Solution values	C_j 0 X_8	0 X_9	0 X_{10}	0 X_{11}	0 X_{12}	0 X_{13}	0 X_{14}	0 X_{15}	0 X_{16}	0 X_{17}	0 X_{18}	0 X_{19}	50 X_1	100 X_2	100 X_3	50 X_4	150 X_5	100 X_6	60 X_7
100	X_3	3	$\frac{1}{3}$	$\frac{1}{4}$					$-\frac{1}{4}$			$-\frac{5}{4}$	$-\frac{1}{2}$	$-\frac{1}{4}$	$\frac{1}{4}$		1				
50	X_4	9	-1	$-\frac{1}{12}$					$-\frac{7}{12}$			$\frac{1}{12}$	$\frac{1}{6}$	$-\frac{7}{12}$	$\frac{19}{12}$			1			
0	X_{10}	117		$-\frac{1}{4}$	1				$\frac{9}{4}$			$\frac{1}{4}$	$-\frac{3}{2}$	$\frac{5}{4}$	$-\frac{21}{4}$						
0	X_{11}	63	$-\frac{2}{3}$	$-\frac{7}{12}$		1			$\frac{11}{12}$			$\frac{19}{12}$	$-\frac{11}{6}$	$\frac{11}{12}$	$-\frac{35}{12}$						
0	X_{12}	103	$-\frac{1}{3}$	$-\frac{1}{6}$			1		$-\frac{25}{6}$			$-\frac{5}{6}$	$-\frac{5}{3}$	$-\frac{19}{6}$	$\frac{7}{6}$						
0	X_{13}	10						1													
100	X_2	5														1					
0	X_{15}	47	$-\frac{1}{3}$	$-\frac{1}{4}$					$\frac{1}{4}$	1		$\frac{5}{4}$	$\frac{1}{2}$	$\frac{1}{4}$	$-\frac{1}{4}$						
0	X_{16}	16		$\frac{1}{12}$					$\frac{7}{12}$		1	$-\frac{1}{12}$	$-\frac{1}{6}$	$\frac{7}{12}$	$-\frac{19}{12}$						
150	X_5	10										1							1		
100	X_6	5											1							1	
60	X_7	20												1							1
	Z_j	4,450	$50\frac{2}{3}$	$20\frac{5}{6}$	0	0	0	0	$45\frac{5}{6}$	0	0	$29\frac{1}{6}$	$58\frac{1}{3}$	$5\frac{5}{6}$	$104\frac{1}{6}$	100	100	50	150	100	60
	$C_j - Z_j$		$-50\frac{2}{3}$	$-20\frac{5}{6}$	0	0	0	0	$-45\frac{5}{6}$	0	0	$-29\frac{1}{6}$	$-58\frac{1}{3}$	$-5\frac{5}{6}$	$-54\frac{1}{6}$	0	0	0	0	0	0

variables. The initial solution indicates that nothing is manufactured internally and all requirements are purchased from outside suppliers. This, of course, is not the optimum, and it gives a saving of zero.

The simplex method can now be applied to Table 14–25. The first column that should come into the solution is X_5, replacing row X_{17}. We do not intend to carry this problem through all the steps of the simplex procedure, since we wish merely to illustrate the formulation of the problem. However, the final simplex tableau is shown as Table 14–26. The solution gives a saving of $4,450. The meanings of the solution variables are shown in Table 14–27.

TABLE 14–27

Part number	Requirement	Manufactured Variable	Manufactured Amount	Purchased Slack variable	Purchased Amount
182	10	X_1 =	0	X_{13} =	10
184	5	X_2 =	5	X_{14} =	0
193	50	X_3 =	3	X_{15} =	47
197	25	X_4 =	9	X_{16} =	16
284	10	X_5 =	10	X_{17} =	0
629	5	X_6 =	5	X_{18} =	0
845	20	X_7 =	20	X_{19} =	0

For the resource constraints, we have:

Variable	Amount	Meaning
X_8 =	0	All machining hours are used (i.e., slack = 0).
X_9 =	0	All assembly hours are used.
X_{10} =	117	117 hours of test are not used.
X_{11} =	63	63 hours of engineering supervision are not used.
X_{12} =	103	$103 of working capital is not used.

A more detailed economic interpretation of this problem can be made. We shall return to this problem again in Chapter 15.

Example 7: No feasible solution

It is possible for the restraint equations to be inconsistent with a feasible solution. For example, suppose we had

$$4X_1 + 2X_2 \leq 10$$
$$X_2 \geq 6$$
$$X_1 \geq 0$$

There are no values of X_1 and X_2 which will satisfy these three conditions. There would be no solution to such a linear programming problem. In a business setting, this result generally indicates an error in formulating the problem.

CONCLUSIONS

Although emphasis has been placed upon understanding the simplex method, the actual computations in a business problem would generally be done on a computer. Linear programming routines based upon the simplex method are available for most electronic computers.

BIBLIOGRAPHY

See the Bibliography of Chapter 13.

PROBLEMS

14–1. Given:

$$5X_1 + 10X_2 = 150$$
$$0 \le X_1 \le 20$$
$$X_2 \ge 14$$

Use the simplex method to find the values of X_1 and X_2 which maximize the function $P = -2X_1 - 8X_2$.

14–2. Given:

$$4X_1 + 2X_2 \le 10$$
$$2X_1 + \tfrac{8}{3}X_2 \le 8$$
$$0 \le X_1 \le 6$$
$$X_2 \ge 0$$

Use the simplex method to find the values of X_1 and X_2 which maximize the function $P = 4X_1 + 3X_2$.

14–3. Given:

$$4X_1 + 2X_2 \le 10$$
$$2X_1 + \tfrac{8}{3}X_2 \le 8$$
$$0 \le X_2 \le 6$$
$$X_1 \ge 0$$

Use the simplex method to find the values of X_1 and X_2 which maximize the function $P = 4X_1 + 3X_2$.

14–4. Given:

$$3X_1 + 2X_2 \ge 12$$
$$\tfrac{1}{2}X_1 + X_2 \ge 4$$
$$X_1 \ge 0$$
$$X_2 \ge 0$$

Use the simplex method to find the values of X_1 and X_2 which minimize the function $C = 6X_1 + 4X_2$.

14–5. The ABC Company has the option of producing two products during periods of slack activity. For the next week, production has been scheduled so that the milling machine is free 10 hours and skilled labor will have 8 hours of available time.

Product A requires four hours of machine time and two hours of skilled labor per unit. Product B requires two hours of machine time and two hours of skilled labor per unit.

Product A contributes $5 per unit to profit, and product B contributes $3 per unit to profit (not including skilled labor or machine time cost).

Use the simplex method to find the amounts of product A and product B which should be produced.

14–6. The XYZ Company combines factors A and B to form a product which must weigh 50 pounds. At least 20 pounds of A and no more than 40 pounds of B can be used. The cost of A is $10 per pound; of B, $25 per pound.

Use the simplex method to find the amounts of factor A and factor B which should be used.

14–7. The Z Company combines factors A and B to form a product which must weigh 50 pounds. At least 20 pounds of A and no more than 40 pounds of B can be used. A costs $25 per pound, and B costs $10 per pound.

Use the simplex method to find the amounts of factor A and factor B which should be used.

14–8. The Ajax Nut Company sells mixed nuts of two quality levels. The more expensive mix has a higher proportion of cashews, whereas the cheaper mix contains more peanuts.

The prices of nuts purchased by Ajax are: cashews, 50 cents a pound; peanuts, 20 cents a pound. The two mixes sold by Ajax and their prices are: mixture A, 80 cents a pound; mixture B, 40 cents a pound. Ajax can sell any amount of each of these mixtures but, due to a shortage of nuts, can obtain no more than 200 pounds of cashews and 400 pounds of peanuts.

Management has decided that mixture A should not contain more than 25 percent peanuts nor less than 40 percent cashews. Mixture B should have no more than 60 percent peanuts and no less than 20 percent cashews.

How should Ajax mix its nuts? That is, how many pounds of mixture A should be produced (and what should be its composition), and how many pounds of mixture B (and its composition)? Formulate the simplex table and solve.

14–9. The advertising department of a certain firm wishes to plan its advertising strategy to reach certain minimum percentages of high-

and low-income groups. Two alternatives are considered—television and magazines. Magazine advertising has an exposure for the high-income group of 2 percent per page, but only a 1 percent per page exposure for the low-income group. Television, on the other hand, exposes 3 percent of the low-income group per show and only 1 percent of the high-income group per show.

Magazine advertising costs $1,000 per page; television, $4,000 per show. If the firm wants a minimal exposure of 50 percent of the high-income group and 30 percent of the low-income group, what strategy should it use to minimize advertising cost? (*Note:* If a person views a show twice, or reads an advertisement twice, or views a show and reads an advertisement, this counts as double exposure. Exposure greater than 100 percent is thus possible.)

Formulate the above as a linear programming problem and solve.

14–10. Solve the following problem by using the simplex method.

Maximize: $P = 3X_1 + 2X_2$
Subject to: $X_1 + 2X_2 \le 6$
$2X_1 + X_2 \le 6$
$X_1, X_2 \ge 0$

15

Linear programming: The dual problem and sensitivity analysis

Every linear programming problem that we have solved has been of the type designated as "primal," the primal being the first problem to which our attention is generally directed. Each primal problem has a companion problem which is called the "dual." The dual has the same optimum solution as the primal, but it is derived by an alternative procedure, and the analysis of this procedure may be instructive for several types of decision problems.

Frequently, the economic problem being solved as the primal involves the maximization of an objective function (for example, profits), subject to constraints that are frequently of a physical nature (such as hours of machine time). In this type of situation the dual involves the minimization of total opportunity costs, subject to the opportunity cost (or equivalently, the value) of the inputs of each product being equal to or greater than the unit profit of the product. We shall discuss further the economic interpretation of the dual after investigating a specific example.

Example: The primal

Assume that two products, X_1 and X_2, are manufactured on two machines, 1 and 2.

Product X_1 requires three hours on machine 1 and one-half hour on machine 2.

Product X_2 requires two hours on machine 1 and one hour on machine 2.

There are six hours of available capacity on machine 1 and four hours on machine 2.

Each unit of X_1 produces a net increase in profit of \$12, and each unit of X_2 an incremental profit of \$4.

The objective function (or profit function) to be maximized is:

$$P = 12X_1 + 4X_2$$

or, after including the slack variables:

$$P = 12X_1 + 4X_2 + 0X_3 + 0X_4$$

The restraints are:

$3X_1 + 2X_2 \leq 6$ There are six hours available on machine 1. Each unit of X_1 requires three hours; X_2 requires two hours.

$\frac{1}{2}X_1 + X_2 \leq 4$ There are four hours available on machine 2. Each unit of X_1 requires one-half hour; X_2 requires one hour.

$X_1 \geq 0, X_2 \geq 0$ The X's cannot be negative. (We cannot produce a negative amount of product.)

After slack variables are introduced to convert the inequalities into equalities, we have:

$$3X_1 + 2X_2 + X_3 + 0X_4 = 6$$
$$\frac{1}{2}X_1 + X_2 + 0X_3 + X_4 = 4$$

The successive simplex tables are shown in Tables 15–1 and 15–2.

TABLE 15–1

C_j			0	0	12	4
	Solution variables	Solution values	X_3	X_4	X_1	X_2
0	$\rightarrow X_3$	6	1	0	3	2
0	X_4	4	0	1	$\frac{1}{2}$	1
	Z_j	0	0	0	0	0
	$C_j - Z_j$		0	0	12	4

$\uparrow$

All the $(C_j - Z_j)$'s are ≤ 0; thus a solution has been reached. Two units of X_1 should be produced, and this will result in a profit of \$24. No other combination of products will result in as high a profit. For

TABLE 15–2

C_j	Solution variables	Solution values	0 X_3	0 X_4	12 X_1	4 X_2
12	X_1	2	$\frac{1}{3}$	0	1	$\frac{2}{3}$
0	X_4	3	$-\frac{1}{6}$	1	0	$\frac{2}{3}$
	Z_j	24	4	0	12	8
	$C_j - Z_j$		-4	0	0	-4

example, producing one unit of X_1 and 1.5 units of X_2 results in a profit of $12 \cdot 1 + \$4 \cdot 1.5$, or \$18. We cannot produce one unit of X_1 and two units of X_2, since this would require more hours than are available on machine 1.

The inclusion of three units of X_4 in the solution indicates that machine 2 will be idle for three hours.

Example: The dual

Continuing the example, we shall examine the dual problem. The following characterizes the dual:

1. If the objective function is *maximized* in the primal, the objective function of the dual is *minimized*. In this example the objective function of the primal is a profit equation, so the objective function of the dual will be a cost equation.

2. The coefficients of the variables of the cost equation (the dual objective function) are the right-hand-side constants of the primal restraints. In this example, they are six and four, and represent the hours of each machine available. The variables U_1 and U_2 of the cost equation of the dual are the respective costs per hour of using machine 1 and machine 2.[1] The cost equation (or objective function) is:

$$C = 6U_1 + 4U_2$$

3. The restraints are formed by *transposing* the coefficients used in the primal. In the primal the equations and coefficients were:

Equation	Coefficients	
$3X_1 + 2X_2 \leq 6$	3	2
$\frac{1}{2}X_1 + X_2 \leq 4$	$\frac{1}{2}$	1

---

[1] The U_1 and U_2 are opportunity cost measures and are not related to conventional accounting costs.

The transposition is as follows (A^T indicates that A has been transposed):

$$A = \begin{pmatrix} 3 & 2 \\ \frac{1}{2} & 1 \end{pmatrix}$$

$$A^T = \begin{pmatrix} 3 & \frac{1}{2} \\ 2 & 1 \end{pmatrix}$$

The first column of A becomes the first row of A^T, and the second column of A becomes the second row of A^T.

The constants for the dual restraints are obtained from the profit function (the objective function) of the primal. Thus the constants will be 12 and 4.

4. If we are maximizing a primal objective function and if the restraints of the primal are "less than or equal to," the restraints of the dual will be "greater than or equal to." Thus the restraints are:

$$3U_1 + \frac{1}{2}U_2 \geq 12$$
$$2U_1 + U_2 \geq 4$$

If this entire procedure is performed on the dual, the original (primal) problem will be obtained. Thus the dual of the dual is the primal.

The interpretation of these restraints should help clarify the relationship between the primal and dual problems. The first inequality states that the time to produce product X_1 on machine 1 (three hours) times the opportunity cost per hour of using machine 1 (U_1) plus the time to produce product X_1 on machine 2 (one-half hour) times the cost per hour of using machine 2 (U_2) is greater than or equal to $12. The $12 is the net profit of a unit of X_1 (see the profit function of the primal). Thus the opportunity cost of producing X_1 is going to be either equal to the net profit (in which case X_1 will be produced) or greater than the net profit (in which case no units of X_1 will be produced).

The interpretation of the second restraint is similar. The total cost per unit of producing product X_2 is $2U_1$ (cost of using machine 1) plus U_2 (cost of using machine 2). The total cost per unit is equal to or greater than $4, where $4 is the net increase in profit per unit of product X_2. Thus the cost of producing X_2 is going to be either equal to the net profit per unit of X_2 (in which case X_2 will be produced) or greater than the net profit (in which case no units of X_2 will be produced).

It should be noted that the form of solution does not allow the opportunity costs of producing either product to be less than the incremental profit of the product. This is reasonable, since the value of the machine-hours is measured by the profit they can produce. To have the total costs less than the profit would imply that we should produce more units of the product; but if the product is produced to the limit of productive capacity, the costs of the last unit will be equal to the profit. The only time the costs will be greater than the incremental profit will be when it is not desirable to produce any units of the product. Remember that these are opportunity, not accounting, costs.

The restraint equations, expanded to include slack variables and artificial variables, are:

$$3U_1 + \tfrac{1}{2}U_2 - U_3 + 0U_4 + U_5 + 0U_6 = 12$$
$$2U_1 + U_2 + 0U_3 - U_4 + 0U_5 + U_6 = 4$$

The expanded cost equation is:

$$C = 6U_1 + 4U_2 + 0U_3 + 0U_4 + MU_5 + MU_6$$

The large coefficient M is assigned to U_5 and U_6 in the expanded cost equation to drive these two variables from the solution; this is done because U_5 and U_6 are artificial variables.

Since we are minimizing a cost function, the replacing column of the simplex tables of this example (Tables 15–3, 15–4, and 15–5) will be the column with the largest negative $(C_j - Z_j)$.

TABLE 15–3

C_j			M	M	0	0	6	4
	Solution variables	Solution values	U_5	U_6	U_3	U_4	U_1	U_2
M	U_5	12	1	0	-1	0	3	$\tfrac{1}{2}$
M	$\rightarrow U_6$	4	0	1	0	-1	2	1
	Z_j	$16M$	M	M	$-M$	$-M$	$5M$	$\tfrac{3}{2}M$
	$C_j - Z_j$		0	0	M	M	$6 - 5M$	$4 - \tfrac{3}{2}M$
							$\uparrow$	

TABLE 15–4

C_j			M	M	0	0	6	4
	Solution variables	Solution values	U_5	U_6	U_3	U_4	U_1	U_2
M	$\rightarrow U_5$	6	1	$-\tfrac{3}{2}$	-1	$\tfrac{3}{2}$	0	-1
6	U_1	2	0	$\tfrac{1}{2}$	0	$-\tfrac{1}{2}$	1	$\tfrac{1}{2}$
	Z_j	$12 + 6M$	M	$3 - \tfrac{3}{2}M$	$-M$	$-3 + \tfrac{3}{2}M$	6	$3 - M$
	$C_j - Z_j$		0	$\tfrac{5}{2}M - 3$	M	$3 - \tfrac{3}{2}M$	0	$1 + M$
						$\uparrow$		

TABLE 15–5

C_j			M	M	0	0	6	4
	Solution variables	Solution values	U_5	U_6	U_3	U_4	U_1	U_2
0	U_4	4	$\frac{2}{3}$	-1	$-\frac{2}{3}$	1	0	$-\frac{2}{3}$
6	U_1	4	$\frac{1}{3}$	0	$-\frac{1}{3}$	0	1	$\frac{1}{6}$
	Z_j	24	2	0	-2	0	6	1
	$C_j - Z_j$		$M-2$	M	2	0	0	3

The minimum of the cost equation is \$24 (see Z_0 of Table 15–5 of the dual). This is equal to the maximum of the profit equation (see Z_0 of Table 15–2 of the primal).

Table 15–5 gives a solution, since all columns have positive $(C_j - Z_j)$ totals. U_1 has a value of \$4, U_2 and U_3 both equal zero, and U_4 has a value of \$4. In the next section, we shall study the significance of these values.

SHADOW PRICES

The economic interpretation of the dual values is of considerable useful-ness. First, consider the dual variables U_1 and U_2. U_1 has a value of \$4, which means an hour of time of machine 1 has a value of \$4. The actual cost of renting additional capacity of machine 1 may be greater or less than \$4. If it is less (say \$3), then the company should consider renting some additional capacity of machine 1, since for each additional hour of available capacity which is rented the return is \$4, whereas the cost is \$3, resulting in an incremental gain of \$1.[2] The value of U_2 is zero, which means the "cost" of an hour of time on machine 2 is zero. This is consistent with the fact that machine 2 has idle hours follow-ing the optimum schedule of production, and profit would not be in-creased by making more time on machine 2 available. The cost informa-tion evolved, using the dual of the linear programming primal problem, is sometimes referred to as a "shadow price."

Shadow prices can be interpreted as the "cost" of a constraint. We can say that a unit of slack of machine 1, which has only six hours available, "costs" at a rate of \$4 per hour (U_1 has a value of \$4 per

---

[2] This statement is true only until the solution mix changes. At some point, as we continue to increase available hours of machine 1, machine 2 will become a bottleneck, and the value of U_1 will fall, reflecting this complication. Thus the cost information obtained from dual variables will only hold true within a certain range. See below for the method of determining this range.

unit). It would be worth $4 per hour in increased profitability to obtain an additional hour on machine 1 (e.g., use a second shift). Thus *the shadow price measures the value or worth of relaxing a constraint by acquiring an additional unit of that factor of production.*

Now consider the dual slack variables, U_3 and U_4. The dual slack variables measure the *opportunity loss* involved in production of the corresponding primal variable. Since U_3 is the slack variable in the first dual constraint, it corresponds to X_1 in the primal. Similarly, U_4 corresponds to X_2. U_4 has a value of $4; this means that the cost of forcing a unit of X_2 into the solution is $4.[3] U_3 has a value of zero, which means that there is no opportunity loss involved in producing X_1. Thus, X_1 is being produced in positive quantity in the optimal solution, whereas X_2 is not being produced. If there is a positive opportunity loss associated with a variable, it will have the value of zero in the optimal solution; conversely, if the opportunity loss associated with a variable is zero, the variable will take on some positive value in the optimal solution.

Note that the values of four for U_1 and U_4 are the same (except for the sign) as the $(C_j - Z_j)$ values for X_3 and X_2 in Table 15–2. This is not a coincidence. The U values of the dual solution are uniquely the $(C_j - Z_j)$ values of corresponding variables in the primal solution. By corresponding variables, it is meant that dual ordinary variables (U_1 and U_2) are associated with primal slack variables (X_3 and X_4, respectively), and dual slack variables (U_3 and U_4) are associated with primal ordinary variables (X_1 and X_2, respectively). These associations make sense, since the dual ordinary variable U_1 measures the opportunity cost per hour of using machine 1, and the primal slack variable X_3 represents the amount of unused capacity of machine 1. Similarly the $(C_j - Z_j)$ values of the dual give the values of the corresponding variables in the primal solution. Thus the simplex table provides both the primal solution and (through the $C_j - Z_j$ values) the values of the dual variables.

Based on the above analysis we can state that the following products are always zero:

$$X_3U_1 = X_4U_2 = 0$$
$$X_1U_3 = X_2U_4 = 0$$

The first products are those of a primal slack variable and the corresponding dual ordinary variable. If a constraint is binding, the primal

---

[3] If we forced a unit of X_2 to be produced, the constraint representing hours on machine 1 would force us to reduce production of X_1 to four thirds of a unit. Our profit would now be $12(4/3) + 4(1) = 20, a drop of $4 from the optimal profit of $24. Hence, U_4 is $4.

slack variable will be zero (as is X_3 in our example), while if a constraint is not binding, then the shadow price of that constraint (U_2 in our example) will be zero. The second products involve a primal ordinary variable and the corresponding dual slack variable. If a primal ordinary variable (here X_1) is positive, the opportunity loss (here U_3) associated with that product will be zero. If an opportunity loss is positive (here U_4) then the corresponding primal ordinary variable (X_2) will be zero. These relationships always hold at the optimum solution.

Another example

Example 6 of Chapter 14 (p. 251) was a somewhat complex linear programming problem. It would be helpful to return to this example and interpret the economic information in the solution. The final solution of this example is reproduced as Table 15–6.

The last row ($C_j - Z_j$) lists the shadow prices. The variables X_8 through X_{12} are the slack variables associated with the constraints on resources (hours of capacity, personnel, and funds). When such slack variables have a zero shadow price (as do X_{10}, X_{11}, and X_{12}), we cannot increase profits by making more of the resources available. The resources are not fully utilized in the optimum solution (e.g., there are $X_{10} = 117$ hours of test unused). On the other hand, the shadow prices associated with X_8 and X_9 give the increased profit associated with making one more unit of these resources available. For example, we could increase profits nearly $21 by making one more hour of assembly time available (i.e., $C_9 - Z_9 = -20\%$). Profits would be decreased $21 by taking away one unit of assembly time.

The variables X_{13} through X_{19} are the slack variables associated with upper limits on production requirements. The shadow prices refer to additional savings (from internal manufacture) if requirements are increased by one unit. If, for example, one more unit of part 284 (X_5) were required, the savings from internal manufacture would increase by $29.16 (the slack variable for requirements of part 284 is X_{17}, and $C_{17} - Z_{17} = -29\frac{1}{6}$). Conversely, if only 9 units of part 284 were needed instead of 10, then the savings from internal manufacture would decrease by $29.16. If all requirements for a part are not manufactured internally, then if the needs for this part were increased, this would merely increase the number of units purchased outside the firm, without affecting the savings from internal manufacture. In like manner, the needs for the part could decrease without the change affecting the savings (the number purchased outside the firm would simply decrease). In the example, X_4, part 197, has a requirement of 25 units, and of these,

TABLE 15–6

C_i	Solution variables	Solution values	0 X_8	0 X_9	0 X_{10}	0 X_{11}	0 X_{12}	0 X_{13}	0 X_{14}	0 X_{15}	0 X_{16}	0 X_{17}	0 X_{18}	0 X_{19}	50 X_1	100 X_2	100 X_3	50 X_4	150 X_5	100 X_6	60 X_7
100	X_3	3	$\frac{1}{3}$	$-\frac{1}{4}$					$-\frac{1}{4}$			$-\frac{5}{4}$	$-\frac{1}{2}$	$-\frac{1}{4}$	$\frac{1}{4}$		1				
50	X_4	9	-1	$-\frac{1}{12}$					$-\frac{7}{12}$			$\frac{1}{12}$	$\frac{1}{6}$	$-\frac{7}{12}$	$19\frac{1}{12}$			1			
0	X_{10}	117	$-\frac{2}{3}$	$-\frac{1}{4}$	1				$\frac{9}{4}$			$\frac{1}{4}$	$-\frac{3}{2}$	$\frac{5}{4}$	$-21\frac{1}{4}$						
0	X_{11}	63	$-\frac{1}{3}$	$-\frac{7}{12}$		1			$11\frac{1}{12}$			$19\frac{1}{12}$	$-11\frac{1}{6}$	$11\frac{1}{12}$	$-35\frac{1}{12}$						
0	X_{12}	103		$-\frac{1}{6}$			1		$-25\frac{1}{6}$			$-\frac{5}{6}$	$-\frac{5}{3}$	$-19\frac{1}{6}$	$\frac{7}{6}$						
0	X_{13}	10						1							1						
100	X_2	5														1					
0	X_{15}	47		$-\frac{1}{4}$					$\frac{1}{4}$	1		$\frac{5}{4}$	$\frac{1}{2}$	$\frac{1}{4}$	$-\frac{1}{4}$						
0	X_{16}	16	$-\frac{1}{3}$	$\frac{1}{12}$					$\frac{7}{12}$		1	$-\frac{1}{12}$	$-\frac{1}{6}$	$\frac{7}{12}$	$-19\frac{1}{12}$						
150	X_5	10										1							1		
100	X_6	5											1							1	
60	X_7	20												1							1
	Z_i	4,450	$5\frac{2}{3}$	$20\frac{5}{6}$	0	0	0	0	$45\frac{5}{6}$	0	0	$29\frac{1}{6}$	$58\frac{1}{3}$	$5\frac{5}{6}$	$104\frac{1}{6}$	100	100	50	150	100	60
	$C_i - Z_i$		$-5\frac{2}{3}$	$-20\frac{5}{6}$	0	0	0	0	$-45\frac{5}{6}$	0	0	$-29\frac{1}{6}$	$-58\frac{1}{3}$	$-5\frac{5}{6}$	$-54\frac{1}{6}$	0	0	0	0	0	0

only 9 units are to be produced internally; and $C_{16} - Z_{16} = 0$. Savings, as measured by the linear programming model, would not be affected by a small change in the needs for X_4.

The shadow prices for X_1 through X_7 indicate the opportunity loss if one unit of a given part must be included in the solution. For X_2 through X_7 the opportunity losses are zero, and each of these variables is in the solution. $C_1 - Z_1 = -54\frac{1}{6}$ indicates that management would reduce its profit by this much if it required that one unit of X_1 (part 182) must be produced internally.

There is a danger in interpreting shadow prices too literally. If a particular constraint is binding and has a high shadow price, management may add capacity to reduce the bottleneck. As capacity is added, at some point another resource will suddenly become an additional bottleneck, and the shadow prices will change.

We shall turn our attention presently to a consideration of these points. The range over which the shadow prices are valid is discussed under sensitivity analysis, and the question of how much additional capacity to add is considered in the section on parametric programming.

Limitations of the examples

The above examples are typical of a large classification of economic problems, but it is important to note the limitations of the procedures described.

The significant characteristics of the problem from the viewpoint of the present discussion were:

1. The objective function of the primal was being maximized.
2. The sense of the primal restraints was "equal to or less than."

With these characteristics, we proceeded to make the sense of the dual restraints opposite to those of the primal. Unfortunately, different combinations of the above characteristics require different procedures in the dual. Two possibilities are shown in Table 15–7.

TABLE 15–7

If primal has—		Then set up dual—		
Objective function	Sense of restraint equation	Objective function		Sense of restraint equation
Maximize...........	$\leq$	Minimize	$\geq$	(Opposite sense)
Minimize...........	$\geq$	Maximize	$\leq$	(Opposite sense)

We may have a primal with an objective function which we are directed to maximize, but the sense of the restraint equations is "equal to or greater than." We can use the above directions by multiplying the objective function by -1 and changing it from a maximizing to a minimizing problem. For example:

$$\text{Maximize:} \quad f = 2X_1 - 3X_2$$

is equivalent to

$$\text{Minimize:} \quad g = -2X_1 + 3X_2$$

but the change would enable us to construct the dual from the primal.

The analyst may prefer to bypass solving the dual as a by-product of the primal. He may initially solve the problem which might be thought of as the dual. The facts of the situation should indicate how the restraints are to be set up.

Dual variables and degeneracy

The previous section has warned that the values of the dual variables may apply only to a small additional increment to the restraint. Here, we shall show that situations may exist where the dual values do not reflect the change in the objective function. The complication arises in a situation where there is degeneracy.

Example: Assume we want to:

$$\text{Maximize:} \quad P = 12X_1 + 9X_2$$
$$\text{Subject to:} \quad 3X_1 + 2X_2 \leq 7$$
$$3X_1 + X_2 \leq 4$$

The optimum solution is $X_1 = 0$ and $X_2 = 3\frac{1}{2}$, resulting in

$$P = 9 \times \frac{7}{2} = 31\frac{1}{2}$$

The dual to this problem is:

$$\text{Minimize:} \quad C = 7U_1 + 4U_2$$
$$\text{Subject to:} \quad 3U_1 + 3U_2 \geq 12$$
$$2U_1 + 1U_2 \geq 9$$

The solution is $U_1 = 4\frac{1}{2}$ and $U_2 = 0$. If we add one unit to the right-hand side of the first constraint of the primal, we obtain:

$$3X_1 + 2X_2 \leq 8$$
$$3X_1 + X_2 \leq 4$$

The optimum solution is $X_1 = 0$ and $X_2 = 4$, resulting in

$$P = 9 \times 4 = 36$$

The profit has increased by $4\frac{1}{2}$ units, as predicted by the dual value $U_1 = 4\frac{1}{2}$. The graphical presentation is of interest (see Figure 15–1).

FIGURE 15–1

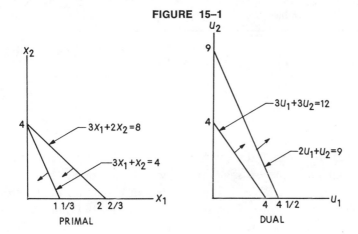

PRIMAL   DUAL

The dual for this situation is:

$$\text{Minimize:} \quad C = 8U_1 + 4U_2$$
$$\text{Subject to:} \quad 3U_1 + 3U_2 \geq 12$$
$$2U_1 + 1U_2 \geq 9$$

We find that this problem has many solutions. Any values for U_1 and U_2 on the line going from $U_1 = 4\frac{1}{2}$ to $U_2 = 9$ will satisfy the above requirements. However, if we add a unit to the first restraint (or the second) of the primal, we will find no change in P (it will still equal 36). The value does not change, since the other unchanged restraint of the primal acts to prevent an improvement unless both restraints are changed. Inspection of Figure 15–1 helps us to understand why this situation can exist. The optimum solution is $X_1 = 0$ and $X_2 = 4$. If we added to either restraint, the other restraint would prevent us from adding to X_2.

SENSITIVITY ANALYSIS

The economic interpretation of the shadow prices (the dual variables) makes linear programming much more valuable to the manager than merely finding the optimum solution. In this section, we shall use sensitivity analysis to determine the range over which the shadow prices are valid.

Let us return to the example at the beginning of the chapter. The final table is repeated in Table 15–8.

TABLE 15–8

C_j			0	0	12	4
	Solution variables	Solution values	X_3	X_4	X_1	X_2
12	X_1	2	$\frac{1}{3}$	0	1	$\frac{2}{3}$
0	X_4	3	$-\frac{1}{6}$	1	0	$\frac{2}{3}$
	Z_j	24	4	0	12	8
	$C_j - Z_j$		-4	0	0	-4

The interpretation of the shadow price on X_3 is that one additional hour of machine time on machine 1 would be worth $4. Recall that X_3 was the slack variable defined to be unused hours on machine 1. We might ask the following question: If we could buy additional hours of machine 1 time for less than $4, could we increase our profit indefinitely by adding more hours?

We can answer this question by examining the X_3 column in Table 15–8. Recall the meaning of the coefficients in the table; if we were to introduce one unit of X_3, it would replace one-third unit of X_1 and $-\frac{1}{6}$ unit of X_4 (i.e., it would actually add one-sixth unit of X_4).

The question posed above, then, can be answered by considering how much X_3 can change before a change in the solution mix will occur.

If we introduce *positive* X_3 into the solution, the interpretation is that additional slack hours are made available on machine 1—and thus those hours to be used for production are *reduced*. In the table the process of introducing X_3 is the same as doing an iteration in the simplex procedure. We divide the "Solution values" column by the amount in the comparable row of the X_3 column. (See page 235 for a review of this step.) The smallest nonnegative number thus obtained gives the number of units of X_3 that can be introduced. In our example:

	Solution values	X_3	Solution values $\overline{X_3}$
X_1.................	2	$\frac{1}{3}$	6
X_4.................	3	$-\frac{1}{6}$	-18

Here the X_1 row is the only positive value, and hence is also the smallest nonnegative value. This means that six units of X_3 can be introduced before variable X_1 goes out of the solution. In terms of the problem, this means that we can cut back a maximum of six hours of those available before production of X_1 stops.

We can also consider adding *negative* X_3. This means that we make additional hours available on machine 1. In order to consider introducing negative X_3 into our tableau, we can proceed as above, except that we must multiply all the values in the X_3 column by -1 before going to the next step in the simplex procedure. Thus, we would have:

	Solution values	$(-1)X_3$	Solution values $(-1)X_3$
X_1.................	2	$-\frac{1}{3}$	-6
X_4.................	3	$\frac{1}{6}$	18

As before, the smallest nonnegative value determines how many units of negative X_3 can be introduced. Here, it is 18; after adding 18 additional hours of time (i.e., negative X_3) on machine 1, we run out of slack time on machine 2 (that is, X_4 goes to zero and out of the solution).

We have derived a range of values relative to the amount of time available on machine 1. We started out with six hours available. Then we found that we could take away 6 hours before the solution mix changed, or we could add 18 hours before the solution mix changed. Hence, we have a range of 0 to 24 for hours available on machine 1, over which the basic solution does not change. Recall that the shadow price for a marginal hour of machine 1 time was $4 (the $C_3 - Z_3$ value in Table 15–8). This value holds over the range we have just determined. In short, machine time on machine 1 has a value of $4 per hour over a range of available hours from 0 to 24 (assuming machine 2 hours remain fixed at 4).

We can make the same kind of analysis relative to the time available on machine 2. Here the slack variable is X_4, and X_4 is in the final solution mix with a value of three (i.e., three unused hours of time on machine 2 are available in the final solution). So we do not proceed as above to look at the coefficients in the X_4 column. However, finding the range over which X_4 can vary without changing the solution mix is relatively simple. With three unused hours available, we know that we can reduce the value of X_4 by only three units before there arises a shortage of machine 2 time and the solution is changed. Also, since we are not currently using all available hours, additional hours can be added indefinitely without changing the solution mix. The original number of hours available on machine 2 was four hours. We have just determined that this can be reduced by three to one hour and increased indefinitely without changing the solution mix or the shadow price of zero associated with X_4 (again, assuming machine 1 hours remain fixed at 6).

A summary of what we have done may be expressed in Table 15–9.

TABLE 15–9

	Original resource constraint (machine-hours available)	Shadow price	Range over which shadow price is valid	
			Lower	Upper
Machine 1 6		$4	0	24
Machine 2 4		0	1	No limit

The above analysis is often referred to as *sensitivity analysis* or *right-hand side ranging* (indicating the limits in the original constant coefficients before the optimum solution mix changes). Many computer programs used to solve linear programming problems provide this kind of sensitivity analysis as part of the output.

An example. Let us turn again to the example used previously in this chapter. The final table was shown in Table 15–6. As an example, the ranges associated with variable X_9—unused assembly time—are determined in Table 15–10.

TABLE 15–10
Determining limits on reduction and addition of assembly hours

Solution variables	Solution values	Determining limit in reduction of hours		Determining limit of additional hours	
			Solution values		Solution values
		X_9	X_9	$-X_9$	$-X_9$
X_3	3	$\frac{1}{4}$	12	$-\frac{1}{4}$	-12
X_4	9	$-\frac{1}{12}$	-108	$\frac{1}{12}$	108
X_{10}	117	$-\frac{1}{4}$	-468	$\frac{1}{4}$	468
X_{11}	63	$-\frac{7}{12}$	-108	$\frac{7}{12}$	108
X_{12}	103	$-\frac{1}{6}$	-618	$\frac{1}{6}$	618
X_{13}	10	0	. . .	0	. . .
X_2	5	0	. . .	0	. . .
X_{15}	47	$-\frac{1}{4}$	-188	$\frac{1}{4}$	188
X_{16}	16	$\frac{1}{12}$	192	$-\frac{1}{12}$	-192
X_5	10	0	. . .	0	. . .
X_6	5	0	. . .	0	. . .
X_7	20	0	. . .	0	. . .

The smallest positive value in the fourth column is 12, associated with variable X_3. Thus, assembly hours can be reduced 12 hours, from the current available 97 to 85, before the solution mix changes.

The smallest positive value in column 6 in Table 15–10 is 108, associated with both X_4 (part No. 197) and X_{11} (engineering supervision hours). Thus, assembly hours can be increased from 97 to 205 before the solution mix changes. Over this range, 85 to 205 hours, the shadow price of $20.83 is valid.

The detailed calculations are not shown for the other variables in this problem, but the ranges are shown in Table 15–11.

TABLE 15–11

Variable name	Associated slack variable	Amount available	Amount used in optimum solution	Shadow price	Lower limit	Upper limit
Resource constraints:						
Machine time	X_8	90	90	$16.67	63	138
Assembly time	X_9	97	97	20.83	85	205
Test time.	X_{10}	200	83	0.00	83	No limit
Supervisory time.	X_{11}	150	87	0.00	87	No limit
Working capital	X_{12}	250	147	0.00	147	No limit
Requirement constraints:						
Part 182	X_{13}	10	0	0.00	0	No limit
Part 184	X_{14}	5	5	45.83	0	17
Part 193	X_{15}	50	3	0.00	3	No limit
Part 197	X_{16}	25	9	0.00	9	No limit
Part 284	X_{17}	10	10	29.17	0	12.4
Part 629	X_{18}	5	5	58.33	0	11
Part 845	X_{19}	20	20	5.83	0	32

Changes in the prices

Another major concern to managers is the sensitivity of the linear programming solution to changes in prices, that is, to changes in the per unit profits (or costs) of variables in the objective function.

In the case of variables that are not in the solution, determining this sensitivity is relatively easy. Recall that the Z_j measures the opportunity cost of introducing one unit of the particular variable into the solution. If the variable is not in the optimum solution, it means that its profitability (C_j) is not as great as the opportunity cost Z_j. In other words, $C_j - Z_j$

is negative.[4] To come into the solution, the profit must exceed Z_j. This is the upper limit before a change occurs. On the other hand, since the variable is not currently profitable enough to be in the solution, any decrease in per unit profit will not change its status.

In summary, for a variable not in the optimum solution, the price ranges are:

Lower limit	Current value	Upper limit
No limit	C_j	Z_j

Within these limits, there is no change in the optimal solution.

As an example, consider variable X_1 in Table 15–6. This variable was the number of units of part No. 182 to be manufactured (see page 252). The current savings from manufacturing this part was $50 (i.e., $C_1 = 50$). From Table 15–6, we see that $Z_1 = 104\frac{1}{6}$. Hence, the savings on X_1 would have to increase from 50 up to over $104\frac{1}{6}$ before any units of this part would be manufactured.

For variables that are already in the solution, determining the sensitivity to per unit profit changes is not so simple. However, the same kind of analysis used above to determine the ranges for the right-hand side coefficients in a primal linear programming problem may also be applied to the dual problem. Recall that in the dual problem, the right-hand side coefficients are the primal prices (the C_j's). Hence, by using the dual problem, we can determine the sensitivity of the optimal solution to changes in the cost or profit coefficients.

Refer to the example described by Table 15–5. The profits associated with the two products were $12 and $4, respectively. In the first dual table (Table 15–3), these were the constant coefficients in the "Solution values" column. The slack variables (in the dual) associated with these two prices are U_3 and U_4, respectively. Using the same procedures described above, the range on the price coefficients can be determined as shown in Table 15–12.

Recall that the solution of this problem called for the production of two units of X_1 and zero units of X_2. Table 15–12 indicates that this solution will not change unless the profit from a unit of X_1 drops below $6 per unit or the profit from a unit of X_2 increases to above $8 per unit.

---

[4] This is true if we are maximizing. If we are minimizing, then the variable will come into the solution if the cost drops below Z_j.

TABLE 15–12

Variable	Associated slack variable	Original value	Range Lower limit	Range Upper limit
Price of X_1........	U_3	$12	$6	No limit
Price of X_2........	U_4	4	No limit	$8

This kind of information is very valuable to management. The C_j's are usually subject to change from time to time. If the changes are within the range determined by the sensitivity analysis, then there is no effect upon the optimum solution.[5] If the changes are outside the range, a new solution is needed, and the programming problem must be re-solved.

The linear programming problem is set up as a decision problem under certainty. Few problems in the real world are truly certain. Often, many factors are unknown and must be estimated using the best judgment available. The use of sensitivity analysis helps to show over what ranges the solution is and is not subject to change. As such, it is an important adjunct to the interpretation of the solution of a linear programming problem.

Addition of new products

The dual solution (and the shadow prices) give the opportunity costs of using the scarce resources in the linear programming problem. In our examples, availability of time on machines has been the scarce factor. It is possible to use these shadow prices to evaluate the value of adding new products or new production processes. Consider the example given in Table 15–6 and Table 15–11. Suppose a new part is introduced and the question is raised whether it should be manufactured internally or purchased outside. The new part requires two hours of machine time, one hour of assembly time, two hours of test time, one-half hour of supervisory time, and 50 cents of working capital. The variable savings from manufacturing the new part internally are $50 per unit.

The opportunity cost of producing this part internally can be determined by multiplying the shadow prices by the requirements, as shown in Table 15–13.

[5] One weakness may be stated, however. The sensitivity analysis described above considers only one variable at a time, with all others held at their original values. A more sophisticated type of analysis would be needed to discover whether the shadow prices changed if, for example, C_1 dropped to $6 *and* C_2 rose to $8.

TABLE 15–13

Scarce resource (1)	Shadow price (2)	Amount required (3)	Opportunity cost (4) = (2) × (3)
Machine time	$16.67	2	$33.33
Assembly time	20.83	1	20.83
Test time.	0.00	2	0.00
Supervisory time.	0.00	½	0.00
Working capital.	0.00	½	0.00
Total opportunity cost.			$54.16

Since the opportunity cost is greater than the incremental savings ($50), the part would not be produced internally. Had the opportunity cost been less than $50, it would have been profitable to produce at least some units of the new part.[6]

PARAMETRIC PROGRAMMING

Sensitivity analysis is concerned with defining a range of values about the optimum solution within which shadow prices remain unchanged. Sometimes it is of interest to examine the changes in the linear programming solution as a given variable is changed over a wide range of values.[7] This type of analysis is called *parametric programming*.

An example will help to illustrate this. Consider the following problem:

$$\text{Maximize:} \quad P = 5X_1 + 8X_2$$
$$\text{Subject to:} \quad 2X_1 + X_2 \leq 14$$
$$X_1 + 3X_2 \leq 12$$
$$X_2 \leq 3$$

Let us suppose the first two constraints represent time used on machine 1 and machine 2, respectively, to produce units of product X_1 and X_2. The third constraint indicates that not more than three units of product X_2 can be sold. This set of constraints is shown graphically in Figure 15–2. The shaded area represents the feasible region.

---

[6] As with the shadow prices, this opportunity cost is good only over a limited range. It is possible to determine the range from the simplex table, and the reader is referred to advanced texts, such as W. W. Garvin, *Introduction to Linear Programming* (New York: McGraw-Hill Book Co., 1960).

[7] We are concerned in this chapter only with variations in one variable at a time. The technique may be extended to consider variations in several variables—in fixed proportions to each other—all at the same time. See *ibid*.

FIGURE 15–2

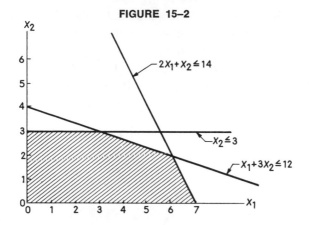

Suppose that we have an additional constraint on working capital, where X_1 and X_2 each require \$1 of working capital per unit:

$$X_1 + X_2 \leq K$$

This states that the total amount of working capital used must be less than an unspecified amount, K. We are interested in knowing how the solution to the problem changes as K varies from zero on up.

If $K = 0$, the only solution is that of no production and $X_1 = X_2 = 0$. As K increases, say up to one, the first dollar of working capital is used to produce one unit of X_2, since X_2 is the more profitable product. Hence, at this stage, each unit of K (i.e., each dollar of working capital) produces \$8 of profit. This holds true until the situation described in Figure 15–3 is reached.

In Figure 15–3, three units of K are available, and all are used to produce units of X_2. However, at this point the market constraint

FIGURE 15–3

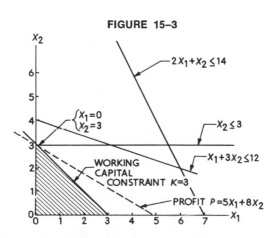

$(X_2 \leq 3)$ becomes binding, and additional units of X_2 cannot be produced. Additional units of working capital now are used to produce units of X_1. Hence, at this stage, each dollar of working capital has an incremental value of $5, the profit associated with selling one unit of X_1. This situation remains true until the situation described in Figure 15–4 is reached.

FIGURE 15-4

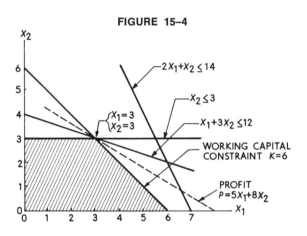

In Figure 15–4 the constraint on time available on machine 2 also becomes binding, at the point at which six units of K are available. Beyond this point, profit can only be increased by moving along the line $X_1 + 3X_2 = 12$, the equation of the constraint on machine 2. This means that for each one-unit reduction in X_2, three units of X_1 can be produced. The incremental value of K now drops to $3.50. (To see this, note that the substitution of one unit of X_2 for three units of X_1 produces $7 additional profit—three times the $5 profit from X_1 minus one times the $8 profit from X_2, or $7. Note also that this requires two units of working capital—three units for the new X_1 less one unit for reduced X_2. Hence the marginal value of K is $7/2, or $3.50.)

Finally, the situation described in Figure 15–5 is reached. Here the constraints on both machine times are binding. Increasing the working capital, K, beyond this point would have no effect on the solution. The marginal value of K at this point becomes zero.

The effects of changes in the value of K are summarized in Figure 15–6. As K increases, the incremental value of additional units of working capital declines in a series of steps—as has been indicated above. The production of X_2 at first increases and later falls; the production of X_1 is zero at first, but then rises up to a level of six units.

An analysis of this sort would be useful to a businessman who was

FIGURE 15–5

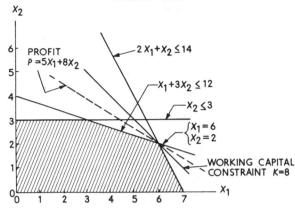

FIGURE 15–6

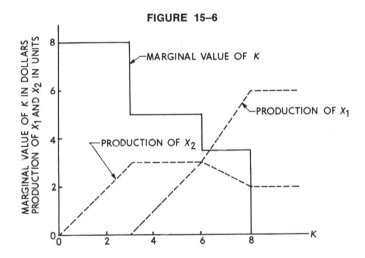

trying to decide how much working capital to invest in this production operation. It is clear he would not invest more than $8. However, he might invest somewhat less if he had profitable alternative uses for his funds. For example, if he could use the working capital elsewhere to return him $4 per unit, then he would not invest more than six units in this operation. Or if he could get a return of $6 per unit elsewhere, he would not use more than three units in this operation.

In building a linear programming model of business systems, often a certain operation is found to be a binding constraint—a bottleneck. Management may consider adding additional capacity. The question arises: How much additional capacity should be obtained? Parametric programming may help answer part of this question by showing what additional revenue or savings will result in adding differing amounts of capacity. When the costs of adding this capacity are determined, then the answer can be obtained.[8]

CONCLUSION

For every linear programming problem, there is a corresponding dual problem. The dual variables contain important information about the implicit values (shadow prices) of capacity constraints of the optimum solution. Sensitivity analysis determines the range over which these shadow prices and unit profits are valid. Parametric programming investigates the changes in the shadow prices and the solution as the capacity in a particular constraint is varied over a wide range of values. These analyses may be even more valuable to a manager than knowing the optimum solution to the linear programming problem. They enable him to make decisions about adding new capacity, about adding new products, about whether the solution changes in response to changes in costs or profitability, and, in general, provide him with an economic interpretation of the optimum solution.

BIBLIOGRAPHY

See the Bibliography of Chapter 13.

PROBLEMS

15–1.   There are two products, X_1 and X_2:

Product	Hours of machine time per unit	Incremental profit per unit
X_1........	4	$2
X_2........	2	4

The machine has four hours of free time.

a)   Using the simplex method, solve the primal and the dual.

b)   Interpret the primal and the dual.

---

[8] The interested reader may attempt to let the linear program solve the problem of additional capacity by defining a new variable, X_3, to represent the increase in capacity. If X_3 is included (with a minus sign) in the relevant capacity constraint and is included in the objective function (with its true cost), then the linear program will solve for the optimal amount of additional capacity.

15–2. Assume two products, X_1 and X_2, are manufactured on two machines, 1 and 2. Product X_1 requires four hours on machine 1 and two hours on machine 2. Product X_2 requires two hours on machine 1 and 8 hours on machine 2. There are 10 hours of excess capacity on machine 1 and 8 hours on machine 2. Each unit of X_1 produces a net increase in profit of $4, and each unit of X_2 an incremental profit of $3.

    a) Determine the maximum profit and the product mix which results in that profit, using the simplex method.

    b) Determine the value of each hour of machine time by solving the dual.

15–3. The XYZ Company has the option of producing two products during periods of slack activity. For the next period, production has been scheduled so that the milling machine is free 10 hours and skilled labor will have 8 hours of time available:

Product	Machine time per unit	Skilled labor per unit	Profit contribution per unit
A............	4	2	$5
B............	2	2	3

    a) Solve the primal problem (the number of units of A and B which should be produced).

    b) Solve the dual problem (the cost of an hour of machine time and an hour of skilled labor).

For Problems 15–4 to 15–7, solve the primal and the dual graphically. For each problem, the primal is described.

15–4. Maximize the objective function:

$$f = 2x_1 + 4x_2$$

subject to restraints:

$$4x_1 + 2x_2 \leq 4$$
$$x_1, x_2 \geq 0$$

15–5. Maximize the objective function:

$$f = 2x_1 - 4x_2$$

subject to restraints:

$$4x_1 + 2x_2 \leq 4$$
$$x_1, x_2 \geq 0$$

15–6. Minimize the objective function:

$$f = 2x_1 + 4x_2$$

subject to restraints:

$$4x_1 + 2x_2 \leq 4$$
$$x_1, x_2 \geq 0$$

15–7. Minimize the objective function:

$$f = 2x_1 - 4x_2$$

subject to restraints:

$$4x_1 + 2x_2 \geq 4$$
$$x_1, x_2 \geq 0$$

15–8. Give a possible economic interpretation of the primal and dual of Problem 15–4.

15–9. Same for Problem 15–5.

15–10. Same for Problem 15–6.

15–11. Same for Problem 15–7.

15–12. The LSM Company can produce two products on two machines. The first product (X_1) sells for $4 and has variable costs of $3 per unit. The second product (X_2) sells for $4.60 and has variable costs of $4.10 per unit. Both products are made on a drill press (X_1 requires 3 hours and X_2 requires 2 hours of time per unit). Product X_1 also requires 5 hours of time on a grinding machine.

There are 12 hours of free time on the drill press and 10 hours of free time on the grinding machine.

a) Using a graphical solution method, solve the primal and the dual. What is the profit for the optimum production mix?

b) Assume one hour of additional drill time can be obtained for no charge. What is the new production mix? The new profit?

c) Assume one hour of additional grinding time can be obtained for no charge. What is the new production mix? The new profit? Compare your answers to (b) and (c) with the dual variables obtained in (a). How much would you pay for an additional hour of time on each machine?

15–13. A manufacturer of television sets made four models—a portable black-and-white set called the Sport, a regular black-and-white set called the Standard, a portable color set called the Traveler, and a regular color set called the Super. Each set required time to assemble and test. The assembly and testing requirements for each model are shown below, together with the amount of time available for assembly and testing. In addition, due to a strike, there was a shortage of picture tubes. The supplier of picture tubes indicated that he would not be able to supply more than a total of 180 picture tubes in the next month; and of these, not more than 100 could be color picture tubes.

	Sport model	Standard model	Traveler model	Super model	Total available
Assembly time (hours)	8	10	12	15	2,000
Test time (hours)	2	2	4	5	500
Marginal profit (dollars)	40	60	80	100	

The manufacturer formulated his decision problem as follows:

Maximize: $P = 40X_1 + 60X_2 + 80X_3 + 100X_4 + 0X_5 + 0X_6$
$+ 0X_7 + 0X_8$

Subject to: $8X_1 + 10X_2 + 12X_3 + 15X_4 + X_5 = 2,000$
$2X_1 + 2X_2 + 4X_3 + 5X_4 + X_6 = 500$
$X_1 + X_2 + X_3 + X_4 + X_7 = 180$
$X_3 + X_4 + X_8 = 100$

In this formulation the variables X_5 through X_8 are slack variables. The problem as formulated was then solved, and the final optimum simplex table is given in Table 15–14.

TABLE 15–14

C_j			40	60	80	100	0	0	0	0
	Solution variables	Solution values	X_1	X_2	X_3	X_4	X_5	X_6	X_7	X_8
0	X_8	50	−0.2		0.2		0.1	−0.5		1
60	X_2	125	0.5	1			0.25	−0.75		
0	X_7	5	0.3		0.2		−0.15	0.25	1	
100	X_4	50	0.2		0.8	1	−0.1	0.5		
	$C_j - Z_j$		−10.0	0	0.0	0	−5.0	−5.0	0	0
	Profit	12,500								

a) What is the optimum production schedule for the television manufacturer? Are there any alternative optimum schedules? What are they?

b) What is the marginal value of an additional hour of assembly time? Over what range of assembly time is this marginal value valid?

c) Suppose that 80 additional hours of test time could be obtained on the outside for $4 per hour. Should this be done? What will be the increase in profit?

d) What is the marginal value of an additional hour of test time? Over what range is this value valid? What constraint next becomes binding as test time is increased?

e) Suppose that a price change is instituted that changes the marginal profit of the Sport model from $40 to $45. Would this change the optimum production plan? If so, what would be the new plan? Suppose that the price of the Sport model changed from $40 to $55. In this case, would there be a change in the production plan? If so, what would be the new plan?

f) Suppose that additional picture tubes can be obtained from another supplier, but at a cost of $2 more than the regular supplier's price for black and white and $5 more for color. Should any of these be purchased? How many?

g) Management is considering the introduction of a new color model called the Mate. The Mate model would require only 10 hours of assembly and 3 hours of test. The marginal profit from this new model would be $70. Should the new model be produced? If so, what will be the marginal value of producing one unit of the Mate model?

15–14. The Paul Bunyan Lumber Company produces pine and fir saw lumber and two types of plywood. The company has a profit contribution of 4 cents a board foot (bf) for pine and 6 cents bf for fir. Type 1 plywood contributes $1.20 per panel and type 2 earns $1.50 per panel.

For the month of December, the company has 2,580 thousand bf (MBF) of pine available for either saw lumber or plywood. Similarly, 2,040 MBF of fir are available. One panel of type 1 plywood requires 16 bf of pine and 8 bf of fir. One panel of type 2 plywood requires 12 bf of each species.

Saw lumber is restricted only by the capacity of the headrig saw. The saw can handle 400 MBF per month of any species.

The plywood mill can be restricted by either the peeler or the dryer. During the month no more than 250 thousand panels of lumber may be peeled, and there are 920 thousand minutes of dryer time available. Each type 1 panel requires 4 minutes of dryer time, and each type 2 panel requires 6 minutes of dryer time.

Market conditions limit the number of type 1 panels sold to no more than 120 thousand and the number of type 2 panels to no more than 100 thousand. Any amounts of saw lumber can be sold.

The company formulated a linear programming model of their operations as follows:

Let

X_1 = MBF of pine saw lumber sold
X_2 = MBF of fir saw lumber sold
X_3 = thousands of panels of type 1 plywood sold
X_4 = thousands of panels of type 2 plywood sold

Maximize: $0.04X_1 + 0.06X_2 + 1.20X_3 + 1.50X_4$
Subject to:

Availability of pine:	X_1	$+ 16X_3 + 12X_4 \leq$	2,580
Availability of fir:		$X_2 + 8X_3 + 12X_4 \leq$	2,040
Sawmill capacity:	$X_1 + X_2$	$\leq$	400
Peeler capacity:		$X_3 + X_4 \leq$	250
Dryer capacity:		$4X_3 + 6X_4 \leq$	920
Market demand, type 1 plywood:		$X_3 \leq$	120
Market demand, type 2 plywood:		$X_4 \leq$	100

Adding appropriate slack variables, the first simplex table is presented in Table 15–15. After several iterations, Table 15–16 is obtained.

a) What is the solution in the second table? Is it optimal? What is the total profit? Are there alternative optimal solutions?
b) Suppose one more unit (thousands of minutes) of dryer time could be made available. What effect would this have on the solution (i.e., what would be the new values for X_1, X_2, X_3, X_4)?
c) What is the incremental profit associated with adding one more unit (thousands of minutes) of dryer time? Over what range is this incremental profit valid?
d) What is the value of additional capacity at the headrig saw in the sawmill? How much is the increase or decrease in this capacity before there is a basic change in the solution variables?
e) Suppose the demand for type 2 plywood could be increased by one unit (thousand panels). What would be the incremental profit of this? Over what range is this valid?
f) A third type of plywood panel is proposed. This would have a profit contribution of $1.60. It would require 8 bf of pine and 16 bf of fir. In addition, the drying time would be 8 minutes. Should any of this type of panel be produced? What would be its incremental profit?

TABLE 15-15

C_j			0	0	0	0	0	0	0	0.04	0.06	1.20	1.50
	Solution variables	Solution values	X_5	X_6	X_7	X_8	X_9	X_{10}	X_{11}	X_1	X_2	X_3	X_4
0	X_5	2,580	1							1		16	12
0	X_6	2,040		1						1	1	8	12
0	X_7	400			1						1		
0	X_8	250				1						1	1
0	X_9	920					1					4	6
0	X_{10}	120						1				1	1
0	X_{11}	100							1				1
	Z_j	0	0	0	0	0	0	0	0	0	0	0	0
	$C_j - Z_j$		0	0	0	0	0	0	0	0.04	0.06	1.20	1.50

TABLE 15-16

C_j			0	0	0	0	0	0	0	0.04	0.06	1.20	1.50
	Solution variables	Solution values	X_5	X_6	X_7	X_8	X_9	X_{10}	X_{11}	X_1	X_2	X_3	X_4
0.04	X_1	100	1				−4.0		12.0	1			
0.06	X_2	200		1			−2.0				1		
0	X_7	100	−1	−1	1		6.0		−12.0				
0	X_8	70				1	−0.25		0.5				
1.20	X_3	80					0.25		−1.5			1	
0	X_{10}	40					−0.25	1	1.5				
1.50	X_4	100							1.0				1
	Z_j	262	0.04	0.06	0	0	0.02	0	0.18	0.04	0.06	1.20	1.50
	$C_j − Z_j$		−0.04	−0.06	0	0	−0.02	0	−0.18	0	0	0	0

16

Linear programming: The transportation problem

There is a type of linear programming problem which may be solved using a simplified version of the simplex technique.[1] Because of its application in solving problems involving several product sources and several destinations of products, this type of problem is frequently called the *transportation problem*. A common characteristic of this type of problem is that all the units available must be assigned. For example, if a source supplies 10 units of a product, an assignment of the 10 units must be made to one or another destination; we cannot assign more or less than 10 units.[2]

BASIC METHOD

In this chapter, we shall describe two possible procedures. The first we shall call the "basic" method. Let us assume there are three factories (F_1, F_2, and F_3) supplying three warehouses (W_1, W_2, and W_3). (See Table 16–1.)

The costs of shipping from each factory to each destination are given in the body of Table 16–2. In the margins of the table are the amounts available at the factories and the requirements of the warehouses.

It is necessary to prepare an initial solution, which may be done in several different ways; the only requirement is that the warehouse needs be met within the constraint of factory production. One popular method is to start in the upper left-hand corner (the northwest corner), first

---

[1] The coefficients of all variables in the restraint equations are either zero or one, and they follow a particular pattern. See the Appendix to this chapter.

[2] This limitation is not really a restriction, since "dummy" sources or destinations may be added to take care of differences between supply and demand. See the Appendix to this chapter.

TABLE 16–1

Factories	Amount available	Warehouses	Amount needed
F_1 20		W_1 5	
F_2 15		W_2 20	
F_3 10		W_3 20	
Total.......... 45		Total 45	

TABLE 16–2
Costs of shipping and physical units

Destination \ Source	F_1	F_2	F_3	Units demanded
W_1	$0.90	$1.00	$1.00	5
W_2	$1.00	$1.40	$0.80	20
W_3	$1.30	$1.00	$0.80	20
Units available	20	15	10	45

supplying the needs of W_1, then W_2, then W_3. Another procedure (the one we shall employ) is to turn to Table 16–2 and find a box which has the lowest value in both its row and its column; place in that box the lower of the values found in its row or its column margin.

A requirement of the initial solution is that the number of routes used must equal the sum of the number of factories, F, plus the number of warehouses, W, minus one; i.e.:

$$\text{Routes used} = F + W - 1$$

If the initial solution uses more routes than $F + W - 1$, then, for one or more zero boxes, there will be more than one possible evaluation. If the initial solution uses less routes than $F + W - 1$, then a problem of degeneracy arises. A method of solving degenerate problems is given later in this chapter.

In establishing early solutions, it is reasonable to aim at using $F + W - 1$ boxes. If more than this number of boxes are used, the solution should be adjusted by making arbitrary changes consistent with the needs of the warehouses and the production capacity of the factories to reduce the number of routes.

The 90 cents in box W_1F_1 of Table 16–2 is the lowest amount in its row and the lowest amount in its column.[3] Since the warehouse only needs 5 units, even though the factory can supply 20 units, we place a 5 in the W_1F_1 box of Table 16–3. In Table 16–3 the costs are in

TABLE 16–3
First solution

Destination \ Source	F_1	F_2	F_3	Units demanded
W_1	$0.90 / 5	$1.00 / 0	$1.00 / 0	5
W_2	$1.00 / 10	$1.40 / 0	$0.80 / 10	20
W_3	$1.30 / 5	$1.00 / 15	$0.80 / 0	20
Units available	20	15	10	45

the upper left corner of each box, the units shipped in the lower right corner.

The 80 cents of costs in W_2F_3 is equal to the 80 cents of W_3F_3. We could take either value, but we shall arbitrarily choose W_2F_3 and place 10 units in that box (the most that can be supplied by factory 3).

To place the remainder of the units, we proceed in a commonsense manner, making certain that no more is taken from a factory than it can produce and no more is sent to a warehouse than it needs. There are 15 units remaining from F_1; we shall assign 10 units to W_2F_1 and 5 units to W_3F_1. The needs of warehouse 2 are satisfied with this allocation.

The 15 units of F_2 are all assigned to W_3F_2, since warehouse 3 is the only location which has unfilled needs.

Table 16–3 shows the first trial solution. Note that five direct routes are used and $F + W - 1$ equals five (i.e., $3 + 3 - 1 = 5$). If possible, we want a solution which uses $F + W - 1$ boxes, to avoid excess routes

---

[3] W_1F_1 indicates that warehouse 1 is being supplied from factory 1.

or degeneracy. We also require that the solution be consistent with the restraints. It would be a coincidence if the trial solution happened to be the optimum solution; but the closer the first solution is to an optimum solution, the less work is required. In any event, we must test to see if costs may be reduced by some rearrangement of routes. Total shipment costs for the first solution are:

$$5(0.90) + 10(1.00) + 10(0.80) + 5(1.30) + 15(1.00) = \$44$$

We shall proceed to test the relative cost advantage of alternative routes. Consider an unused route, such as shipping to warehouse 1 from factory 2 (i.e., box W_1F_2 has a zero entry in its lower right corner). The direct cost of using this route is the amount in the upper left corner of the box, $1; this amount is to be contrasted with the current costs of the indirect route from F_2 to W_1. The indirect route is identified as the path a unit would have to follow from a given factory to a given warehouse, using only established channels (i.e., the shipment must avoid zero boxes; otherwise, we are shipping from a box which has no units, or introducing two new boxes into the solution instead of one). In this case the indirect route from F_2 to W_1 for a unit is (the arrows represent cost flows, not the flow of goods):

	F_1	F_2	F_3
W_1	5		
W_2	↑		
W_3	5	15	

The cost of shipping one unit from F_2 to W_1 by this indirect route is:

+$1.00   Charge for shipping from F_2 to W_3
− 1.30   Every unit F_2 sends to W_3 saves the cost
          of supplying W_3 from F_1
+ 0.90   Charge for shipping from F_1 to W_1
———
+$0.60

The cost of presently avoiding box W_1F_2 is 60 cents (the additional outlay of $1 for using W_3F_2, the saving of $1.30 resulting from not using W_3F_1 to as large an extent as possible and the 90-cent cost of using box W_1F_1). Compared with this total indirect cost, 60 cents, is a cost of $1 which would result from using the direct route W_1F_2; thus the indirect route is to be preferred.

An alternative manner of describing the analysis is to say that the use of W_1F_2 would require the following change in the flow of goods:

	F_1	F_2	F_3
W_1	5	↑	
W_2	↓	↑	
W_3	5	5	

W_1F_1 could supply as many as five units to W_3F_1, and W_3F_2 could supply five units to W_1F_2. The net cost of this indirect route per unit is:

$$
\begin{array}{rl}
+\$1.00 & \text{Cost of } W_1F_2 \\
- 1.00 & \text{Saving of } W_3F_2 \\
+ 1.30 & \text{Cost of } W_3F_1 \\
- 0.90 & \text{Saving of } W_1F_1 \\
\hline
+\$0.40 & \text{Net cost of the change}
\end{array}
$$

The net cost of the change is positive; thus the change is not desirable. If the cost of the direct shipment ($1) is greater than the cost of the indirect shipment (60 cents), as in this case, the direct route should not be used (i.e., the zero entry should be retained). There can be only one indirect route for each zero box, unless the previous trial solution contained more than $F + W - 1$ direct routes.

The other zero boxes may be evaluated in a comparable manner. For example, the indirect shipment from F_2 to W_2 is the charge from F_2 to W_3 ($1) less the W_3F_1 charge ($1.30) plus the W_2F_1 charge ($1) = 70 cents. Again, this is less than the cost of direct shipment ($1.40), so the current indirect route should be continued. The W_1F_3 box is also found to have a 70-cent cost for the indirect shipment; and again, this is less than the direct route cost ($1). However, the evaluation of the last unused route, W_3F_3, yields a cost for the indirect route of

$$\$0.80 - \$1.00 + \$1.30 = \$1.10$$

and this is greater than the direct route cost of 80 cents. The direct route W_3F_3 should be used rather than the indirect route of

$$W_2F_3 - W_2F_1 + W_3F_1$$

since a saving of

$$\$1.10 - \$0.80 = \$0.30$$

per unit can be made by using the direct route. (See Table 16–4.)

TABLE 16-4

Unused route	Cost of direct route	Cost of indirect route
W_1F_2	$1.00	$0.60
W_1F_3	1.00	0.70
W_2F_2	1.40	0.70
W_3F_3	0.80	1.10

How many units can be shifted from the indirect route to the direct route? The answer is the minimum number in any of the connections of the indirect route which must supply units for the transfer. This is five units, from box W_3F_1. Thus, we ship 5 units by the direct route W_3F_3; since F_3 produces only 10 units, this imposes a reduction in the W_2F_3 box to 5. An additional five units now are required at warehouse 2. This deficiency is met readily by factory 1, which has been forced to reduce its shipment to W_3 by exactly five units as a result of W_3's new source of supply. The new pattern is shown in Table 16–5. Again,

TABLE 16-5

Destination \ Source	F_1	F_2	F_3	Units demanded
W_1	$0.90 / 5	$1.00 / 0	$1.00 / 0	5
W_2	$1.00 / 15	$1.40 / 0	$0.80 / 5	20
W_3	$1.30 / 0	$1.00 / 15	$0.80 / 5	20
Units available	20	15	10	45

all of the unused routes, identified by the zero entries in Table 16–5, must be evaluated to see if a further reduction in cost is possible. This may be done in the now established manner shown in Table 16–6. In every case the cost of the indirect route is less than the cost of the direct

TABLE 16–6

Unused route	Cost of using direct route	Cost of using indirect route
$W_3 F_1$	$1.30	$1.00
$W_1 F_2$	1.00	0.90
$W_2 F_2$	1.40	1.00
$W_1 F_3$	1.00	0.70

route, indicating that we are minimizing the shipment costs. The total cost of shipment from factories to warehouses is:

$$(5)(\$0.90) + (15)(\$1.00) + (15)(\$1.00)$$
$$+ 5(\$0.80) + 5(\$0.80) = \$42.50$$

Note that the final solution uses five direct routes, where

$$F + W - 1 = 5$$

F plus W may be generalized and called the sum of the number of margin requirements, since we may be dealing with entities other than warehouses and factories.

Degeneracy: Basic method

In some programming situations the problem of degeneracy appears. Degeneracy is caused by less than $F + W - 1$ boxes being used, which makes it impossible to evaluate a zero box by the direct methods described above.[4]

To resolve the degeneracy case, record some very small amount, say d, in one of the zero boxes. We shall treat d as if it were a standard quantity, and therefore an eligible node for evaluating indirect routes. The box with the d entry may either ship or receive goods, but in the final solution the d is assigned a value of zero if it is still present in the calculations.

Degeneracy example. Consider the same problem as previously discussed, but let us choose a first trial solution that is degenerate. Say the first solution is that shown in Table 16–7. Only four boxes are being used in this trial solution, but $W + F - 1 = 5$; thus the trial solution is degenerate. The zero boxes cannot be evaluated without introducing d. Let us put d units in box $W_1 F_1$, so that the shipping schedule appears as shown in Table 16–8. Total shipping cost for this example is $43.

---

[4] Degeneracy may also occur where a factory ships its entire output to one warehouse and satisfies the total needs of that warehouse.

TABLE 16–7

Destination \ Source	F_1	F_2	F_3	Units demanded
W_1	0.90 / 0	1.00 / 5	1.00 / 0	5
W_2	1.00 / 20	1.40 / 0	0.80 / 0	20
W_3	1.30 / 0	1.00 / 10	0.80 / 10	20
Units available	20	15	10	45

TABLE 16–8

Destination \ Source	F_1	F_2	F_3	Units demanded
W_1	d	5	0	$5 + d$
W_2	20	0	0	20
W_3	0	10	10	20
Units available	$20 + d$	15	10	$45 + d$

The zero boxes now may be evaluated in the established manner. Consider $W_3 F_1$. The cost of the direct route to W_3 from F_1 is \$1.30. The indirect route is from F_1 to W_1, which may be used by virtue of the d, which permits a reduction of shipment from F_2 to W_1; but this in turn requires an increase in the shipment from F_2 to W_3. This completes the indirect shipment from F_1 to W_3, with these costs:

$$
\begin{array}{ll}
W_1 F_1 \dots\dots\dots\dots\dots\dots\dots\dots\dots\dots & \$0.90 \\
-W_1 F_2 \dots\dots\dots\dots\dots\dots\dots\dots\dots\dots & -1.00 \\
W_3 F_2 \dots\dots\dots\dots\dots\dots\dots\dots\dots\dots & \underline{1.00} \\
\text{Cost of indirect shipment from } F_1 \text{ to } W_3 \dots\dots & \$0.90
\end{array}
$$

This indirect route cost is lower than the direct route cost ($1.30); therefore the indirect route should continue to be used. The other zero boxes may be evaluated in the same manner, with the result shown in Table 16–9. The direct route cost of using the zero box is in the upper left

TABLE 16–9

Destination \ Source	F_1	F_2	F_3
W_1			$1.00 / $0.80
W_2		$1.40 / $1.10	$0.80 / $0.90
W_3	$1.30 / $0.90		

corner of the box; the indirect route cost of using the zero box is in the lower right of the zero box. The indirect cost exceeds the direct cost in only one instance, shipping from F_3 to W_2 (this indirect route is F_3 to W_3, less W_3F_2, plus W_1F_2, less W_1F_1, plus W_2F_1). This is the only place it pays to shift from the indirect to the direct route. The maximum amount which can be shifted is five units, since this is the minimum amount in a box which must be reduced (box W_1F_2). The new trial solution is shown in Table 16–10. The zero boxes of this trial solution must be evaluated. This procedure is not subject to degeneracy, for we now have five boxes being used, which meets the standard requirement. As was established before, all these zero boxes have direct route costs which exceed their indirect route costs; thus, this solution is optimal.

Although degeneracy disappeared in one step in our example above, it is possible for degeneracy to remain through several iterations; in fact, the optimal solution may be degenerate.

SAME EXAMPLE: ALTERNATIVE METHOD

Returning to the example in the beginning of this chapter, we shall prepare an array of costs using the direct route costs where the warehouse-factory combination is used in the solution, and the indirect route

TABLE 16–10

Destination \ Source	F_1	F_2	F_3	Units demanded
W_1	$0.90 / 5	$1.00 / 0	$1.00 / 0	5
W_2	$1.00 / 15	$1.40 / 0	$0.80 / 5	20
W_3	$1.30 / 0	$1.00 / 15	$0.80 / 5	20
Units available	20	15	10	45

costs where the combination is not used (there is a line under each in-direct cost) :

	F_1	F_2	F_3
W_1.............	$0.90	$0.60	$0.70
W_2.............	1.00	0.70	0.80
W_3.............	1.30	1.00	1.10

Now, for each warehouse, take the difference between the amounts in columns F_1 and F_2, and note that for each line the difference is 30 cents. We can do the same for columns F_2 and F_3; note the difference for each line is 10 cents. The alternative method is a means of using these relationships to find the cost array reproduced above.[5]

The first trial solution appearing in Table 16-3 would apply here, just as it did in the basic method. Table 16–3 is now separated into three tables (Tables 16–11, 16–12a, and 16–12b). This is done to make the cost information more accessible for computation.

---

[5] The reader is also referred to G. B. Dantzig's paper, "Applications of the Simplex Method to a Transportation Problem," in T. C. Koopmans (ed.), *Activity Analysis of Production and Allocation* (New York: John Wiley & Sons, Inc., 1951). This paper is the basis of the several procedures presented in this chapter.

TABLE 16–11

Destination \ Source	F_1	F_2	F_3	Units demanded
W_1	5			5
W_2	10		10	20
W_3	5	15		20
Units available.	20	15	10	45

TABLE 16–12a
Unit costs: First solution

Destination \ Source	F_1	F_2	F_3	Row value
W_1	$0.90			$0.00
W_2	$1.00		$0.80	$0.10
W_3	$1.30	$1.00		$0.40
Column value	$0.90	$0.60	$0.70	

TABLE 16–12b
Computation of unit costs: First solution

Destination \ Source	F_1	F_2	F_3	Row value
W_1	$0.90			$0.00 ← ① Arbitrary choice
W_2	$1.00		$0.80	$0.10 ← ③ ($1.00 − $0.90)
W_3	$1.30	$1.00		$0.40 ← ④ ($1.30 − $0.90)
Column value	$0.90	$0.60	$0.70	

②   ⑤   ⑥
($0.90 − $0.00)   ($1.00 − $0.40)   ($0.80 − $0.10)

In order to start the calculation, the first-row value is arbitrarily chosen to be zero cents. Each cost figure in the body of Table 16–12a is equal to the sum of amounts in the margins of its row and its column. We have presented Table 16–12b to show the computation of the row values and column values. The steps are numbered in sequential order.

Table 16–13 shows the unit costs of all direct routes; the unit cost of indirect routes is calculated by summing the cost entries in the relevant column and row margins, and these computations are also shown in Table 16–13.

TABLE 16–13
Unit costs and cost savings: First solution

($0.60 + $0.10)   ($0.60 + $0.00)   ($0.70 + $0.00)

Destination \ Source	F_1	F_2	F_3	Row value
W_1	$0.90	$0.60	$0.70	$0.00
W_2	$1.00	$0.70	$0.80	$0.10
W_3	$1.30	$1.00	$1.10	$0.40
Column value.....	$0.90	$0.60	$0.70	

—($0.70 + $0.40)

The next step is to compare the unit costs of each route as shown in Table 16–13 with the costs of Table 16–10. Comparison of the tables shows that only one box of Table 16–13, W_3F_3, is larger than the comparable box of Table 16–10. Thus, that direct route is more desirable than the indirect route presently being used. The basic method indicated the same decision.

Table 16–14 shows the rearrangement of units shipped (X is the number of units transferred). The maximum size of X is five, if we obey the requirement that no deliveries may be negative. Box W_3F_1 is the limiting factor, since it can supply only five units of product.

Table 16–15 shows the number of units shipped from each factory to each warehouse after the adjustment. Table 16–16 shows the unit costs of using the routes specified in Table 16–15. Table 16–17 adds the information concerning the cost saving which will result from using routes not presently being used.

None of the presently unused routes will reduce costs if they are sub-

TABLE 16–14

Add X units

Destination \ Source	F_1	F_2	F_3	Units demanded	
W_1	5			5	
W_2	$10 + X$		$10 - X$	20	Subtract X units
W_3	$5 - X$	15	X	20	
Units available.	20	15	10	45	

Subtract X units   Add X units

stituted for currently employed routes. We have reached an optimum solution, as shown in Table 16–15.

Comparison of the two methods illustrated in this chapter reveals that they differ only in technique. The alternative method would seem to

TABLE 16–15
Units shipped: Second solution

Destination \ Source	F_1	F_2	F_3	Units demanded
W_1	5			5
W_2	15		5	20
W_3		15	5	20
Units available.	20	15	10	45

be simpler to execute, though the basic method tends more to connect the computations with their meaning. Both methods have the desirable feature that an error made in one table may be eliminated in future tables.

In some situations the amount demanded will be less than the amount supplied. The solution is to introduce a destination—say W_4—which

TABLE 16–16
Cost per unit: Second solution

Source Destination	F_1	F_2	F_3	Row value	
W_1	$0.90			$0.00	
W_2	$1.00		$0.80	$0.10 ← ②	($1.00 – $0.90)
W_3		$1.00	$0.80	$0.10 ← ④	($0.80 – $0.70)
Column value.....	$0.90	$0.90	$0.70		

① ($0.90 – $0.00)   ⑤ ($1.00 – $0.10)   ③ ($0.80 – $0.10)

TABLE 16–17
Cost per unit and cost savings: Second solution

($0.90 + $0.00)   ($0.90 + $0.10)

Source Destination	F_1	F_2	F_3	Row value
W_1	$0.90	$0.90	$0.70 ←	$0.00
W_2	$1.00	$1.00	$0.80	$0.10
W_3	$1.00	$1.00	$0.80	$0.10
($0.90 + $0.10) Column value.....	$0.90	$0.90	$0.70	

($0.70 + $0.00)

Box	From Table 16–17: cost of using indirect route	From Table 16–2: cost of using direct route	Net profit (or loss) of using direct route
$W_1 F_2$	$0.90	$1.00	$(0.10)
$W_1 F_3$	0.70	1.00	(0.30)
$W_2 F_2$	1.00	1.40	(0.40)
$W_3 F_1$	1.00	1.30	(0.30)

is a fiction, but which receives the slack. A cost of zero may be placed in these slack boxes, since no transportation is involved.

Degeneracy: Alternative method

In some situations, it is necessary to alter normal procedures because of degeneracy. When the problem is degenerate and the basic method is used, one of the zero boxes cannot be evaluated. That is, one of the boxes being tested for supplying units to the new box does not have any units to supply. In the alternative method of solution, degeneracy makes it impossible to complete the row and column values which are necessary to determine the cost savings of the routes which are currently not being used.

The method of handling degeneracy in the alternative method is the same as that in the basic method. A small amount d is put in one of the unused routes. The calculations for the row and column values can then be performed by treating the amount d as if it were a real amount.

ECONOMIC INTERPRETATIONS

The row and column values calculated in the alternative method and the costs of the indirect routes calculated in both methods have important economic interpretations that are useful in management decisions.

The costs of indirect routes

The costs of the indirect routes are equivalent to the Z_j values in standard linear programming and can be used in the same way. Suppose, for example, after completing our analysis in Tables 16–15 and 16–17, we were informed that the requirements for W_2 had increased one unit, and that the capacity of F_2 would be expanded to handle this increase. What will be the incremental increase in the shipping costs?

The cost of the indirect route for F_2W_2 immediately gives us the answer. The direct route would cost \$1.40, and the indirect only \$1. Hence, the incremental cost of supplying this unit is simply \$1. Table 16–18 shows how the original solution would be modified. Note that up to five units could be shipped using this indirect route.

Changes in shipping costs

We can also examine the sensitivity of the solution to changes in shipping costs. For example, if the shipping cost from F_1 to W_3 (which is now \$1.30) were to change, would our solution change? Note that the

TABLE 16–18
Effect of one additional unit for F_2 and W_2

Destination \ Source	F_1	F_2	F_3	Units demanded
W_1	5			5
W_2	15	5 + 1		20 + 1
W_3		15 + 1	5 – 1	20
Units available.	20	15 + 1	10	45 + 1

cost of the indirect route for $F_1 W_3$ is \$1. The shipping cost would have to fall below \$1 before the direct route was used, i.e., before the solution in Table 16–15 changed.

Locational advantages

Suppose one unit was added to the requirements of W_1 (from five units to six units). Which factory should be expanded to meet this requirement? Using the method presented above, we can find the cost of supplying one unit to W_1 for each factory:

Factory	Route used	Cost
F_1	Direct	\$0.90
F_2	Indirect	0.90
F_3	Indirect	0.70

Note that it costs \$0.20 less (considering only shipping costs) to supply the additional unit from F_3 than from either F_1 or F_2. F_3 has a *locational advantage* of \$0.20. Actually, this same advantage holds even if the additional unit is required at W_2 or W_3.[6] It is not necessary to determine the locational advantages as we have done above, for they can be easily seen by examining the column values at the bottom of Table 16–17. These show the \$0.20 relative advantage for F_3, and also that F_1 and F_2 are equal in this respect.

---

[6] Just as with shadow prices in standard linear programming, the locational advantage is a marginal value. It holds only over a limited range of changes in capacity or requirements.

In a similar fashion, by examining the row values in Table 16–17, we can see that W_1 has a \$0.10 locational advantage over W_2 and W_3.

Knowledge of these locational advantages can be quite useful in management decisions about which of several plants to expand, or about which regions to attempt to increase sales.

CONCLUSION

If a linear programming problem has coefficients in the restraint equations which are all either zero or one and which follow a particular pattern (see Appendix at end of chapter), the problem is of a special type called the transportation problem. We have illustrated two methods of solving this type of problem.

Just as an ordinary linear programming problem is solved in practice by using a computer program to perform the necessary steps, a computer may be used to solve the less complicated transportation problem. The specific steps are demonstrated so that a better understanding of the problem and the solution may be obtained.

APPENDIX. THE TRANSPORTATION PROBLEM EXPRESSED IN CONVENTIONAL EQUATION FORM

F_1, F_2, and F_3 are the production capacities of three factories.

W_1, W_2, and W_3 are the needs of three warehouses.

C_{11}, C_{12}, . . . , C_{ij}, . . . , C_{33} are the unit costs associated with factory i supplying warehouse j.

The total transportation cost is f (we want to minimize f).

X_{ij} is the amount transferred from the ith factory to the jth warehouse. This amount may be zero.

Minimize: $f = C_{11}X_{11} + C_{12}X_{12} + \cdots + C_{ij}X_{ij} + \cdots + C_{33}X_{33}$

Subject to: $X_{11} + X_{12} + X_{13} = F_1$

$$X_{21} + X_{22} + X_{23} = F_2$$
$$X_{31} + X_{32} + X_{33} = F_3$$
$$X_{11} + X_{21} + X_{31} = W_1$$
$$X_{12} + X_{22} + X_{32} = W_2$$
$$X_{13} + X_{23} + X_{33} = W_3$$

All $X_{ij} \geq 0$. Note that the coefficients of all X_{ij} in the restraint equations will be either zero or one, and they form a distinct pattern. Also, there are six restrictions, one of which is redundant since total supply equals total demand. With the choice of five appropriate values of X_{ij}, we can effectively limit the choice of the rest of the X_{ij}'s; thus,

$W + F - 1$ is the required number of positive values of X_{ij} in order to avoid degeneracy.

SUPPLY NOT EQUAL TO DEMAND

If supply is not equal to demand, a "dummy" source or destination may be added to remove the discrepancy. For example, suppose the supply available $(F_1 + F_2 + F_3)$ exceeded the total warehouse requirements $(W_1 + W_2 + W_3)$ by 10 units. Then we would create a dummy warehouse 4 with requirement $W_4 = 10$ units, and shipments from any of the three factories to warehouse 4 would have a zero cost in the objective function. The factories supplying the dummy warehouse would actually reduce their production by the amount going to warehouse 4 (the reductions would be X_{14}, X_{24} and X_{34} respectively). Our revised problem would be:

Minimize: $f = C_{11}X_{11} + \cdots + C_{33}X_{33} + 0X_{14} + 0X_{24} + 0X_{34}$
Subject to: $X_{11} + X_{12} + X_{13} + X_{14} = F_1$
$X_{21} + X_{22} + X_{23} + X_{24} = F_2$
$X_{31} + X_{32} + X_{33} + X_{34} = F_3$
$X_{11} + X_{21} + X_{31} = W_1$
$X_{12} + X_{22} + X_{32} = W_2$
$X_{13} + X_{23} + X_{33} = W_3$
$X_{14} + X_{24} + X_{34} = W_4$

All $X_{ij} \geq 0$

BIBLIOGRAPHY

See the Bibliography of Chapter 13.

PROBLEMS

16–1.   Using the basic method of solving the transportation type of problem, prepare a table of optimum allocation of shipments from the factories to the warehouses:

Factories	Amount available	Warehouses	Amount needed
F_1	10	W_1	15
F_2	20	W_2	28
F_3	30	W_3	17
Total	60	Total	60

The unit costs of shipping are:

	F_1	F_2	F_3
W_1	$0.90	$1.00	$1.05
W_2	0.95	1.40	0.85
W_3	1.30	0.95	1.10

16–2. Solve Problem 16–1 using the alternative method. Use the same first trial solution as you used in Problem 16–1.

16–3. Using the basic method of solution, prepare a table of optimum allocation of shipments from the factories to the warehouses:

Factories	Amount available	Warehouses	Amount needed
F_1	20	W_1	10
F_2	15	W_2	26
F_3	30	W_3	29
Total	65	Total.	65

The unit costs of shipping are:

	F_1	F_2	F_3
W_1	$1.10	$1.20	$1.10
W_2	1.12	1.00	0.90
W_3	1.20	1.05	0.95

16–4. Solve Problem 16–3 using the alternative method. Use the same first trial solution as you used in Problem 16–3.

16–5. Using the basic method of solution, attempt to prepare a table of optimum allocation of shipments from the factories to the warehouses. Use the initial solution which is given.

Unit costs and units supplied and demanded

Destination \ Source	F_1	F_2	F_3	Units demanded
W_1	$0.80	$0.90	$1.00	10
W_2	$0.85	$0.70	$0.60	28
W_3	$1.45	$1.05	$1.15	22
Units available.	10	20	30	60

First solution

Destination \ Source	F_1	F_2	F_3	Units demanded
W_1	10			10
W_2		20	8	28
W_3			22	22
Units available.	10	20	30	60

16–6. Instead of using the first solution as given in Problem 16–5, solve Problem 16–5 starting from the solution given below:

First solution

Destination \ Source	F_1	F_2	F_3	Units demanded
W_1	5	5		10
W_2	5		23	28
W_3		15	7	22
Units available.	10	20	30	60

16–7. Solve Problem 16–5 using the alternative method. Use the same first trial solution as in Problem 16–5.

16–8. Three classifications of workers (P_1, P_2, P_3) may be used on three jobs (J_1, J_2, J_3). Each man has a different cost for each job, as follows:

Direct costs

Destination \ Source	P_1	P_2	P_3	Workers needed
J_1	$1.00	$0.90	$0.80	5
J_2	$1.10	$0.80	$0.85	10
J_3	$1.20	$1.10	$1.15	30
Workers available.	10	15	20	45

The number of workers required on each job and the number of workers available are in the margins of the above table.

Use the basic method to find the optimum allocation.

16–9. Solve Problem 16–8 using the alternative method.

16–10. A firm has two factories that ship to three regional warehouses. The unit costs of transportation are:

Unit transportation costs

Warehouse	Factory F_1	Factory F_2
W_1.	$2	$4
W_2.	2	1
W_3.	5	1

Factory 2 is old and has a variable manufacturing cost of $2 per unit. Factory 1 is modern and produces for $1 per unit. Factory 2 has a capacity of 25 units, and factory 1 has a capacity of 40 units. The needs at the warehouses are:

Warehouse	Units needed
W_1.	20
W_2	10
W_3.	25

How much should each factory ship to each warehouse?

Hint: Add the manufacturing cost to the transportation cost to obtain a "unit delivered" cost. Minimize this. Also, set up a dummy warehouse to handle the excess capacity.

16–11.   A company manufactures two lines of its products, regular and super. The products are subject to seasonal sales fluctuations. In order to keep costs low, the company produces during low-volume months and stores the goods as inventory for the high-volume months. The projected sales of the two lines of product are given in the table below:

| | Sales (thousands of cases) | | |
Month	Regular line	Super line	Total
January	4	2	6
February	6	2	8
March	6	6	12
April.	8	10	18
May	8	12	20
June	4	8	12
Totals.	36	40	76

The production facility of the factory has a capacity of 10,000 cases per month on the regular shift. Overtime can be used up to a capacity of 8,000 cases per month. However, it costs $1.20 per case more to produce on the overtime shift than on the regular shift.

Inventory of the finished product can be stored for any number of months. However, it costs 80 cents per case to store the regular product for one month, and the cost to store the super product is $1 per case per month.

What production schedule for the company minimizes the total overtime production and inventory storage costs?

Hint: Treat the different shifts each month as the sources; the product requirements in the different months are the destinations. Then solve as a transportation problem.

16–12.   The ABC Company has four factories shipping to five warehouses. The shipping costs, requirements, and capacities are shown below:

| | Shipping costs (dollars per case) | | | | | Requirements (thousands of cases) | |
	F_1	F_2	F_3	F_4			
					W_1	80
					W_2	50
W_1	1	2	1	5	W_3	50
W_2	3	2	5	2	W_4	30
W_3	4	1	1	4	W_5	40
W_4	5	4	3	5		
W_5	6	5	1	4		

Factory capacities
(thousands of cases)

F_1 100
F_2 60
F_3 60
F_4 50

The company was considering closing down the fourth factory (F_4) because of high operating costs. If this were done, 30 units of capacity would be added to factory 3. The transportation manager was worried about the effect of this move on the company's transportation costs. He noted that warehouse 2 (W_2) received about 30 thousand cases from F_4. Since the shipping cost from F_3 to W_2 was $5 (compared to $2 from F_4 to W_2), the transportation manager estimated that the effect of closing F_4 would be a $90 thousand increase in transportation costs. Do you agree with the transportation manager? What effect do you think closing F_4 will have on transportation costs?

16–13. The Zeta Products Company has four factories that supply five warehouses. The variable costs of manufacturing and shipping of one ton of product from each factory to each warehouse are shown as small numbers in the upper left-hand corner of the boxes in the table below. The factory capacities and warehouse requirements in thousands of tons are shown in the margins of the table. Note that there is a dummy warehouse (labeled "slack") to account for the difference between total capacity and total requirements.

Sources / Destinations	F_1	F_2	F_3	F_4	Requirements
W_1	17	13 10	8 30	15	40
W_2	9	6 20	17	20	20
W_3	14 25	11 15	9	11 10	50
W_4	10 30	11	12	14	30
W_5	14	12	12	6 40	40
Slack	0 20	0	0	0	20
Capacities	75	45	30	50	

After several iterations, a solution is obtained (the boldface numbers in the table).

a) Is this solution optimal? If so, what is the total cost?

b) Is there an alternative optimum? If so, what is the alternative optimum solution?

c) Suppose some new equipment was installed that reduced the variable operating cost by $2 per ton in the second factory (F_2). Is the shipping schedule still optimal? If not, what is the new optimum solution?

d) Suppose the freight charge from F_1 to W_1 were reduced by $2. Would this change the shipping schedule? If so, what would be the new optimum solution?

e) How much would the manufacturing cost have to be reduced in factory 1 before production would be increased above 55 (thousand) tons?

f) Suppose that new estimates indicated that requirements at W_2 would be 25 rather than the 20 originally estimated. What would be the total incremental cost if:

(1) No expansion of any plant were undertaken?

(2) F_3 was expanded by 5 to meet the additional requirements?

g) A program to increase sales in one of the warehouse districts is about to be undertaken. If the effectiveness of this program were the same in all districts, in which district would you suggest that the program be undertaken? Why? (Assume the selling price is the same in each warehouse district.)

17

Utility as a basis for decision making

Assume that you are given a choice in each of the following paired alternatives. You may select one of the A choices, one of the B choices, and one of the C choices. Make a note of the set of alternatives you choose.

$A_1 =$ The certainty of a $100,000 gift, tax-free *or* $A_2 =$ On the flip of a fair coin, nothing if it comes up heads, or a tax-exempt gift of $250,000 if the coin turns up tails

$B_1 =$ No gain or loss *or* $B_2 =$ One chance out of 100 of incurring a $9,000 debt, and a 99/100 chance of winning $100.

$C_1 =$ A gift of $10,000 tax-free *or* $C_2 =$ A payment of 2^N cents, where N is the number of times a fair coin is flipped until tails comes up. If tails appears on the first toss, you receive 2 cents; if the coin shows heads on the first toss and tails on the second, you receive 4 cents; two heads in a row followed by tails yields 8 cents; and so forth. However, you are allowed to participate only once; the sequence stops with the first showing of tails.

Most people would choose the set A_1, B_1, and C_1. However, the mathematical expectation (or expected monetary value) favors the alternatives A_2, B_2, and C_2. The expected value of alternative A_2 is one half (the

314

probability of the fair coin showing heads) times zero (the monetary value associated with heads) plus one half (the probability of tails) times $250,000, or $125,000. Since this expected value is $25,000 more than the expected value of choice A_1, you should have selected A_2 *if you wanted to maximize expected monetary value.*

Similarly, with B_2 the expected net gain is $99/100$ (the appropriate probability) times $100 (the amount of gain) less $1/100$ times $9,000. This amount is $9, which is larger than the zero-dollar gain associated with B_1. If you made decisions so as to maximize expected monetary gain, you would accept the very small chance of a large loss, but most of us would choose B_1.

The expected monetary value of the game described in C_2 is infinite. The chance of the first tail appearing on the first toss is $1/2$; on the second toss, $1/4$; on the third, $1/8$; on the fourth, $1/16$; and so on. The related rewards would be 2 cents, 4 cents, 8 cents, 16 cents, etc. The expected monetary value, by definition, is the sum of the monetary outcomes, weighted by the associated probabilities. In this case:

$$EMV = \tfrac{1}{2}(2\cent) + \tfrac{1}{4}(4\cent) + \tfrac{1}{8}(8\cent) + \tfrac{1}{16}(16\cent) + \cdots$$
$$= 1\cent + 1\cent + 1\cent + 1\cent + \cdots = \infty\,\cent$$

The fact that no prudent man would choose this game in preference to the certainty of a modest amount provides the essentials of the famous St. Petersburg paradox. This paradox led Daniel Bernoulli to the first investigations of utility rather than the expectation of monetary value as a basis of decision making.

UTILITY

Since most people would choose A_1, B_1, and C_1 rather than the alternatives with greater monetary expectation, it seems reasonable to conclude that people do not always make decisions so as to maximize expected monetary value. What, then, is an alternative criterion for decision making? Von Neumann and Morgenstern[1] constructed a framework which was consistent with choices such as A_1, B_1, and C_1. They argued that decisions were made so as to maximize expected *utility* rather than expected monetary value. If you selected A_1 over A_2, we would conclude that alternative A_1 had more utility for you than alternative A_2. If you were indifferent between two alternatives—say B_1 and B_2—we would conclude that each alternative offered the same expected utility to you. Indifference might be defined as your willingness to take either result

[1] J. von Neumann and O. Morgenstern, *Theory of Games and Economic Behavior* (Princeton: Princeton University Press, 1944).

at random, or have some stranger make the choice for you. It is possible to derive generalizations about a person's utility function for some commodity (most often money) that are consistent with logic and observation of repeated decisions. It follows that it is reasonable to assume that people make decisions so as to maximize expected utility rather than expected value. This is not a painless choice, for expected monetary value is an unambiguous concept and is relatively easy to calculate. It would be quite convenient if we were able to associate different monetary outcomes with indices of the decision maker's preferences. A complex set of alternatives then might be transformed into utility measures for purposes of decision making. It is our purpose in this chapter to relate money and a utility index, and to derive generalizations about this relationship in situations involving risk.

MEASURING UTILITY[2]

Is it possible to measure the utility of money? In an attempt to answer this question, we shall consider three different types of measurement scales:

1.   Nominal or classification scale
2.   Ordinal or ranking scale
3.   Cardinal or interval scale

A *nominal* scale assigns a description to a set of elements. The elements may be a physical unit or a condition. The description may be a number, as in a numbering system for baseball players; or it may be an adjective, as when a person says he is hungry or not hungry. A nominal scale can be useful for decision analysis. For example, a set of possible returns might be divided into subsets or classifications of satisfactory and unsatisfactory returns. Investments may be divided into two classes, acceptable and unacceptable, on a nominal scale. A form of grading procedure could assign two grades, passing or failing. It is not difficult to conceive of nominal measures of utility. For example, acts could be classified as having negative utility (disutility) or positive utility.

An *ordinal* measure adds the concept of relative ordering or ranking. Objects become "more" or "less" than other objects. A person can declare a sound is louder than another sound. Different light sources may be ranked by brightness without a number measure being placed on

---

[2] The material presented in this section is to a great extent based on the authors' interpretation of the following two sources: M. Friedman and L. J. Savage, "The Utility Analysis of Choices Involving Risk," *Journal of Political Economy*, August, 1948; and R. D. Luce and H. Raiffa, *Games and Decisions*, New York: John Wiley & Sons, Inc., 1957).

the amount of light. We can choose the winner of a race without the use of a stopwatch. An attempt may be made to rank all investments according to their relative desirability (though this process may be easier to describe than to accomplish).

Ordinal measures of utility are used in analyzing situations with riskless choices. Indifference curve analysis collects alternatives with equal utility (i.e., a person is indifferent to these choices), and we compare any of these choices with the choices on another indifference curve which is higher (and more desirable) or lower (and less desirable). If we could rank investments, this would imply that we have an ordinal measure of desirability.

With a *cardinal* measure, a number is assigned which is an interval measure of a characteristic. Thus a piece of wood may be a number of inches long, a number of pounds in weight, and a number of cubic inches in volume. We can measure in a cardinal sense such things as distance, weight, light, sound, time, and heat. We can do some mathematical manipulations with a cardinal measure. For example, all 5-pound bags of sugar weigh the same; and if we have two 5-pound bags, we then have 10 pounds of sugar.

The von Neumann-Morgenstern measure of utility is a special type of cardinal measure (some would say it is a special type of ordinal measure). It measures utility in situations involving risk for the individual decision maker. The use of this utility measure allows us to predict which of several lotteries a person will prefer, and thus enables a manager to make the decision for his employer. Sometimes the employer will make decisions inconsistent with his utility function, but this type of inconsistency can generally be straightened out if the employer reconsiders his decisions.

One justification for the use of utility in investment situations evolves from the fact that other measures cannot adequately cope with uncertainty. Neither net present value nor rate of return are sufficient measures of the worth of an investment with uncertainty. An individual making his own investments will automatically apply his own utility function to the situation. He may do this without knowing that such a function exists. Making the decision helps determine the function. Formal utility analysis finds its most effective use in situations too complex for an individual's intuition, and where a manager is making decisions for his employer.

Any utility function is the result of a person's attitudes towards risk. There are no right or wrong answers (though inconsistencies may arise because of misunderstandings). Thus if you are asked what amount you will accept for certain instead of engaging in a lottery involving a 0.5

probability of losing $500 and 0.5 probability of winning $1,000, the answer is a personal preference rather than a mathematical calculation. (In a class of 50 students it is likely that close to 50 different answers will be obtained.)

THE PSYCHOLOGICAL ASSUMPTIONS

The use of utility for purposes of making decisions in the manner described involves assumptions about how an individual reacts to choices. Since we are attempting to measure attitudes toward uncertain situations, it is important that the model used in making the decisions be consistent with the psychological makeup of people.

The following assumptions will be made:

1.   With any two alternatives, we can decide whether we are indifferent to them or which one we prefer. This seems to be a trivial requirement, but it is very necessary. In fact, we may find that it is difficult to determine a specific unequivocal reaction to pairs of alternatives. For example, would you prefer $200 for certain or a lottery involving a 50–50 chance of getting zero dollars or $1,000? Change the $200 until your preference is different. Finding the exact point of indifference between the two lotteries is very difficult, and the answer is frequently indecisive.

2.   Alternatives are transitive; i.e., if A is preferred to B, and B is preferred to C, then A is preferred to C. Also, if A equals B, and B equals C, then A is equal to C. It is possible, where the degree of preference is slight and the alternatives are many, for a person to give rankings of pairs that are intransitive. This means that on close decisions a person may be inconsistent. For example, a person might say that he prefers a trip to Nassau to a trip to Bermuda, and a trip to Bermuda to a trip to Hawaii, but then say that he prefers a trip to Hawaii to a trip to Nassau. This is intransitive, but it may result from the fact that all three trips sound fine; and although he is trying to give preferences, he is close to being indifferent between three choices. He should be able to eliminate this type of intransitivity by reexamining his decisions.

3.   If a person is indifferent to two lotteries, then they may be substituted for each other for purposes of analysis. For example, we previously compared a 50–50 chance of zero dollars and $1,000 with $200 for certain. If you are indifferent between these two lotteries, then we can use the second lottery ($200 for certain) as a substitute for the first. Further, we can say the utilities of the two lotteries are equal.

4.   If two lotteries have the same two possible outcomes, but the outcomes have different probabilities, then the lottery with the more favorable outcome having the higher probability is the preferred lottery.

Example. Consider the two lotteries shown in Table 17–1. Lottery *A* must be preferred over lottery *B*.

TABLE 17–1

Possible outcomes	Probability of outcomes for lottery:	
	A	*B*
$1,000............	0.80	0.50
0............	0.20	0.50

5. If *A* is preferred to *B*, and *B* is preferred to *C*, then there is some lottery involving *A* and *C* which is indifferent to *B* for certain.

Example. Let:

$$A = \$1,000$$
$$B = \$400$$
$$C = \$0$$

We shall make up a lottery involving *A* with probability *p* and *C* with probability $(1 - p)$. The expected *monetary* value of the lottery will be:

$$A(p) + C(1 - p) = 1,000p + 0(1 - p)$$

What is the value of *p* which will make you indifferent to the above lottery and *B* for certain? If there is some value, then assumption 5 is satisfied; *B* would be called the *certainty equivalent* of the lottery.

6. If *A* is preferred to *B*, and there is some third alternative, *C*, then any combination of *A* plus *C* is preferred to a combination of *B* plus *C*, provided the probability of assignments are the same in both lotteries. It is required that the probability attached to *C* be less than one.

Example. Let:

$$A = \$1,000$$
$$B = \$400$$
$$C = \$200$$

$A(p) + C(1 - p)$ is preferred over $B(p) + C(1 - p)$. If *p* equals 0.6, then $\$1,000 \times 0.6 + \$200 \times 0.4$ is preferred over $\$400 \times 0.6 + \$200 \times 0.4$.

Assumption 6 can also be expressed as follows: If a combination of

A plus *C* is preferred over a combination of *B* plus *C*, with *C* having the same probability (less than one) in both combinations, then *A* is preferred to *B*.

7.   The utility of a lottery is defined to be equal to the expected utility of its components.

The assumption that the utility of a lottery is the expectation of the component utilities is a convenient assumption for mathematical manipulation.[3] Let us assume a lottery, L_1, has the outcomes shown in Table 17–2, with each outcome assigned a utility measure and a probability of occurrence.

TABLE 17–2

Outcomes	Utility of outcomes	Probability
A_1...............	$U(A_1)$	p_1
A_2...............	$U(A_2)$	p_2
....	.....	...
....	.....	...
A_n...............	$U(A_n)$	p_n

The utility of the lottery is defined as:

$$U(L_1) = p_1 U(A_1) + p_2 U(A_2) + \cdots + p_n U(A_n)$$

The lottery L_1 may itself have a probability of occurrence. Assume lottery L_1 has a probability of r and lottery L_2 has a probability of $(1 - r)$. The utility of the two lotteries is $U(L)$:

$$U(L) = r U(L_1) + (1 - r) U(L_2)$$

Example. Assume two lotteries (see Table 17–3):

$$U(L_1) = 0.6 \times 50 + 0.4 \times 0 = 30$$
$$U(L_2) = 1.0 \times 40 = 40$$

TABLE 17–3

Lottery	Outcomes	Utility of outcomes	Probability
L_1.........	\$1,000	50	0.6
	0	0	0.4
L_2.........	400	40	1.0

---

[3] See R. Dorfman, P. A. Samuelson, and R. M. Solow, *Linear Programming and Economic Analysis* (New York: McGraw-Hill Book Co., 1958), pp. 465–69, for a proof.

Assume L_1 has a probability of 0.8 and L_2 has a probability of 0.2. The expected utility of the gamble (i.e., the two lotteries) is:

$$U(L) = 0.8 \times 30 + 0.2 \times 40 = 32$$

Since the scale of utility is arbitrary, we can change the scale and origin without contradicting our assumptions. In particular, if a and b are any two constants, $b > 0$, and if $U(L)$ is a utility function, then $F(L)$ is also a utility function where:

$$F(L) = a + bU(L)$$

That is to say, we can add a constant to a utility function, or we can change the unit (or the slope). It is said that a utility function is unique up to an order-preserving linear transformation.[4]

DERIVATION OF A UTILITY FUNCTION FOR MONEY

To be of use in decision making, utility values must be assigned to all outcomes. In many circumstances, such outcomes are nonmonetary in nature. For example, in making a medical diagnosis, a physician has to weigh such factors as pain and suffering, loss of work from hospitalization, psychological effects, costs, and even death. It is possible using the von Neumann-Morgenstern approach to assign utility values to such outcomes. However, in most business decision problems, the monetary consequence is of major importance. Hence, in this book, we shall be concerned primarily with evaluating the utility function for money.

The shape of utility functions

Some generalizations about the usual shape of the utility function are possible. People usually regard money as a desirable commodity and prefer more of it to less of it. The utility measure of a large sum is normally greater than the utility measure of a small sum, and the utility function rises over any relevant range of money.[5] We can describe the utility function as having a positive slope over this relevant range. The slope in this case is the ratio of an incremental change in the utility index

---

[4] The sense in which von Neumann and Morgenstern use the term *utility* differs somewhat from the traditional use in economics. Utility in the von Neumann sense is associated with choices involving uncertainty; in the older economic version, utility represented the intrinsic satisfaction possessed by a commodity. The distinction will be sharpened in the following discussion. The word *preference* has been used instead of *utility* in some recent books to avoid this confusion.

[5] If more and more money is acquired, a saturation point is approached, and the utility function levels off—it is bounded from above. It is also bounded from below for large losses.

$[\Delta U(M)]$ as a result of an incremental change in the stock of money (ΔM). The incremental changes will always have the same sign, so we may write:

$$\text{Slope} = \frac{\Delta U(M)}{\Delta M} > 0$$

This measure of the slope is called the marginal utility of money and, except for the algebraic sign, is an arbitrary measure. This follows from the utility function being unique only to a linear transformation.

The slope of the utility function is positive and probably does not vary in response to small changes in the stock of money. It follows that for small changes in the amount of money going to an individual, his utility function over that range has approximately a constant slope and may be regarded as linear. If the utility function is linear [$U(M)$ in Figure 17–1], the person maximizes expected utility by maximizing expected

FIGURE 17–1
Utility for money

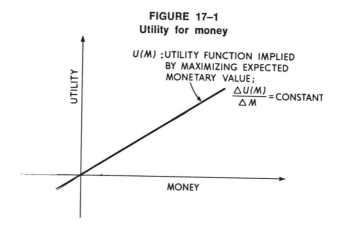

monetary value. Thus, expected monetary value may properly be used as a guide in decision making only when there is reason to believe the pertinent utility function is linear over the range of possible outcomes. We have seen that for large variations in the amount of money, this is a most unlikely condition. At the extremes, for large losses and large gains, the utility function is almost certain to approach upper and lower limits. The slope of the curve usually will increase sharply as the amount of the loss increases, implying that the disutility of a large loss is proportionately more than the disutility of a small loss, but the curve will flatten as the loss becomes very large. Similarly, for large stocks of money, the slope of the utility function grows smaller with further additions to that stock. These observations are consistent with the traditional "diminishing marginal utility" view of consumer psychology. It is also consistent with the notion of "risk aversion" which pervades most business decision problems. An example of a risk averse utility function is shown in Figure 17–2. If an individual is risk averse, then the expected utility of a gamble is less than the utility of the expected monetary value.

FIGURE 17–2
Utility functions

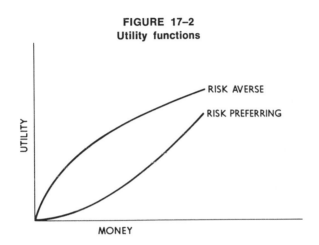

It is possible for a decision maker to be risk preferring, at least over a range of the utility function. In this case, the expected utility of a gamble is more than the utility of the expected monetary value. A risk preferring utility function is also shown in Figure 17- 2.

Assessing a utility function

The first step in actually deriving a utility function is to determine two values to use as reference points. For convenience, these can be the largest and smallest monetary values involved in the decision problem. The utility of these values are arbitrarily selected—for convenience we might assign utility values of zero and one to these monetary values. For example, if the decision problem included monetary values ranging from −$10,000 to +$100,000, we would assign a zero utility to −$10,000 and a utility of 1.0 to $100,000. That is:

$$U(-10,000) = 0 \quad \text{and} \quad U(100,000) = 1.0$$

The selection of utility values of zero and one is arbitrary. Values of −29 and +132 or other values could have been selected. In this sense, the utility scale is like that for temperature. Both the Centigrade and Fahrenheit scales measure temperature but have different readings for the freezing point of water ($0°$ and $32°$ respectively) and for the boiling point ($100°$ and $212°$ respectively).

Next, formulate an alternative A_1 which offers a one-half chance at $-\$10,000$ and a one-half chance at $+\$100,000$. The expected utility of this alternative is the sum of the utility assignments to the possible events, weighted by the appropriate probabilities. In this case

$$U(A_1) = \tfrac{1}{2}U(-10,000) + \tfrac{1}{2}U(\$100,000) = \tfrac{1}{2}(0) + \tfrac{1}{2}(1) = 0.5$$

Now formulate an alternative line of action (A_2) which yields some amount of money with certainty—say, $\$25,000$. You now have to choose between the two courses of action, A_1 and A_2. Say you choose A_2, or $\$25,000$ for certain. We infer that:

$$U(A_2) > U(A_1) = 0.5$$

or $U(\$25,000) > \tfrac{1}{2}U(-\$10,000) + \tfrac{1}{2}U(\$100,000) = 0.5$; that is, the utility of $\$25,000$ is greater than one half. Because the $\$25,000$ is preferred to A_1, we conclude that the utility index of A_2 is greater than one half. Assume next that you were offered $\$5,000$ for certain (A_3) and found that you preferred A_1 to A_3. This would imply that the utility index associated with $\$5,000$ should be less than one half. If your patience held out, you could continue proposing alternative acts yielding sums of money with certainty until you discovered one that was exactly as attractive as A_1. Suppose this offer was in the amount of $\$15,000$, so that we could infer that you were indifferent between $\$15,000$ for certain and the original proposal. Thus the utility assignment to $\$15,000$ should be:

$$U(\$15,000) = \tfrac{1}{2}U(-\$10,000) + \tfrac{1}{2}U(\$100,000) = 0.5$$

We now have three points through which your utility function passes. Additional utility evaluations may be made in a similar manner. For example, pose an alternative which offers a 0.5 probability of $\$15,000$ and a 0.5 probability of $\$100,000$. Find the sum which must be offered with certainty to make you indifferent to the opportunity involving risk. Say this amount is $\$47,000$. We could conclude that the appropriate utility assignment for $\$47,000$ is:

$$U(\$47,000) = \cdot\tfrac{1}{2}U(\$15,000) + \tfrac{1}{2}U(\$100,000)$$
$$= \tfrac{1}{2}(0.5) + \tfrac{1}{2}(1.0) = 0.75$$

Next, pose the alternative involving a one-half chance at $\$15,000$ and one-half chance at $-\$10,000$. You may consider this alternative unfavorable, and in fact be willing to pay some amount to be relieved of the alternative (in the same way that one buys insurance to be relieved of a risk). Suppose you are indifferent to −$2,500 (that is a payment of $2,500) and the opportunity involving risk. Then:

$$U(-\$2,500) = \tfrac{1}{2}U(-\$10,000) + \tfrac{1}{2}U(\$15,000)$$
$$= \tfrac{1}{2}(0) + \tfrac{1}{2}(0.5) = 0.25$$

You now have the five points of the utility function shown in Table 17–4 and Figure 17–3. These can be connected by a smooth curve to

TABLE 17–4
Assessed utility points

Monetary value M	Utility index U(M)
−$ 10,000.	0
− 2,500.	0.25
15,000.	0.50
47,000.	0.75
100,000.	1.0

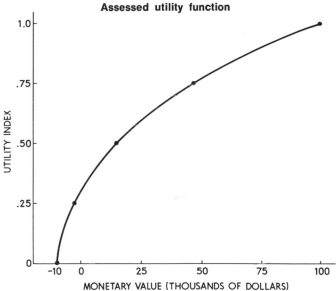

FIGURE 17–3
Assessed utility function

give an approximation for the utility function over the entire range −$10,000 to $100,000.

Note that

$$U(\$15,000) = 0.5$$

and

$$\tfrac{1}{2}U(-\$2,500) + \tfrac{1}{2}U(\$47,000) = \tfrac{1}{2}(0.25) + \tfrac{1}{2}(0.75) = 0.5$$

Hence, as a final check on your assessments, you should be indifferent between $15,000 for sure and an alternative involving a one-half chance at −$2,500 and one-half chance at $47,000. If this is not true, your assessments are not consistent and must be revised.

An alternative procedure for assessing the utility function is to pick a certain monetary value and then determine the probabilities that make a gamble involving the maximum and minimum values equivalent to the certain amount.[6] For example, if we picked a certain amount L we then formulate the equation:

$$pU(\$100,000) + (1 - p)U(-\$10,000) = U(L)$$

and we find the probability p that makes the decision maker indifferent between the two sides of this equation. As an illustration, if L were $25,000, the decision maker would have to assess a probability p such that he was indifferent between $25,000 for sure, and a p chance at $100,000 and a $(1 - p)$ chance at −$10,000. In this case p might be 0.60. Then

$$U(L) = U(25,000) = 0.6U(100,000) + 0.4U(-10,000)$$
$$= 0.6(1) + 0.4(0) = 0.6$$

(because we have set $U(100,000) = 1.0$ and $U(-10,000) = 0$, $U(L) = p$). To obtain other values on the utility curve, other values of L would be selected and the p probability assessed. In this manner, a curve similar to that of Figure 17–3 could be obtained.

USING UTILITY FUNCTIONS

A utility function represents the subjective attitude of a decision maker to risk. Hence, a utility function of a person can be used to evaluate his decision problems involving uncertain outcomes.

Example. Suppose a decision maker had to make a choice between two alternatives. Alternative A involved a contract in which the company was sure to make a profit of $20,000. Alternative B, on the other hand, was the introduction of a new product. The sales that the product would achieve, and hence the profit, were unknown. Management assigned the probabilities shown in Table 17–5 to the various profit possibilities.

---

[6] If the mathematical form of the utility function is of certain types, it is possible to assess the curve using only a single indifference evaluation. This is the case for constant risk aversion, or constant proportional risk aversion. For a discussion of mathematical forms for utility functions, see "The Consistent Assessment and Fairing of Preference Functions," by R. Meyer and J. W. Pratt in *IEEE Transactions on Systems Science and Cybernetics* (Special Issue on Decision Analysis), Vol. SSC-4, No. 3 (September 1968).

TABLE 17–5
Probabilities, payoffs, utilities for alternative B

Probability	Profit (thousands of dollars)	Utility
0.1	−10	0
0.3	0	0.30
0.2	20	0.55
0.2	40	0.71
0.1	60	0.82
0.1	80	0.90
Expected values	25	0.524

The expected monetary value for alternative B is $25,000. On this basis, it would be preferred to A. On the other hand, if the decision maker were risk averse, this may not be true. Note that there is a 30 percent chance of no profit and a 10 percent chance of a loss with alternative B. If the decision maker had the utility function given in Figure 17–3, we would evaluate this alternative by using utility values instead of monetary values. By interpolating in Figure 17–3, we could find the utility values associated with each profit amount. These are given in Table 17–5. Using the probabilities in the same table, the *expected utility* would be calculated (by multiplying the probabilities by the utility amounts and summing). The expected utility is calculated as 0.524. Note that the utility of $20,000 is given in the table as 0.55. Hence the expected utility of alternative B is not as great as the utility of the contract involving $20,000 for sure, and the sure contract should be accepted.

Certainty equivalents

The notion of a certainty equivalent has been presented several times in this chapter. Let us now consider its meaning more explicitly. Consider an uncertain decision situation, which may be represented by a lottery, L, with dollar outcomes A_1 and A_2, and corresponding probabilities p and $(1 - p)$. The certainty equivalent is a certain or sure dollar amount A^* which is equivalent, for the decision maker, to the lottery L.

The certainty equivalent can be interpreted as the maximum insurance that the decision maker would pay to be freed of an undesirable risk (for example, the maximum premium to guard against a fire in one's house). Or we might consider the certainty equivalent as the minimum amount one would be willing to accept for selling a desirable risk.

Once we have obtained the utility function for a decision maker and also obtained the probabilities in a given decision situation, the certainty equivalent can be obtained directly by the methods used in this chapter. In our example above, the alternative of introducing the new product has an expected utility of 0.524. Reading from the curve in Figure 17–3, we can see that $17,500 also has a utility of 0.524. Hence we can say that the amount $17,500 is the *certainty equivalent* of the alternative involving the new product introduction. When faced with an uncertain decision situation, it would be beneficial to determine the certainty equivalent directly by asking the decision maker. If this does not agree with the value computed using the utility function and the probabilities, then we have come up with an inconsistency; it may be due either to the utility curve or to the probabilities assigned to the outcomes. Hence the use of the certainty equivalent is a check on the validity of our analysis.

The certainty equivalent also has another use in analyzing complex decision situations. Our procedure so far has called for obtaining probabilities of various outcomes and a utility function as separate inputs to the decision-making process. Since both of these often represent subjective judgments on the part of the decision maker, it is sometimes convenient to shortcut the analysis and come up with a certainty equivalent directly.

Example. A manufacturer is bidding on a contract to supply 1,000 units of a certain electronic component. He has to decide his bid price. One uncertain factor in the decision process is the possibility of a strike by his workers. If they do strike, it would mean delays and penalties associated with meeting the deadline on the contract. To simplify the decision analysis, we might simply ask our manufacturer how much he would be willing to pay for insurance against losses due to the possible strike. He might answer, for example, $3,000. This amount is the certainty equivalent to the uncertain situation related to the strike (the dollar outcomes with and without a strike *and* the related probabilities). The decision maker may not actually be able to purchase insurance of this type, but the certainty equivalent provides a figure that we can use in our analysis to determine the proper bid to be made by the manufacturer.

Risk premium

Suppose an individual has assessed his utility function $U(I)$ as shown in Figure 17–4. He is presented first with a gamble involving a one-half chance for the amount I_1 and a one-half chance for the amount I_3. The expected monetary value (EMV) of this gamble is I_2. The certainty equivalent of the gamble is I^* [i.e., $\frac{1}{2} U(I_1) + \frac{1}{2} U(I_3) = U(I^*)$].

FIGURE 17–4
Utility function

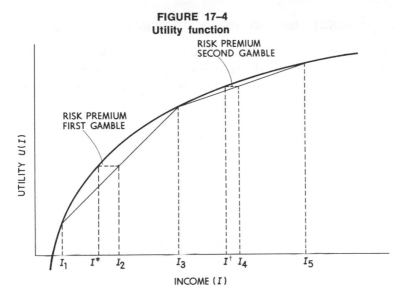

The difference between the EMV and the certainty equivalent of the gamble (i.e., $I_2 - I^*$) is the *risk premium* associated with the gamble for that individual. The risk premium is a measure of how much risk aversion there is in a given portion of an individual's utility function. For two individuals presented with the same gamble, the one with the higher risk premium is the more risk averse.

For a given individual, the risk premium will generally not be the same at different parts of the utility function.[7] Consider a second gamble involving a one-half chance at I_3 and a one-half chance at I_5, where I_5 is such that the distance from I_3 to I_5 is the same as that from I_1 to I_3 (i.e., $I_5 - I_3 = I_3 - I_1$). We can think of this second gamble as if it were composed of a sure amount of $(I_3 - I_1)$ plus the first gamble above involving I_1 and I_3. In this sense, the second gamble is the same as the first, except for a different starting point (I_3 versus I_1). Note that the risk premium in the second gamble is $(I_4 - I\dagger)$ and is less than the risk premium of first gamble. Thus the utility function shown in Figure 17–4 has the property of *decreasing risk aversion*. In other words, the individual becomes less risk averse as his money amount I increases.

This property of decreasing risk aversion is one that seems reasonable for most business and many personal decisions, at least over reasonable sized increases or decreases in wealth.

---

[7] If the risk premium is the same everywhere on the curve (the case of *constant risk aversion*), the utility function has the form $U(I) = (1 - e^{rI})/(1 - e^{r})$ where r is the risk aversion parameter. See Meyer and Pratt, *IEEE Transactions*.

UTILITY FUNCTIONS AND RISK PREFERENCE

There is empirical evidence that for individuals, the utility function actually has an area of risk preference.[8] In this area, the slope of the utility function increases up to a point of inflection and decreases thereafter (see Figure 17–5).

FIGURE 17–5
Utility for wealth

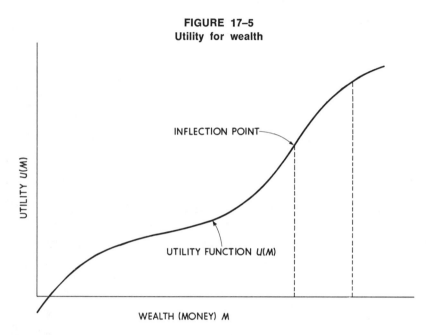

It is quite consistent for an individual with a utility function of this shape [$U(M)$ in Figure 17–5] to (1) pay a small premium for insurance against large losses, even when the premiums include a "loading" charge above the actuarial cost of bearing the risk; and (2) simultaneously accept risky propositions which promise a chance at relatively large gains in return for modest investments, even though the mathematical expectation may make the gamble an unfair one.

Example. Consider the entrepreneur whose utility table contains the pairs shown in Table 17–6. Say that he is faced with two decisions: (*a*) Should he pay a $100 premium to insure against a potential $10,000 fire loss when he knows that the insurance company has calculated the probability of fire on his class of property to be 1 out of 200? (*b*) Should

---

[8] The original conjecture was by Friedman and Savage, "The Utility Analysis of Choices Involving Risk," supported by empirical observations that many people were willing to accept long-shot risky ventures (e.g., lotteries) at the same time that they insured against large losses. Since then, there has been some experimental support of this view.

TABLE 17–6

$U(M)$	M
−800.	−$10,000
− 2.	− 200
− 1.	− 100
0.	0
250.	10,000

he invest $100 in an oil-drilling venture where the geologist has said there is only 1 chance in 200 of striking oil (with the expectation of $10,000 profit) and a 199/200 chance of losing the $100 investment? Let us analyze these decisions in terms of expectations calculated from the utility measures. The decision to insure or not is described in Table 17–7.

The expected utility of act 1 is less than the expected utility of act 2; the entrepreneur maximizes his utility by taking act 2 (insuring).

TABLE 17–7
Conditional and expected utility

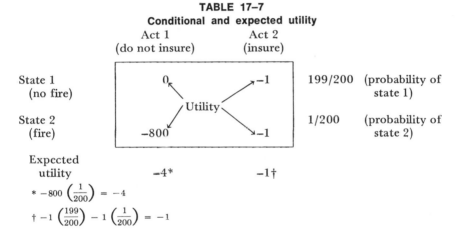

	Act 1 (do not insure)	Act 2 (insure)		
State 1 (no fire)	0	−1	199/200	(probability of state 1)
State 2 (fire)	−800	−1	1/200	(probability of state 2)
Expected utility	−4*	−1†		

$$* -800 \left(\frac{1}{200}\right) = -4$$
$$† -1 \left(\frac{199}{200}\right) - 1 \left(\frac{1}{200}\right) = -1$$

The decision to invest or not may be analyzed in the same manner. The utility table shown in Table 17–8 may be constructed on the basis

TABLE 17–8
Conditional and expected utility

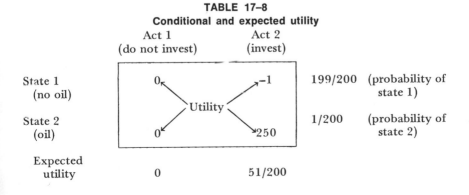

	Act 1 (do not invest)	Act 2 (invest)		
State 1 (no oil)	0	−1	199/200	(probability of state 1)
State 2 (oil)	0	250	1/200	(probability of state 2)
Expected utility	0	51/200		

of the available information. It follows that the expected utility of act 1 is less than the expected utility of act 2. It is seen that the entrepreneur maximizes utility by taking act 2 (investing). The risky venture would be accepted at the same time the entrepreneur was insuring against a loss, contrary to the decisions indicated by expected monetary value.

CONCLUSIONS

There is general agreement that under some conditions, expected monetary value will not be an appropriate basis on which to make decisions. This implies that utility functions for money exist. A set of assumptions has been presented in this chapter which leads to the method illustrated of deriving a utility function. If the assumptions are not valid, then we would have to change the method of derivation and the manner in which we use the utility function.

This chapter dealt with utility functions of individuals. We know less about how to deal with groups of individuals with different preferences (as in the case of a corporation). While our knowledge is imperfect in this area, we do know that the decision maker in a corporation must take risk, and attitudes towards risk, into consideration; he should not assume that the use of expected monetary value is always correct.

BIBLIOGRAPHY

EDWARDS, W., and TVERSKY, A. (eds.). *Decision Making.* Baltimore: Penguin Books Inc., 1967.

FISHBURN, P. C. *Utility Theory for Decision Making.* New York: John Wiley & Sons, Inc., 1970.

FRIEDMAN, M., and SAVAGE, L. J. "The Utility Analysis of Choices Involving Risk," *Journal of Political Economy,* August 1948.

HAMMOND, J. S. "Better Decisions with Preference Theory," *Harvard Business Review,* November–December 1967.

IEEE Transactions on Systems Science and Cybernetics, (Special Issue on Decision Analysis), Vol. SSC-4, No. 3 (September 1968).

LUCE, R. D., and RAIFFA, H. *Games and Decisions.* New York: John Wiley & Sons, Inc., 1957.

PRATT, J. W.; RAIFFA, H.; and SCHLAIFER, R. "The Foundations of Decision under Uncertainty: An Elementary Exposition," *Journal of the American Statistical Association,* June 1964.

SAVAGE, L. J. *The Foundations of Statistics.* New York: John Wiley & Sons, Inc., 1954.

SCHLAIFER, R. *Analysis of Decisions under Uncertainty.* New York: McGraw-Hill Book Co., 1969.

SIEGEL, S. "Level of Aspiration and Decision Making," *Psychological Review*, 1957.

SIMON, H. A. *Models of Man.* New York: John Wiley & Sons, Inc., 1957.

SWALM, R. O. "Utility Theory—Insights into Risk Taking," *Harvard Business Review*, November–December 1966.

VON NEUMANN, J., and MORGENSTERN, O. *Theory of Games and Economic Behavior.* Princeton: Princeton University Press, 1944.

PROBLEMS

17–1. Entrepreneur W has a utility index of 5 for a loss of $1,000, and 12 for a profit of $3,000. He says that he is indifferent between $10 for certain and the following lottery: a 0.4 chance at a $1,000 loss and a 0.6 chance at a $3,000 profit. What is his utility index for $10?

17–2. Entrepreneur X has a utility index for $-\$2$ of 0.50; his index for $500 is 0.60. He maintains that he is indifferent between $500 for certain and a lottery of a 0.8 chance at $-\$2$ and a 0.2 chance at $20,000. What is his utility index for $20,000?

17–3. Entrepreneur Y has a utility index of -108 for $11,000, and -275 for zero dollars. He is indifferent between a 0.5 chance at $11,000 plus a 0.5 chance at a $20,000 loss and a certainty of zero. What is his utility index for a loss of $20,000?

17–4. Entrepreneur Z has a utility index of 10 for $18,750, 6 for $11,200, and 0 for zero dollars. What probability combination of zero dollars and $18,750 would make him indifferent to $11,200 for certain?

17–5. Entrepreneur W has a utility index of five for a loss of $1,000 and a utility index of six for a loss of $500. What is the slope of his utility function between these points?

17–6. Two economists, Alfred M. Noxie and J. Maynard K. Bampton, are arguing about the relative merits of their respective decision rules. Noxie says he always takes that act with the greatest expected monetary value; Bampton says he always takes the act with the greatest expected utility, and his utility function for money is $U = 10 + 0.2M$. For decisions involving monetary payoffs, who will make the better choices?

17–7. You are a fire insurance salesman confronted by a balky mathematician who argues that he should not insure his house against fire because of the small loading charge which provides the overhead for the insurance company. If his analysis is correct, what does this imply about the shape of his utility function?

17–8. You have a date for the quantitative analysis ball; the admission is $10, which you do not have. On the day of the dance, your psychology instructor offers you either $8 for certain or a 50–50 chance at nothing or $12. Which choice would you make, assuming you had no other source of funds or credit? Why? If the utility of $8 is 20, and the utility of zero dollars is 0, what does this imply about the utility of $12?

17–9. You are the plant manager for a small manufacturing concern. The parking lot next to the factory must be repaved. A large contractor has told you that he will submit a bid at any time consisting of the expected full cost plus 10 percent profit. The only uncertainty in the cost calculation on this job is the weather. If it is clear, the incremental cost of the job will be $40,000. If it rains, the incremental cost will be $55,000. The Weather Bureau has informed you that the chance of rain for the relevant period is 1 out of 10, and that all contractors know and accept this information.

You know you will get two other bids on the job. Two small local contractors, Willie and Joe, have been engaged in a bitter rivalry ever since World War II. In recent years the object of their rivalry has been to see who would be the first to enter the Six-Figure Club. Requirements for admission consist of making a profit of $100,000 or more for one year. You know that Willie has made profits this year of $109,500, and Joe has made profits of $95,000. There is so little time left in the year that your job will be the last possible job for each of them. Also, they both have excess capacity and can undertake the job. What bids would you expect? How would you explain the bids?

17–10. Suppose that Smith has a utility function $U(x) = x^{2/3}$, where x is in dollars ($0 \leq x \leq 1,000$). Smith is offered the following choices:

A—$8 for sure

B—A lottery with a one-half chance for zero dollars and a one-half chance for $64

Which lottery would you predict Smith will choose?

17–11. The Iota Engineering Company does subcontracting on government contracts. Iota is a small company with limited capital. The utility function is described as follows:

$$U(x) = -x/100 - x^2/5,000, \qquad x < -1,000$$
$$U(x) = x/100 - 170, \qquad -1,000 \leq x \leq 10,000$$
$$U(x) = \sqrt{x}, \qquad x > 10,000$$

a) Suppose Iota is considering bidding on a given contract. It will cost $2,000 to prepare the bid. If the bid is lost, the $2,000 cost is also lost. If Iota wins the bid, it will make $40,000 and recover the $2,000 bid preparation cost. If Iota feels that the odds are 50–50 of winning the contract if a bid is submitted, what should it do?

b) What would the probability of winning have to be before Iota would submit a bid?

17–12. Suppose a decision maker, when asked to find the certainty equivalents for the gambles shown in the first column below, responded with the answers in the second column.

	Gamble	Assessed certainty equivalent
1.	½ chance at –$100,000 and ½ chance at $200,000	$ 10,000
2.	½ chance at $10,000 and ½ chance at $200,000	100,000
3.	½ chance at $10,000 and ½ chance at –$100,000	– 55,000

a) Using graph paper, plot the utility points associated with the above gambles and draw a smooth utility curve through the points.
b) Using this curve, find the certainty equivalent for the following gamble:

Payoff	Probability
–$ 80,000	0.2
0	0.4
80,000	0.2
160,000	0.2

17–13. Refer to Problem 3–19. Suppose that the utility function for money for the drilling problem is the same as that assessed in Problem 17–12 above.
a) Should the company drill or sell the lease?
b) Suppose, before the company began drilling, another firm offered to buy the lease. What is the minimum price the company should accept?
c) Suppose, before drilling began, an outside syndicate of investors offered the following proposition: The syndicate would pay the company $20,000 for a 50 percent share in the costs and revenues associated with drilling. (That is, revenues to the company would be $20,000 plus one half of the values listed in Problem 3- 19.) Should the company accept the offer?

17–14. Refer to Problem 3–13. Suppose the concessionnaire in that problem gave the following certainty equivalents for the gambles shown below:

	Gamble	Assessed certainty equivalent
1.	½ chance at –$20,000 and	
	½ chance at $40,000.............	–$ 5,000
2.	½ chance at –$5,000 and	
	½ chance at $40,000.............	13,000
3.	½ chance at –$5,000 and	
	½ chance at –$20,000............	– 16,000

a) Using these values, draw a utility function for the concession-naire on graph paper.

b) How much food should the concessionnaire order to be consistent with this set of utility assessments?

18

Game theory

We shall now develop a mathematical model which has its primary application to the relationships between two independent competing entities (i.e., individuals or organizations). This analysis is derived from the monumental work of von Neumann and Morgenstern, *Theory of Games and Economic Behavior*.[1]

While game theory is not widely used in industry, a knowledge of the subject does give insights that are helpful in arriving at decisions. The assumptions of each game theory model should be carefully noted since the assumptions frequently will limit the application.

GAMES

In the context of this chapter the word *games* is a generic term, incorporating conflict situations of a particular sort. In these situations the motives of the participants are dichotomized; the success of one party tends to be at the expense of the others, so they are in a conflict, or rivalrous relationship. However, any one of a wide range of agreements is preferable to no agreement, from the standpoint of all concerned, so it is in their mutual interest to cooperate to the extent of participating in the process and reaching some decision. Most parlor games are characterized by this condition and have some advantages for analytical purposes (the objectives usually are unambiguous and known to all parties; the rules and procedures are specified; there is a terminal point for play; etc.). However, the essential characteristics are shared by most instances of social or business conflict, so the mathematics of games is of general interest.

We shall introduce a two-person zero-sum game and a two-person non-constant-sum game in this chapter. Since the mathematics becomes diffi-

---

[1] Princeton, N.J.: Princeton University Press, 1944.

338 Quantitative analysis for business decisions

cult very quickly in response to minor modifications of the problem, we shall investigate relatively simple situations.

TWO-PERSON ZERO-SUM GAMES

In a two-person zero-sum game the interests of the two opponents are opposed in such a manner that the sum of their utilities add to zero for every outcome of the game. An example of a zero-sum game would be two persons matching pennies, where each person has a linear utility function with respect to money. The sum of money (utility) won by one is the sum of money (utility) lost by the other. Both participants know the payoff matrix in game theory terms.

It is a characteristic of two-person zero-sum games that there is a unique minimax solution. The prime advantage of a minimax solution in this situation is that it is the best choice of the decision maker if the other participant has chosen a minimax solution. Unlike a game against nature, where the sole advantage of a minimax solution is a form of conservatism, in a game against a thinking opponent, minimax is likely to be a desirable procedure. However, minimax may not lead to the best possible outcome if the opponent does not use a minimax solution.

We shall use a payoff table which shows the profits of the party whose strategies are listed down the left side of the table. The profits of the opponent (his strategies or acts are listed across the top of the table) are not listed, since they are the negative values of the payoffs shown. Table 18–1 illustrates a payoff table.

TABLE 18–1
Payoffs to player I

I \ II	Strategy 1	Strategy 2	Minimum of row
Strategy 1	10	14	10 ←
Strategy 2	7	12	7
Maximum of column	10	14	

↑

In the margins of the payoff table are the row minimums and column maximums. The minimax solution attempts to maximize a security level for the players (minimize the maximum possible loss, or maximize the minimum gain).

For each strategy of player I, we find the minimum gain we would make if faced by the best strategy of player II (these are the row minimums). For each strategy of player II, we find the maximum gain of player I (this is also the maximum loss of player II). These are the column maximums. Player I will choose the largest of the row minimums (in this case strategy 1), and player II will choose the smallest of the column maximums (in this case strategy 1). Since the maximum equals the minimax (both have values of 10), we have an equilibrium. The values are called an "equilibrium" pair. If one of the parties tried to move from this equilibrium while the other maintained his position, the mover would not improve his position. A *pure* strategy (i.e., a choice of only one strategy by each player) leads to a strictly determined game when the maximum of the minimum values of a row is equal to the minimum of the maximum values of the columns.[2] The value 10 is called a *saddle point.*

It should be noted that the margins of Table 18–1 give the guaranteed minimum profits of player I or the guaranteed maximum costs of player II. Since the values listed in the table may be expectations, these may be guaranteed expected values.

An example: Company versus union

The labor contract between your company and the union will terminate in the near future. A new contract must be negotiated, preferably before the old one expires. You are a member of a management group charged with selecting the company representatives and a strategy for them to follow during the coming negotiations. After a consideration of past experience, the group agrees that the feasible strategies for the company are as follows:

C_1 = all-out attack; hard, aggressive bargaining
C_2 = a reasoning, logical approach
C_3 = a legalistic strategy
C_4 = an agreeable, conciliatory approach

Which strategy is best for the company? That depends on the strategy adopted by the union, and that knowledge is not available. However, assume the history of the union suggests that it is considering one of the following set of approaches:

U_1 = all-out attack; hard, aggressive bargaining
U_2 = a reasoning, logical approach
U_3 = a legalistic strategy
U_4 = an agreeable, conciliatory approach

---

[2] This statement is valid as long as the decision maker whose positive gains are described in the payoff matrix has his strategies listed down the side of the matrix; otherwise, we would have to modify the description of a strictly determined game with pure strategies.

We now must consider the consequences of each of our lines of action, conditional upon the union adopting any one of its available strategies. With the aid of an outside mediator, we construct Table 18–2.

TABLE 18–2
Conditional gains of union (costs to company)

Union strategies	Company strategies				Row minimums
	C_1	C_2	C_3	C_4	
U_1	+20¢	+15¢	+12¢	+35¢	+12¢ ←
U_2	+25	+14	+ 8	+10	+ 8
U_3	+40	+ 2	+10	+ 5	+ 2
U_4	– 5	+ 4	+11	0	– 5
Column maximums	+40¢	+15¢	+12¢	+35¢	

↑

If the company adopts strategy C_1 and the union adopts strategy U_1, the final contract will involve a 20-cent-per-hour increase in wages and benefits to the average worker. If the union adopts strategy U_2 in response to C_1, it will secure a 25-cent-per-hour increase; strategy U_3 is even better for the union against the company's C_1—it yields a 40-cent-per-hour raise. However, if the union adopts U_4 against C_1, it will end up with a 5-cent cut in wages. The other entries have a similar connotation. Both union and company must decide on the overall strategy before negotiations begin; an attitude cannot be taken and then changed when the other party commits itself. Assume the company's utility function is approximately linear in money, so that these figures may serve as the utility index for the company.[3] The mediator informs the management group that he has been in touch with the union; it has also been considering alternative strategies and possible results of these lines of action. The mediator indicates that the union has constructed a table that does not vary significantly from Table 18–2, and he has provided the union with comparable information. Assume the union also has a linear utility function.

Given these conditions, what will the bargainers do? The company would prefer the union to be conciliatory (U_4) in response to its aggres-

[3] In general, this will not be the case unless the wage costs are a relatively unimportant part of the firm's total costs and the negotiations do not have strong emotional or symbolic significance. Where the union and the company are both large and strong, this is not likely to be the situation, and the possible wage changes should be converted to utility terms.

sive attack (C_1), with the result of a 5-cent reduction in wages. But if the company adopts C_1, it is quite possible the union will select a legalistic approach (U_3) and "sock" the firm for a 40-cent wage boost. The second best solution from the company's viewpoint would result from both the company and the union being agreeable (C_4, U_4). But if the company chooses C_4, the union might select an aggressive strategy (U_1) and win a 35-cent wage increase.

The union experiences the same difficulty: If it adopts U_3 in the hope of a 40-cent raise, the company may select a reasoning approach (C_2), which yields only 2 cents to the union. It is clear, however, that the union will never follow a conciliatory strategy (U_4), for it can gain more from U_1 no matter what strategy the company adopts. We may say that strategy U_1 *dominates* strategy U_4.

One rule the participants might adopt in such a situation is the minimax strategy. The company might adopt that strategy which minimizes the maximum wage increase it would have to grant, regardless of the action of the union. If the union adopted this rule, it would choose that strategy which maximized the mimimum wage increase. In the case at hand, the minimax strategy for the company is C_3, with a maximum wage increase of 12 cents; the minimax strategy for the union is U_1, with a minimum wage increase of 12 cents. Since, in Table 18–2, 12 cents is both the maximum of its C_3 column and the minimum of its U_1 row, it is the equilibrium solution of this situation. In game theory, 12 is designated as the value of the game. The pure strategies (U_1, C_3) provide equilibrium in this case, for if the company follows C_3, then U_1 is the union's best defense. If the union follows U_1, then C_3 is the company's best defense.[4]

MIXED STRATEGIES: A ZERO-SUM GAME

Not every conflict situation has a minimax equilibrium attainable by pure strategies. By changing one of the critical figures in Table 18–2, we can transform it into such a case. Say the intersection of C_3 and U_3 now is $+19$ cents rather than $+10$ cents, so that $+12$ cents is no longer the maximum of its column. This is shown in Table 18–3. Now C_2 is the strategy which minimizes the company's maximum loss; the union's maximum strategy remains U_1. The intersection of these strategies is not an equilibrium point, however, because $+15$ cents is not the maxi-

---

[4] A zero-sum game may have more than one equilibrium pair; however, all of the equilibrium pairs will have the same value, so the players will be indifferent among them.

TABLE 18-3
Conditional gains to union (costs to company)

Union strategies	Company strategies				Row minimums
	C_1	C_2	C_3	C_4	
U_1	+20¢	+15¢	+12¢	+35¢	+12¢ ←
U_2	+25	+14	+ 8	+10	+ 8
U_3	+40	+ 2	+19	+ 5	+ 2
U_4	− 5	+ 4	+11	+ 0	− 5
Column maximums	+40¢	+15¢	+19¢	+35¢	

↑

mum of its column *and* the minimum of its row. If the union adopts strategy U_1, the company would prefer to have strategy C_3, not C_2. But if the company chooses strategy C_3, the union would like U_3 better than U_1. If the union selects U_3, the company's optimum strategy would be C_2. Yet C_2 is the strategy against which the union would take U_1, as indicated initially. We have completed the full circle. The pure strategies (U_1, C_2) are not an equilibrium pair; they are not best against each other.

Let us reduce Table 18–3 to the strategies shown in Table 18–4. This is done by successive elimination of dominated strategies. Union strategy

TABLE 18-4

Union strategies	Company strategies	
	C_2	C_3
U_1	+15¢	+12¢
U_3	+ 2	+19

U_4 is dominated by U_1, so U_4 may be dropped. Then company strategy C_1 is dominated by either C_2 or C_3; thus, C_1 may be dropped. This leaves union strategy U_2 dominated by U_1, so that the only remaining union strategies are U_1 and U_3. At this point, company strategy C_4 is dominated by C_2, so the only pertinent strategies for the company are C_2 and C_3. Our objective now is to derive some *probability mixture* of the strategies (that is, a *mixed strategy*) which will improve the position of both parties with respect to the available pure strategies. For example, assume that it is possible for the company to use strategy C_2, at random, one half of the time, and strategy C_3, at random, the other half. Then, if the union used strategy U_1, the expected wage increase would be:

$$\tfrac{1}{2}(+15\cent) + \tfrac{1}{2}(+12\cent) = +13\tfrac{1}{2}\cent$$

If the union used U_3, the expected wage increase would be:

$$\tfrac{1}{2}(+2\cent) + \tfrac{1}{2}(+19\cent) = +10\tfrac{1}{2}\cent$$

Either of these is preferable from the company viewpoint to the +15 cents indicated by the minimax rule. The union, of course, also may adopt such a mixed strategy. One of von Neumann's great contributions was to prove that every two-person zero-sum game, regardless of the number of strategies available to the participants, has a unique equilibrium value. As a special case, the solution may involve pure strategies, as shown initially. If this is not the case, we still know that for some pair of *mixed* strategies an equilibrium exists.

Graphical solution

A simple and instructive way to find the solution for the two-person two-strategy case is the geometric method suggested by Luce and Raiffa.[5] First, we shall derive the optimum mixed strategy for the company. Consider Figure 18–1, where possible mixed company strategies may be

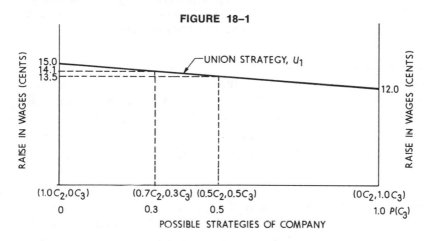

FIGURE 18–1

evaluated against the union's strategy U_1. On the vertical axes the possible raises are plotted. the horizontal axis is scaled in terms of mixed strategies for the company from the limit of $(1.0C_2, 0C_3)$—the pure strategy C_2—to the limit $(0C_2, 1.0C_3)$, the pure strategy C_3. At the ex-

[5] R. D. Luce and H. Raiffa, *Games and Decisions* (New York: John Wiley & Sons, Inc., 1957).

tremes the payoffs are $+15$ cents and $+12$ cents, as shown in Table 18–4. The device of the mixed strategy enables us to select any point on the line connecting $+15$ cents and $+12$ cents as a payoff to the union's strategy, U_1. For example, if we wanted to choose $+13.5$ cents in response to U_1, we would select the mixed strategy $(0.5C_2, 0.5C_3)$. If we chose the mixed strategy $(0.7C_2, 0.3C_3)$, the payoff would be $+14.1$ cents. Any point on the straight line in Figure 18–1 is feasible if the union follows strategy U_1.

Now, in Figure 18–2, we construct the appropriate mixed-strategies payoff line for U_3, and consider it in conjunction with the U_1 line devel-

FIGURE 18–2

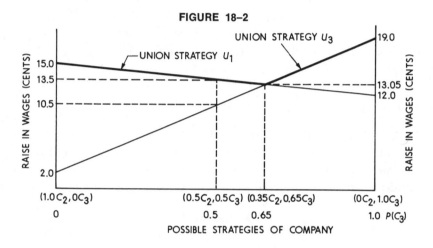

oped in Figure 18–1. The new line indicates the returns to the union for strategy U_3, assuming the company selects a mixed strategy between $(1.0C_2, 0C_3)$ and $(0C_2, 1.0C_3)$. For example, if the company adopts $(0.5C_2, 0.5C_3)$, the raise is 13.5 cents if the union adopts strategy U_1 and 10.5 cents if the union adopts U_3. From the company's standpoint the maximum payoff for this strategy is 13.5 cents. For mixed strategies between $(1.0C_2, 0C_3)$ and $(0.35C_2, 0.65C_3)$, the maximum raise to the union is obtained if the union follows strategy U_1; for mixed strategies between $(0.35C_2, 0.65C_3)$ and $(0C_2, 1.0C_3)$, the maximum raise to the union is associated with union strategy U_3. The heavy line in Figure 18–2 defines the set of maximum raises the company would have to provide, assuming the union always adopted the most favorable strategy available to it in response to any mixed strategy adopted by the company. If the company follows the rule of minimizing the maximum raise it would have to pay, it would adopt the mixed strategy $(0.35C_2, 0.65C_3)$ and give the union a raise of $0.35(15¢) + 0.65(12¢) = 13.05¢$ if it adopts strategy U_1, or $0.35(2¢) + 0.65(19¢) = 13.05¢$ if the union adopts strategy U_3. Regardless of the union's action, it cannot get more than 13.05 cents per hour of expected wage increase (i.e., its best average increase is 13.05).

What strategy could we expect the union to follow? The minimax philosophy dictates that the union assume the company will erect the stoutest defense against any strategy it selects. We have sketched in Figure 18–3

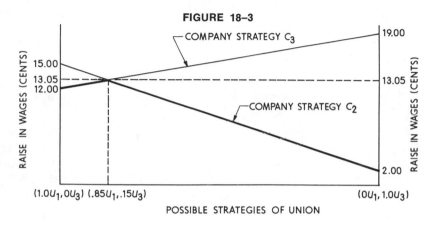

FIGURE 18–3

the strategies available to the union and the set of minimum wage increases associated with those strategies. If the company adopts strategy C_3, the wage increases to the union in return for various mixed strategies are indicated by the line joining 12 cents and 19 cents. This line would indicate the minimum raise for strategies between $(1.0U_1, 0U_3)$ and $(0.85U_1, 0.15U_3)$. The line joining 15 cents and 2 cents defines the wage increases in response to various union mixed strategies if the company follows strategy C_2. This strategy provides the minimum wage boost for union action in the range $(0.85U_1, 0.15U_3)$ to $(0U_1, 1.0U_3)$. If the union wishes to maximize the minimum wage increase, it will adopt the strategy $(0.85U_1, 0.15U_3)$. This provides an expected increase of

$$0.85(15\cent) + 0.15(2\cent) = 13.05\cent$$

if the company adopts strategy C_2, and

$$0.85(12\cent) + 0.15(19\cent) = 13.05\cent$$

if the company adopts strategy C_3. The sum 13.05 cents is a saddle point in this game and provides the equilibrium solution.

It should be remembered that the example assumes that the monetary measures are also utility measures. The 13.05 is the expected utility of the cost to the company of following the mixed strategy, and it is also the expected utility of the wage increase to the union. If we fail to recognize that the 13.05 measures utility (as well as money), then we may fall into the trap of thinking that the mixed strategy is not a minimax strategy because one possible event is a wage increase of 19 cents following the mixed strategy, but the maximum wage increase following C_2 is only 15 cents. For example, the expected utility of the cost to the company of U_3 is equal to

$$0.35U(2\cent) + 0.65U(19\cent) = 0.35(2) + 0.65(19) = 13.05$$

The 13.05 is a utility measure and, as such, leads us to conclude that the mixed strategy results in minimum maximum cost for the company and maximum minimum wage increase to the union (in terms of expected utility or, equivalently in this example, expected monetary values).

Algebraic solution

Instead of a graphical solution, we can solve algebraically for the probability that will cause the expected utility, from the point of view of the union, to be independent of the strategy of the company. Thus no matter what strategy the company uses, the expected utility of the union strategy will be the same. Assume that the union uses a random device that leads to a probability of p for strategy U_1 and $(1 - p)$ for strategy U_3.

If the company uses strategy C_2, the union's expected utility is (see Table 18–4 for the source of the numbers):

$$E(U|C_2) = 0.15p + 0.02(1 - p)$$

If the company uses strategy C_3 the union has for its expected utility:

$$E(U|C_3) = 0.12p + 0.19(1 - p)$$

Set these two expected utilities equal and solve for p:

$$0.15p + 0.02(1 - p) = 0.12p + 0.19(1 - p)$$
$$0.03p = 0.17(1 - p)$$
$$p = \frac{17}{20} = 0.85$$

The expected utility of the union's mixed strategy using a p of 0.85 is:

$$E(U|C_2) = E(U|C_3) = 0.15 \times \frac{17}{20} + 0.02 \times \frac{3}{20} = \frac{2.55 + 0.06}{20}$$

$$= \frac{2.61}{20} = 0.1305 \text{ or } 13.05\cent.$$

This expected value is larger than the minimum values that could result if either pure strategy is followed.

Solving the same problem from the point of view of the company, we now let p represent the probability that the *company* chooses strategy C_2. We have for the expected costs for the two strategies of the union:

$$E(C|U_1) = 0.15p + 0.12(1 - p)$$
$$E(C|U_3) = 0.02p + 0.19(1 - p)$$

Set these two expressions equal and solve for p:

$$0.15p + 0.12(1 - p) = 0.02p + 0.19(1 - p)$$
$$0.13p = 0.07(1 - p)$$
$$p = \frac{7}{20} = 0.35$$
$$1 - p = 0.65$$

With a p of $\frac{7}{20}$ for the company's mixed strategy the expected cost to the company is:

$$E(C|U_1) = E(C|U_3) = 0.15\left(\frac{7}{20}\right) + 0.12\left(\frac{13}{20}\right) = \frac{1.05 + 1.56}{20}$$
$$= 0.1305 \text{ or } 13.05\cancel{c}$$

This expected cost is independent of the union's strategy.

The algebraic solution method can be used to solve for mixed strategies among more than two possible acts, while the graphical solution shown earlier is limited to games in which at least one player has only two possible choices.

Linear programming solution

It is also possible to formulate the problem of finding the equilibrium mixed strategy as a linear programming problem. This has decided computational advantages if the number of pure strategies available to the players is large, since efficient computer programs exist for linear programming problems. The Appendix to this chapter describes the formulation of a two-person zero-sum game as a linear programming problem.

MIXED STRATEGIES AND GAMES AGAINST NATURE

This section questions whether mixed strategies can be used to help the decision maker in a game against nature. Let us consider an example used in Dorfman, Samuelson, and Solow and originally provided by Williams.[6]

The problem involves the firm of Gunning and Kappler and their testing procedure. We shall consider two tests and two possible states of nature. The payoff table is given in terms of costs (see Table 18–5).

TABLE 18–5
Costs

| Nature | Gunning and Kappler's strategy | |
	s_1 ($1 test)	s_2 (sure-fire test)
Defect..........	4¼	1
No defect	2	10

Let p be the probability of Gunning and Kappler taking strategy s_1, and solve for p so that the expected cost is the same no matter which strategy ("defect" or "no defect") nature uses. We obtain:

$$4.25p + 1(1 - p) = 2p + 10(1 - p)$$
$$p = \frac{4}{5}$$

The expected cost is $3.60 no matter what state nature chooses:

$$E(\text{cost}) = 4.25 \times \tfrac{4}{5} + 1 \times \tfrac{1}{5} = 3.4 + 0.2$$
$$= \$3.60 \text{ if nature chooses "defect"}$$

$$E(\text{cost}) = 2 \times \tfrac{4}{5} + 10 \times \tfrac{1}{5} = 1.6 + 2$$
$$= \$3.60 \text{ if nature chooses "no defect"}$$

The above procedure may be criticized because it omits any consideration of the likelihood of the states of nature and substitutes an implicit assumption that nature will behave like a conscious opponent and follow a minimax strategy. The consequences of these assumptions may be seen by changing the problem slightly. Now assume that the cost for the $1 test and the state "no defect" is $1.25 rather than $2. This improves the cost picture associated with the $1 test; and intuitively, we should expect the probability of choosing this test to be increased. Table 18–6 shows the new payoffs.

───────
    [6] See R. Dorfman, P. A. Samuelson, and R. M. Solow, *Linear Programming and Economic Analysis* (New York: McGraw-Hill Book Co., 1958), pp. 435–36; or J. D. Williams, *The Compleat Strategyst* (New York: McGraw-Hill Book Co., 1954), pp. 76–78.

TABLE 18–6
Costs

	Gunning and Kappler's strategy	
Nature	s_1 ($1 test)	s_2 (sure-fire test)
Defect.	4¼	1
No defect	1¼	10

Solving for p:

$$4.25p + (1 - p) = 1.25p + 10(1 - p)$$
$$p = \tfrac{3}{4}$$

The improvement in the payoffs associated with strategy s_1 results in a *reduction* in the probability of choosing s_1 from 0.8 to 0.75. This is not consistent with our intuition. We would have expected an improvement in the consequences associated with an act to increase the probability of choosing that act. This is not the case using a minimax mixed-strategy approach. The expected cost is now:

$$E(\text{cost}) = 4.25 \times \tfrac{3}{4} + 1 \times \tfrac{1}{4}$$
$$= \$3.44 \text{ if nature chooses "defect"}$$

$$E(\text{cost}) = 1.25 \times \tfrac{3}{4} + 10 \times \tfrac{1}{4}$$
$$= \$3.44 \text{ if nature chooses "no defect"}$$

The expected cost has decreased from $3.60 to $3.44, as we would expect with the improved cost situation.

Assume that nature is a thinking opponent. It realizes that the $1 test is now a better test; thus the firm is more likely to choose it than when the cost was $2. If this is the case, then nature should tend to choose "defect" rather than "no defect." But if nature follows this course, the firm should tend to choose the sure-fire test. This reasoning, in the case of a thinking opponent, leads to the choice of a mixed strategy. However, where nature is not a thinking opponent, the mixed-strategy approach does not apply.

EVALUATION OF MINIMAX STRATEGY

In games against nature, minimax strategy is very conservative, and minimax is not a very desirable criterion. However, in a two-person constant-sum game against a thinking opponent, it is reasonable, since it provides a participant with maximum security. It insures a minimum outcome for you and a maximum for your opponent, regardless of the behavior of the opponent. No matter how cunning, how clever, how unscrupulous he may be, his best outcome is determined by your actions. You are indifferent to the strategy he selects, for you are prepared for all contingencies.

Minimax has a particular appeal to students on academic scholarships who are preparing for exams, football coaches, and most credit officers and bankers. It is not a good strategy for those who think they can outguess their opponents and are willing to accept the risk of going on the offensive in nonzero-sum games.

The notion of using a mixed strategy for "one-shot" business decisions is criticized by some analysts. You might imagine the reaction of a seasoned buisnessman, for example, if you recommended that he adopt a marketing strategy against his competitor (price changes, advertising budget, etc.) by letting the decision depend on the spin of a roulette wheel or some other randomizing device.

While there isn't any direct answer to this criticism, there are some insights gained from game theory that are relevant. Recall that one assumption of game theory implied perfect information for both opponents about the other's strategies and payoffs (or utilities). In this setting, a mixed strategy is a means of camouflaging your intentions. In the real world such perfect information is rarely available. Your opponent does not know exactly your payoffs and strategies, and you do not know his. Hence there is less need of camouflage. The uncertainty present serves somewhat the same purpose as randomizing.[7]

Secondly, when there is no pure strategy solution, a game player is, in a sense, exploitable. That is, for any pure strategy he adopts, there is some strategy of his opponent that can hurt or exploit him. A mixed strategy can be viewed as a means of compromising or hedging against such exploitation.

NONZERO-SUM GAMES

For most two-person conflict situations the utilities of the participants will not sum to a constant for all outcomes of the game. Some solutions will yield more joint satisfaction to the participants than others. These games are called nonzero-sum games. A famous example, originally called the "prisoner's dilemma," is given here.

---

[7] An interesting example of this idea is developed by Robert B. Wilson in the context of a bidding problem. See R. Wilson, "Competitive Bidding with Disparate Information," *Management Science,* March 1969; and "Competitive Bidding with Asymmetrical Information," *Management Science,* July 1967.

Assume two firms are faced with a decision relative to whether or not they will advertise. They each have two possible decisions—no advertising, or advertising. The table of payoffs is as shown in Table 18–7.

TABLE 18–7

I \ II	No advertising	Advertise
No advertising. . . .	+ 2 +2	+ 5 −15
Advertise	−15 +5	−10 −10

The numbers in the table refer to the utilities of the two firms for each pair of decisions: firm I's utility and firm II's utility. For example, if firm I advertises and firm II does not, firm I will have a utility of 5 and firm II a utility of −15.

The payoff table for firm II is shown in Table 18–8.

TABLE 18–8

I \ II	No advertising	Advertise
No advertising. . . . Advertise	+ 2 −15	+ 5 −10

No matter what firm I's decision is, firm II is better off if it advertises. That is, if firm I does not advertise, firm II will, for it prefers a payoff of five rather than a payoff of two. If firm I advertises, so will firm II, for it prefers a payoff of −10 to one of −15. Thus the advertising strategy dominates the no-advertising strategy for firm II, and firm II is led to the decision to advertise. Exactly the same analysis holds for firm I, since the decision it faces is exactly the same as that of firm II. Firms I and II are both led by a rational decision process to advertise and incur a loss of −10 each. If they were not so rational, they might each follow the dominated strategy of no advertising and receive a payoff of +2 each.

Of course, the above analysis assumes the two parties cannot co-operate (i.e., communicate their intentions), since this would change the nature of the game. It also assumes a one-shot playing of the game, with no learning by the parties concerned. It is possible that firms I and II would learn by the unhappy experience of their first try at this game and co-operate during a later playing of the game, even without actually communicating.

The above is an example of a two-person nonzero-sum game. Although there is a type of solution because the advertising decision dominates the no-advertising decision, it is not a very satisfactory solution. A pair of nonrational players may arrive at the more desirable solution where both parties do not advertise. Nonzero-sum games frequently do not have easily determined satisfactory solutions.

UNCERTAIN PAYOFFS

In the above example the payoffs were certain amounts. It is possible for the payoffs of a game to be subject to probability distributions. For example, instead of firm II knowing that its loss will be 10 if both firms advertise, it can be told that the payoff will be either a loss of 40 with a 0.5 probability or a gain of 20 with a probability of 0.5. The expected loss is:

$$-40 \times 0.5 = -20$$
$$20 \times 0.5 = \underline{10}$$
$$-10$$

When the payoffs are the result of a stochastic process, it necessitates an additional computation. Before we analyze the possible decisions, the expected utility of each pair of decisions is computed and inserted into the matrix. It should be remembered that we are using expectations of utility and not expected monetary values.

CONCLUSIONS

The reader should ask himself if there are any situations in the real world where two or more parties are competing with each other where the gains come close to being zero sum (what one person loses the other gains) or are nonzero sum. Are the results of such games always beneficial to society?

Examples of real life "games" range from wars (where one party can only win at the expense of the other and where both parties are likely to lose) to the automobile industry and college football where escalation in "selling" expenditures sometimes results in all parties being worse off than they would have been with different strategies.

It is far from clear that in the real world exact solutions can be obtained to game situations, or that the theories can be applied exactly. On the other hand, game theory helps us to learn how to approach and understand a conflict situation, and to improve the decision process.

APPENDIX. LINEAR PROGRAMMING SOLUTION TO TWO-PERSON ZERO-SUM GAMES

Suppose the game has two players, A and B. Player A has possible pure strategies $A_1, A_2, \ldots A_m$. Player B has strategies $B_1, B_2, \ldots B_n$. And a_{ij} is the payoff to player A when player A is using strategy A_i and player B is using B_j. This is shown in Table 18–9.

TABLE 18–9
Generalized game problem (payoffs to player A)

Strategies for player A	Strategies for player B			
	B_1	B_2	$\cdots$	B_n
A_1	a_{11}	a_{12}	$\cdots$	a_{1n}
A_2	a_{21}	a_{22}	$\cdots$	a_{2n}
A_3	a_{31}	a_{32}	$\cdots$	a_{3n}
.	.	.		.
.	.	.		.
.	.	.		.
A_m	a_{m1}	a_{m2}		a_{mn}

A mixed strategy for player A consists of a set of probabilities X_i (for $i = 1$ to m), such that $\sum_{i=1}^{m} X_i = 1.0$. Each X_i represents the probability of using pure strategy A_i. The objective for player A is to obtain an expected value V (the value of the game) as large as possible. He can only be sure of the expected value V, if his strategy will guarantee that regardless of what strategy his opponent adopts, he will obtain an expectation of V or more. For example, if player B were to adopt B_1, then A's strategy must be such that:

$$a_{11}X_1 + a_{21}X_2 + a_{31}X_3 + \cdots + a_{m1}X_m \geq V$$

Similarly if player B uses B_2, then to guarantee V, A must have:

$$a_{12}X_1 + a_{22}X_2 + a_{32}X_3 + \cdots + a_{m2}X_m \geq V$$

A similar condition holds for any strategy B may play. Hence, the linear programming problem for A is:[8]

Maximize: V

Subject to: $a_{11}X_1 + a_{21}X_2 + \cdots + a_{m1}X_m - V \geq 0$

$a_{12}X_1 + a_{22}X_2 + \cdots + a_{m2}X_m - V \geq 0$

.

.

.

$a_{1n}X_1 + a_{2n}X_2 + \cdots + a_{mn}X_m - V \geq 0$

$X_1 + \quad X_2 + \cdots + \quad X_m \qquad = 1$

all $X_i \geq 0$

The last equation guarantees that the probabilities add to one.

The solution to this problem gives the equilibrium mixed strategy $(X_1, X_2, \ldots, X_m)$ for player A and the value of the game V.

It is interesting to note that the dual of the linear programming problem for player A is the primal problem from player B's point of view. Let $(U_1, U_2, \ldots, U_n)$ be the mixed strategy probabilities for player B. He wishes to minimize the expected payoff to his opponent. His problem is thus:

Minimize: W

Subject to: $a_{11}U_1 + a_{12}U_2 + \cdots + a_{1n}U_n \leq W$

$a_{21}U_1 + a_{22}U_2 + \cdots + a_{2n}U_n \leq W$

.

.

.

$a_{m1}U_1 + a_{m2}U_2 + \cdots + a_{mn}U_n \leq W$

$U_1 + \quad U_2 + \cdots + \quad U_n = 1$

all $U_i \geq 0$

The solution gives the optimum strategy for B $(U_1, U_2, \ldots U_n)$ and the value of the game W. Note that W must equal V.

BIBLIOGRAPHY

DAVIS, M. D. *Game Theory, a Nontechnical Introduction.* New York: Basic Books, Inc., 1970.

DORFMAN, R., SAMUELSON, P. A., and SOLOW, R. M. *Linear Programming and Economic Analysis.* New York: McGraw-Hill Book Co., 1958.

---

[8] There is one minor problem that may arise. If the game is such that the value of the game to player A is negative (i.e., $V < 0$), then standard linear programming computer codes will not solve the problem. An easy way around this is to add a constant K to every a_{ij} so that all $a_{ij} \geq 0$. This will guarantee that $V \geq 0$. The solution obtained is optimal, and the value of the game is $V - K$.

FRIEDMAN, L. "Game Theory Models in the Allocation of Advertising Expenditures," *Operations Research,* September-October 1958.

LUCE, R. D., and RAIFFA, H. *Games and Decisions.* New York: John Wiley & Sons, Inc., 1957.

OWEN, G. *Game Theory.* Philadelphia: W. B. Saunders Co., 1968.

RAPOPORT, A. *Two Person Game Theory.* Ann Arbor: University of Michigan Press, 1966.

SHUBIK, M. (ed.). *Game Theory and Related Approaches to Social Behavior.* New York: John Wiley & Sons, Inc., 1964.

———. *Strategy and Market Structure.* New York: John Wiley & Sons, Inc., 1959.

VON NEUMANN, J., and MORGENSTERN, O. *Theory of Games and Economic Behavior.* Princeton: Princeton University Press, 1944.

WILLIAMS, J. D. *The Compleat Strategyst.* Rev. ed. New York: McGraw-Hill Book Co., 1966.

PROBLEMS

18–1. Prepare the payoff matrix for matching pennies, player 1 saying he can match player 2. What does this assume about the utilities of players 1 and 2?

18–2. In matching pennies, is the minimax strategy a pure strategy?

18–3. If a player follows a pure strategy in matching pennies, what is the most he is likely to lose on a series of n plays?

18–4. Assume the following payoff matrix for two opponents, A and B, the amounts being the utility gained by A and lost by B for any given intersection of strategies:

	B_1	B_2
A_1	10	6
A_2	8	2

a) What strategy will A follow?
b) What strategy will B follow?
c) What is the "value" of the game?
d) Plot the payoffs from these strategies from player A's standpoint.

18–5. Assume the following payoff matrix for A and B, the amounts being the utilities gained by A and lost by B for any given intersection of strategies:

	B_1	B_2
A_1	10	6
A_2	8	12

a) What is the maximum minimum gain A can make for sure by following a pure strategy?

b) What is the minimum maximum loss B can incur for sure by following a pure strategy?

c) What is the mixed strategy for A?

d) Plot the mixed strategies for A and B.

e) If A and B follow mixed strategies, what is the value of the game?

18–6. What type of conflict situation is more likely—a zero-sum game or a nonzero-sum game?

18–7. Say the following payoff matrix is appropriate for the merchandising strategies of two opponents:

Strategies of a	Strategies of b	
	b_1	b_2
a_1	0 ⟍ 0	1 ⟍ 2
a_2	4 ⟍ 1	5 ⟍ 3

a) What strategy will a follow? Why?

b) What strategy will b follow? Why?

c) What outcome would you predict for this situation?

18–8. Two firms, f and g, face the following profit payoff for alternative merchandising strategies:

Strategies of g	Strategies of f	
	f_1	f_2
g_1	8 ⟍ 8	1 ⟍ 10
g_2	10 ⟍ 1	2 ⟍ 2

a) What strategy will *f* follow? Why?

b) What strategy will *g* follow? Why?

c) What is the solution of the game?

d) Identify the equilibrium pair, if there is one.

18–9.   If Problem 18–8 were repeated daily for *n* days, where *n* is large, do you think the players would continue to follow an equilibrium strategy? What does this suggest?

18–10.   The ABC Company and the XYZ Company are both currently distributing, through a subsidiary, automobiles in the country of Akro. The profits per year of the two subsidiaries are currently as follows: ABC, $10 million; and XYZ, $20 million.

The ABC Company is considering establishing a manufacturing plant in Akro. An analyst has projected a profit of $38 million after the plant begins operations (this assumes the XYZ Company continues to distribute automobiles, but not to manufacture them, in the country).

An analyst for the XYZ Company has heard of the plans of the ABC Company. If the plant is built by ABC, he projects XYZ's profits to fall to $4 million. If the XYZ Company builds a plant and the ABC Company does not, he anticipates profits of $38 million and a decrease in the profits of ABC to $4 million.

If both companies build plants, it is expected that they would both earn $5 million per year. What should the companies do?

18–11.   Two computer manufacturers, A and B, are attempting to sell computer systems to two banks, 1 and 2. Company A has four salesmen, company B has only three available. The computer companies must decide upon how many salesmen to assign to call on each bank. Thus, company A can assign four salesmen to bank 1 and none to bank 2, or three to bank 1 and one to bank 2, etc.

Each bank will buy one computer system. The probability that a bank will buy from a particular computer company is directly related to the number of salesmen calling from that company relative to total salesmen calling. Thus, if company A assigned three men to bank 1 and company B assigned two men, the odds would be three out of five that bank 1 would purchase a company A computer system. (As a special case, if none call from either company, the odds are one half for buying either computer.)

Let the payoff be the expected number of computer systems that company A sells. (Then two minus this payoff is the expected number company B sells.)

What strategy should company A use in allocating its salesmen? What strategy should company B use? What is the value of the game to company A? What is the meaning of the value of the game in this problem?

18–12.   Refer to Problem 18–11. Suppose that bank 1 is going to buy two computer systems, whereas bank 2 will buy only one. In this case, what is the optimum strategy for company A? For company B? What is the value of the game?

18–13. Refer to Problem 18–11. Suppose that each bank bought the computer system from the company sending the larger number of salesmen. (If both companies send equal numbers, the decision is made by the flip of a fair coin.) In this case, what is the optimum strategy for company A? For company B? What is the value of the game?

18–14. Firms I and II are competing for business. Whatever I gains II loses. The table shows the utilities to firm I for various market shares (assume the game is zero-sum).

Firm I's utility

I \ II	No advertising	Medium advertising	Large advertising	Row minimums
No advertising.	60	50	40	40
Medium advertising	70	70	50	50
Large advertising	80	60	75	60
Column maximums	80	70	75	

Find an equilibrium solution.

19

Waiting lines: Queuing theory

Queues or waiting lines are very common in everyday life. There are few individuals in modern society who have not had to wait in line for a bus, a taxi, a movie ticket, a grocery check-out, a haircut, or registration material at the beginning of the school year. Most of us consider lines an unavoidable part of our civilized life, and we put up with them with more or less good humor. Occasionally, the size of a line or the wait we encounter discourages us, and we abandon the project, and a sale is lost by some enterprise. This chapter is concerned with the decision-making process of the business firm (or government agency) which has charge of the queue and makes decisions relative to the number of service facilities which are operating.

Queuing theory or waiting line theory is primarily concerned with processes which have the characteristics of having random arrivals (i.e., arrivals at random time intervals), and the servicing of the customer is also a random process. If we assume there are costs associated with waiting in line, and if there are costs of adding more channels (i.e., adding more service facilities), we want to minimize the sum of the costs of waiting and the costs of providing service facilities. The computations will lead to such measures as the expected number of people in line or the expected waiting time of the arrivals. These measures can then be used in the cost computations to determine the number of service facilities which are desirable.

Queuing theory may be applied to determining the optimum number of:

Toll booths for a bridge or toll road
Doctors available for clinic calls
Repairmen servicing machines
Landing strips for aircraft

Docks for ships
Clerks for a spare-parts counter
Windows for a post office

The above are a few examples of the many different waiting line situations encountered by managers.

EXPERIENCE AND QUEUES

Fortunately for the businessman, reasonable queuing decisions can frequently be made based on past experience or on the facts of the current situation. Thus the management of a grocery chain knows approximately how many check-out counters should be installed in a new store by looking at the experience of comparable stores. At any time of the day the store manager can tell how many of the installed counters should be manned by noting the lengths of the queues and adding personnel from other chores, or sending the present check-out personnel to other tasks. Also, historical records (say of machine down-time) can indicate the amount of time that machines had to queue for repairs rather than relying upon the computations resulting from a mathematical model to determine the amount of downtime.

Although a number of problems encountered by an executive can be reasonably solved by the use of intuition or past experience, there will be many situations which are too complex for our intuition or where we desire a more accurate answer than we can expect to be supplied by intuition. In these situations the problem can be approached by either simulation or a mathematical model procedure. In this chapter we shall investigate several mathematical models of waiting-line situations; the next chapter demonstrates how simulation can be used to study more complex waiting-line problems.

MATHEMATICAL MODELS OF QUEUING

The presentation of this chapter has been designed so that no special mathematical knowledge is required. An Appendix to the chapter contains a derivation of a model, but we have not tried to show the origin of the formulas in the body of the chapter. We could consider the following types of situations:

1. Arrivals and services occurring following a given time schedule
2. Arrivals coming randomly from an infinite universe where:
    a)   There is one service facility
    b)   There are multiple service facilities

3. Arrivals coming from a finite population where:
    a)   There is one service facility
    b)   There are multiple service facilities

A solution to the first situation is to have the facilities exactly scheduled to meet the arrivals. A mass-production assembly line could be an example of arrivals with a given time schedule.

Both single- and multiple-service facility situations will be illustrated for the situation where random arrivals come from an infinite universe, but only the single-service facility situation will be explored when the arrivals come from a finite universe.

A SINGLE-SERVICE FACILITY: ARRIVALS FROM AN INFINITE POPULATION

To simplify the analysis, we shall first assume there is one channel or service facility. Those waiting accept service on a "first come, first served" basis and do not get discouraged by the length of the line (i.e., there is no balking and going elsewhere for service). We shall assume that arrivals and services are coming individually from an infinite universe and that the process for both arrivals and services is Poisson.[1] The assumptions are:

1. Arrivals are independent of each other. Services are also independent. That is, what happened in previous time periods is not relevant to the future (we can start at time *t*, or time *t* plus *x*, and it does not affect the probability of an arrival or of a service completion).
2. Both arrivals and services are homogeneous relative to time. That is, the average arrival and service rates do not change over time.

These assumptions may seem somewhat restrictive. Later, we shall relax the assumption of one channel and an infinite universe, but we shall retain the other assumptions in this chapter. The flavor of queuing theory may be gained for the described models, but the expert operations researcher has at his disposal many more models than the ones described in this chapter. However, the business manager should realize that any model will have to make assumptions about the probabilities of arrivals and services. There are three basic elements of uncertainty:

1. We may not know the form of the theoretical probability distribution which applies.
2. Even if we know which probability distribution applies, we shall probably not know the parameters of the process.

---
[1] See Appendix 1 at the end of this chapter for a description of a Poisson process.

3. If items 1 and 2 were known, we would still not know the actual outcome, but only the expected outcome (or the probability distribution of outcomes).

Thus, although the model builder may seem to come up with exact answers as a result of applying his model, there is a great deal of uncertainty associated with solutions. Even if the form of the probability distribution were known (say we knew the distribution was Poisson), and even if we knew the parameters of the process (say we knew the mean), the output of the model would still be in the form of an expected value, and the distribution would have a variance. Thus, we are still solving a problem under conditions of uncertainty.

THE MODEL

We shall first assume there is one service facility and the arrivals are emanating from an infinite universe. The arrivals and services occur in accordance with a Poisson process. Arrivals are served on a "first come, first served" basis. All the formulas assume the process has been operating long enough to remove the effects of initial conditions. Let:

A = average number of customers arriving in one unit of time

S = average number of customers the facility services in one unit of time, assuming no shortage of customers

n = number of units either being serviced or waiting in the system

n_q = number in the queue (the number in the queue does not include the unit being serviced)

p_n = probability of having n units in the system

w = time an arrival must wait in the queue

There are several relationships of interest:[2]

$$(19\text{--}1) \qquad\qquad p_0 = 1 - A/S$$

$$(19\text{--}2) \qquad\qquad p_n = (A/S)^n p_0$$

$$(19\text{--}3) \qquad\qquad p_n = (A/S)p_{n-1}$$

The expected number in the waiting line or being serviced is:

$$(19\text{--}4) \qquad\qquad E(n) = \frac{A}{(S - A)}$$

---

[2] See Appendix 2 at the end of this chapter for the derivation of equation (19–2).

The expected number in the queue is:

$$\text{(19–5)} \qquad E(n_q) = \frac{A^2}{S(S - A)}$$

The average waiting time (in the queue) of an arrival is:

$$\text{(19–6)} \qquad E(w) = \frac{E(n_q)}{A}$$

The probability that the number in the queue and being serviced is greater than k is:

$$\text{(19–7)} \qquad P(n > k) = (A/S)^{k+1}$$

Equations 19–1 to 19–7 apply only if $\frac{A}{S} < 1$. If the arrival rate, A, is greater than the service rate, the queue will grow without end.

Example

Assume patients for the medical office of a very large plant arrive randomly following a Poisson process. The office can process patients at an average rate of five patients an hour (one at a time); the service process is also Poisson. Patients arrive at an average of four per hour (we shall assume the process is Poisson, though this is not exact, since the population is not infinite, although it is very large). The plant operates 24 hours a day.

$$A = 4$$
$$S = 5$$

Since $\frac{A}{S} < 1$, we can use the following relationships:

$$E(n) = \frac{A}{(S - A)} = \frac{4}{(5 - 4)} = 4$$

There will be an average of four persons in line or being serviced.

$$E(n_q) = \frac{A^2}{S(S - A)} = \frac{4 \times 4}{5(5 - 4)} = \frac{16}{5} = 3.2$$

There will be an average of 3.2 persons in line.

$$E(w) = \frac{E(n_q)}{A} = \frac{16/5}{4} = \frac{4}{5} = 0.8$$

The average waiting time of a patient is 0.8 of an hour. All of the above measures assume the process has been operating long enough for the probabilities resulting from the physical characteristics of the problem to have made themselves felt; i.e., the system is in equilibrium.

We now know:

1. The average number of patients in the office is four.
2. The average number of patients waiting is 3.2.
3. A patient will wait for four fifths of an hour, on the average.

If we assume a 24-hour workday, there will be an average of 96 patients arriving per day, and the expected total lost time of patients waiting will be:

$$T = A \times 24 \text{ hours} \times E(w)$$
$$T = 4 \times 24 \times 0.8 = 76.8 \text{ hours}$$

There will be a cost associated with these 76.8 hours. Assume the cost to the corporation is $10 for each hour lost by a worker waiting. The average cost per day from waiting is:

$$76.8 \times \$10 = \$768$$

We can also compute the cumulative probability distribution of patients in the office. (See Table 19–1).

TABLE 19–1

More than this number in office k	Probability $P(n > k) = \left(\dfrac{A}{S}\right)^{k+1} = \left(\dfrac{4}{5}\right)^{k+1}$
0	0.8000
1	0.6400
2	0.5120
3	0.4096
4	0.3277
5	0.2621
6	0.2097

It may be that we want to limit the probability of a given occurrence. For example, if we are willing to accept a 0.41 probability that more than three persons will be in the office (i.e., more than two waiting), then one office is acceptable.

Suppose that we could in some fashion increase the service rate to six per hour and thereby decrease the average time spent in service from 12 minutes to 10 minutes. What would be the effect of this change?

With $S = 6$, the expected number in the queue, $E(n_q)$, is 1.3 instead of the 3.2 found above. This can be seen as follows:

$$E(n_q) = \frac{A^2}{S(S-A)} = \frac{4 \times 4}{6(6-4)} = \frac{16}{12} = 1.33$$

The average wait for a patient is:

$$E(w) = \frac{E(n_q)}{A} = \frac{1.33}{4} = \frac{1}{3}$$

Before the change each patient spent an average of 12 minutes being served and 48 minutes waiting. After the change each patient will spend an average of 10 minutes being served and 20 minutes waiting. Each day there are 96 patients (4×24) and each patient will save one-half hour in total. At a cost of $10 per hour, the daily cost saving is:

$$96 \times \tfrac{1}{2} \times 10 = \$480$$

It would be worth $480 per day or $175,200 per year to the company to increase the service rate to six patients per hour.

Another approach which could be used to reduce the cost of $768 per day for waiting would be to open another office (i.e., another channel). This situation would involve a multiple-service facility.

MULTIPLE-SERVICE FACILITIES

We shall now assume there are C channels and there is one waiting line if all the service facilities are busy. Each channel has the same service rate, S. We shall again use n to represent the sum of the customers being served and in the waiting line.

$$(19\text{-}8) \quad p_0 = \left[\frac{(A/S)^C}{C!\left(1 - \dfrac{A/S}{C}\right)} + 1 + \frac{(A/S)^1}{1!} + \frac{(A/S)^2}{2!} \right.$$
$$\left. + \cdots + \frac{(A/S)^{C-1}}{(C-1)!} \right]^{-1}$$

$$(19\text{-}9) \quad p_n = p_0 \frac{(A/S)^n}{n!} \qquad \text{if} \quad n \leq C$$

$$(19\text{-}10) \quad p_n = p_0 \frac{(A/S)^n}{C!C^{n-C}} \qquad \text{if} \quad n > C$$

We can use the above equations if $\dfrac{A}{CS} < 1$. If $\dfrac{A}{CS} > 1$, then the waiting line grows larger and larger; i.e., n becomes infinite if the process runs long enough.

When $C = 1$ (there is one service facility), equations (19–9) and (19–10) reduce to equation (19–2). From equation (19–9), we have:

$$p_n = p_0 \frac{(A/S)^n}{n!} \text{ if } n \leq C$$

But n can only take on values of zero or one if $n \leq C = 1$. Thus:

(19–2) $$p_n = p_0(A/S)^n$$

If $C = 1$, equation (19–10) also reduces to equation (19–2).

With C service facilities, the average number of customers in the queue is:

(19–11) $$E(n_q) = \frac{(A/S)^{C+1}}{C \cdot C! \left(1 - \dfrac{A/S}{C}\right)^2} p_0$$

and, as before, the expected waiting time for an arrival is:

(19–12) $$E(w) = \frac{E(n_q)}{A}$$

Example

We shall continue the medical example of the previous section and consider the characteristics of the process if a second office is added.

$$A = 4$$
$$S = 5$$
$$C = 2$$
$$\frac{A}{S} = 0.8$$

$$p_0 = \frac{1}{\dfrac{(A/S)^C}{C! \left(1 - \dfrac{A/S}{C}\right)} + 1 + \dfrac{(A/S)^1}{1!} + \cdots + \dfrac{(A/S)^{C-1}}{(C-1)!}}$$

$$p_0 = \frac{1}{\dfrac{(0.8)^2}{2(1 - 0.8/2)} + 1 + \dfrac{0.8}{1}} = \frac{1}{\dfrac{0.64}{1.2} + 1.8}$$

$$= \frac{1}{2.3} = 0.43$$

For different values of n, we would obtain:

$$n = 1 \qquad p_1 = p_0 \frac{(A/S)^n}{n!} = 0.43 \times \frac{0.8}{1} = 0.34 \left.\begin{array}{c}\\\\\\\end{array}\right\} n \le C$$

$$n = 2 \qquad p_2 = 0.43 \times \frac{(0.8)^2}{2} = 0.13$$

$$n = 3 \qquad p_3 = p_0 \frac{(A/S)^n}{C!C^{n-C}} = 0.43 \times \frac{0.8^3}{2 \times 2} = 0.06 \left.\begin{array}{c}\\\\\\\\\\\\\\\end{array}\right\} n > C$$

$$n = 4 \qquad p_4 = 0.43 \times \frac{0.8^4}{2 \times 2^2} = 0.02$$

$$n = 5 \qquad p_5 = 0.43 \times \frac{0.8^5}{2 \times 2^3} = 0.01$$

The average number in the system is shown in Table 19–2.

TABLE 19–2

n	p_n	np_n
0	0.43	0.00
1	0.34	0.34
2	0.13	0.26
3	0.06	0.18
4	0.02	0.08
5	0.01	0.05
		Approximately 0.91

(ignoring the values greater than $n = 5$)

The expected number in the waiting line is:

$$E(n_q) = \frac{(0.8)^3}{2 \cdot 2(1 - 0.8/2)^2} \times 0.43 = \frac{0.512 \times 0.43}{4 \times 0.36} = 0.15$$

The expected waiting time is:

$$E(w) = \frac{E(n_q)}{A} = \frac{0.15}{4} = 0.0375 \text{ hours}$$

We previously computed the expected time lost waiting with one office to be 76.8 hours. The expected total time lost waiting is now:

$$T = A \times 24 \text{ hours} \times E(w)$$
$$= 4 \times 24 \times 0.0375 = 3.60 \text{ hours}$$

Again assuming a cost of $10 for each hour, the average cost per day of waiting is:

$$3.60 \times \$10 = \$36$$

There has been a saving in expected cost of $732 (i.e., $768 − $36). If the cost of adding the second office is less than $732 per day, then the decision should be to go from one to two offices. We could also consider adding a third office; but since the expected cost of waiting is now only $36 per day, the adding of a third office is not likely to be worthwhile from an economic standpoint.

ONE-SERVICE FACILITY: ARRIVALS FROM A FINITE SOURCE

Assume a situation where one repairman is servicing m machines. The Poisson probability law does not apply, since the arrivals are not independent. If k machines are down for repairs, the set of potential arrivals is reduced to $m - k$.

A = average number of machines needing repairs during a unit time period

S = average number of machines that can be repaired in a unit of time, assuming machines are available for repair

$\dfrac{A}{S}$ = service factor, and $\dfrac{A}{S} < 1$

m = total number of machines

n = number of machines being serviced plus the queue

k = number of machines operating

The probability of all m machines waiting or being serviced, assuming the process has been operating long enough to reach a period of equilibrium, is:

$$(19\text{--}13) \qquad p_m = \left\{ 1 + \frac{1}{1!}\left(\frac{S}{A}\right)^1 + \cdots + \frac{1}{m!}\left(\frac{S}{A}\right)^m \right\}^{-1}$$

The probability of $m - k$ machines waiting or being serviced is:

$$(19\text{--}14) \qquad p_{m-k} = \frac{1}{k!}\left(\frac{S}{A}\right)^k p_m$$

The expected number of machines in the waiting line is:

$$(19\text{--}15) \qquad E(n_q) = m - \frac{A + S}{A}(1 - p_0)$$

The average time spent by a machine in the waiting line is:

$$(19\text{--}16) \qquad E(w) = \frac{1}{S}\left(\frac{m}{1 - p_0} - \frac{1 + A/S}{A/S}\right)$$

Example 1. There is one repairman servicing three machines.

$$A = \text{one machine per day}$$
$$S = \text{ten machines per day}$$
$$\frac{A}{S} = 0.1$$
$$\frac{S}{A} = 10$$
$$\frac{A}{S} < 1$$
$$m = 3$$

$$(19\text{--}17) \qquad p_m = \left\{1 + \frac{1}{1}\left(\frac{S}{A}\right)^1 + \cdots \frac{1}{m!}\left(\frac{S}{A}\right)^m\right\}^{-1}$$

$$p_3 = \left\{1 + (10) + \frac{1}{2}(10)^2 + \frac{1}{3 \cdot 2}(10)^3\right\}^{-1}$$

$$= \{228\}^{-1} = \frac{1}{228}$$

Table 19–3 shows the computation of p_{m-k} for $k = 1, 2, 3$.

TABLE 19–3

k	$\frac{1}{k!}(10)^k \frac{1}{228}$	=	p_{m-k}
0...........	$\frac{1}{228}$	$\frac{1}{228}$	p_3
1...........	$10 \times \frac{1}{228}$	$\frac{10}{228}$	p_2
2...........	$\frac{1}{2}(10)^2 \times \frac{1}{228}$	$\frac{50}{228}$	p_1
3...........	$\frac{1}{(3 \cdot 2)}(10)^3 \times \frac{1}{228}$	$\frac{167}{228}$	p_0
Total........		$\frac{228}{228}$	

The expected number of machines in the waiting line is:

$$(19\text{--}18) \qquad E(n_q) = m - \frac{A+S}{A}(1 - p_0)$$

$$= 3 - \frac{11}{1}\left(1 - \frac{167}{228}\right) = 3 - 11\left(\frac{61}{228}\right)$$

$$= 3 - 2.94 = 0.06$$

The average time spent waiting is:

$$(19\text{--}19) \qquad E(w) = \frac{1}{S}\left(\frac{m}{1 - p_0} - \frac{1 + A/S}{A/S}\right)$$

$$= \frac{1}{10}\left(\frac{3}{61/228} - \frac{1.1}{0.1}\right)$$

$$= \frac{1}{10}(11.21 - 11) = 0.021 \text{ days}$$

Example 2. In the second example the likelihood of breakdown and the average servicing time will be increased. There is one repairman servicing three machines.

$$A = \text{Two machines per day}$$
$$S = \text{Two and one-half machines per day}$$
$$m = 3$$
$$\frac{A}{S} = 0.8$$
$$\frac{S}{A} = 1.25$$
$$\frac{A}{S} < 1$$

$$p_m = \{1 + (1.25)^1 + \tfrac{1}{2}(1.25)^2 + \tfrac{1}{6}(1.25)^3\}^{-1}$$
$$= \{1 + 1.25 + 0.7812 + 0.3255\}^{-1}$$
$$= (3.36)^{-1} = 1/3.36 = 0.298$$

$$E(n_q) = m - \frac{A+S}{A}(1 - p_0) = 3 - \frac{4.5}{2}(0.903) = 3 - 2.03 = 0.97$$

$$E(w) = \frac{1}{S}\left(\frac{m}{1 - p_0} - \frac{1 + A/S}{A/S}\right) = \frac{1}{2.5}\left(\frac{3}{0.903} - \frac{1.8}{0.8}\right)$$

$$= \frac{1}{2.5}(3.32 - 2.25) = \frac{1}{2.5}(1.07) = 0.44$$

TABLE 19–4

k	$\dfrac{1}{k!}(1.25)^k 0.298$	$=$	p_{m-k}
0.............	0.298	0.298	p_3
1.............	1.25×0.298	0.372	p_2
2.............	$\dfrac{1}{2} \times 1.25^2 \times 0.298$	0.233	p_1
3.............	$\dfrac{1}{6} \times 1.25^3 \times 0.298$	0.097	p_0
		1.000	

The average waiting time is 0.44 days. Machines are breaking down at the rate of two per day, so the average time lost per day is 2×0.44, or 0.88 equipment-days. Assuming a value per equipment-day of $100 per machine, this would be a waiting cost of $88 (i.e., $0.88 \times \$100$).

CONCLUSION

A number of more complex queuing models exist for queuing situations which do not fit the assumptions made above. However, not all assumptions can be analytically manipulated and solved for the information of interest. For the average situation we may find it easier to use the technique of simulation (described in the next chapter) even when a theoretical model exists, since a simulation may easily be modified to include any specific characteristics of the problem setting (e.g., there may be space for only three trucks to wait at an unloading dock). As computer simulation languages and time-sharing computer systems combine to make computer simulation more accessible at lower cost, simulation is likely to be used to a greater degree to study specific queuing situations.

APPENDIX 1. THE POISSON PROCESS AND DISTRIBUTION

In a Poisson process the probability of occurrence of an event is constant, and the occurrence of an event is independent of what has happened immediately preceding the present observation. We may be interested in what happens over a continuous interval. This interval may be a measure of distance—for example, a yard, or a unit of time such as a day. Printing errors per page of a book is an example of a process which may be Poisson; other examples are the manufacturing of textiles, rolled steel, pipe, wire, etc., where there are X defects per unit measure of product.

The sales for a product may behave like a Poisson process. Suppose we have had 1,500 individual sales of one unit of product per person during the last 50 weeks, or an average sale of 30 per week. We may wish to know the probability of different weekly sales in the next five weeks.

The Poisson probability distribution applied to a Poisson process gives the probability of a number of events in a measure of distance or time, given that we know (1) the expected number of events *per unit* of distance or time and (2) the length of distance or time. Suppose we use the symbol L to be the expected number of events per unit measure, i.e., the rate or intensity of the process.[3] Examples of L are 30 units of sales per week, 6 units of sales per day, 25 telephone calls per hour, 3 defects per 100 feet of pipe, etc. We shall let T be the unit of time or space during which events are to be counted. Then:[4]

$$(19\text{--}20) \qquad P_{po}(R = r | L, T) = \frac{e^{-LT}(LT)^r}{r!}$$

is the Poisson probability of exactly r events occurring during time T, given the average number of events per unit of time is L.

In using the Poisson probability distribution, we may combine L and T by multiplication to obtain m; i.e., $m = LT$, where m is the expected number of events in the specified time period. We *expect* m events in a specified time, T. For example, if $L = 2$ (the average number of events per week) and $T = 5$ (the time period is five weeks), the average number of events per five-week period is $2 \cdot 5 = 10$. A Poisson distribution has the special property that its variance is always equal to its mean, m, so the standard deviation is $\sqrt{m}$.

The Poisson probability distribution may also be used as an approximation to the binomial probability distribution if the number of Bernoulli trials, n, is large, and if p, the probability of success, is small. This approximation is especially useful when n is large, since the computations involved in solving the binomial problem become tedious (even with a computer).

THE EXPONENTIAL DISTRIBUTION

In connection with the Poisson process, we have discussed the Poisson probability distribution, which gives the probability of the number of occurrences of an event, given an intensity L and a certain time period T.

---

[3] Frequently, in literature in this area, the Greek letter λ (lambda) is used to represent the process intensity.

[4] $e = 2.718 \ldots$, the base for natural logarithms.

For the same Poisson process, we could ask about the waiting time be-tween successive events (that is, the so-called "interarrival time"). In other words, what is the probability distribution of time, *t*, *between* events? This probability distribution is called the *exponential distribution* (see Figure 19–1).

FIGURE 19–1
Exponential probability density function

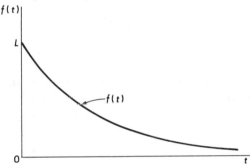

The exponential probability density function is:

(19–21) $$f(t) = Le^{-Lt}; \quad 0 < t < \infty$$

The mean of the exponential distribution is $\bar{t} = (1/L)$.

The right-hand tail of the exponential distribution is:[5]

$$P(t > T) = e^{-m} \quad \text{where } m = LT$$

That is, the probability that the time between events (arrivals) is greater than *T* is e^{-m}. Note that this is also the value of a Poisson mass function for zero occurrences (arrivals) in a time period *T*.[6]

Thus the Poisson distribution for arrivals per unit time and the expo-nential distribution for interarrival times provide two alternative ways of describing the same thing. We can say that the number of arrivals per unit time is Poisson with mean rate $L = 5$ per hour, for example, or alternatively, say that the interarrival times are exponentially distributed

---

[5] $\int_T^\infty Le^{-Lx}dx = -e^{-Lx}\Big|_T^\infty = 0 + e^{-LT} = e^{-LT} = e^{-m}$

[6] The Poisson mass function is:
$$P_{po}(R = r|L, T) = e^{-m}\frac{m^r}{r!}$$

where $m = LT$.
   If $r = 0$, then:
$$P_{po}(R = 0|L, T) = e^{-m}$$

i.e., the probability of no events in time *T* is e^{-m}.

with mean interarrival time $(1/L) = \frac{1}{5}$ hour; each statement implies the other.

APPENDIX 2.   DERIVATION OF BASIC QUEUING FORMULA

We want to derive the relationship:

$$p_n = (A/S)^n p_0$$

Assume arrivals and services occur in accordance with a Poisson process. There is one service facility with a single "first come, first served" queue. Let:

A = average number arriving in one unit of time

S = average number the station can service in one unit of time

n = number of units in the system either being serviced or waiting

$P_n(t)$ = probability of having n units in the system at time t

p_n = probability of having n units in the system, assuming equilibrium

Ah = probability of an arrival during time period h, when h is very small

Sh = probability of a service completion during time period h

We can reasonably assume that the probability of more than one change during time period h is very close to zero; to simplify the development, we shall assume it actually to be zero (i.e., the probability of two or more services or arrivals or a service and arrival is zero in a very small time interval). Thus:

$$1 - Ah - Sh = \text{probability of no changes}$$

We can reach state n (i.e., n units in the system) by one of four events, occurring as follows:

Event (a)—be at n, and no change occurs.

Event (b)—be at $n - 1$, and have an arrival take place.

Event (c)—be at $n + 1$, and have a service completion.

Event (d)—be at $n - y$ or $n + y$, and have y changes take place when $y > 1$ (we have assumed the probability of this event to be zero).

Since the events a, b, and c are mutually exclusive, we may add their probabilities:

$$P_n(t + h) = P(a) + P(b) + P(c), \qquad 1 \leq n < \infty$$

(19–22)
$$P_n(t + h) = P_n(t)(1 - Ah - Sh) + P_{n-1}(t)(Ah) + P_{n+1}(t)(Sh)$$

(19–23) $$\frac{P_n(t + h) - P_n(t)}{h} = -(A + S)P_n(t) + AP_{n-1}(t) + SP_{n+1}(t)$$

Rearranging terms and letting h approach zero:

(19–24) $$\frac{dP_n(t)}{dt} = AP_{n-1}(t) - (A + S)P_n(t) + SP_{n+1}(t)$$

In equilibrium, $\dfrac{dP_n(t)}{dt} = 0$, and we obtain:

(19–25) $$p_{n+1} = -\frac{A}{S}p_{n-1} + \frac{A + S}{S}p_n$$

Returning to equation (19–22):

(19–26)
$$P_n(t + h) = P_n(t)(1 - Ah - Sh) + P_{n-1}(t)(Ah) + P_{n+1}(t)(Sh)$$

If we solve for $P_0(t + h)$, then $n = 0$, $P_{n-1}(t) = 0$, and the term $-Sh$ drops out because with zero customers a service completion is impossible. We obtain:

(19–27) $$P_0(t + h) = P_0(t)(1 - Ah) + P_1(t)(Sh)$$

Subtract $P_0(t)$ from both sides and divide by h:

(19–28) $$\frac{P_0(t + h) - P_0(t)}{h} = -AP_0(t) + SP_1(t)$$

In equilibrium, this last equation is equal to zero as h goes to zero:

$$-Ap_0 + Sp_1 = 0$$

(19–29) $$p_1 = \frac{A}{S}p_0$$

Using equation (19–25), we obtain:

(19–30) $$p_2 = -\frac{A}{S}p_0 + \frac{A + S}{S}p_1$$

Substituting $\dfrac{A}{S}p_0$ for p_1:

$$p_2 = -\frac{A}{S}p_0 + \frac{A + S}{S}\left(\frac{A}{S}p_0\right)$$

$$= \left(-\frac{AS}{S^2} + \frac{A^2 + AS}{S^2}\right)p_0 = \frac{A^2}{S^2}p_0 = \left(\frac{A}{S}\right)^2 p_0$$

Continuing this procedure, we find:

$$(19\text{--}31) \qquad\qquad p_n = (A/S)^n p_0$$

The reader interested in further derivations is referred to W. Feller, *An Introduction to Probability Theory and Its Applications;* and A. Kaufmann, *Methods and Models of Operations Research* (see the Bibliography that follows for these references and others).

BIBLIOGRAPHY

FELLER, W. *An Introduction to Probability Theory and Its Applications,* Vol. I. 3d ed. New York: John Wiley & Sons, Inc., 1968.

————. *An Introduction to Probability Theory and Its Applications,* Vol. II. New York: John Wiley & Sons, Inc., 1966.

HILLIER, F., and LIEBERMAN, G. J. *Introduction to Operations Research.* San Francisco: Holden-Day, Inc., 1967.

KAUFMANN, A. *Methods and Models of Operations Research.* Englewood Cliffs, N.J.: Prentice-Hall, Inc., 1963.

LEE, A. M. *Applied Queueing Theory.* London: Macmillan & Co., Ltd., 1966.

MORSE, P. M. *Queues, Inventories, and Maintenance.* New York: John Wiley & Sons, Inc., 1958.

NEWELL, G. F. *Applications of Queueing Theory.* London: Chapman & Hall, Ltd., 1971.

PRABHU, N. U. *Queues and Inventories.* New York: John Wiley & Sons, Inc., 1965.

SAATY, T. L. *Elements of Queueing Theory.* New York: McGraw-Hill Book Co., 1961.

WAGNER, H. M. *Principles of Operations Research.* Englewood Cliffs, N.J.: Prentice-Hall, Inc., 1969.

PROBLEMS

19–1. Ace Airline has one reservations clerk on duty at a time. He handles information about flight schedules and makes reservations. All calls to Ace Airline are answered by an operator. If a caller requests information or reservations, the operator transfers the call to the reservations clerk. If the clerk is busy, the operator asks the caller to wait. When the clerk becomes free, the operator transfers to him the call of the person who has been waiting the longest.

Assume that arrivals and services follow a Poisson process. Calls arrive at a rate of 10 per hour, and the reservations clerk can service a call in four minutes, on the average (i.e., $S = 15$ per hour).

a) What is the average number of calls waiting to be connected to the reservations clerk?

b)   What is the average time a caller must wait before reaching the reservations clerk?

c)   What is the average time for a caller to complete a call (i.e., waiting time plus service time)?

19–2.   Refer to Problem 19–1 above. Suppose that the management of Ace Airline is considering installing some visual display equipment and a new reservations system. One of the benefits of this system is that it will reduce the average time required to service a call from four to three minutes.

a)   What would be the average number of calls waiting to be connected to the reservations clerk if this new system were installed?

b)   What would be the expected waiting time before a caller was connected to the reservations clerk with the new system?

19–3.   Refer to Problems 19–1 and 19–2. Suppose that instead of installing a new reservations system, Ace Airline was considering adding a second reservations clerk. The telephone operator could then refer calls to whichever clerk was free.

a)   What would then be the average number of calls waiting to be connected to a reservations clerk?

b)   What would then be the expected waiting time before a caller was connected to a reservations clerk?

19–4.   Refer to Problem 19–3. Suppose that the cost of manning an additional station would be $50 per day. Ace Airline is undecided about incurring this additional cost.

a)   If the goodwill cost of having a customer wait is 10 cents per minute spent waiting (before being connected to a clerk), should Ace Airline add the second clerk?

b)   At what goodwill cost would Ace Airline be indifferent as to whether or not to add the second clerk?

c)   What assumption is made about the expected number of calls for each hour of the day?

19–5.   Two typists have identical jobs. Each types letters dictated by a manager. Suppose that letters to be typed arrive at random (following a Poisson process) at a rate of three per hour for each typist. Suppose that each typist can type four letters per hour, on the average (also a Poisson process).

a)   Assuming that each typist does her own work, what is the expected waiting time for a letter (time before work is started on a letter)?

b)   Suppose that the two typists are "pooled." That is, letters are sent to the two together and are done by whoever is free, in the order of arrival. What is the expected waiting time for a letter under this arrangement?

c)   Comment on this example.

19–6.   The Speedo Computer Company maintains a technical repairman to service the five Speedo electronic computers that are located in Bay City. Speedo receives a rental of $100 per hour on each of these computers. This fee is paid only for the number of hours that the computers are operative and excludes downtime (time spent awaiting repair and repair time).

Past experience shows that a Speedo computer develops trouble and needs repair about once in five days. Hence, with the five computers in Bay City, requests for repair are made on an average of one per day ($A = 1$). The time required to repair a computer, on the average, takes about one third of a day (i.e., $S = 3$). Both arrivals and service times are Poisson.

a) What is the expected total amount of machine downtime per week? Include repair time as well as waiting time. Also, assume an eight-hour day, five-day week for both the computers and the serviceman.

b) Suppose that some new diagnostic equipment could be developed that would enable the serviceman to repair four computers per day (instead of the three above). How much would this equipment be worth per week to Speedo?

19–7. An integrated petroleum company is considering expansion of its one unloading facility at its Australian refinery. Due to random variations in weather, loading delays, and other factors, ships arriving at the refinery to unload crude oil arrive according to the Poisson distribution with average rate $A = 5$ ships per week. Service time is also Poisson with average service rate $S = 10$ ships per week.

a) What is the average number of ships waiting to deliver crude oil?

b) What is the average time a ship must wait before beginning to deliver its cargo to the refinery?

c) What is the average total time (waiting plus actual delivery) that a ship spends at the refinery?

19–8. Refer to Problem 19–7. The company has under consideration a second unloading berth which could be rented for $5,000 per week. The service time for this berth would also be Poisson with the same rate $S = 10$ as the company's own berth. For each week of a ship spent idle waiting in line, the company loses $20,000.

a) If the second berth is rented, what will be the average number of ships waiting?

b) What would be the average time a ship would wait?

c) Is the benefit of reduced waiting time (in dollars) worth the rental cost for the second berth?

19–9. Refer to Problem 19–8. An alternative way to improve unloading facilities is for the company to rent a new high-speed unloading device. With the new device, the service rate would be Poisson with mean rate $S' = 15$ ships per week. The weekly rental cost of the new device is $5,000.

a) Compute the (new) average number of ships waiting if the device is installed.

b) Compute the (new) expected waiting time for ships.

c) Is the benefit of reduced waiting time (in dollars) worth the rental cost for the new device?

19–10. Refer to Problems 19–8 and 19–9. An analyst for the company, after studying the costs and benefits of the two suggested modifications, suggests "In each case the benefit exceeds the cost, so let's *both* install the high-speed unloading device on our own berth *and* rent the second berth." Unfortunately, there are no formulas in the chapter which are appropriate for a two-channel queue with differing service rates ($S_1 = 15$, $S_2 = 10$). Find a way to calculate an upper limit on the potential saving from avoidance of waiting delays, and use this limit to comment on the analyst's suggestion.

20

Simulation

It is an accepted practice for an airplane manufacturer to test a scale model of a new type of aircraft in an air tunnel before building a full-sized plane. Flood control measures are frequently tested on scale models before the actual projects are carried out. In recent years, techniques for testing the results of some business decisions before they are actually executed have been developed. The anticipated actual business processes are simulated using either manual labor (pencil, paper, and desk calculator) or large electronic computers. The electronic computers have the advantage of being able to handle large amounts of data rapidly. However, the basic simulation procedure is independent of how the computations are made.

Waiting line problems of the type discussed in the previous chapter can be analyzed by building such an artificial or simulation model. Where we can adequately solve the problem by mathematical methods, it is generally preferable to do so. However, there are many queuing (and other) situations which cannot be solved easily by mathematics, and hence we must resort to simulation.

Consider, as an example, a warehouse that has one dock which is used to unload railroad freight cars. Incoming freight cars are delivered to the warehouse during the night. It takes exactly half a day to unload a car. If more than two cars are waiting to be unloaded on a given day, some are postponed until the following day.

Past experience has indicated that the number of cars arriving during the night have the frequencies shown in Table 20–1. Furthermore, there is no apparent pattern, so that the number arriving on any night is independent of the number arriving on any other night.

This is a one-channel queuing problem with an average service rate of two per day and an average arrival rate of 1.5 per day. However, it can be shown that the arrivals are not Poisson; and the services clearly are

TABLE 20–1

x number of cars arriving	f(x) relative frequency
0.	0.23
1.	0.30
2.	0.30
3.	0.10
4.	0.05
5.	0.02
6 or more.	0.00
	1.00

Average = $E(x)$ = 1.5 cars per night

not, since the service time is fixed at exactly half a day. Hence the queuing model presented in the previous chapter does not apply.

The first step in simulating this queuing process is to generate a history or time series of arrivals for a number of nights. This is done using a randomized or *Monte Carlo* process. One way to do this would be to take 100 chips and write the number 0 on 23 of them; the number 1 on 30 of them; the number 2 on 30 of them; and so on, corresponding to the frequencies in Table 20–1. We could then draw a chip from a hat, and the number on the chip would indicate the number of freight cars arriving in a given simulated period.

A simpler procedure is to use a table of random numbers such as Table 20–2. Each entry in Table 20–2 was drawn in such a way that each digit (zero through nine) had an equal chance of being drawn.

We could then assign two-digit random numbers to each of the possible outcomes (i.e., to the number of arrivals), as shown in Table 20–3.

There are 100 two-digit pairs of numbers. Note that 23 are assigned to the event "zero cars arrive"; 30 to the event "one car arrives"; 30 to the event "two cars arrive"; etc. Since each two-digit number has a 1/100 chance of coming up, the probability that the event "zero cars arrive" will occur is 23/100, or 0.23.

We are now prepared to simulate the queuing process. This is done in Table 20–4.

Three days are used to start the process (marked x). For the first day, the random number (taken from Table 20–2) is 97. Since 97 corresponds to the event "four cars arrive" in Table 20–3, we list four in the third column. Of these four cars, two are unloaded, and the unloading of the other two is postponed until the following day. The random

TABLE 20–2
Table of random digits

97	95	12	11	90	49	57	13	86	81
02	92	75	91	24	58	39	22	13	02
80	67	14	99	16	89	96	63	67	60
66	24	72	57	32	15	49	63	00	04
96	76	20	28	72	12	77	23	79	46
55	64	82	61	73	94	26	18	37	31
50	02	74	70	16	85	95	32	85	67
29	53	08	33	81	34	30	21	24	25
58	16	01	91	70	07	50	13	18	24
51	16	69	67	16	53	11	06	36	10
04	55	36	97	30	99	80	10	52	40
86	54	35	61	59	89	64	97	16	02
24	23	52	11	59	10	88	68	17	39
39	36	99	50	74	27	69	48	32	68
47	44	41	86	83	50	24	51	02	08
60	71	41	25	90	93	07	24	29	59
65	88	48	06	68	92	70	97	02	66
44	74	11	60	14	57	08	54	12	90
93	10	95	80	32	50	40	44	08	12
20	46	36	19	47	78	16	90	59	64
86	54	24	88	94	14	58	49	80	79
12	88	12	25	19	70	40	06	40	31
42	00	50	24	60	90	69	60	07	86
29	98	81	68	61	24	90	92	32	68
36	63	02	37	89	40	81	77	74	82
01	77	82	78	20	72	35	38	56	89
41	69	43	37	41	21	36	39	57	80
54	40	76	04	05	01	45	84	55	11
68	03	82	32	22	80	92	47	77	62
21	31	77	75	43	13	83	43	70	16
53	64	54	21	04	23	85	44	81	36
91	66	21	47	95	69	58	91	47	59
48	72	74	40	97	92	05	01	61	18
36	21	47	71	84	46	09	85	32	82
55	95	24	85	84	51	61	60	62	13
70	27	01	88	84	85	77	94	67	35
38	13	66	15	38	54	43	64	25	43
36	80	25	24	92	98	35	12	17	62
98	10	91	61	04	90	05	22	75	20
50	54	29	19	26	26	87	94	27	73

TABLE 20–3

Number of cars arriving	Random digits	Relative frequency
0	00 to 22	0.23
1	23 to 52	0.30
2	53 to 82	0.30
3	83 to 92	0.10
4	93 to 97	0.05
5	98 and 99	0.02
		1.00

TABLE 20–4 Queuing system simulation

Day number	Random number	Number of arrivals	Total number to be unloaded	Number unloaded	Number delayed to following day
x.........	97	4	4	2	2
x.........	02	0	2	2	0
x.........	80	2	2	2	0
1.........	66	2	2	2	0
2.........	96	4	4	2	2
3.........	55	2	4	2	2
4.........	50	1	3	2	1
5.........	29	1	2	2	0
6.........	58	2	2	2	0
7.........	51	1	1	1	0
8.........	04	0	0	0	0
9.........	86	3	3	2	1
10.........	24	1	2	2	0
11.........	39	1	1	1	0
12.........	47	1	1	1	0
13.........	60	2	2	2	0
14.........	65	2	2	2	0
15.........	44	1	1	1	0
16.........	93	4	4	2	2
17.........	20	0	2	2	0
18.........	86	3	3	2	1
19.........	12	0	1	1	0
20.........	42	1	1	1	0
21.........	29	1	1	1	0
22.........	36	1	1	1	0
23.........	01	0	0	0	0
24.........	41	1	1	1	0
25.........	54	2	2	2	0
26.........	68	2	2	2	0
27.........	21	0	0	0	0
28.........	53	2	2	2	0
29.........	91	3	3	2	1
30.........	48	1	2	2	0
31.........	36	1	1	1	0
32.........	55	2	2	2	0
33.........	70	2	2	2	0
34.........	38	1	1	1	0
35.........	36	1	1	1	0
36.........	98	5	5	2	3
37.........	50	1	4	2	2
38.........	95	4	6	2	4
39.........	92	3	7	2	5
40.........	67	2	7	2	5
41.........	24	1	6	2	4
42.........	76	2	6	2	4
43.........	64	2	6	2	4
44.........	02	0	4	2	2
45.........	53	2	4	2	2
46.........	16	0	2	2	0
47.........	16	0	0	0	0
48.........	55	2	2	2	0
49.........	54	2	2	2	0
50.........	23	1	1	1	0
Totals.....		79			45
Average		1.58			0.90

number for the second day is 02 (again from Table 20–2). This means zero cars arrive, and the two cars from the previous day are unloaded. We continue in the same fashion.

Table 20–4 simulates 50 days' operations (in addition to the three days to get started). During most of the period, there is little delay. Note that there is, however, considerable delay starting around period 36. The average number of arrivals per day (1.58) over the sample period of 50 days is slightly larger than the expected number per day (1.50). On the average, 0.90 cars are delayed per day. For more accurate results, the simulation could be carried on for more days.

We could use the simulation model in much the same way that we used mathematical waiting line models. That is, we can compare the effects of feasible alternatives upon waiting time and cost. For example, in this case we could compare delays under the current service rate of two per day with a service rate of three per day. Or we could introduce one or more additional channels.

SIMULATION AND INVENTORY CONTROL

The use of simulation is not restricted to queuing processes. Many phases of business operations have been simulated with successful results. We shall illustrate by a brief example how simulation could be applied to the solution of an inventory problem.

Suppose that the weekly demand of a certain product has the distribution shown in Table 20–5.

TABLE 20–5

Number demanded	Probability	Random numbers assigned
0	0.10	00 to 09
1	0.40	10 to 49
2	0.30	50 to 79
3	0.20	80 to 99
	1.00	

When an order is placed to replenish inventory, there is a delivery lag which is a random variable, as shown in Table 20–6.

We should like to determine an order quantity, Q, and an order point, R. We can do this by trying several values of Q and R, and simulating to determine the best.

TABLE 20-6

Number of weeks from order to delivery	Probability	Random numbers assigned
2.............	0.20	00 to 19
3.............	0.60	20 to 79
4.............	0.20	80 to 99
	1.00	

An illustration with $Q = 15$ and $R = 5$ is shown in Table 20-7. We assume that no backorders are allowed. If we established the cost of ordering, the cost of holding inventory, and the cost of being out of stock, we could estimate the cost of the inventory system under the rule $Q = 15$, $R = 5$. Alternative rules could be compared to this. For example, the formulas for optimal order quantity and optimum reorder point [equations (12–1) and (12–2) in Chapter 12] could be used, even though the assumptions needed for these formulas are not met in our example (the replenishment lead time is not constant). The amount of error introduced by using the formulas may be estimated by the simulation. Frequently, a method of solution may be operationally useful even when it is not strictly applicable theoretically.

RISK ANALYSIS

Consider the decision on a major capital investment such as the introduction of a new product. The profitability of the investment depends upon several factors which are generally uncertain. Estimates of total market for the product; the market share that the firm can attain; the growth in the market; the cost of producing the product; the selling price; the life of the product; and even the cost of the equipment needed—all are generally subject to substantial uncertainty.

The usual approach is to make single-number "best estimates" for each of the uncertain factors above and then to calculate measures of profitability such as net present value or rate of return for the project.[1] This

---

[1] The net present value of an investment is defined to be $NPV = \sum_{i=1}^{N} P_i \left(\frac{1}{1+r} \right)^i - I_0$

where P_i is the benefit (cash flow) of the project in the ith year, I_0 is the investment, r is the discount or interest rate, and N is the life of the project. The rate of return is determined by finding a value of r such that $NPV = 0$. Both measures are a means of adjusting for the time value of money. That is, $1 a year from now is worth $1 \cdot (1 + r)^{-1}$ now if r is the appropriate discount rate.

TABLE 20–7
Inventory simulation illustration

Week number	Receipts	Beginning inventory	Random number	Sales (units)	Ending inventory	Lost sales (outages)	Orders	Random number for orders	Number of weeks hence when order will arrive
0.....	15	15	11	1	14				
1.....		14	91	3	11				
2.....		11	99	3	8				
3.....		8	57	2	6				
4.....		6	28	1	5		15	61	3
5.....		5	70	2	3				
6.....		3	33	1	2				
7.....	15	17	91	3	14				
8.....		14	67	2	12				
9.....		12	97	3	9				
10.....		9	61	2	7				
11.....		7	11	1	6				
12.....		6	50	2	4		15	86	4
13.....		4	25	1	3				
14.....		3	06	0	3				
15.....		3	60	2	1				
16.....	15	16	80	3	13				
17.....		13	19	1	12				
18.....		12	88	3	9				
19.....		9	25	1	8				
20.....		8	24	1	7				
21.....		7	68	2	5		15	37	3
22.....		5	78	2	3				
23.....		3	37	1	2				
24.....	15	17	04	0	17				
25.....		17	32	1	16				
26.....		16	75	2	14				
27.....		14	21	1	13				
28.....		13	47	1	12				
29.....		12	40	1	11				
30.....		11	71	2	9				
31.....		9	85	3	6				
32.....		6	88	3	3		15	15	2
33.....		3	24	1	2				
34.....	15	17	61	2	15				
35.....		15	19	1	14				
36.....		14	90	3	11				
37.....		11	24	1	10				
38.....		10	16	1	9				
39.....		9	32	1	8				
40.....		8	72	2	6				
Totals		412				0			
Average		10.3							

approach has two drawbacks:

a) There is no guarantee that using the "best estimates" will give the true expected profitability of the project.

b) There is no way to measure the risk associated with the investment. In particular, the manager has no way of determining the probability that the project will lose money or the probability that very large profits will result. For example, using only the one-number approach, a manager would not be able to distinguish between the two projects shown in Figure 20–1. And yet such information is necessary if techniques for dealing with risk, such as the utility measures of Chapter 17, are to be applied.

FIGURE 20–1
Comparison of two projects

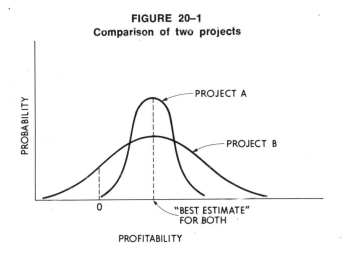

Risk analysis is a technique designed to circumvent these two disadvantages. The general approach is to assign a subjective probability distribution to each unknown factor and to combine these, using the Monte Carlo simulation approach, into a probability distribution for the project profitability as a whole. This can be shown with a simple example.

Example

Suppose we are considering marketing a new product. The investment required is $5,000. There are three factors which are uncertain: selling price, variable cost, and annual sales volume. The product has a life of only one year. Table 20–8 contains the various possible levels of these factors, together with the estimated probability of each. We will assume that the factors in Table 20–8 are statistically *independent*. (This is an important assumption. If it were not so, we would

TABLE 20–8
Factors in risk analysis example

Selling price	(Prob.)	Variable cost	(Prob.)	Sales volume (units)	(Prob.)
$4	(0.3)	$2.	(0.1)	3,000	(0.2)
5	(0.5)	3.	(0.6)	4,000	(0.4)
6	(0.2)	4.	(0.3)	5,000	(0.4)

want to modify our simulation to include whatever probabilistic dependence we felt appropriate.)

Because this is a very simple example, it is possible to use the decision tree and probability tree techniques of Chapter 3 to calculate the various outcomes and probabilities. In this case, we have only $3 \times 3 \times 3 = 27$ possible distinct outcomes, but in a more realistic problem with many uncertain factors each having 10 or 20 levels, we could easily have a million possible outcomes. In these circumstances, the technique of simulation can be very useful in estimating both the average profitability of the investment and the "riskiness" of it, described by the probability of achieving various levels of profit.

We first need a way of generating random values for the elements of Table 20–8 according to the stated probabilities. As before, we associate various random numbers with various outcomes as in Table 20–9.

TABLE 20–9
Random number assignments in risk example

Selling price	Random numbers	Variable cost	Random numbers	Sales volume	Random numbers
$4	(0, 1, 2)	$2.	(0)	3,000.	(0, 1)
5	(3–7)	3.	(1–6)	4,000.	(2–5)
6	(8, 9)	4.	(7–9)	5,000.	(6–9)

Now we can begin the simulation. We generate single-digit random numbers from the random number table (Table 20–2) and, in turn, determine a price, a cost, and a volume. Once these elements have been determined, profit is computed as follows:

$$\text{Profit} = (\text{price} - \text{cost}) \times \text{volume} - \$5,000$$

Then the process is repeated a large number of times to generate a large number of profit outcomes. See Table 20–10 for a sample of 25 trials.

TABLE 20–10
Risk analysis—twenty-five trials

Trial	R.N.*	Price	R.N.*	Cost	R.N.*	Volume (000 units)	Profit ($000)
1	8	$6	0	$2	6	5	15
2	0	4	4	3	3	4	−1
3	6	5	2	3	2	4	3
4	1	4	4	3	0	3	−2
5	3	5	6	3	0	3	1
6	5	5	6	3	9	5	5
7	1	4	6	3	7	5	0
8	3	5	8	4	6	5	0
9	2	4	8	4	8	5	−5
10	1	4	6	3	1	3	−2
11	5	5	7	4	3	4	−1
12	9	6	9	4	6	5	5
13	4	5	9	4	7	5	0
14	7	5	2	3	6	5	5
15	9	6	5	3	3	4	7
16	0	4	5	3	0	3	−2
17	1	4	1	3	8	5	0
18	0	4	6	3	4	4	−1
19	8	6	8	4	6	5	5
20	9	6	2	3	4	4	7
21	0	4	7	4	7	5	−5
22	0	4	0	2	8	5	5
23	4	5	0	2	1	3	4
24	6	5	5	3	8	5	5
25	4	5	0	2	1	3	4
						Average	2.08

* Random number.

Twenty-five trials is not enough to make a precise estimate of the average profitability or of the probability distribution of profits. If this process were programmed on a computer, several hundred trials could be easily simulated. However, for illustrative purposes, we will base our discussion on the results of these 25 trials.

Note that the average profit is 2.08 or $2,080. It is interesting to compare this with simpler methods of analysis. For example, if we had used the one-number approach, and used the most likely value for each factor, our estimate of profit would have been:

$$(\text{Most likely profit}) = (\$5 - \$3) \times (4,000) - \$5,000 = \$3,000$$

Thus the simple one-number approach, in this case, significantly overstates the expected profitability of the investment.

Because it is a simple case, computation of the expected profit (the profit of each of the 27 outcomes, weighted by the probabilities) can be performed;[2] this expected profit is $2,140. Thus, as one would expect, our sample average for 25 trials is not precisely equal to expected profit. However, the expected profit calculation sheds no light on the *risk* associated with the investment, whereas the set of 25 sample outcomes clearly indicates that one may actually incur a loss (for example, trial 4 in Table 20–10). A convenient way to represent this risk from the results of a risk analysis is to rank the outcomes by profitability and plot a graph of the sample cumulative probability function (see Figure 20–2).

FIGURE 20–2
Risk analysis (sample cumulative probability function)

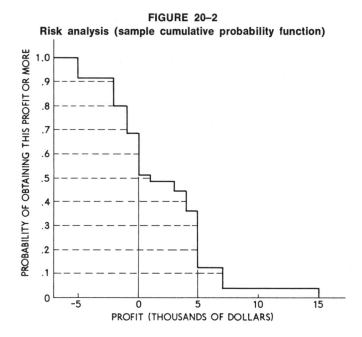

PROFIT (THOUSANDS OF DOLLARS)

From Figure 20–2 we see that there is a 68 percent chance of making 0 profit or more (and a 32 percent chance of incurring a loss); there is a 36 percent chance of making $5,000 or more; and no chance of making more than $15,000. As larger numbers of trials are simulated, the curve of Figure 20–2 would smooth out somewhat (although it would continue to have the staircase shape because there are only a discrete number of alternative outcomes rather than a continuous curve).

---

[2] In this case, since the factors are independent and related by simple multiplication and addition, we can compute the expected profit from the expected values of price, cost, and volume. (See Chapter 4.) If, however, these elements were not linearly related or independent, then the complete set of branches of the probability tree would have to be evaluated.

SIMULATION OF COMPLEX SYSTEMS

While simulation is a useful tool in dealing with queuing, inventory, risk analysis, and other problems, perhaps its greatest contribution is in the analysis of complex systems. Many real-world problems involve systems made up of many component parts that are interrelated; the system may be dynamic and changing over time; and the system may involve probabilistic or uncertain events. Simulation is the only technique for quantitative analysis of such problems.

We shall use an example to illustrate the use of simulation for these problems. Consider the operations of a barge line down the Ohio–Mississippi river system.[3] This barge company is a subsidiary of a steel company and receives barge loads of steel at its home port in Pittsburgh for shipment down the river to various ports, and to Gulf Coast ports by another barge line. Figure 20–3 sketches the operations of this system. Barge loads of steel arrive at the Pittsburgh port in a random fashion represented by a probability distribution in Figure 20–3. The destinations of these barges also vary from time to time, shown by the frequency distribution in the figure. If a barge is available the steel is loaded. Otherwise, it must be shipped by another (i.e., a foreign) barge company. A tug will start with a tow of full barges (tow size is limited because of the locks in the river system) and calls on the various ports downstream. The number of ports is simplified to six in the illustration. At each port, barges designated for that port are dropped. At New Orleans, the tug turns upstream and picks up available empty barges from the ports as it goes. These empty barges are available after a turnaround time (for unloading) which is a random event. Back at the home port, the tug returns to the available tug queue (after a short time for restocking, repairs, etc.) and the barges go to the empty barge queue, both ready to move back into the system again.

The company has 4 tugs and 127 barges, and, at any one time, these may be scattered throughout the system.

A simulation model of this system may be constructed and programmed on a computer. The probabilistic elements (arrivals of steel, destinations for barges, and turnaround times) would be incorporated using the Monte Carlo (simulation) technique. The computer model must also keep track of time in the system, keep track of the barges and tugs and the physical limitations in the system, move the tugs and barges from port to port in accordance with travel distances (four days from Pittsburgh to Cincinnati for example), and so on.

---

[3] This example was adapted from G. G. O'Brien and R. R. Crane, "The Scheduling of a Barge Line," *Operations Research,* vol. 7 (1959), pp. 561–70.

FIGURE 20–3
Operations of barge company

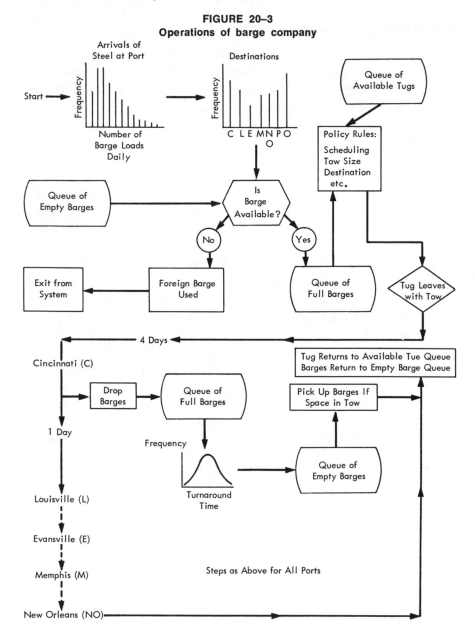

Once such a simulation model has been developed, management can use the model to try out possible alternative policies. For example, several scheduling rules might be tried including:

a)   Having a tug leave Pittsburgh at fixed intervals—8 or 10 days apart—regardless of how many barges it has.

b)   Having a tug leave when it has a tow of at least so many barges—
16 for example.

Other scheduling policies are of course possible. In addition, the company could examine the effects on the system of additional equipment—more barges or tugs, or faster tugs.

The simulation models allows the company to experiment with these and other changes without having to try them out on the real system. Besides the costs of disruption which would be incurred, it is hard to evaluate results of experiments in the real world because other external factors are constantly changing. It is hard to know if the observed results are attributable to the external factors or to the changes in the system. This problem does not exist in simulation models because the external factors can be controlled.

Although simulation models of complex systems can be very valuable, there are some disadvantages. They tend to be relatively costly to build. And, of course, like all models they are simplifications of the real world and may fail to adequately represent important elements or relationships.

APPENDIX. SIMULATION WITH CONTINUOUS PROBABILITY DISTRIBUTIONS

In the risk analysis example above the random variables were discrete (e.g., selling price took on only three distinct possible values; $4, $5, and $6). There may be situations in which we would like to assume that elements are random variables drawn from some continuous probability distribution. Suppose, for example, that we felt that annual sales volume in the risk analysis example would be normally distributed with mean $\mu = 3,000$ units and standard deviation $\sigma = 500$ units. How can we generate random values of sales volume for use in a simulation?

Graphical method

One way to generate random variables from continuous distributions is to plot the cumulative distribution function (see Chapter 7). For the normal distribution just mentioned, the cumulative distribution function is illustrated in Figure 20–4.

In order to use the cumulative distribution function, we first use a table of random numbers (like Table 20–2) to generate a random decimal between zero and one. This can be done by taking three random numbers from Table 20–2 and placing the decimal point in front of them. For example, if the random numbers 7, 3, and 6 were drawn, the corresponding decimal would be 0.736.

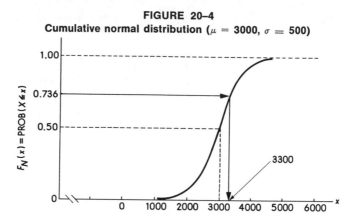

FIGURE 20–4
Cumulative normal distribution ($\mu = 3000$, $\sigma = 500$)

Then the cumulative curve of Figure 20–4 is *entered* on the vertical axis at the corresponding decimal value (0.736 in our example). Draw a horizontal line over to the cumulative curve, and when the line at height 0.736 hits the curve, drop straight down to the horizontal axis. Then read off the value reached; this value will be the particular random value desired. In our case this value is approximately 3,300.

This method of generating random values works because the choice of a random decimal between zero and one is equivalent to choosing a random *percentile* of the distribution. Then the figure is used to convert the random percentile (in our case, the 73.6 percentile) to a particular value (3,300). The method is general and can be used for *any* cumulative probability distribution, either continuous or discrete.

Algebraic method

Sometimes it is possible to perform the above process algebraically. Specifically, suppose the cumulative distribution function of interest can be expressed in closed form (i.e., in a formula as a function of x without any integration signs); then the graphical process can be replaced by an equivalent algebraic relationship.

For example, consider the exponential probability density function discussed in Appendix 1 of Chapter 19:

(20–1) $$f(t) = Le^{-Lt}, \quad 0 < t < \infty$$

The cumulative distribution function of the exponential distribution is:[4]

(20–2) $$F(t) = 1 - e^{-Lt}$$

---
[4] See footnote 5 of Chapter 19.

Now we set a hypothetical random decimal (R.D.) equal to the cumulative distribution function and solve for t:

(20–3)
$$R.D. = 1 - e^{-Lt}$$
$$e^{-Lt} = 1 - R.D.$$

Since our random decimal is between zero and one, so is $1 - R.D.$; thus *this* quantity $(1 - R.D.)$ can be considered directly as a random decimal. So

(20–4)
$$e^{-Lt} = R.D.$$

Taking natural logarithms,

(20–5)
$$-Lt = \log_e(R.D.)$$

or

(20–6)
$$t = -(1/L) \log_e(R.D.)$$

Equation 20–6 can be used directly to generate values from an exponential distribution with parameter L. First, a random decimal (R.D.) is obtained from a random number table such as Table 20–2; then the particular value obtained is substituted into the right-hand side of equation (20–6) and solved to produce a particular value for t. The value obtained will be a random draw from an exponential distribution with parameter L.

For example, if $L = 5$ and the random decimal were R.D. $= 0.475$, then from tables of natural logarithms, $\log_e(0.475) = -0.744$; and $t = -(1/5)(-0.744) = 0.1488$. This value would be a random draw from an exponential distribution with parameter $L = 5$ (mean $1/L = 1/5$).

Computer generation of random variables

Most digital computers have programs available to generate "equally likely" random decimals between zero and one. Many computers have been programmed to use equation (20–6) to generate exponentially distributed random variables after one specifies the appropriate value for the parameter L. Also, many computers have routines for generating standard normal random variables Z ($\mu = 0$, $\sigma = 1$) from which one can quickly generate values for Normal random variables with any specified parameters by rearranging the transformation

$$Z = \frac{X - \mu}{\sigma}$$

so that $X = \mu + \sigma Z$ (see Chapter 7).

BIBLIOGRAPHY

HERTZ, D. B. "Risk Analysis in Capital Investment." *Harvard Business Review,* January–February 1964.

HILLIER, F., and LIEBERMAN, G. J. *Introduction to Operations Research.* San Francisco: Holden-Day, Inc., 1967.

IBM CORPORATION. *Bibliography on Simulation.* White Plains, N.Y., 1966.

KAUFMANN, A. *Methods and Models of Operations Research.* Englewood Cliffs, N.J.: Prentice-Hall, Inc., 1963.

MEIER, R. C.; NEWELL, W. T.; and PAZER, H. L. *Simulation in Business and Economics.* Englewood Cliffs, N.J.: Prentice-Hall, Inc., 1969.

NAYLOR, T. H. *Computer Simulation Experiments with Models of Economic Systems.* New York: John Wiley & Sons, Inc., 1971.

————. "Simulation and Gaming." *Computing Reviews,* Vol. 10, No. 1 (January 1969). A bibliography.

————.; BALINTFY, J. L.; BURDICK, D. S.; and CHU, K. *Computer Simulation Techniques.* New York: John Wiley & Sons, Inc., 1966.

RAND CORPORATION. *A Million Random Digits.* Glencoe, Ill.: Free Press, Inc., 1955.

SCHLAIFER, R. *Analysis of Decisions under Uncertainty.* New York: McGraw-Hill Book Co., 1969.

WAGNER, H. M. *Principles of Operations Research.* Englewood Cliffs, N.J.: Prentice-Hall, Inc., 1969.

$TC = 9.44 \left(50\right) + 5\frac{1}{2}\left(10\right) + 2 \times 3.00 = \$65.72$

PROBLEMS

20–1.   *a)*   Using the same history of arrivals shown in Table 20–4, simulate the waiting line process of the warehouse-railroad car example with a known service rate of three per day.

b)   Assuming that the warehouse company pays $20 per day for freight cars kept over one day, estimate the annual savings (250 days = one year) from a service rate of three per day (instead of two per day).

20–2.   Continue Table 20–7 to 100 periods, using random numbers from Table 20–2. Estimate the total annual cost (one year = 50 weeks) if the cost of placing an order is $10, the cost of holding one unit of inventory is 50 cents per year, and the cost of outage is $3 per unit of lost sales. (Use average beginning inventory in determining cost of holding inventory.) $Q = 15$ $R = 5$ $T.C. \, Av_5 = 9.44$

 Cost of outage 4 il orders

20–3.   Pick an inventory rule that you consider good for the situation described in Problem 20–2. (That is, pick a number Q and a number R.) Simulate for 100 periods and compare the cost of your rule with the cost in Problem 20–2. $Q = 20$ $R = 5$

20–4.   Continue Table 20–10 to 50 trials, using random numbers from

Table 20–2. Plot your results on a diagram similar to Figure 20–2. Out of your sample of 25 trials, what is the probability of the profit being less than zero? What is the average profit for your sample of 25 trials? Compare your answer with those obtained in Table 20–10 and with the expected profit of $2,140; also, compute the *exact* probability of profit being less than zero and compare it to your sample outcome.

20–5. Refer to Problem 20–4. Suppose that the selling price and annual sales volume were *not* independent variables but were jointly distributed with the following probabilities:

Sales volume

		3,000	4,000	5,000	Row sums
	$4	0	0	0.3	0.3
Price	$5	0	0.4	0.1	0.5
	$6	0.2	0	0	0.2
	Column sums	0.2	0.4	0.4	1.0

Note that the marginal probabilities are the same as in the chapter; but now the assumption of independence does not apply.

a) Simply by studying the joint probability table above, can you predict whether expected profit under the new assumption will be higher or lower than previously? Why or why not?

b) Devise a scheme similar to Table 20–9 which uses random numbers to produce random values for the elements price and volume when they are related as specified.

c) Use your scheme in part (b) to generate 25 trials of the investment as in Table 20–10, but now assuming price and volume are dependent as specified.

d) Plot a figure similar to Figure 20–2 for your data in part (c).

e) Compare your figure of part (d) to Figure 20–2. Which investment would you prefer? Why?

20–6. Refer to Problem 19–7 in Chapter 19. Suppose now that arrivals are still Poisson with average rate $A = 5$ ships per week, but that service times are constant at 0.1 week. Simulate two weeks of operation, keeping track of the waiting time of each ship. (*Hint:* The times between arrivals are exponential random variables with parameter $A = 5$. Starting from zero, generate random interarrival times as described in the Appendix.)

21

PERT (Program Evaluation and Review Technique)

In many business situations, there are a number of different activities which must be performed in a specified sequence in order to accomplish some project. Some of the activities may be in series (for example, market research cannot be performed before the research design is planned), whereas others may be in parallel (for example, the engines for a ship can be built at the same time the hull is being constructed). For a large, complex project the complete set of activities will usually contain a combination of series and parallel elements. The technique of PERT (Program Evaluation and Review Technique) is designed to aid a manager in planning and controlling a project. For planning purposes prior to the start of the project, the PERT technique allows a manager to calculate the expected total amount of time the entire project will take to complete. The technique highlights the bottleneck activities in the project so that the manager may either allocate more resources to them or keep a careful watch on them as the project progresses. For purposes of control after the project has begun, the technique provides a way of monitoring progress and calling attention to those delays in activities which will cause a delay in the project's completion date.

INFORMATION REQUIREMENTS

In order to use PERT, two types of information are needed for each activity in the project.[1] The sequencing requirements for an activity must be known. For example, we need to know the set of activities which

---

[1] A closely related procedure called CPM (Critical Path Method) also exists. In this chapter the terminology of PERT is used, although the method of network analysis follows the convention of CPM.

must be completed prior to the beginning of each specific activity. In addition, we require an estimate of the time each activity will take.

CASE I: KNOWN ACTIVITY TIMES

In the first part of the chapter we will assume that there is a precise, known time that each activity in the project will take. In the second part, we will assume that the time to perform each activity is uncertain (i.e., a random variable).

NETWORK DIAGRAM

The network diagram is a graphical representation of the entire project. Each activity in the project is represented by a circle, and arrows are used to indicate sequencing requirements.[2]

Example

Table 21–1 contains a list of six activities which constitute a project, together with the sequencing requirements and the estimated times for

TABLE 21–1

Activity	Immediate predecessors	Estimated time (days)
A.........	....	2
B.........	A	3
C.........	A	4
D.........	B, C	6
E.........	....	2
F.........	E	8

each activity. The immediate predecessor of activity B is activity A; this means that activity A must be completed before activity B can begin. If activities are represented by circles, then the network diagram for our example is contained in Figure 21–1. The arrows in the network diagram illustrate the sequencing requirements of the problem. For example, the arrow from circle A to circle B indicates that activity A must be completed before activity B can begin. Similarly, activities B and C must *both* be completed before activity D can begin.

---

[2] In PERT the arrows are used to represent activities; however, the CPM convention is easier to understand.

FIGURE 21–1
Network diagram

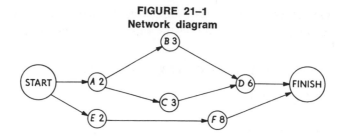

The estimated time for each activity has been placed in the circle representing that activity. Once the network diagram is completed, it may be used to develop the critical path for the project.

THE CRITICAL PATH

A *path* is defined as a sequence of connected activities in the project. In our example, there are only three possible paths: *ABD*, which has a length of 11 days; *ACD*, which has a length of 12 days; and *EF*, which has a length of 10 days. The critical path is the path which has the largest amount of time associated with it. In our example, it is *ACD*, with a length of 12 days. The length of the critical path determines the minimum time in which the entire project may be completed. The activities on the critical path are the bottleneck activities in the project.

The critical path is important for two reasons. First, the completion time for the project cannot be reduced unless one or more of the activities on the critical path can be completed in less time than the initial time estimate. The critical path highlights those activities which must be performed more rapidly if the total project completion time is to be reduced. Second, any delays in activities which are on the critical path will produce delays in completion of the project, whereas delays in noncritical activities may not actually delay the completion of the project. In our example the estimated project completion time is 12 days. If we desire to reduce this time, we must reduce the time to complete one of the three activities on the critical path—*A*, *C*, or *D*. We obtain no benefit from reducing the time required to perform activities *B*, *E*, and *F*, since these activities are not on the critical path. Also, a delay of up to one day in the time required to perform activity *B* could be tolerated, since this would have no effect on the project completion time. On the other hand, any delay in activities *A*, *C*, or *D* would directly affect the project completion time adversely. If activity *C* was delayed 3 days, the project would take 15 days rather than 12 to be completed.

For simple projects such as the one in our example, the critical path may be found by inspection of the network diagram. However, the PERT technique is typically used for planning and control of a large-scale, complex project (e.g., the construction of a 50-story building, or the development and implementation of a new military defense system). In such a situation, there may be hundreds or even thousands of activities which must be performed to complete the project, and some systematic way of finding the critical path is needed.

ALGORITHM FOR CRITICAL PATH

An algorithm is a well-defined systematic procedure. The algorithm to find the critical path in a network is presented below. Let:

$$ES_i = \text{earliest start time for activity } i$$
$$EF_i = \text{earliest finish time for activity } i$$

where the earliest start time for an activity is the earliest possible time that the activity can begin, assuming that all of its predecessors also started at the earliest possible times. The earliest finish time for an activity is the sum of the earliest start time and the estimated time to perform the activity. The earliest finish time represents the earliest possible time that an activity could be finished, assuming all of its predecessors started at their earliest start times.

The ES and the EF for each activity in the network are obtained as follows: First, set the ES of the first activity equal to zero. Then add the estimated time to perform the first activity to its ES (zero), obtaining the EF for the first activity. Now consider any activity for which all of its immediate predecessors have ES and EF values. The ES of such an activity is equal to the largest of the EF values of its immediate predecessors. Again, the EF is obtained by adding the estimated time to perform the activity to its ES time.

Figure 21–2 contains ES and EF times for the activities in our first example. Activities A and E are the first activities, so ES for A and E is zero. Since activity A takes two days, the EF for activity A is two. Similarly, the EF for activity E is two. Then the ES for activities B and C is two. The EF for B is $2 + 3$, or 5; and the EF for C is $2 + 4$, or 6. Since activity D requires both B and C to be completed before it can begin, the ES for activity D is the larger of 5 or 6, namely, 6. The EF for D is $6 + 6$, or 12. The ES for activity F is 2, and the EF for activity F is 10.

Continuing with our algorithm, define:

$$LS_i = \text{latest start time for activity } i$$
$$LF_i = \text{latest finish time for activity } i$$

FIGURE 21–2
Earliest start, earliest finish time

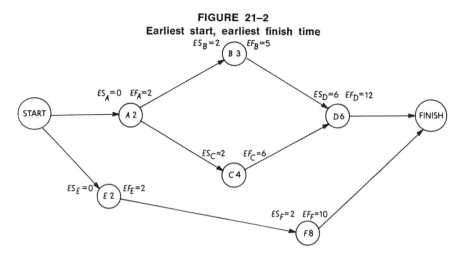

where the latest finish time for an activity is the latest possible time an activity can finish without delaying the project beyond its deadline, assuming all of the subsequent activities are performed as planned. The latest start time for an activity is the difference between the latest finish time and the estimated time for the activity to be performed.

To obtain the *LS* and *LF* for each activity, we start at the end of the network diagram and first set the *LF* for the last activity equal to the *EF* for that activity.[3] Then we subtract the estimated time to perform the last activity from the *LF* to obtain the *LS*. Now consider any activity for which all of its immediate successors have *LS* and *LF* values. The *LF* of such an activity is equal to the smallest of the *LS* values of its immediate successors. Then the *LS* is obtained by subtracting the estimated time to perform the activity from its *LF* time. Figure 21–3 contains *LS* and *LF* times for the activities in our example, assuming the deadline for project completion is 12 days. Activities *D* and *F* are the last activities, so the *LF* for *D* and for *F* is set equal to the project deadline of 12 days. Since activity *D* takes 6 days, the *LS* for activity *D* is 12 — 6, or 6. Activity *F* takes 8 days, so the *LS* for *F* is 12 — 8, or 4. The *LF* for both *B* and *C* is 6, since they both have the same successor activity. The *LS* for activity *B* is 6 — 3, or 3; and the *LS* for activity *C* is 6 — 4, or 2. Activity *A*'s *LF* is the smallest of the *LS* values of its immediate successors; the smaller of three and two is two. Since activity *A* takes 2 days, the *LS* for *A* is 2 — 2, or 0. Finally, the *LF* for activity *E* is four, and its *LS* is two.

---

[3] In practice, the *LF* for the last activity is set equal to the project due date, or deadline. However, it is also instructive to set the *LF* of the last activity equal to its *EF* time, so that the critical path will have no slack. See below.

FIGURE 21-3
Latest start, latest finish time

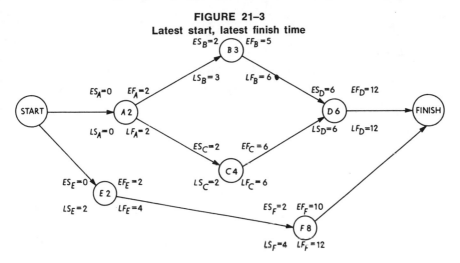

SLACK AND CRITICAL PATH

Slack refers to the number of days an activity can be delayed without forcing the total project to be delayed beyond its due date. After the *ES*, *EF*, *LS*, and *LF* have been calculated for each activity in the project, the slack for each activity is calculated as the difference between the *LS* and the *ES* for that activity (or equivalently, the difference between the *LF* and the *EF*). In our example, we specified that the project deadline was the length of the critical path, or 12 days. Thus, there will be zero slack for those activities which are on the critical path. Table 21–2 presents the slack for each activity in our example. Activity *B* has

TABLE 21-2

Activity	LS	ES	Slack
A........	0	0	0
B........	3	2	1
C........	2	2	0
D........	6	6	0
E........	4	2	2
F........	2	0	2

slack of one day; activities *E* and *F* have slack of two days; and activities *A*, *C*, and *D* have zero slack. If the project deadline is set equal to the length of the critical path, then all activities with zero slack must be on the critical path, since the definition of the critical path implies that any delay in a critical activity will delay the total project. Conversely, any activity which has positive slack may be delayed beyond its *ES* by an amount of time up to the amount of slack, since such a delay will by itself have no effect on the duration of the total project.[4]

The algorithm to compute slack and find the critical path for a network diagram has been programmed for computer calculation, and a number of computer codes are available to perform the calculations.

TIME-COST TRADE-OFFS

In the analysis above, we have assumed that the time needed to complete any activity was fixed. Sometimes this is true; but more generally, management can alter the time needed to complete an activity by allocating more resources to the task. For example, an activity—the painting of a house—may be assigned six days. However, this time can be shortened if more painters are assigned to the task or if they are scheduled to work overtime. The time for most activities may be thus shortened, usually at an increase in cost.[5] In this section, we shall examine how a manager might allocate resources to shorten the total project time.

To do this, let us consider the same example that we have been using. However, we shall allow the possibility that each activity may be done on a hurry-up or "crash" basis. The times and costs for the regular and crash programs are given in Table 21–3.

TABLE 21–3

	Time required		Cost (dollars)	
Activity	Regular program	Crash program	Regular program	Crash program
A	2	1½	$ 100	$ 150
B	3	2	200	250
C	4	3	300	375
D	6	4½	500	740
E	2	1½	180	210
F	8	5½	1,000	1,200
			$2,280	$2,925

Recall that the critical path is *ACD* and has a length of 12 days.

---

[4] If a group of noncritical activities are in series, the slack is shared among them. Once one such activity uses up its slack, the other activities in series will have zero slack. For example, activities *E* and *F* share two days of slack.

[5] Note that the activity times are now assumed to be controllable but are still deterministic; i.e., they still have no random components. Case II below considers the situation in which activity times are random variables.

This is under the assumption that the regular programs are used for each activity. In this case the cost may be obtained by adding the figures in the fourth column of Table 21–3. The total is $2,280. Now, suppose that the manager of the project decides that 12 days is too long and that the project has to be completed in a shorter period of time. He can obtain a shorter project completion time by doing some of the activities on a crash basis, while incurring the additional cost of doing so. But which activities should he do on a crash basis?

The activities which are *not* on the critical path already have slack time. Cutting down the time needed for these activities would have no effect on the total project time. So the manager needs only to examine those activities *on* the critical path. Shortening the time of any activity on the critical path will shorten total project time. The three critical-path activities, their incremental savings in days due to a crash program, and the incremental costs are shown in Table 21–4.

TABLE 21–4

Activity	Days shortened by crash program	Incremental cost of crash program	Incremental cost per day
A..........	½	$ 50	$100
C..........	1	75	75
D..........	1½	240	160

From Table 21–4, we can see that the activity that can be shortened most inexpensively is activity *C*. The cost per day for this is only $75, compared to $100 and $160 for activities *A* and *D*, respectively. If activity *C* is done on a crash basis, the total project completion time is cut by one day. The network now looks as shown in Figure 21–4. Both paths,

FIGURE 21–4
Network with activity C shortened to three days

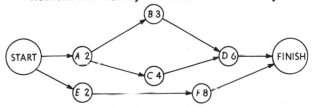

ACD and *ABD*, are now critical, each being 11 days long. The cost of this crash program is $2,355, the additional $75 being the incremental cost of putting activity *C* on a crash basis.

If the manager wished to cut the project completion time even more, he could do so by putting more activities on a crash basis. The critical activities are now A, B, C, and D. Activity C cannot be shortened further. Shortening B would shorten the path ABD but would leave the path ACD unchanged at 11 days and hence would not cut total project time. The project time can be cut only by reducing activities A or D. Referring to Table 21–4, we see that activity A is the less expensive. This reduction amounts to one-half day, with an additional cost of $50, making the total cost $2,405. The two reductions are summarized in the second and third rows of Table 21–5.

TABLE 21–5

Activities on:				
Regular program	Crash program	Critical path(s)	Project completion time	Project total cost
All	None	ACD	12	$2,280
A, B, D, E, F.	C	ABD, ACD	11	2,355
B, D, E, F	A, C	ABD, ACD	10½	2,405
B, C, E, F	A, D	ACD, EF	10	2,570
A, B, F	C, D, E	ABD, ACD, EF	9½	2,625
B	A, C, D, E, F	ABD, ACD	9	2,875

If the manager wished to reduce the project time even further, he would next put activity D on a crash basis. However, this would eliminate the need to have *both* A and C on a crash basis, since the critical path would shift to EF; path EF takes 10 days, while if A, C, and D are all crashed, path ACD takes only 9 days. Thus, after deciding that activity D must be crashed to reduce the project time below 10½ days, the manager must review tentatively-crashed activities A and C to ascertain which of these should be moved back to the regular program.

Assuming D and C are crashed (and A is not), then path ACD takes 9½ days, and path EF with 10 days is the critical path; the cost of crashing D and C is $2,280 + $75 + $240 = $2,595. However, suppose that D and A are crashed, while C is restricted to the regular program. Then path ACD takes 10 days, and there are two critical paths: ACD and EF. The cost of crashing A and D is $2,280 + $50 + $240 = $2,570. Thus, for a target of 10 project days, this alternative meets the target at lowest cost. The example illustrates the complexity of making optimal time-cost trade-offs.

Since there are now two critical paths (ACD and EF), the manager must simultaneously shorten *both* of these paths in order to reduce further the project time. Consider each of these paths in turn; for path *EF*, he can reduce activity *E* by one-half day at a cost of $60 per day or activity *F* by 2½ days at a cost of $80 per day. Activity *E* is the less expensive, and the manager tentatively plans to crash activity *E*. Since this reduces path *EF* to 9½ days, he next considers ways to lower path *ACD* to 9½ days (or less). Path *ACD* will take precisely 9½ days if activities *C* and *D* are crashed. Now we must check to see whether any other paths have become critical. If activities *C, D,* and *E* are crashed, then path *ABD* becomes critical with time 9½ days. The fifth line in Table 21–5 shows this situation. All three paths are now critical; total project time is 9½ days, and total cost is $2,625.

In order to reduce further the total project time, all three critical paths must be shortened simultaneously. This can be done by doing both activity *A* and activity *F* on a crash basis. The sixth line in Table 21–5 shows this situation. Total project time is nine days, with total cost of $2,875. It is not possible to reduce project time further. Activity *B* remains at the regular program level; all others are on a crash basis.

Figure 21–5 summarizes the results of our analysis. The curve can be labeled a time-cost trade-off curve, indicative of the fact that the manager

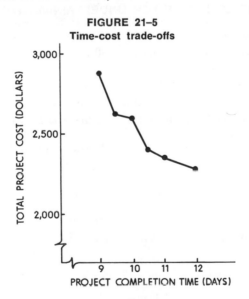

FIGURE 21–5
Time-cost trade-offs

can have different project completion times, depending upon how much he is willing to pay.[6]

---

[6] Only the points indicated in Figure 21–5 are feasible alternatives. The lines connecting the points are drawn only to give a proper graphic effect.

The determination of the time-cost trade-offs above has been deliberately simplified in order to increase understanding of what is happening. But there is no reason why only two possible programs should be considered for each activity. There may be many alternative levels in addition to regular and crash programs. In fact, one could assume a continuum of possibilities, expressed by a straight line or other curve between the cost and time of the regular and crash programs. Some PERT or critical-path computer programs allow the user to find these resource allocation or trade-off alternatives as a part of the solution of the critical-path network.

CASE II: UNCERTAIN ACTIVITY TIMES

We now make a more realistic assumption concerning activity times; namely, that they are not known (or controllable) with certainty. Suppose activity times are treated as random variables. Then we need to obtain information concerning the probability density functions of these random variables before we may begin manipulating them. One technique to obtain such information is called the multiple-estimate approach.

MULTIPLE TIME ESTIMATES FOR UNCERTAIN ACTIVITY TIMES

Instead of asking for an estimate of expected activity time directly, three time estimates are requested, as follows:

$$a_i = \text{most optimistic time for activity } i$$
$$b_i = \text{most pessimistic time for activity } i$$
$$m_i = \text{most likely time for activity } i \text{ (i.e., the mode)}$$

Then equation (21–1) is used to estimate expected (mean) activity time:

(21–1) $$t_i = \tfrac{1}{6}(a_i + 4m_i + b_i)$$

where t_i is the expected activity time for activity i. For example, suppose the estimates for activity B are:

$$a_B = 1$$
$$b_B = 8$$
$$m_B = 3$$

Then the expected time for activity B is:

$$t_B = \tfrac{1}{6}(1 + 4 \cdot 3 + 8) = \tfrac{1}{6}(21) = 3.5$$

The modal estimate for activity B is 3, but the expected time for the completion is 3.5. This occurs because the pessimistic time estimate is quite large. The formula for expected time in equation (21–1) is used because this formula approximates the mean of a beta distribution whose end points are a_i and b_i, and whose mode is m_i. It is not possible to justify the use of the beta distribution in a rigorous sense, but the distribution has the following characteristics: It is unimodal, it is continuous, and it has a finite range. Intuitively, the formula in equation (21–1) gives some weight to the end points (a_i and b_i) as well as the mode (m_i) in calculating the mean time for completion.

The multiple-estimate approach is supposed to produce improved estimates of the expected time to complete an activity. In practice, it is not obvious that the multiple-estimate approach leads to a better expected value than the one-estimate approach; however, the multiple-estimate approach allows us to consider the variability of the time for completion of an activity. Equation (21–2) is used to estimate the standard deviation of the time required to complete an activity, based on the three time estimates:

$$(21\text{–}2) \qquad\qquad \sigma_i = \tfrac{1}{6}(b_i - a_i)$$

where σ_i represents the standard deviation of the time required to complete activity i. Again, this formula is only an approximation used if the time to complete an activity is beta-distributed. The value of the standard deviation is that it may be used for those activities on a path to obtain an estimate of the standard deviation of the duration of the path. For instance, suppose the multiple time estimates shown in Table 21–6 were made for the project in our example. The numbers in the

TABLE 21–6
Multiple time estimates

Activity	a_i	b_i	m_i	t_i	$\sigma_i = \tfrac{1}{6}(b_i - a_i)$	σ_i^2
A..........	1	3	2	2	0.33	0.11
B..........	1	5	3	3	0.67	0.45
C..........	2	6	4	4	0.67	0.45
D..........	4	8	6	6	0.67	0.45
E..........	1	3	2	2	0.33	0.11
F..........	1	15	8	8	2.33	5.43

table were chosen so that the estimated time, t_i, would be the same as the initial estimates in Figure 21–1. Thus the critical path is still ACD, with an expected length of 12 days. Path ABD has an expected length of 11 days, and path EF has an expected length of 10 days. Table 21–6 contains the expected time for each activity and the standard deviation of time for each activity.

Some authors suggest computing the standard deviation of the length of each path. Starting with the critical path, if we assume that the activity times are independent random variables, then the variance of the time to complete the critical path may be computed as the sum of the variances of the activities on the critical path.[7] In our example the path ACD is the critical path. If we add the variances along this path, we obtain:

$$\sigma^2_{ACD} = 0.11 + 0.45 + 0.45 = 1.01$$

The standard deviation of the length of path ACD is:

$$\sigma_{ACD} = \sqrt{1.01} = 1.005$$

If there is a large number of independent activities on the critical path, the distribution of the total time for the path can be assumed to be normal.[8] Our example only has three activities, so the assumption of normality would not be strictly appropriate; but for illustration, our results may be interpreted as follows: The length of time it takes to complete path ACD is a normally distributed random variable with a mean of 12 days and a standard deviation of 1.005 days. Given this information, it is possible to use tables of the cumulative normal distribution to make probability statements concerning various completion times for the critical path.[9] For example, the probability of path ACD being completed within 14 days is:

$$F\left(\frac{X - \mu}{\sigma}\right) = F\left(\frac{14 - 12}{1.005}\right) = F(2) = 0.977 \text{ from Table A}$$

There is a major problem in performing this type of analysis on the critical path. Apart from the difficulties involved in assuming that all activity times are independent and beta-distributed, it is not necessarily true that the path with the longest expected length (i.e., the critical path) will in fact *turn out to be* the longest path. In our example, the path EF has an expected length of 10 days. The variance of that path is:

$$\sigma^2_{EF} = 0.11 + 5.43 = 5.54$$

---

[7] The variance of a sum of random variables equals the sum of the variances of each random variable if the variables are independent.

[8] The sum of n independent random variables with finite mean and variance tends toward normality by the central limit theorem as n tends toward infinity.

[9] See Chapter 7 for a review of the standardized normal variate

$$Z = \frac{X - \mu}{\sigma}$$

The standard deviation is:

$$\sigma_{EF} = \sqrt{5.54} = 2.35$$

If we assume that the distribution of the length of path EF is normal, then it has mean 10.0 and standard deviation 2.35. The probability of path EF being completed within 14 days is:

$$F\left(\frac{14 - 10}{2.35}\right) = F(1.70) = 0.955 \text{ from table A}$$

Path ACD and path EF must both be completed within 14 days for the project to be completed within 14 days, since the project is not completed until all activities are completed. The probability that both paths (ACD and EF) are completed within 14 days is:

$$(0.977)(0.955) = 0.933$$

If we had considered only the critical path, the probability of not completing the project in 14 days would have been $1 - 0.977$, or 0.023. After path EF is also considered, the probability of not completing the project in 14 days is $1 - 0.933$, or 0.067, almost three times the probability of the critical path not being completed. Another way of describing the situation is to say that if the project takes more than 14 days, path EF has a larger chance of causing the delay than path ACD does.

A final difficulty remains. Path ABD may also turn out to be the most constraining path, and we could compute the variance of that path, as we did above for paths ACD and EF. However, there are two activities in common between path ABD and path ACD, and thus the lengths of the two paths are not independent variables. In order to calculate the probability that both path ABD and path ACD are completed in less than 14 days, we must deal with the joint probability of dependent events, and we are beyond the methods of calculation presented in this book. The problems we have encountered in a six-activity sample project are greatly magnified when a realistic project with hundreds of activities is considered. Thus, there is a serious danger in using the mean and variance of the length of the critical path to estimate the probability that the project will be completed within some specified time. Since some noncritical paths may in fact turn out to be constraining, the mean estimate of project completion time obtained by studying the critical path alone is too optimistic an estimate; i.e., it is biased and always tends to underestimate the average project completion time.

Fortunately, even though the analytical calculation of the distribution of the project completion time is exceedingly difficult in a real-sized network, it is relatively easy to use the technique of Monte Carlo or simulation (see Chapter 20) to obtain information about the project when activity times are uncertain.

SIMULATION OF PERT NETWORKS

To overcome the problem described above, it is possible to simulate any PERT network. In general terms, the steps would proceed as follows:

1. Using (for example) a normal distribution of activity times for each activity, and using each activity's calculated mean and standard deviation from equations (21–1) and (21–2), generate a random value (a realization) for the time to complete each activity in the network.
2. Treat the generated times as actual times for each activity, and use the critical-path algorithm described earlier to find both the "critical path" (*ex post*) and the actual project duration.
3. Repeat steps (1) and (2) above for some large number of trials, recording a histogram of project completion times and the percentage of time each activity was on the *ex post* critical path.

Example

Suppose a simulation were run 100 times for the sample network of the chapter, using means and standard deviations from Table 21–6. Figure 21–6 contains a representative histogram of the type which might be produced from the simulation. While the information contained in Figure 21–6 would be useful in deciding whether the risk of project lateness were tolerable or not, it is of no direct help in deciding how to "crash" activities so as to speed the project. For this purpose, the

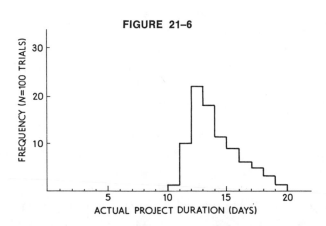

FIGURE 21–6

simulation can record the percentage of times each activity was on the *ex post* critical path (that is, the path which actually turned out to be critical in a given simulation run). Table 21–7 is an example of such a record.

TABLE 21–7
Percentage of time activities were critical

$$
\begin{array}{ll}
A \ldots \ldots \ldots \ldots & 42\% \\
B \ldots \ldots \ldots \ldots & 11 \\
C \ldots \ldots \ldots \ldots & 31 \\
D \ldots \ldots \ldots \ldots & 42 \\
E \ldots \ldots \ldots \ldots & 58 \\
F \ldots \ldots \ldots \ldots & 58 \\
\end{array}
$$

Activities E and F constitute one potentially critical path, and thus have identical percentages in Table 21–7. Activities A and D are in series in two paths (ABD and ACD), and hence also have identical percentages. Activities B and C are in parallel, and thus the sum of their percentages (11 percent + 31 percent) must add to 42 percent, which is the percentage for activities A and D in series with the B–C parallel link.

For a large network, a simulation of the regular program would produce a histogram like Figure 21–6. If the project performance needed to be improved, study of a table like Table 21–7 would indicate the set of activities which, on the average, were causing delays various percentages of the time. Then, after some of those "critical activities" were crashed, the simulation could be repeated to see whether project performance had been sufficiently improved.

EVALUATION OF PERT

The PERT technique forces the planner to specify in detail the set of activities which constitute the project, and to estimate their times and state their sequencing requirements. The construction of the network diagram can often point out major problems in the project. If the critical path is longer than desired, the project can be replanned, with more resources committed to critical activities. Once the project has begun, the PERT technique may be used to provide periodic reports on the status of the project, including any changes in the critical path. If there is a path which is almost critical, the PERT technique can provide this information by pointing out activities with a small amount of slack.

The time estimates to perform activities constitute a major potential defect in the PERT technique. If the time estimates are poor, then the initial network diagram and initial critical path will have little real meaning after the project begins. Also, if there is uncertainty in how long it will take to complete the tasks, then this uncertainty must be taken into account in estimating the probability of project completion within any specified time. As we have seen, when activity times are random, one may compute the probability of the "critical path" being completed in any given time; but with random activity times, the actual *ex post* critical path may differ from the *ex ante* critical path. The best way of dealing with this complexity involves simulation of the network. In the simulation both the probability of project lateness and the probability that each activity will be "critical" can be estimated, thereby providing guidance to the project planner.

Finally, the simple PERT technique does not consider the resources required at various stages of the project. For example, if a certain resource must be used to perform both activity *B* and activity *C* in our example, and if it can only be used for one activity at a time, then the diagram in Figure 21–3 is infeasible, and activity *C* must not be performed in parallel with activity *B*. Various extensions of the PERT technique have been developed which allow for resource constraints and keep track of costs as well as time as the project progresses.

Many project managers experienced in using PERT and CPM now feel that the major advantages of the technique are in the planning stage of a project. Using PERT for active control of a project requires frequent updating and rerunning of the PERT calculations, while often a simple bar-chart of progress to date can provide an adequate record for control purposes at much less cost.

BIBLIOGRAPHY

EVARTS, H. F. *Introduction to PERT*. Boston: Allyn and Bacon, Inc., 1964.

FORD, L. R., JR., and FULKERSON, D. R. *Flows in Networks*. Princeton: Princeton University Press, 1962.

LEVY, F. K.; THOMPSON, G. L.; and WIEST, J. D. "The ABC's of the Critical Path Method." *Harvard Business Review,* September–October 1963.

MILLER, R. W. "How to Plan and Control with PERT." *Harvard Business Review,* March–April 1962.

————. *Schedule, Cost, and Profit Control with PERT: A Comprehensive Guide for Program Management*. New York: McGraw-Hill Book Co., 1963.

WIEST, J. D., and LEVY, F. K. *A Management Guide to PERT/CPM.* Englewood Cliffs, N.J.: Prentice-Hall, Inc., 1969.

PROBLEMS

21–1. Consider the following data for the activities in a project:

Activity	Immediate predecessors	Estimated time (days)
A	. . . .	5
B	A	4
C	. . . .	7
D	B, C	3
E	B	4
F	D, E	2

a) Draw a network diagram for the project.
b) Compute the *ES, EF, LS,* and *LF* for each activity, assuming the *EF* and the *LF* for the last activity are the same. What is the minimum project completion time?
c) List the activities which are on the critical path.

21–2. Consider the data in Problem 21–1, but suppose now that activity *C* takes nine days to complete rather than seven days.
a) Does the critical path change?
b) If activity *C* were to take 11 days to complete, would the critical path change?

21–3. The table below contains a list of activities and sequencing requirements as indicated, which comprise necessary activities for the completion of a thesis.

Activity	Description	Prerequisite activity	Expected time (weeks)
a	Literature search	None	6
b	Topic formulation	None	5
c	Committee selection	b	2
d	Formal proposal	c	2
e	Company selection and contact	a, d	2
f	Progress report	d	1
g	Formal research	a, d	6
h	Data collection	e	5
i	Data analysis	g, h	6
j	Conclusions	i	2
k	Rough draft (without conclusions)	g	4
l	Final copy	j, k	3
m	Oral examination	l	1

a) Draw a network diagram illustrating the sequencing require-ments for the set of activities in the table. Be sure to portray activities by circles and sequencing requirements by arrows.

b) Compute the *ES*, *EF*, *LS*, and *LF* for each activity, assuming the *EF* and the *LF* for the last activity are the same. What is the minimum project completion time?

c) List the activities which are on the critical path.

21–4. You are given the following data concerning the activities in a project:

Activity	Immediate predecessor	a_i	b_i (days)	m_i
A................	...	2	6	4
B................	...	6	10	8
C................	A	1	15	5
D................	C	1	9	5
E................	B	6	10	8

a) Compute the expectation (t_i) and the variance (σ_i^2) of the time required to complete each activity.

b) Draw a network diagram and find the critical path by inspection. What is the expected length of the critical path?

c) Assume the time required to complete a path is normally distri-buted. Compute the probability that path *ACD* will be completed in less than 16 days. Also compute the probability that path *BE* will be completed in less than 16 days.

d) What is the probability that the project will be completed in less than 16 days?

21–5. Consider the estimate of total project duration as calculated by the usual PERT algorithm (adding up expected time estimates of all activities which are on the critical path).

a) Suppose you are dealing with a pure "series" network:

$$\boxed{\text{START}} \rightarrow \text{\textcircled{A}} \rightarrow \text{\textcircled{B}} \rightarrow \text{\textcircled{C}} \rightarrow \cdots \rightarrow \text{\textcircled{X}} \rightarrow \text{\textcircled{Y}} \rightarrow \text{\textcircled{Z}} \rightarrow \boxed{\text{FINISH}}$$

Can you argue logically that the PERT estimate of total project duration is unbiased? (*Hint:* Recall that the expectation of a sum equals the sum of the expectations.)

b) Suppose you are dealing with a pure "parallel" network:

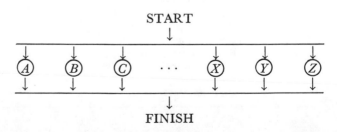

Assume that all activities in this network have the same expected time for completion. Can you argue logically that the PERT estimate of total project duration is biased in this case? In which direction is the estimate biased?

c) From your conclusions in (a) and (b) above, make a valid generalization about the bias (or lack thereof) inherent in a PERT project duration estimate when we have a large, complex network combining series and parallel portions.

21–6. The Ocean Hardware Company was a chain of retail hardware and appliance stores. The company was considering the installation of a new computer system to do the payroll for the company, to do the sales accounting (paying for purchases and sending bills), and to do inventory record keeping. The company controller was trying to lay

No.	Activity	Time to complete (in months)	Predecessor activities
a	Analyze alternative computer systems and order computer from the manufacturer	2	. . .
b	Wait for delivery of computer from manufacturer	4	a
c	Hire computer programmers	1	a
d	Do preliminary work on payroll program	1½	c
e	Do preliminary work on accounting program	2½	c
f	Do final work on both payroll and accounting programs	2	d, e
g	Hire outside consultant for work on inventory control program	1	a
h	Do preliminary work on inventory control program	2	e, g
i	Do final work on inventory control program	2	f, h
j	Do preliminary testing of payroll and accounting programs on rented machine	½	f
k	Revise payroll and accounting programs	½	j
l	Install and test computer upon delivery from manufacturer	½	b
m	Test payroll and accounting programs on installed computer	½	k, l
n	Prepare manuals describing payroll and accounting programs	1	j
o	Implement payroll and accounting programs	½	m, n
p	Test inventory control program on installed computer	½	i, l
q	Prepare manuals describing inventory control program	1	i
r	Implement inventory control program	½	p, q
s	Done	0	o, r

out a schedule for the various tasks involved in putting the new computer system into operation.

The company planned to hire programmers to develop the payroll and accounting programs. However, an outside consulting firm was to be hired to do the inventory control program. Certain aspects of the inventory control program depended upon the accounting program, and hence it had to be developed after the accounting program was completed.

The job of completing each program involved preliminary work, final work, testing, revising, writing of manuals, and implementation. The new manager of the computer operations identified the following list of tasks (activities) that had to be performed, together with the times needed to accomplish each and the activities that had to be completed before the given activity could begin (the predecessor activities).

a) How long will it take before the computer system with the three programs is completed? What activities are critical in achieving this time?

b) Suppose that management is concerned only with minimizing the time to get the accounting and payroll programs implemented. How long will this take? What activities are critical in this case?

21–7. A project is characterized by activities A through F below. The predecessor activities and the times required, and costs for both a regular and a crash program for each activity, are shown in the table below.

		Time (weeks)		Cost (hundreds of dollars)	
Activity	Predecessor activities	Regular program	Crash program	Regular program	Crash program
A (start)	. . .	0	.	0	. .
B	A	5	3	10	22
C	A	2	1	6	15
D	B, C	3	2	6	15
E	B	4	2	10	25
F (finish).	D, E	0	.	0	. .

a) Using only the times for the regular program activities, draw a PERT network for this problem. What is the critical path? How long will it take to complete the total project?

b) What is the cost of the project as given in (a) above?

c) Find the time-cost trade-off points that are possible. What is the minimum time in which the project can be completed? What is the cost of this program?

21-8. Refer to Problem 21–4. Assume for purposes of this exercise that each activity time is equally likely between its a_i and b_i time estimates (i.e., ignore the m_i column and consider activity times to be rectangularly distributed over the appropriate range). Using the table of random digits (Table 20–2 on page 382), perform a hand simulation of the network for 10 trials, recording for each trial the project completion time and the activities which were critical. Which activities were critical the largest percentage of the time?

21-9. A network for a project is shown below:

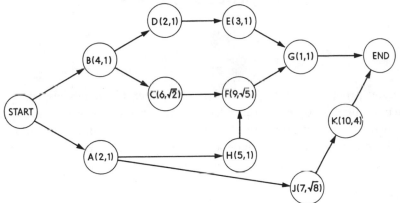

The (t_i, σ_i) attached to each node represents the (expected time, standard deviation) *in months*, of this segment of the project.
a) Identify the critical path and calculate its expected length.
b) Assuming that the length of the "critical path" is normally distributed, calculate the probability that the *path* of (a) above will be completed in less than 23 months.
c) Will the actual *project* be completed by 23 months—
   (1) With the same probability as in (b)?
   (2) With lower probability?
   (3) With higher probability?
   Why?
d) Suppose you wish to reduce the probability that the project will take longer than 23 months. You can "crash" *one* of the following activities, and *only one*, by one month: A, C, E, or H. Which one would you choose to crash? *Why?*
   (*Note:* Assume that crashing will reduce the *mean* activity time by one month and leave the variance unchanged.)

22

Markov processes

Markov processes are a special class of mathematical models which are often applicable to decision problems. In a Markov process, various states are defined. The probability of going to each of the states depends only on the present state and is independent of how we arrived at that state. A simple Markov process is illustrated in Example 1.

Example 1

A machine which produces parts may either be *in adjustment* or *out of adjustment*. If the machine is in adjustment, the probability that it will be in adjustment a day later is 0.7, and the probability that it will be out of adjustment a day later is 0.3. If the machine is out of adjustment, the probability that it will be in adjustment a day later is 0.6, and the probability that it will be out of adjustment a day later is 0.4.[1] If we let state 1 represent the situation in which the machine is in adjustment and let state 2 represent its being out of adjustment, then the probabilities of change are as given in Table 22–1. Note that the sum of the probabilities in any row is equal to one.

TABLE 22–1
Probabilities of change

From \ To	In adjustment (state 1)	Out of adjustment (state 2)
In adjustment (state 1)	0.7	0.3
Out of adjustment (state 2)	0.6	0.4

---
[1] Assume the machine has a self-adjusting mechanism which functions imperfectly.

The process is represented in Figure 22–1 by two probability trees whose upward branches indicate moving to state 1 and whose downward branches indicate moving to state 2.

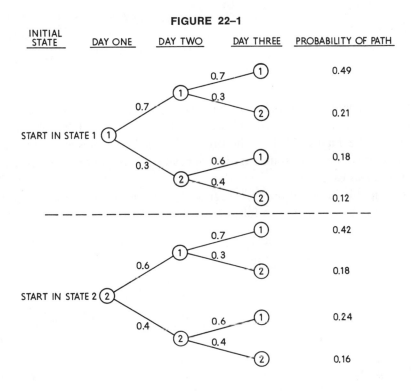

FIGURE 22–1

Suppose the machine starts out in state 1 (in adjustment). Table 22–1 and Figure 22–1 show there is a 0.7 probability that the machine will be in state 1 on the second day. Now, consider the state of the machine on the third day. The probability that the machine is in state 1 on the third day is 0.49 plus 0.18, or 0.67 (see Figure 22–1). This probability may also be computed as follows:

Let:

$$P\left(\begin{array}{c|c} \text{state 1} & \text{state 1} \\ \text{on day 3} & \text{on day 1} \end{array}\right) = \begin{array}{c} \text{probability that the machine will} \\ \text{be in state 1 on day 3, } \textit{given} \\ \text{that it was in state 1 on day 1} \end{array}$$

Recognizing that

$$P\left(\begin{array}{c|c} \text{state 1} & \text{state 1} \\ \text{on day 3} & \text{on day 2} \end{array}\right) = 0.7 \text{ and } P\left(\begin{array}{c|c} \text{state 1} & \text{state 2} \\ \text{on day 3} & \text{on day 2} \end{array}\right) = 0.6,$$

we have:

$$P\left(\begin{array}{c|c}\text{state 1} & \text{state 1} \\ \text{on day 3} & \text{on day 1}\end{array}\right) = (0.7)P\left(\begin{array}{c|c}\text{state 1} & \text{state 1} \\ \text{on day 2} & \text{on day 1}\end{array}\right)$$

(22–1)
$$+ (0.6)P\left(\begin{array}{c|c}\text{state 2} & \text{state 1} \\ \text{on day 2} & \text{on day 1}\end{array}\right)$$

$$= (0.7)(0.7) + (0.6)(0.3)$$
$$= 0.49 + 0.18$$
$$= 0.67$$

The corresponding probability that the machine will be in state 2 on day 3, given that it started off in state 1 on day 1, is 0.21 plus 0.12, or 0.33 (see Figure 22–1). The probability of being in state 1 plus the probability of being in state 2 add to one, since there are only two possible states in this example.

Given this information (see Figure 22–2), the state probabilities on day 4 may be calculated as follows:

$$P\left(\begin{array}{c|c}\text{state 1} & \text{state 1} \\ \text{on day 4} & \text{on day 1}\end{array}\right) = (0.7)P\left(\begin{array}{c|c}\text{state 1} & \text{state 1} \\ \text{on day 3} & \text{on day 1}\end{array}\right)$$

(22–2)
$$+ (0.6)P\left(\begin{array}{c|c}\text{state 2} & \text{state 1} \\ \text{on day 3} & \text{on day 1}\end{array}\right)$$

$$= (0.7)(0.67) + (0.6)(0.33)$$
$$= 0.469 + 0.198$$
$$= 0.667$$

The corresponding probability that the machine will be in state 2 on day 4, given that it started off in state 1 on day 1, is 1 minus 0.667, or 0.333. This procedure may be continued to calculate the probability of the machine being in state 1 on any future day, given that it started off in state 1 on day 1; Table 22–2 contains the results of additional calculations.

TABLE 22–2

Day number	Probability of machine being in state 1 on a future day, given that it started off in state 1 on day 1
1.	1.0
2.	0.7
3.	0.67
4.	0.667
5.	0.6667
6.	0.66667
7.	0.666667
8.	0.6666667

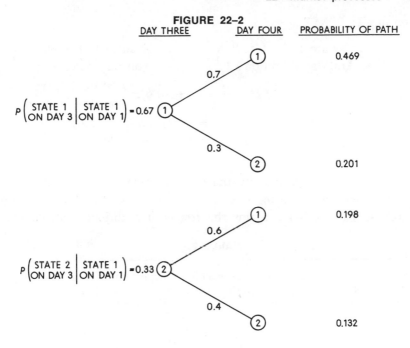

FIGURE 22–2

The corresponding part of the figure shows:

DAY THREE   DAY FOUR   PROBABILITY OF PATH

$P\left(\begin{array}{c|c}\text{STATE 1} & \text{STATE 1} \\ \text{ON DAY 3} & \text{ON DAY 1}\end{array}\right) = 0.67$ ① with branches 0.7 to ① (0.469) and 0.3 to ② (0.201)

$P\left(\begin{array}{c|c}\text{STATE 2} & \text{STATE 1} \\ \text{ON DAY 3} & \text{ON DAY 1}\end{array}\right) = 0.33$ ② with branches 0.6 to ① (0.198) and 0.4 to ② (0.132)

Table 22–2 shows that the probability of the machine being in state 1 on any future day, given that it started off in state 1 on day 1, tends toward the value 2/3 as the day number increases.

Now, consider a related set of calculations for the probability of the machine being in state 1 on future days, given that it started out in state 2, the out-of-adjustment case. The probability that the machine will be in state 1 on day 3, given that it started off in state 2 on day 1, is 0.42 plus 0.24, or 0.66 (see Figure 22–1); it may also be computed as follows:

(22–3)
$$P\left(\begin{array}{c|c}\text{state 1} & \text{state 2} \\ \text{on day 3} & \text{on day 1}\end{array}\right) = (0.7)P\left(\begin{array}{c|c}\text{state 1} & \text{state 2} \\ \text{on day 2} & \text{on day 1}\end{array}\right)$$
$$+ (0.6)P\left(\begin{array}{c|c}\text{state 2} & \text{state 2} \\ \text{on day 2} & \text{on day 1}\end{array}\right)$$
$$= (0.7)(0.6) + (0.6)(0.4)$$
$$= 0.42 + 0.24$$
$$= 0.66$$

The corresponding probability that the machine will be in state 2 on day 3, given that it started off in state 2 on day 1, is 0.18 plus 0.16, or 0.34 (see Figure 22–1). The state probabilities on day 4 may be calculated as follows, again assuming that the machine started off in state

2 on day 1:

$$P\left(\begin{array}{c} \text{state 1} \\ \text{on day 4} \end{array} \middle| \begin{array}{c} \text{state 2} \\ \text{on day 1} \end{array}\right) = (0.7)P\left(\begin{array}{c} \text{state 1} \\ \text{on day 3} \end{array} \middle| \begin{array}{c} \text{state 2} \\ \text{on day 1} \end{array}\right)$$

(22–4)
$$+ (0.6)P\left(\begin{array}{c} \text{state 2} \\ \text{on day 3} \end{array} \middle| \begin{array}{c} \text{state 2} \\ \text{on day 1} \end{array}\right)$$
$$= (0.7)(0.66) + (0.6)(0.34)$$
$$= 0.462 + 0.204$$
$$= 0.666$$

The corresponding probability that the machine will be in state 2 on day 4, given that it started out in state 2 on day 1, is 1 minus 0.666, or 0.334. Table 22–3 contains the results of additional calculations.

TABLE 22–3

Day number	Probability of machine being in state 1 on a future day, given that it started off in state 2 on day 1
1.	0.0
2.	0.6
3.	0.66
4.	0.666
5.	0.6666
6.	0.66666
7.	0.666666
8.	0.6666666

Tables 22–2 and 22–3 show that the probability of the machine being in state 1 on any future day tends toward 2/3, irrespective of the initial state of the machine on day 1. This probability is called the *steady-state* probability of being in state 1; the corresponding probability of being in state 2 (1 minus 2/3, or 1/3) is called the steady-state probability of being in state 2. The steady-state probabilities are often significant for decision purposes. For example, if we were deciding to lease either this machine or some other machine, the steady-state probability of state 2 would indicate the fraction of time the machine would be out of adjustment in the long run, and this fraction (1/3 in our example) would be of interest to us in making the decision.

CALCULATION OF STEADY-STATE PROBABILITIES

The steady-state probabilities for a Markov process may be derived in a more efficient manner than by completing tables such as Tables 22–2 and 22–3. We reason as follows: As the day number (n) increases to a very large number, the state probabilities for day n and for day $n + 1$ become nearly identical. As n approaches infinity, the probability of being in state 1 after n periods should be the same as the probability of being in state 1 after $n + 1$ periods. Thus, we write:

$$P\left(\begin{matrix} \text{state 1} \\ \text{on day } n + 1 \end{matrix} \middle| \begin{matrix} \text{state 1} \\ \text{on day 1} \end{matrix}\right) = (0.7)P\left(\begin{matrix} \text{state 1} \\ \text{on day } n \end{matrix} \middle| \begin{matrix} \text{state 1} \\ \text{on day 1} \end{matrix}\right)$$

(22–5)
$$+ (0.6)P\left(\begin{matrix} \text{state 2} \\ \text{on day } n \end{matrix} \middle| \begin{matrix} \text{state 1} \\ \text{on day 1} \end{matrix}\right)$$

and in addition, we reason that:

$$P\left(\begin{matrix} \text{state 1} \\ \text{on day } n + 1 \end{matrix} \middle| \begin{matrix} \text{state 1} \\ \text{on day 1} \end{matrix}\right) = P\left(\begin{matrix} \text{state 1} \\ \text{on day } n \end{matrix} \middle| \begin{matrix} \text{state 1} \\ \text{on day 1} \end{matrix}\right) \text{ as } n \to \infty$$

(22–6)

Substituting equation (22–6) into equation (22–5), we obtain:

$$P\left(\begin{matrix} \text{state 1} \\ \text{on day } n \end{matrix} \middle| \begin{matrix} \text{state 1} \\ \text{on day 1} \end{matrix}\right) = (0.7)P\left(\begin{matrix} \text{state 1} \\ \text{on day } n \end{matrix} \middle| \begin{matrix} \text{state 1} \\ \text{on day 1} \end{matrix}\right)$$

$$+ (0.6)P\left(\begin{matrix} \text{state 2} \\ \text{on day } n \end{matrix} \middle| \begin{matrix} \text{state 1} \\ \text{on day 1} \end{matrix}\right)$$

(22–7)
$$= (0.7)P\left(\begin{matrix} \text{state 1} \\ \text{on day } n \end{matrix} \middle| \begin{matrix} \text{state 1} \\ \text{on day 1} \end{matrix}\right)$$

$$+ (0.6)\left\{1 - P\left(\begin{matrix} \text{state 1} \\ \text{on day } n \end{matrix} \middle| \begin{matrix} \text{state 1} \\ \text{on day 1} \end{matrix}\right)\right\}$$

Solving:

$$P\left(\begin{matrix} \text{state 1} \\ \text{on day } n \end{matrix} \middle| \begin{matrix} \text{state 1} \\ \text{on day 1} \end{matrix}\right) = \frac{0.6}{1 - 0.7 + 0.6} = \frac{0.6}{0.9} = \frac{2}{3} \text{ as } n \to \infty$$

(22–8)

It was not important that we assumed the machine started out in state 1; in the steady state the effects of the initial conditions disappear. To demonstrate this fact, our computations are repeated, this time assuming that the machine started out in state 2:

$$P\left(\begin{matrix} \text{state 1} \\ \text{on day } n + 1 \end{matrix} \middle| \begin{matrix} \text{state 2} \\ \text{on day 1} \end{matrix}\right) = (0.7)P\left(\begin{matrix} \text{state 1} \\ \text{on day } n \end{matrix} \middle| \begin{matrix} \text{state 2} \\ \text{on day 1} \end{matrix}\right)$$

(22–9)
$$+ (0.6)P\left(\begin{matrix} \text{state 2} \\ \text{on day } n \end{matrix} \middle| \begin{matrix} \text{state 2} \\ \text{on day 1} \end{matrix}\right)$$

and

$$P\left(\begin{matrix} \text{state 1} \\ \text{on day } n + 1 \end{matrix} \middle| \begin{matrix} \text{state 2} \\ \text{on day 1} \end{matrix}\right) = P\left(\begin{matrix} \text{state 1} \\ \text{on day } n \end{matrix} \middle| \begin{matrix} \text{state 2} \\ \text{on day 1} \end{matrix}\right) \text{ as } n \to \infty$$

(22–10)

Substituting equation (22–10) into equation (22–9), we obtain:

$$P\left(\begin{array}{c}\text{state 1} \\ \text{on day } n\end{array}\middle|\begin{array}{c}\text{state 2} \\ \text{on day 1}\end{array}\right) = (0.7)P\left(\begin{array}{c}\text{state 1} \\ \text{on day } n\end{array}\middle|\begin{array}{c}\text{state 2} \\ \text{on day 1}\end{array}\right)$$

$$+ (0.6)P\left(\begin{array}{c}\text{state 2} \\ \text{on day } n\end{array}\middle|\begin{array}{c}\text{state 2} \\ \text{on day 1}\end{array}\right)$$

(22–11)
$$= (0.7)P\left(\begin{array}{c}\text{state 1} \\ \text{on day } n\end{array}\middle|\begin{array}{c}\text{state 2} \\ \text{on day 1}\end{array}\right)$$

$$+ (0.6)\left\{1 - P\left(\begin{array}{c}\text{state 1} \\ \text{on day } n\end{array}\middle|\begin{array}{c}\text{state 2} \\ \text{on day 1}\end{array}\right)\right\}$$

Solving:

$$P\left(\begin{array}{c}\text{state 1} \\ \text{on day } n\end{array}\middle|\begin{array}{c}\text{state 2} \\ \text{on day 1}\end{array}\right) = \frac{0.6}{(1 - 0.7 + 0.6)} = \frac{0.6}{0.9} = \frac{2}{3} \text{ as } n \to \infty$$

(22–12)

To simplify our notation, we shall hereafter let P_i represent the steady-state probability of being in state i. That is,

$$P_1 = P\left(\begin{array}{c}\text{state 1} \\ \text{on day } n\end{array}\middle|\begin{array}{c}\text{state 1} \\ \text{on day 1}\end{array}\right) = P\left(\begin{array}{c}\text{state 1} \\ \text{on day } n\end{array}\middle|\begin{array}{c}\text{state 2} \\ \text{on day 1}\end{array}\right) \text{ as } n \to \infty$$

$$P_2 = P\left(\begin{array}{c}\text{state 2} \\ \text{on day } n\end{array}\middle|\begin{array}{c}\text{state 1} \\ \text{on day 1}\end{array}\right) = P\left(\begin{array}{c}\text{state 2} \\ \text{on day } n\end{array}\middle|\begin{array}{c}\text{state 2} \\ \text{on day 1}\end{array}\right) \text{ as } n \to \infty$$

and so on.

CHARACTERISTICS OF A MARKOV PROCESS

Example 1 demonstrates some properties of Markov processes. The basic assumption of a Markov process is that the probabilities of going to each of the states depend only on the current state and not on the manner in which the current state was reached. For example, if the machine is in state 1 on day 2, the probability of its changing to state 2 on day 3 is 0.3, irrespective of the state of the machine on day 1. This property is often called the property of "no memory." There is no need to remember how the process reached a particular state at a particular period; the state of the process at a particular period of time contains all necessary information about the process and the likelihood of future changes.

A second characteristic of Markov processes is that there are initial conditions which take on less and less importance as the process operates, eventually "washing out" when the process reaches the steady state.[2] The steady-state probabilities are defined to be the long-run probabilities of being in particular states, after the process has been operating long enough to wash out the initial conditions. In deriving the steady-state probabilities for Example 1, we let the day number (n) tend toward infinity. In theory, the steady state would never be precisely reached, but the concept is useful. For example, if the initial state of the machine is unknown and the machine has been running for some time, then it would be appropriate to assign initial-state probabilities which are equal to the steady-state probabilities. If the process is started by assigning steady-state probabilities to initial-state probabilities, then the probabilities of future states will all be equal to the steady-state probabilities.

It is important to distinguish between the steady-state probabilistic behavior of the process and the actual state values attained as the process operates. For any particular set of days or time periods, the machine will take on a pattern of states, one on each day. However, when the process is analyzed before it is operated, then the steady-state probabilities are relevant. When one observes the machine and records the current state, this state becomes an initial state, and Tables 22–2 and 22–3 indicate the short-run probabilities of future changes. However, in the long run the steady-state probabilities are of interest.

Example 1 has a discrete number of states (two), and potential changes occur once every time period (once a day in the example). We may describe these characteristics by saying that the process is discrete in state space (a discrete number of possible states) and in time (potential changes occur only once every time period). Sometimes the more precise label of *Markov chain* is used to distinguish this process from other Markov processes in which either the state space and/or the time periods between changes may be continuous instead of being discrete. In this chapter, we shall continue to use the general term *Markov process* even though all of our examples will be discrete in state space as well as time periods between changes.

---

[2] We are assuming there are no "trapping states," where the probability of staying in a state is one. With a trapping state the initial state may be of importance. Also, we are assuming that the process is not cyclic. An example of a cyclic process is:

To From	1	2
1	0	1.0
2	1.0	0

Note that in this case the process moves continually back and forth between state 1 and state 2.

USE OF MARKOV PROCESSES IN DECISION PROBLEMS

Some decision problems can be solved by formulating a Markov process model of the situation and computing the steady-state probabilities from the probabilities of change. Let us extend our first example and assume that we have the alternative of leasing machine A (the one analyzed above) or machine B for the same annual cost. Suppose the probabilities of change for machine B are as shown in Table 22–4. By comparing

TABLE 22–4
Probabilities of change (machine B)

| From | To | |
	In adjustment (state 1)	Out of adjustment (state 2)
In adjustment (state 1)	0.8	0.2
Out of adjustment (state 2)	0.5	0.5

Table 22–4 with Table 22–1, we see that machine B has a lower probability of changing from the state of "in adjustment" to the state of "out of adjustment" (0.2 versus 0.3). On the other hand, there is also a lower probability that the self-adjusting mechanism will correct itself and return to the in-adjustment state from the out-of-adjustment state (0.5 versus 0.6). It is not immediately clear which machine is more desirable to lease. However, let us calculate the steady-state probabilities for machine B:

$$P\left(\begin{array}{c|c}\text{state 1} & \text{state 1}\\ \text{on day } n & \text{on day 1}\end{array}\right) = (0.8)P\left(\begin{array}{c|c}\text{state 1} & \text{state 1}\\ \text{on day } n & \text{on day 1}\end{array}\right)$$

$$(22\text{–}13) \qquad + (0.5)\left\{1 - P\left(\begin{array}{c|c}\text{state 1} & \text{state 1}\\ \text{on day } n & \text{on day 1}\end{array}\right)\right\}$$

That is,

$$P_1 = (0.8)P_1 + (0.5)[1 - P_1]$$

or

$$(22\text{–}14) \qquad P_1 = \frac{0.5}{1 - 0.8 + 0.5} = \frac{0.5}{0.7} = \frac{5}{7} \text{ as } n \to \infty$$

Now we may compare the steady-state probabilities of being in state 1 for machines A and B. Since machine B has a 5/7 probability of being in adjustment in the steady state, whereas machine A has a 2/3 probability, we would choose machine B (5/7 is greater than 2/3).

Example 2

Suppose the manufacturer of a brand of coffee is considering an extensive advertising campaign designed to cause consumers to try his brand of coffee. From panel data obtained through market research, he has been able to estimate the current probabilities of consumers changing from "our brand" to "any other" and vice versa, as given in Table 22–5. Also, suppose that market researchers have estimated the corre-

TABLE 22–5
Probabilities of changing brands of coffee
(no advertising campaign)

From \ To	Our brand (state 1)	Any other (state 2)
Our brand (state 1)	0.8	0.2
Any other (state 2)	0.2	0.8

TABLE 22–6
Probabilities of changing brands of coffee
(after advertising campaign)

From \ To	Our brand (state 1)	Any other (state 2)
Our brand (state 1)	0.8	0.2
Any other (state 2)	0.3	0.7

sponding probabilities that will exist after the advertising campaign has taken place, after taking into account any expected competitive reactions (see Table 22–6). Note that the probability of customers switching from "any other" to "our brand" has increased from 0.2 to 0.3, but the probability of retaining our current customers has not changed.

Suppose that the advertising campaign will cost $12 million per year, and that there are 50 million coffee purchasers in the market. For each customer the average annual profit before taxes is $2. Should the manufacturer undertake the advertising campaign?

In order to solve this decision problem, we first calculate the steady-state probabilities that a customer will be buying our brand under the current conditions (no advertising). Letting state 1 represent our brand and state 2 represent any other, using Table 22–5, the steady-state probabilities without advertising are calculated as follows:

$$(22-15) \qquad P_1 = (0.8)P_1 + (0.2)[1 - P_1]$$

and

$$(22-16) \qquad P_1 = \frac{0.2}{1 - 0.8 + 0.2} = \frac{0.2}{0.4} = \frac{1}{2} \text{ as } n \to \infty$$

Then, after the advertising campaign has taken place:

$$(22-17) \qquad P_1 = (0.8)P_1 + (0.3)[1 - P_1]$$

and

$$(22-18) \qquad P_1 = \frac{0.3}{(1 - 0.8 + 0.3)} = \frac{0.3}{0.5} = \frac{3}{5} \text{ as } n \to \infty$$

The steady-state probabilities may be used to make an economic evaluation of the advertising campaign. If the campaign is undertaken, we shall incur $12 million of costs per year. The benefits of the campaign are that the steady-state probability that a purchaser buys our brand of coffee will increase from 50 percent to 60 percent.[3] If we have an additional 10 percent of the total market, that represents 5 million customers. Each customer represents average annual profit of $2, so that we shall obtain additional profits of $2 times 5 million, or $10 million each year. The value of the benefits is less than the value of the costs ($12 million), and the advertising campaign should not be undertaken.

Extension of Example 2. Now, suppose the manufacturer were faced with an alternative advertising campaign which also has $12 million of costs per year but which would alter the probabilities of change as shown in Table 22–7. This advertising campaign increases the probability of retaining our own customers from 0.8 to 0.9, but leaves the probability of switching from any other brand to our brand unchanged.

In order to evaluate this second advertising campaign, we first compute the steady-state probabilities after the campaign, as follows:

$$(22-19) \qquad P_1 = (0.9)P_1 + (0.2)[1 - P_1]$$

$$P_1 = \frac{0.2}{(1 - 0.9 + 0.2)} = \frac{0.2}{0.3} = \frac{2}{3} \text{ as } n \to \infty$$

---

[3] There is a problem in deciding how quickly the campaign will take effect. Here, we assume that the change is instantaneous; but if purchase decisions are made once a month, it could take three or four periods of "transition" before we get close to the new steady state. The calculations could be modified to handle this difficulty (see Tables 22–2 and 22–3 as examples of how to calculate short-run transition probabilities).

Since the steady-state probability that a purchaser buys our brand increases from 1/2 to 2/3, we expect to gain an additional 1/6 of the total market of 50 million people, or 8⅓ million people. A stream of

TABLE 22–7
Probabilities of changing brands of coffee
(after second advertising campaign)

From	To — Our brand (state 1)	Any other (state 2)
Our brand (state 1)	0.9	0.1
Any other (state 2)	0.2	0.8

payments of $16.67 million (i.e., $2 times 8⅓ million) per year is obtained. In this case the value of the benefits ($16.7 million per year) exceeds the annual cost ($12 million), and the second advertising campaign is a profitable one to undertake.

Example 3

A warehouse manager must decide whether or not to stock an infrequently demanded product. Each week, there may be demands for zero, one, or two units, each with the probabilities shown in Table

TABLE 22–8

Units demanded	Probability
0	0.8
1	0.1
2	0.1

22–8. If the manager stocks the product, he plans to use the following ordering policy: Order one unit when inventory on hand is zero. Assume that the carrying cost per unit per week is $1 and that the profit on a single sale is $5. Any demands that cannot be met from stock are lost. Units ordered at the end of one week arrive at the beginning of the next week. The manager needs to calculate the expected profits from stocking in order to make his decision.

To solve this problem, we first specify the following state possibilities:

State 1 :   Zero units on hand at the end of the week and one on order (0, 1).

State 2 :   One unit on hand at the end of the week and zero on order (1, 0).

These two states exhaust the feasible alternatives if the manager follows his ordering policy; he would never have zero units on order when his inventory was zero, and he would never have more than one unit on hand. Now, using the probabilities of demand as given in Table 22–8, let us assume that he stocks the product. Then the probabilities of changing from one state to another from one week to the next are contained in Table 22–9. The reader should study the probabilities of change in

TABLE 22–9
Probabilities of change

From	To State 1 (0, 1)	State 2 (1, 0)
State 1 (0, 1)	0.2	0.8
State 2 (1, 0)	0.2	0.8

Table 22–9 to see how they are determined. For example, if we are in state 1 (zero on hand and one on order), then if zero units are demanded (probability 0.8), we shall have one unit on hand and zero units on order one week later (state 2). Thus the probability of going from state 1 to state 2 is 0.8. If one unit is demanded (probability 0.1), then the unit on order will be used to satisfy that demand, and we shall have zero units on hand. However, our decision rule is to place an order when inventory falls to zero. This action will take place if a demand for one unit occurs, and we shall return to state 1 (zero units on hand and one unit on order). Similarly, we shall return to state 1 if two units are demanded (probability 0.1), even though only one demand will be met. Thus the probability of staying in state 1 is 0.1 plus 0.1, or 0.2.

The change probabilities from state 2 are similar to those from state 1. Zero demand signals remaining in state 2, and demand for either one or two units causes a move from state 2 to state 1.

Solution. The steady-state probabilities are obtained as follows:

$$(22\text{–}20) \qquad P_1 = (0.2)P_1 + (0.2)[1 - P_1]$$

$$= \frac{0.2}{1 - 0.2 + 0.2} = 0.2 \text{ as } n \rightarrow \infty$$

The steady-state probabilities for state 1 and state 2 are 0.2 and 0.8, respectively.[4]

Now, we may calculate the expected profit per week. When the process is in state 1, we have just sold one unit for a profit of $5. When the process is in state 2, we have just experienced zero demand, so we have incurred a carrying charge of $1. Thus our weekly expected profit is:

$$EP = (0.2)(\$5) + (0.8)(-\$1) = \$1 - \$0.80 = \$0.20$$

Since the expected profit is positive, the manager should stock the product.

STEADY-STATE SOLUTION TO LARGER PROBLEMS

All the examples solved thus far in the chapter have involved only two different states. However, the same approach to a solution can be used for larger problems with three or more states. The only complication is that instead of having just one equation like that of (22–20) above, for larger problems there will be two or more simultaneous linear equations which, when solved, will produce the steady-state probabilities.[5]

Example 4

Consider the Markov process whose probabilities of change are contained in Table 22–10. This is a three-state process; in order to find the steady-state probabilities, we write two equations which are similar in

TABLE 22–10
Daily probabilities of change

From \ To	State 1	State 2	State 3
State 1	0.6	0.3	0.1
State 2	0.7	0.2	0.1
State 3	0.2	0.4	0.4

---

[4] As shown in Table 22–9, the probabilities of going to state 1 and going to state 2 are the same in each row. Thus, these probabilities must be the steady-state probabilities. Whenever all rows of a transition probability table are identical, the steady-state probabilities may be obtained by inspection.

[5] The number of simultaneous equations to be solved will always equal one less than the number of states.

form to equation $(22\text{--}20)$ above:

$(22\text{--}21)$ $P\left(\begin{array}{c}\text{state 1}\\ \text{in day } n\end{array}\middle|\begin{array}{c}\text{state 1}\\ \text{in day 1}\end{array}\right) = (0.6)P\left(\begin{array}{c}\text{state 1}\\ \text{in day } n\end{array}\middle|\begin{array}{c}\text{state 1}\\ \text{in day 1}\end{array}\right)$

$+ (0.7)P\left(\begin{array}{c}\text{state 2}\\ \text{in day } n\end{array}\middle|\begin{array}{c}\text{state 1}\\ \text{in day 1}\end{array}\right)$

$+ (0.2)P\left(\begin{array}{c}\text{state 3}\\ \text{in day } n\end{array}\middle|\begin{array}{c}\text{state 1}\\ \text{in day 1}\end{array}\right)$

$(22\text{--}22)$ $P\left(\begin{array}{c}\text{state 2}\\ \text{in day } n\end{array}\middle|\begin{array}{c}\text{state 1}\\ \text{in day 1}\end{array}\right) = (0.3)P\left(\begin{array}{c}\text{state 1}\\ \text{in day } n\end{array}\middle|\begin{array}{c}\text{state 1}\\ \text{in day 1}\end{array}\right)$

$+ (0.2)P\left(\begin{array}{c}\text{state 2}\\ \text{in day } n\end{array}\middle|\begin{array}{c}\text{state 1}\\ \text{in day 1}\end{array}\right)$

$+ (0.4)P\left(\begin{array}{c}\text{state 3}\\ \text{in day } n\end{array}\middle|\begin{array}{c}\text{state 1}\\ \text{in day 1}\end{array}\right)$

Equations $(22\text{--}21)$ and $(22\text{--}22)$ are two equations in three unknowns. However, since the sum of the steady-state probabilities must be 1.0, we may substitute in for the third unknown as follows:

$(22\text{--}23)$ $P\left(\begin{array}{c}\text{state 3}\\ \text{in day } n\end{array}\middle|\begin{array}{c}\text{state 1}\\ \text{in day 1}\end{array}\right) = 1 - P\left(\begin{array}{c}\text{state 1}\\ \text{in day } n\end{array}\middle|\begin{array}{c}\text{state 1}\\ \text{in day 1}\end{array}\right)$

$- P\left(\begin{array}{c}\text{state 2}\\ \text{in day } n\end{array}\middle|\begin{array}{c}\text{state 1}\\ \text{in day 1}\end{array}\right)$

Letting P_1, P_2, and P_3 represent the steady-state probabilities, and substituting equation $(22\text{--}23)$ into equations $(22\text{--}21)$ and $(22\text{--}22)$, we obtain:

$(22\text{--}24)$ $\qquad P_1 = 0.6P_1 + 0.7P_2 + 0.2(1 - P_1 - P_2)$

$(22\text{--}25)$ $\qquad P_2 = 0.3P_1 + 0.2P_2 + 0.4(1 - P_1 - P_2)$

which, collecting terms, are:

$(22\text{--}26)$ $\qquad\qquad 0.6P_1 - 0.5P_2 = 0.2$

$(22\text{--}27)$ $\qquad\qquad 0.1P_1 + 1.2P_2 = 0.4$

Equations $(22\text{--}26)$ and $(22\text{--}27)$ can be solved simultaneously to obtain the steady-state probabilities. Multiplying the second equation by six and subtracting to remove the P_1 term, we obtain:

$(22\text{--}28)$ $\qquad\qquad -7.7P_2 = -2.2$

or

$$P_2 = \frac{2.2}{7.7} = \frac{2}{7}$$

and substituting $P_2 = \frac{2}{7}$ into equation (22–26),

(22–29) $0.6P_1 - 0.5(\frac{2}{7}) = 0.2$ or $0.6P_1 = \frac{24}{70}$

or

$$P_1 = \frac{4}{7}$$

Finally, using the fact that the steady-state probabilities must sum to 1.0, we see that $P_3 = 1 - P_1 - P_2 = 1.0 - \frac{6}{7} = \frac{1}{7}$.

This same approach may be used in solving for the steady-state probabilities for Markov processes with a larger number of states.

CONCLUSION

In this chapter, we have considered Markov processes which are discrete in state space and time period. The Markovian property of "no memory" has been discussed. Calculations of the steady-state probabilities have been demonstrated, and the steady-state probabilities have been used to solve some managerial decision problems. The concepts have been illustrated using basic mathematics. The solution to more complex problems can be facilitated by the use of more sophisticated mathematical techniques.

APPENDIX. STEADY-STATE AND TRANSIENT BEHAVIOR OF A TWO-STATE MARKOV PROCESS[6]

This chapter has dealt with the numerical solution of Markov processes to obtain steady-state probabilities. For the case of a two-state Markov process, it is convenient to obtain general formulas for the steady-state probabilities in terms of the probabilities of change.

General steady-state solution to two-state Markov process

Suppose the transition probability matrix for a two-state Markov process is represented as follows:

(22–30) $P = \begin{bmatrix} p_{11} & p_{12} \\ p_{21} & p_{22} \end{bmatrix}$

We will use a prime after a vector to indicate a row vector. Thus if π_1 and π_2 represent the steady-state probabilities of being in state 1 and

---

[6] This Appendix uses matrix notation and matrix multiplication. For basic presentation of these concepts, see either of the following references: J. G. Kemeny and J. L. Snell, *Finite Markov Chains* (Princeton: D. Van Nostrand Co., Inc., 1959); or S. R. Searle and W. H. Hausman, *Matrix Algebra for Business and Economics* (with assistance from H. Bierman, Jr., J. E. Hass, and L. J. Thomas) (New York: John Wiley & Sons, Inc., 1970).

state 2, respectively, then the row vector π' may be defined as follows:

(22–31) $$\pi' = (\pi_1 \quad \pi_2)$$

In the steady state, equation (22–32) must hold:

(22–32) $$\pi' = \pi'P$$

or equivalently:

(22–33) $$(\pi_1 \quad \pi_2) = (\pi_1 \quad \pi_2)\begin{bmatrix} p_{11} & p_{12} \\ p_{21} & p_{22} \end{bmatrix}$$

These equations hold because once the steady state is reached, the state probabilities in a given period must be identical to the state probabilities one period later. If the matrix multiplication in equation (22–33) is performed, we obtain:

(22–34) $$(\pi_1 \quad \pi_2) = (\pi_1 p_{11} + \pi_2 p_{21} \quad \pi_1 p_{12} + \pi_2 p_{22})$$

Equating terms in the vector:

(22–35) $$\pi_1 = \pi_1 p_{11} + \pi_2 p_{21}$$

and

(22–36) $$\pi_2 = \pi_1 p_{12} + \pi_2 p_{22}$$

Equations (22–35) and (22–36) are two linear simultaneous equations, but one of the two equations is redundant (i.e., one equation may be derived from the other). However, the two state probabilities must add to one, so the substitution $\pi_2 = 1 - \pi_1$ may be made in equation (22–35) to obtain:

(22–37) $$\pi_1 = \frac{p_{21}}{p_{12} + p_{21}}$$

Then:

(22–38) $$\pi_2 = \frac{p_{12}}{p_{12} + p_{21}}$$

Equations (22–37) and (22–38) contain the general formulas for the steady-state probabilities of a two-state Markov process.

Example

Consider Example 1 (p. 420), involving a machine which may be either in adjustment (state 1) or out of adjustment (state 2). The probabilities of change from one state to the other are given in

Table 22–1. Substituting into equation (22–37) to obtain the steady-state probability for state 1:

$$(22-39) \qquad \pi_1 = \frac{p_{21}}{p_{12} + p_{21}} = \frac{0.6}{0.3 + 0.6} = \frac{2}{3}$$

For state 2:

$$(22-40) \qquad \pi_2 = 1 - \pi_1 = \frac{1}{3}$$

These answers are identical to the steady-state probabilities calculated directly in the chapter.

Transient-state probabilities

In some situations, we need to know more than the steady-state probabilities in order to use a Markov process in a decision problem. The state probabilities for particular periods of time are called transient probabilities. The following example illustrates a Markov process model where we are interested in the operating results before the steady state is reached. In this type of situation the transient probabilities are relevant to the decision.

Example

Consider the machine described in Example 1 of the chapter (p. 420). The machine moves from state 1 (in adjustment) to state 2 (out of adjustment), and vice versa, with the probabilities of change as given in Table 22–1.

Suppose that when the machine is in state 1 for a day, a profit of $200 is gained, and if the machine is in state 2 for a day a loss of $100 is incurred. If the decision maker is concerned with the long run, he would proceed as before and calculate the steady-state probabilities of 2/3 and 1/3, respectively, as computed in equations (22–39) and (22–40). The expected profit per day in the steady state would be:

$$EP = \$200(2/3) + (-\$100)(1/3) = \$100$$

Now, suppose the decision maker is concerned with the short-run or transient behavior of the process. If the machine is in state 1 on day 1, he may wish to know the expected profit over the next five days. This expected profit may be calculated by evaluating all branches of the probability tree in Figure 22–3, weighted by the appropriate profit for each branch. However, an alternative approach is presented below

FIGURE 22–3

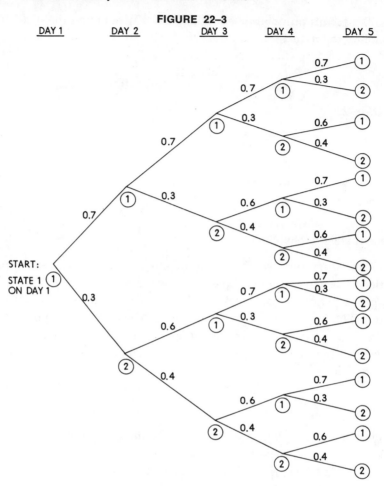

where the transient-state probabilities are calculated by matrix multiplication. Once the transient-state probabilities are obtained for each day, they may be multiplied by the profit payoffs and summed to obtain the expected profit over the five-day period.

Matrix calculation of transient-state probabilities

Let $\pi(n)$ represent the vector of transient-state probabilities at period n, given that the initial-state probabilities at time zero are $\pi(0)$. The individual transient-state probabilities $\pi_1(n)$ and $\pi_2(n)$ are the two components of the vector $\pi(n)$:

(22–41) $\pi'(n) = [\pi_1(n) \quad \pi_2(n)]$

The transition probability matrix P defined in equation (22–30) above may be used to calculate the transient-state probability vector $\pi(n)$ recursively. For period 1:

$$(22\text{–}42) \qquad\qquad \pi'(1) = \pi'(0) \cdot P$$

For period 2:

$$(22\text{–}43) \qquad\qquad \pi'(2) = \pi'(1) \cdot P = \pi'(0) \cdot P^2$$

For any general period n:

$$(22\text{–}44) \qquad\qquad \pi'(n) = \pi'(n - 1) \cdot P = \pi'(0) \cdot P^n$$

Equation (22–44) states that the transient probability vector for any period n may be calculated by postmultiplying the initial-state (row) vector by the transition probability matrix raised to the nth power.

Example

For the machine example, suppose the initial state on day 1 is state 1. Then the transient-state probability vector for day 1 is:

$$(22\text{–}45) \qquad\qquad \pi'(1) = (1 \quad 0)$$

For day 2, using equation (22–44):

$$\pi'(2) = \pi'(1) \cdot P$$

$$(22\text{–}46) \qquad = (1 \quad 0) \begin{bmatrix} 0.7 & 0.3 \\ 0.6 & 0.4 \end{bmatrix} = (0.7 + 0 \quad 0.3 + 0)$$

$$= (0.7 \quad 0.3)$$

The individual transient-state probabilities on day 2 are:

$$\pi_1(2) = 0.7$$
$$\pi_2(2) = 0.3$$

For day 3:

$$\pi'(3) = \pi'(2) \cdot P$$

$$(22\text{–}47) \qquad = (0.7 \quad 0.3) \begin{bmatrix} 0.7 & 0.3 \\ 0.6 & 0.4 \end{bmatrix} = (0.49 + 0.18 \quad 0.21 + 0.12)$$

$$= (0.67 \quad 0.33)$$

For day 4:

$$\pi'(4) = \pi'(3) \cdot P$$

$$(22\text{–}48) \qquad = (0.67 \quad 0.33) \begin{bmatrix} 0.7 & 0.3 \\ 0.6 & 0.4 \end{bmatrix} = (0.469 + 0.198 \quad 0.201 + 0.132)$$

$$= (0.667 \quad 0.333)$$

Finally, for day 5:

$$\pi'(5) = \pi'(4) \cdot P$$

(22–49)
$$= (0.667 \quad 0.333) \begin{bmatrix} 0.7 & 0.3 \\ 0.6 & 0.4 \end{bmatrix}$$

$$= (0.4669 + 0.1998 \quad 0.2001 + 0.1332)$$

$$= (0.6667 \quad 0.3333)$$

To calculate the expected profit for day n, we write:

$$EP(n) = \pi'(n) \cdot \begin{bmatrix} \$200 \\ -\$100 \end{bmatrix}$$

For example, expected profit for day 2 is:

$$EP(2) = \pi'(2) \cdot \begin{bmatrix} \$200 \\ -\$100 \end{bmatrix} = (0.7 \quad 0.3) \begin{bmatrix} \$200 \\ -\$100 \end{bmatrix}$$

$$= 0.7(200) + 0.3(-100)$$

$$= 140 - 30 = 110$$

Table 22–11 contains calculations of expected profit for days 1–5. Thus the expected profit for the next five days, given that the machine

TABLE 22–11

Day number n	Transient-state probability vector $\pi'(n)$	Expected profit for day n $EP(n) = \pi'(n) \cdot \begin{bmatrix} 200 \\ -100 \end{bmatrix}$		
1..........	(1 0)	$200 - 0$	$= 200$
2..........	(0.7 0.3)	$140 - 30$	$= 110$
3..........	(0.67 0.33)	$134 - 33$	$= 101$
4..........	(0.667 0.333)	$133.4 - 33.3$	$= 100.1$
5..........	(0.6667 0.3333)	$133.34 - 33.33$	$= 100.01$
		Total......	$\$611.11$

starts off in state 1 (in adjustment), is $611.11, or an average daily profit of $122.22, as compared to the steady-state expected daily profit of $100. If the analysis were performed for more days than five, the average daily profit would move closer to $100.

BIBLIOGRAPHY

DERMAN, C. *Finite State Markov Decision Processes.* New York: Academic Press, 1970.

FELLER, W. *An Introduction to Probability Theory and Its Applications,* Vol. I. 3d ed. New York: John Wiley & Sons, Inc., 1968.

————. *An Introduction to Probability Theory and Its Applications,* Vol. II. New York: John Wiley & Sons, Inc., 1966.

Howard, R. A. *Dynamic Programming and Markov Processes.* Cambridge: M.I.T. Press, 1960.

————. *Dynamic Probabilistic Systems* (2 vols.). New York: John Wiley & Sons, Inc., 1971.

Karlin, S. *A First Course in Stochastic Processes.* New York: Academic Press, Inc., 1969.

Kemeny, J. G.; Schleifer, A., Jr.; Snell, J. L.; and Thompson, G. L. *Finite Mathematics with Business Applications.* 2d ed. Englewood Cliffs, N.J.: Prentice-Hall Inc., 1972.

————, and Snell, J. L. *Finite Markov Chains.* Princeton, N.J.: D. Van Nostrand Co., Inc., 1960.

Searle, S. R., and Hausman, W. H. *Matrix Algebra for Business and Economics* (with assistance from H. Bierman, Jr., J. E. Hass, and L. J. Thomas). New York: John Wiley & Sons, Inc., 1970.

PROBLEMS

22–1. Two machines, A and B, are candidates for leasing. The two machines have differing probabilities of changing from an in-adjustment state (state 1) to an out-of-adjustment state (state 2), as follows:

Probabilities of change: machine A

From \ To	In adjustment (state 1)	Out of adjustment (state 2)
In adjustment (state 1)	0.9	0.1
Out of adjustment (state 2)	0.6	0.4

Probabilities of change: machine B

From \ To	In adjustment (state 1)	Out of adjustment (state 2)
In adjustment (state 1)	0.8	0.2
Out of adjustment (state 2)	0.7	0.3

Solve for the steady-state probabilities for each machine. Which machine would be the more desirable to lease?

22–2. The ABC Ski Resort has found that after a clear day the probability of stormy weather is 0.3, whereas after a stormy day the probability of clear weather is 0.8. Write down the transition probability table. What are the steady-state probabilities for clear days and stormy days?

22–3. The Acme Car Rental Company rents cars from three airports—A, B, and C. Customers return cars to each of the airports according to the following probabilities:

From \ To	A (state 1)	B (state 2)	C (state 3)
A (state 1)	0.8	0.2	0.0
B (state 2)	0.2	0.0	0.8
C (state 3)	0.2	0.2	0.6

a) Calculate the steady-state probabilities.
b) The Acme Company is planning to build a maintenance facility at one of the three airports. Which airport would you recommend for this purpose? Why?

22–4. The following table contains various probabilities of a manager moving among three floors of a department store:

From \ To	Floor 1	Floor 2	Floor 3
Floor 1	0.0	0.4	0.6
Floor 2	0.8	0.0	0.2
Floor 3	0.8	0.2	0.0

Compute the steady-state probabilities.

22–5. The Acme Company has obtained the following transition probability table for car rental customers:

To From	No. 1	Acme	All others
No. 1	0.6	0.2	0.2
Acme	0.2	0.6	0.2
All others	0.4	0.2	0.4

A typical customer rents a car once every six months

a) Solve for the steady-state probabilities.

b) Acme is considering a new program to provide all potential customers with credit cards before its competitors do. In order to estimate the benefit of such a move, Acme must know the expected incremental benefit of new customers starting with Acme with probability 1, as compared to starting in the steady state. Suppose the expected profit per rental is $10 and there are 10,000 new car rental customers every six months. What is the approximate expected value of having all new customers start with Acme?

22–6. The stock price for the XYZ Company has been observed for 100 days. Each day the price either goes up one point or falls by one point, according to the following probabilities:

To From	Up one (state 1)	Down one (state 2)
Up one (state 1)	0.4	0.6
Down one (state 2)	0.6	0.4

What are the steady-state probabilities?

22–7. Consider the XYZ Company stock in Problem 22–6. Suppose now that if the stock goes up on one day, the probability that it goes up the next day is 0.6; and if the stock goes down on one day, the probability that it goes down the next day is 0.5. Write down the transition probability table and compute the steady-state probabilities.

22–8.   Consider a Markov process with the following transition table:

From \ To	State 1	State 2	State 3
State 1	0.7	0.3	0.0
State 2	0.8	0.2	0.0
State 3	0.0	0.2	0.8

a)   If the process starts in state 1 and a very large number of transitions occur, what fraction of these transitions is from state 1 to state 2? (*Hint:* First calculate the steady-state probability of being in state 1.)

b)   Repeat part (*a*) assuming the process starts in state 2.

22–9.   A cabdriver has found that if he is in town 1 there is a 0.8 probability that his next fare will take him to town 2 and a 0.2 probability that he will stay in town 1. If he is in town 2, there is a 0.4 probability that his next fare will take him to town 1 and a 0.6 probability that his next fare will keep him in town 2. The average profit for each type of trip is as follows:

$$\begin{array}{ll} \text{Within town 1:} & \$1 \\ \text{Within town 2:} & \$1 \\ \text{Between towns:} & \$2 \end{array}$$

a)   Write down the transition probability table for two states and compute the steady-state probabilities for being in town 1 and town 2.

b)   Use the two steady-state probabilities of part (*a*) in conjunction with the transition probabilities to compute expected profit per fare.

c)   Alternatively, set up the process as a four-state process by defining states as the type of trip encountered rather than the location. Write down the transition probability table for the four-state formulation. Is this approach an easier way to calculate the expected profitability than that of part (*b*) above?

22–10.   The following transition probability table represents the behavior of department store customers in paying (or not paying) their monthly bills:

From \ To	Paid (state 1)	Not paid (state 2)
Paid (state 1)	0.95	0.05
Not paid (state 2)	0.95	0.05

a) What are the steady-state probabilities?
b) Should the credit manager attempt to discontinue credit to those customers who have not paid previous bills? Why, or why not?

22–11. Refer to Problem 22–10. Suppose one set of customers (called "unpredictable") have the transition probability table of that problem, while another set (called "predictable") have the following:

Probabilities of change—predictable customers

From \ To	Paid (state 1)	Not paid (state 2)
Paid (state 1)	0.99	0.01
Not paid (state 2)	0.49	0.51

a) What are the steady-state probabilities for the predictable customers? How do they compare to those of the unpredictable customers?
b) Now suppose the department store has determined that it "breaks even" when the probability of payment is 0.949. If a new customer can be precisely classified as "unpredictable," should the store accept him for credit or not? Why?
c) Given the break-even probability of part (b) above, should the store accept a new customer who is classified as "predictable" but whose state is unknown?
d) Given (b) and (c) above, suppose a new customer applies for credit and he is predictable. Suppose also that his last state (paid or not paid) is known. Should the store accept him or not, depending on his last state? Why?

22–12. Refer to Example 3 on page 431. Consider the following order policy: order two units if stock on hand is zero; otherwise do not order. Set up the transition probability table for this case, and calculate the steady state probabilities and the expected profit. [*Hint:* There are three states: (1) zero on hand and two on order; (2) one on hand and zero on order; and (3) two on hand and zero on order.]

22–13. Refer to Example 3 on page 431 and Problem 22–12 above. Consider the following policy: order two units if stock on hand is zero; order one unit if stock on hand is one; order no units if stock on hand is two. Set up the transition probability table for this case and calculate the steady-state probabilities and the expected profit.

22–14. Ajax Novelty Company is a mail-order shipper of a wide range of novelty and gift items. The company has a mailing list of 100,000 potential customers. Current policy calls for Ajax to mail its catalog to the complete list every six months. In the past, about 50 percent of previous customers order after any catalog mailing (a previous customer is one who placed an order in the last six-month period). On the other hand, only about 10 percent of persons previously noncustomers order. Typically, a customer places one order during a six-month period and Ajax makes an average profit of $8 per order.

   Ajax was considering changing current policies. Two new alternatives were considered for analysis.

   The first possibility involved using a fancier catalog than previously. The cost of this would add 25 cents to the catalog cost (or $25,000 to the cost of a mailing). This change was not expected to affect the percentage of previous customers who reordered. However, the percentage of noncustomers who ordered was expected to increase from 10 to 15 percent.

   A second alternative was to offer special discounts to previous customers. This would reduce the average profit from $8.00 to $7.50 for these customers, but the plan was expected to increase the number of customers who reordered from 50 percent to 60 percent. The plan would have no effect on previous noncustomers (the percent who order would remain at 10 percent and profit would be $8 per order.)

   a) Consider the three plans presented above. Formulate each as a Markov process (i.e., define the states and give the transition probability table.)

   b) Estimate the profitability of each plan. Which should Ajax adopt?

22–15. A magazine made a profit of $1 on its regular one-year subscriptions. Eighty percent of subscriptions were renewed. The magazine was debating methods of obtaining new subscriptions. One method involved mail solicitation of potential customers on selected mailing lists The costs of mail solicitation would be $0.25 per mailing. It was estimated that 5 percent of those mailed would become regular subscribers.

A second method involved personal solicitation of a selected group of potential customers. The cost of this would be $1 per solicitation, but 20 percent were expected to become regular customers. Which method should the magazine adopt?

23

Dynamic programming

Dynamic programming is a mathematical technique designed to solve certain decision problems. The method of solution is to divide the total problem into a number of subproblems.

The basic ideas used in dynamic programming may be seen in the following example.

Example 1: A pricing problem

Consider a problem involving pricing strategy. A manager must decide which price level to choose in pricing a new product over the next five years. He is considering four different prices: $5, $6, $7, or $8 per unit. After evaluating potential pricing moves by his competitors, he has constructed a payoff table which relates his price in a given year to the present value of the profit expected that year. The payoff values are presented in Table 23–1.

TABLE 23–1
Payoff table (in millions of dollars)

Price \ Year	1	2	3	4	5
$5	9	2	4	5	8
$6	7	4	8	2	1
$7	6	5	9	6	4
$8	8	7	1	7	3
	↑ Decision 1	↑ Decision 2	↑ Decision 3	↑ Decision 4	↑ Decision 5

Under these circumstances, the manager should treat each year separately and choose the price in each year which maximizes the present value of his profit. However, the manager wishes to avoid making drastic changes in price from one year to the next, and he has decided that the change in price from one year to the next must not be greater than $1. For example, if the price in year 1 is $6, then in year 2 the price must be either $5, $6, or $7; it cannot be $8. Figure 23–1 illustrates

FIGURE 23–1
Allowable movements

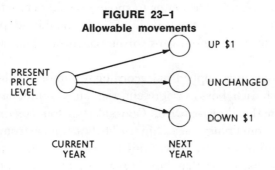

the allowable price movements. The problem may be restated as follows: The manager must decide which way to move his price from one year to the next. The objective is to choose a set of prices over the five years which maximizes the present value of his profits.[1] This problem can be solved by the basic concepts of dynamic programming.

Basic concepts

The three basic concepts used in dynamic programming are:

1. The total problem is divided into a number of subproblems.
2. Working backward from the natural end of the problem, each subproblem is solved in turn.
3. After each subproblem is solved, the answer is recorded, and the payoff (profit, cost, etc.) from that stage on to the end of the problem is also recorded.

In order to apply the first concept to our example, our total problem is divided into a series of five subproblems. In our example the five subproblems represent the five decisions on which way to move the price level.

---

[1] This is a simplified example and an alert reader might be able to obtain the correct answer merely by inspecting Table 23–1. To illustrate how complex even this small problem is, consider how the solution changes (if at all) if profits in year 2 with a price of $6 were 6 instead of 4. Or if profits in year 4 with a price of $5 were to be 7 instead of 5. Or make year 3's payoff with a price of $5, 7 instead of 4. It is difficult to determine the consequence of these changes without the use of the dynamic programming approach.

Table 23–1 indicates the five decisions to be made on which way to move. The second concept is applied by solving the last subproblem first, and working backward from the right-hand side to the left-hand side of the table. For example, the last subproblem is which way to move when you are at one of the price levels in the fourth year. This subproblem may be solved by studying each allowable move from each price level and choosing the move with the highest payoff. For example, from the $5 price level in year 4, it is better to move directly across to the payoff of 8 rather than down to the payoff of 1. From the $8 price level in year 4, it is better to move upward to the payoff of 4 rather than across to the payoff of 3.

The third concept is applied by recording a number in the upper left-hand corner of each box to represent the sum of the payoffs on the best path from that box onward. Consider the top box in the fourth year (the one containing five). Since the best move from this box is a move across to 8, we add 8 to 5 and record 13 in the upper left-hand corner of that box. Once that box is reached, the best path from that box onward to the end of the table has a sum of 13. We also record the best decision by drawing an arrow from that box across toward the value of eight. Table 23–2 illustrates this procedure carried out for all

TABLE 23–2

Price \ Year	1	2	3	4	5
$5	9	2	17 / 4	13 / 5	8 / 8
$6	7	4	21 / 8	10 / 2	1 / 1
$7	6	5	20 / 9	10 / 6	4 / 4
$8	8	7	12 / 1	11 / 7	3 / 3

↑ Decision 1   ↑ Decision 2   ↑ Decision 3   ↑ Decision 4   ↑ Decision 5

the boxes in column 4. For completeness, the numbers in column 5 have been placed in their respective upper left-hand corners.

Now we work backward and consider decision 4, the price to charge at the beginning of year 4. If this decision were approached without prior preparation, our answer might be the following: "It would depend on which way you planned to move after this move." But since the last decision has already been solved, the numbers in the upper left-hand corners of the boxes in column 4 may be used to represent the relative attractiveness of the various boxes in column 4. For example, consider the top box in column 3 (the one containing four). By studying the upper left-hand corner numbers in column 4, we see that it is better to move across and incur a payoff of 13 rather than down to a payoff of 10. Repeating our earlier recording procedure, the value of 13 plus 4, or 17, is recorded in the upper left-hand corner of the top box in column 3. We also record the best decision by an arrow from that box across toward the top box of column 4. By following this same procedure for the other boxes in column 3, we may solve decision 4.

Then we work backward again and begin to solve decision 3. Using the same procedure as above, the reader may fill in the upper left-hand corners of column 2 in Table 23–2 and draw arrows indicating the best move to make. The same procedure is used again for decision 2; and finally, decision 1 involves choosing the largest of the values in the upper left-hand corners of the boxes in column 1. The completed solution is contained in Table 23–3. From Table 23–3, the optimal strategy is to

TABLE 23-3

Price	Year 1	2	3	4	5
$5	34 / 9	23 / 2	17 / 4 →	13 / 5 →	8 / 8
$6	33 / 7	25 / 4 →	21 / 8	10 / 2	1 / 1
$7	33 / 6	26 / 5	20 / 9	10 / 6 →	4 / 4
$8	35 / 8	27 / 7 →	12 / 1	11 / 7	3 / 3
	↑ Decision 1	↑ Decision 2	↑ Decision 3	↑ Decision 4	↑ Decision 5

begin with a price of $8 in year 1, keep it unchanged at $8 in year 2, change it to $7 in year 3, change it back to $8 in year 4, and change it to $7 in the fifth year. The profit from this strategy is recorded in the upper left-hand corner of the fourth box in the first column, and amounts to 35. No other strategy results in a payoff this large. If for some reason the manager did not wish to set a price of $8 the first year, his next best alternative would be a price of $5. The payoff from starting with a $5 price and making optimal decisions from year 1 onward is 34, as recorded in the upper left-hand corner of the first box in column 1.

FORMALIZING THE DYNAMIC PROGRAMMING TECHNIQUE

The dynamic programming technique is formalized by referring to stages, state variables, optimal decision rules, and optimal policies. A *stage* refers to the particular decision we are facing; in Example 1, there are five decision stages (see Table 23–1). A *state variable* is a variable defining the current situation at any stage. The state variable for Example 1 would be the current price level at a given stage. An *optimal decision rule* specifies which decision to make, as a function of the state variable and the stage number. The optimal decision rule for decision 5 (stage 5) in our example would specify: "Keep the price constant if the price is $5, and lower the price if the price is $6; keep the price constant if the price is $7, and lower the price if the price is $8" (see Table 23–3). An *optimal policy* is a *set* of optimal decision rules which guides one's decisions through all stages of the entire problem. The optimal policy for Example 1 is the set of arrows in Table 23–3 which specifies the optimal moves to make through the five-year span of time.

PRINCIPLE OF OPTIMALITY

The principle behind the operation of the dynamic programming technique is called the principle of optimality: "An optimal policy has the property that whatever the initial state and initial decision are, the remaining decisions must constitute an optimal policy with regard to the state resulting from the first decision."[2] The principle of optimality allows one to divide the total problem and solve the last decision stage, then work backward and solve the second-to-last decision, etc., until the first decision is solved.

Example 2: An inventory-production problem

A firm is faced with demand for its product in each of the next four periods as shown in Table 23–4. It must decide upon a production sched-

---

[2] R. E. Bellman, *Dynamic Programming* (Princeton: Princeton University Press, 1957), p. 83.

TABLE 23–4
Demand requirements

Period n	Units required D_n
1	2
2	3
3	2
4	4

ule to meet these demands. In any period the cost of production is $1 per unit plus a setup cost of $3. The setup cost is not incurred if zero units are produced. No more than six units can be produced in any period. The requirements can be summarized as:

$$\text{Production cost} = \$3 + 1 \cdot X \quad \text{if } 0 < X \le 6$$
$$= 0 \quad \text{if } X = 0$$

In addition, there is an inventory holding cost of $0.50 per unit per period. The firm has zero inventory on hand at the beginning of period 1 and wishes to have zero inventory at the end of period 4. The problem is to find a production schedule that will meet the demand requirements at minimum cost (production plus inventory costs). We formulate this problem as a dynamic programming problem:

Stages: each period is a stage, $n = 1, 2, 3, 4$.
State variable: the amount of inventory at the *beginning* of a period, designated by I_n.
Decision variable: the production level each period, designated X_n.
Optimal decision rule: (to be determined) this will specify the optimal production $X_n{}^*$ as a function of beginning inventory. That is:

$$X_n{}^* = X_n(I_n)$$

for each period.

Note that the periods are linked by the inventory balance equation relating inventory in one period to that in the next:

$$(23\text{--}1) \qquad I_{n+1} = I_n + X_n - D_n$$

where D_n is the demand in the nth period (Table 23–4).

The cost in any period is the sum of production and inventory costs:

$$(23\text{--}2) \quad \text{Period cost} = C_n(X_n, I_n) = \begin{cases} 3 + 1X_n & \text{if } X_n > 0 \\ 0 & \text{if } X_n = 0 \end{cases} + 0.5I_n$$

Finally, let $f_n(I_n)$ represent the optimal (minimum) cost from the

nth period to the end, given an inventory of I_n at the beginning of period n. For example, $f_2(3)$ would be the cost of the optimal production schedule from the second period through the fourth, given a beginning inventory of 3 units in period 2. This function $f_n(I_n)$ is called the *return function*.

Now we can write a series of equations defining the return function for each period. Let us first go to the last period of the process $(n = 4)$:

$$(23\text{--}3) \qquad f_4(I_4) = \underset{\substack{0 \leq X_4 \leq 6 \\ \text{and } X_4 + I_4 \geq D_4}}{\text{Minimum}} \{C_4(X_4, I_4)\}$$

Backing up one period, the return function at period $n = 3$ is:

$$(23\text{--}4) \quad f_3(I_3) = \underset{\substack{0 \leq X_3 \leq 6 \\ \text{and } X_3 + I_3 \geq D_3}}{\text{Minimum}} \{C_3(X_3, I_3) + f_4(I_3 + X_3 - D_3)\}$$

For the general period n, the dynamic programming recursion can be given as:

$$(23\text{--}5) \quad f_n(I_n) = \underset{\substack{0 \leq X_n \leq 6 \\ \text{and } X_n + I_n \geq D_n}}{\text{Minimum}} \{C_n(X_n, I_n) + f_{n+1}(I_n + X_n - D_n)\}$$

This recursion is solved, starting with the last period, and working backwards. At each stage, the optimal decision is found, minimizing the cost for that period plus subsequent-period costs. This conforms to the principle of optimality stated above. Each stage involves finding an optimum value of X_n for each I_n. Note the restrictions on X_n because of the production limitations $(0 \leq X_n \leq 6)$ and because of the need to meet each period's demand from either production or inventory $(X_n + I_n \geq D_n)$.

To find the actual numerical solution to the problem, we start with period 4. Since the firm wishes to have no inventory at the end of the period, the production amounts are easily determined (Table 23–5). Recall that demand in period 4 is four units. Hence only enough is produced to meet this need. Values of beginning inventory larger than four need not be considered.

TABLE 23–5
Period 4 solution

Beginning inventory I_4	Optimal production $X_4{}^* = X_4(I_4)$	Cost Production	Cost Inventory	Total cost $f_4(I_4)$
0	4	$7	$0	$7.0
1	3	6	0.5	6.5
2	2	5	1.0	6.0
3	1	4	1.5	5.5
4	0	0	2.0	2.0

We now turn to period three. Beginning inventory in period 3 can range from zero units on hand to six units. More than six units would be excess, since demand in periods 3 and 4 totals six units. We construct Table 23–6 which examines all feasible production plans.

TABLE 23–6
Period 3: Determination of optimal production

Beginning inventory I_3	Possible production amounts X_3	Cost in period 3 Production	Cost in period 3 Inventory	Cost in period 3 Total $C_3(X_3, I_3)$	Ending inventory I_4	Subsequent costs $f_4(I_4)$	Total costs $C_3(X_3, I_3) + f_4(I_4)$
0	2	$5	$0	$5.0	0	$7.0	$12.0
	3	6	0	6.0	1	6.5	12.5
	4	7	0	7.0	2	6.0	13.0
	5	8	0	8.0	3	5.5	13.5
	6*	9	0	9.0	4	2.0	11.0*
1	1	4	0.5	4.5	0	7.0	11.5
	2	5	0.5	5.5	1	6.5	12.0
	3	6	0.5	6.5	2	6.0	12.5
	4	7	0.5	7.5	3	5.5	13.0
	5*	8	0.5	8.5	4	2.0	10.5*
2	0*	0	1.0	1.0	0	7.0	8.0*
	1	4	1.0	5.0	1	6.5	11.5
	2	5	1.0	6.0	2	6.0	12.0
	3	6	1.0	7.0	3	5.5	12.5
	4	7	1.0	8.0	4	2.0	10.0
3	0*	0	1.5	1.5	1	6.5	8.0*
	1	4	1.5	5.5	2	6.0	11.5
	2	5	1.5	6.5	3	5.5	12.0
	3	6	1.5	7.5	4	2.0	9.5
4	0*	0	2.0	2.0	2	6.0	8.0*
	1	4	2.0	6.0	3	5.5	11.5
	2	5	2.0	7.0	4	2.0	9.0
5	0*	0	2.5	2.5	3	5.5	8.0*
	1	4	2.5	6.5	4	2.0	8.5
6	0*	0	3.0	3.0	4	2.0	5.0*

* Indicates optimum for the given beginning inventory.

Note that in Table 23–6 the optimum production amount is marked with an * for each level of beginning inventory. The costs under the "Subsequent costs" column are taken from Table 23–5.

TABLE 23–7. Summary for period 3

Beginning inventory I_3	Optimal production X_3*	Total cost periods 3 and 4 $f_3(I_3)$	Ending inventory I_4
0	6	$11.0	2
1	5	10.5	2
2	0	8.0	0
3	0	8.0	1
4	0	8.0	2
5	0	8.0	3
6	0	5.0	4

TABLE 23–8. Period 2: Determination of optimal production

Beginning inventory I_2	Possible production amounts X_2	Cost in period 2			Ending inventory I_3	Subsequent costs $f_3(I_3)$	Total costs $C_2(X_2, I_2) + f_3(I_3)$
		Production	Inventory	Total $C_2(X_2, I_2)$			
0	3	$6	$0	$ 6.0	0	$11.0	$17.0
	4	7	0	7.0	1	10.5	17.5
	5*	8	0	8.0	2	8.0	16.0*
	6	9	0	9.0	3	8.0	17.0
1	2	5	0.5	5.5	0	11.0	16.5
	3	6	0.5	6.5	1	10.5	17.0
	4*	7	0.5	7.5	2	8.0	15.5*
	5	8	0.5	8.5	3	8.0	16.5
	6	9	0.5	9.5	4	8.0	17.5
2	1	4	1.0	5.0	0	11.0	16.0
	2	5	1.0	6.0	1	10.5	16.5
	3*	6	1.0	7.0	2	8.0	15.0*
	4	7	1.0	8.0	3	8.0	16.0
	5	8	1.0	9.0	4	8.0	17.0
	6	9	1.0	10.0	5	8.0	18.0
3	0*	0	1.5	1.5	0	11.0	12.5*
	1	4	1.5	5.5	1	10.5	16.0
	2	5	1.5	6.5	2	8.0	14.5
	3	6	1.5	7.5	3	8.0	15.5
	4	7	1.5	8.5	4	8.0	16.5
	5	8	1.5	9.5	5	8.0	17.5
	6	9	1.5	10.5	6	5.0	15.5
4	0*	0	2.0	2.0	1	10.5	12.5*
	1	4	2.0	6.0	2	8.0	14.0
	2	5	2.0	7.0	3	8.0	15.0
	3	6	2.0	8.0	4	8.0	16.0
	4	7	2.0	9.0	5	8.0	17.0
	5	8	2.0	10.0	6	5.0	15.0

* Indicates optimum for given beginning inventory.

The results of the analysis in Table 23–6 may be summarized in Table 23–7. Thus, for any beginning inventory, we have determined the optimal production schedule for periods 3 and 4.

We now turn to period 2. Beginning inventory can range from zero to four units. The four-unit upper limit results from the fact that at most six units can be produced in period 1, and two of these must be used to satisfy period 1 demand. The analysis for period 2 is shown in Table 23–8. Note that the values in the column labeled "Subsequent costs" are the costs for periods 3 *and* 4, and are obtained from Table 23–7. A summary for period 2 is provided in Table 23–9.

TABLE 23–9
Summary for period 2

Beginning inventory I_2	Optimal production $X_2{}^*$	Total costs periods 2, 3, and 4 $f_2(I_2)$	Ending inventory I_3
0	5	$16.0	2
1	4	15.5	2
2	3	15.0	2
3	0	12.5	0
4	0	12.5	1

TABLE 23–10
Period 1: Determination of optimal production

Beginning inventory I_1	Possible production amounts X_1	Cost in period 1			Ending inventory I_2	Subsequent costs $f_2(I_2)$	Total costs $C_1(X_1, I_1) + f_2(I_2)$
		Production	Inventory	Total $C_1(X_1, I_1)$			
0	2	$5	$0	$5.0	0	$16.0	$21.0
	3	6	0	6.0	1	15.5	21.5
	4	7	0	7.0	2	15.0	22.0
	5*	8	0	8.0	3	12.5	20.5*
	6	9	0	9.0	4	12.5	21.5

Finally, we come to period 1. The analysis for this period is shown in Table 23–10. This table is short since we have a known beginning inventory of zero units.

As can be seen from Table 23–10, the optimum production in period 1 is five units, and the total cost for all four periods is $20.5. The optimum schedule for periods 2, 3, and 4 can now be determined by working through Tables 23–9, 23–7, and 23–5:

Period	Beginning inventory	Optimal production	Ending inventory = beginning inventory next period
1	0	5	3
2	3	0	0
3	0	6	2
4	2	0	0

Example 3: A breeding problem

Consider a decision faced by a cattle breeder. The breeder must decide how many cattle he should sell in the market each year and how many he should retain for breeding purposes. Suppose the breeder starts with a herd of 200 cattle. If he breeds cattle, he obtains 1.4 times as many cattle per year as he started with. The cost of breeding is $30 for each head of cattle not sold. Breeding takes one year, and the $30 cost includes all expenses of maintaining an animal and its offspring. Alternatively, the breeder may sell cattle in the market, at a price which depends on how many cattle he sells. If Y represents the number of cattle which are sold in a given year, then the price, P, is given by equation (23–6):

$$(23\text{–}6) \qquad P = 200 - 0.2Y, \quad 0 \leq Y \leq 1{,}000$$

Assume that the breeder plans to sell his entire herd at the beginning of 10 years from now and retire, and that the buyer of his herd will pay him $150 per head at that time. The breeder must decide how many cattle to sell in the market each year and how many cattle to breed so that his profit is maximized.

This problem may be solved by dynamic programming. Define the following:

X_n = size of herd at the beginning of year n (the state variable)

$f_n(X_n)$ = maximum return from year n to year 10 when X_n cattle are in the herd at the beginning of year n and optimal decisions are made from year n to year 10 (the return function)

Y_n = number of cattle to be sold at the beginning of year n

$Y_n{}^*(X_n)$ = optimal number of cattle to sell at the beginning of year n, given a herd size of X_n at that time

Note that n, the stage number, refers to the year in which a decision is being made; $n = 1, 2, \ldots , 10$. Also note that the maximum return, $f_n(X_n)$, is a function of both the stage number (n) and the current state variable (X_n), representing the size of the herd. Then, starting at the end of the actual decision process, the size of the herd in year 10 is represented as X_{10}. Since the herd is to be sold at $150 per head at the beginning of year 10, we may write:

(23–7) $$f_{10}(X_{10}) = 150X_{10}$$

Working backward, the decision at the beginning of year 9 and the corresponding maximum return from year 9 onward may be written as:

(23–8)

$$f_9(X_9) = \max_{0 \le Y_9 \le X_9} \{ \overset{\textit{Sell } Y_9}{(200 - 0.2Y_9) \cdot Y_9} + \overset{\textit{Breed } (X_9 - Y_9)}{[f_{10}(1.4(X_9 - Y_9)) - 30(X_9 - Y_9)]} \}$$

Equation (23–8) says in words that the maximum return available from year 9 onward, given a current herd size of X_9, is equal to the maximum amount which may be obtained by selling Y_9 cattle and breeding the remainder $(X_9 - Y_9)$. The terms in braces { } in equation (23–8) represent the return from selling Y_9 cattle plus the gross return from breeding $(X_9 - Y_9)$ cattle, less the cost of breeding the $(X_9 - Y_9)$ cattle. Note that the gross return from breeding $(X_9 - Y_9)$ cattle is written as $f_{10}(1.4(X_9 - Y_9))$ and not $150(1.4)(X_9 - Y_9)$. This is done to emphasize that a *recurrence relation* is being developed between the maximum return at any stage (n) and the maximum return at the succeeding stage $(n + 1)$. Figure 23–2 is an illustration of the decision at year 9.

The optimal decision in year 9, $Y_9{}^*(X_9)$, will typically be a function of the herd size, X_9. A similar equation exists for the decision problem

FIGURE 23–2

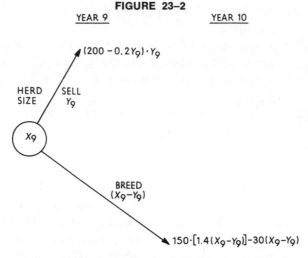

Total payoff to be maximized:

$$(200 - 0.2Y_9) \cdot Y_9 + 150[1.4(X_9 - Y_9)] - 30(X_9 - Y_9)$$

faced in year 8:

(23–9)

$$\text{Sell } Y_8 \qquad\qquad \text{Breed } (X_8 - Y_8)$$

$$f_8(X_8) = \max_{0 \le Y_8 \le X_8} \{(200 - 0.2Y_8) \cdot Y_8 + [f_9(1.4(X_8 - Y_8)) - 30(X_8 - Y_8)]\}$$

It is possible to write the equation in general for year n:

(23–10)

$$\text{Sell } Y_n \qquad\qquad \text{Breed } (X_n - Y_n)$$

$$f_n(X_n) = \max_{0 \le Y_n \le X_n} \{(200 - 0.2Y_n) \cdot Y_n + [f_{n+1}(1.4(X_n - Y_n)) - 30(X_n - Y_n)]\}$$

$$\text{for } n = 1, 2, \ldots, 9$$

Equation (23–10) illustrates the basic recurrence relationship for our dynamic programming problem.

The set of equations represented in equations (23–7) and (23–10) may be solved *recursively*, starting with equation (23–7) and working backward. As each equation is solved, we must record both the optimal decision rule relating $Y_n{}^*$ to X_n and the maximum return obtained as a function of X_n. First, we solve equation (23–7):

$$f_{10}(X_{10}) = 150X_{10}$$

We sell the entire herd at the beginning of year 10, irrespective of its size. The solution to equation (23–7) is trivial because the problem states that the breeder will sell his entire herd at year 10. Thus $Y_{10}{}^*(X_{10}) = X_{10}$.

Next consider equation (23–8) for year 9; substituting the solution for equation (23–7) into equation (23–8):

(23–11)

$$\underset{0\le Y_9\le X_9}{\text{Max}} \quad \overset{Sell\ Y_9}{\{(200 - 0.2Y_9)\cdot Y_9 + \overset{Breed\ (X_9 - Y_9)}{[150(1.4)(X_9 - Y_9) - 30(X_9 - Y_9)]}\}}$$

$$f_9(X_9) = \underset{0\le Y_9\le X_9}{\text{Max}} \quad \{(200 - 0.2Y_9)\cdot Y_9 + [150(1.4)(X_9 - Y_9) - 30(X_9 - Y_9)]\}$$

or:

(23–12)
$$f_9(X_9) = \underset{0\le Y_9\le X_9}{\text{Max}} \quad \{200Y_9 - 0.2(Y_9)^2 + 210(X_9 - Y_9) - 30(X_9 - Y_9)\}$$

Simplifying, we obtain:

$$(23\text{–}13)\quad f_9(X_9) = \underset{0\le Y_9\le X_9}{\text{Max}} \quad \{-0.2(Y_9)^2 + 20Y_9 + 180X_9\}$$

The set of terms in the braces { } in equation (23–13) forms a quadratic equation. To find the value of Y_9 which maximizes the return, we use calculus. Take the first derivative and set it equal to zero:

$$(23\text{–}14)\qquad \frac{d\{\ \}}{dY_9} = -0.2(2)Y_9 + 20 = 0$$

so that:

$$(23\text{–}15)\qquad Y_9{}^* = \frac{20}{0.4} = 50$$

Thus, at year 9 the breeder should sell 50 head of cattle and breed the rest.[3] His maximum return from year 9 to year 10 may be calculated by substituting the optimal decision value into equation (23–11):

(23–16)
$$\begin{aligned}
f_9(X_9) &= [200 - 0.2(50)]\cdot 50 + 210(X_9 - 50) - 30(X_9 - 50)\\
&= [190]\cdot 50 + 180(X_9 - 50)\\
&= 9{,}500 + 180X_9 - 9{,}000\\
&= 180X_9 + 500
\end{aligned}$$

assuming X_9 is greater than 50. If less than 50 cattle are in the herd at year 9, then all should be sold.

Now consider the decision in year 8. We may write:

(23–17)

$$\overset{Sell\ Y_8}{\qquad} \qquad \overset{Breed\ (X_8 - Y_8)}{\qquad}$$

$$f_8(X_8) = \underset{0\le Y_8\le X_8}{\text{Max}} \quad \{(200 - 0.2Y_8)\cdot Y_8 + [f_9(1.4(X_8 - Y_8)) - 30(X_8 - Y_8)\}$$

---

[3] Note that in this example the optimal decision in year 9 is not a function of the herd size. The marginal revenue from selling the fiftieth animal is $180. The benefit from not selling it in period 9 is also $180 (that is, $1.4 \times \$150$ less $30).

Since $X_9 = 1.4(X_8 - Y_8)$ and we have established that $f_9(X_9) = 180X_9 + 500 = 180(1.4)(X_8 - Y_8) + 500$, we may write:

(23–18)

$$f_8(X_8) = \max_{0 \le Y_8 \le X_8} \{(200 - 0.2Y_8) \cdot Y_8 + [180(1.4)(X_8 - Y_8) + 500] - 30(X_8 - Y_8)\}$$

or:

(23–19)

$$f_8(X_8) = \max_{0 \le Y_8 \le X_8} \{200Y_8 - 0.2(Y_8)^2 + 252(X_8 - Y_8) + 500 - 30(X_8 - Y_8)\}$$

Simplifying, we obtain:

$$(23\text{–}20) \quad f_8(X_8) = \max_{0 \le Y_8 \le X_8} \{-0.2(Y_8)^2 - 22Y_8 + 222X_8 + 500\}$$

Again, the value of Y_8 which maximizes the return is obtained by setting the derivative of the term in braces in equation (23–20) equal to zero, and solving for $Y_8{}^*$:

$$(23\text{–}21) \qquad \frac{d\{\ \}}{dY_8} = -0.2(2)Y_8 - 22 = 0$$

so that:

$$(23\text{–}22) \qquad Y_8{}^* = \frac{-22}{0.4} = -55$$

The value of Y_8 which maximizes the return is negative, but negative values are not allowed. Thus, we set $Y_8{}^*$ equal to zero for maximum feasible return. Then:

$$(23\text{–}23) \qquad f_8(X_8) = 222X_8 + 500$$

The reason that we find that we should not sell any of the cattle for $200 is that an animal retained will lead to 1.92 animals in two periods which when sold will bring $288 (that is, $1.92 \times \$150$). The cost of maintaining the animal the first period is $30 and maintaining 1.4 animals the second period is $42. Thus the benefit from not selling now is $216 compared with $200 obtained from selling now.

The solution process could be continued for year 7 and earlier years, each time obtaining the optimal decision $Y_n{}^*$. In this manner the optimal policy or set of decision rules would be obtained. For this example the optimal policy involves breeding all the herd every year until year 9, and selling 50 head in that year. The value of $f_1(X_1)$ for X_1 equal to 200 would indicate the maximum profit available to the breeder, assuming he followed the optimal policy for the 10 years.

FORMULATION AND SOLUTION OF DYNAMIC PROGRAMMING PROBLEMS

In order to formulate a managerial decision problem as a dynamic programming problem, it is necessary to divide the problem into a number of subproblems or decision stages, as the examples have shown. It is also necessary to be able to describe the state of the system by a state variable.[4] Finally, one must be able to write the general recurrence relation between the maximum return at one stage and the maximum return at the next stage [see equations (23–5) and (23–10) as examples]. The stage often refers to a time period, but need not necessarily represent time.

The actual numerical solution to a dynamic programming problem is rarely worked out by hand; a computer is generally required to perform the calculations. Sometimes the particular structure of a problem will allow the maximization or minimization in the recurrence relation to be performed by calculus, as in our third example, or by other analytical methods. At other times, it may be necessary to program a computer to search over a grid of allowable values in order to determine an approximate value for the optimal decision. This search procedure was used in our first and second examples, where we simply looked at all the available possibilities and chose the one with the highest payoff at each stage. Although the basic concepts of dynamic programming are present in every dynamic programming formulation and solution, the actual numerical procedures used for solution may vary widely. For this reason, no prepared computer library program or code exists for the solution of dynamic programming problems comparable to well-known computer codes for solving linear programming problems. In fact, a dynamic programming problem is not nearly so well-defined as a linear programming problem; all one knows is that decision stages are present, a state variable exists, and recurrence relations have been recorded. The complexity of the recurrence relations determines in large part whether the dynamic programming problem is easy to solve, hard to solve, or impossible to solve.

DYNAMIC PROGRAMMING UNDER UNCERTAINTY

It is possible to expand the range of problems which may be formulated as dynamic programming problems to include problems where uncertainty exists (in the sense of a known probability distribution). The particular maximization or minimization in the recurrence relation may

---

[4] The state variable may actually be more than one variable, but if its dimensionality exceeds two or three, then it is generally impossible to obtain numerical solutions.

contain random variables. The following example illustrates the use of dynamic programming under uncertainty.

Example 4: A purchasing problem

A purchasing manager must obtain a raw material in five weeks. The price of the raw material varies each week, according to the probabilities in the following table. If the manager decides to purchase the raw material at the end of a week, he pays the price which prevails in that week.

Price	Probability
$500............	0.3
600............	0.3
700............	0.4

If he chooses to delay his purchase, he must obtain the raw material in some future week, at whatever price prevails when he decides to purchase the material. If he has not purchased the material before week 5, he is forced to purchase it at the end of week 5, since it is needed for production. The objective is to find a purchasing policy which will minimize the expected cost of the material.

This problem may be solved by dynamic programming. Let:

n = week number; n = 1, 2, . . . , 5 (the stage number)
X_n = price observed in week n (the state variable)
$f_n(X_n)$ = minimum expected cost if price observed in week n is X_n and an optimal policy is followed from week n to the end of the process (the return function)

We work backward and consider the last week (week 5):

(23–24) $$f_5(X_5) = X_5$$

since the manager must purchase the material in week 5 if he has not already done so. Now, in the next-to-last week (week 4):

(23–25)

$$\text{Act} \qquad\qquad\qquad \text{Wait}$$
$$f_4(X_4) = \text{Min}\{X_4; \quad (500) \cdot (0.3) + (600) \cdot (0.3) + (700) \cdot (0.4)\}$$

That is, the manager may either act and obtain the price X_4, or wait and obtain the expected value of the price in the last week. Let us rewrite equation (23–25) in terms of $f_5(X_5)$, where $f_5(X_5) = X_5$:

(23–26)

$$\text{Act} \qquad\qquad\qquad \text{Wait}$$
$$_4(X_4) = \text{Min}\{X_4; \quad f_5(500) \cdot (0.3) + f_5(600) \cdot (0.3) + f_5(700) \cdot (0.4)\}$$

Figure 23–3 illustrates the alternatives faced in week 4.

FIGURE 23–3

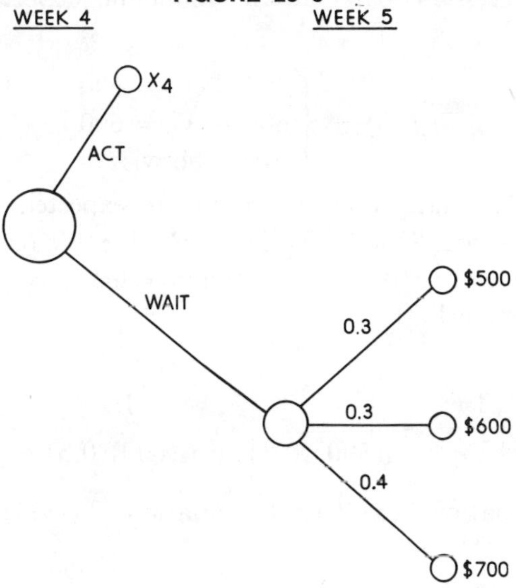

WEEK 4   WEEK 5

The situation in week 3 is:

(23–27)

$$f_3(X_3) = \text{Min}\{\underset{Act}{X_3;} \quad \underset{Wait}{f_4(500) \cdot (0.3) + f_4(600) \cdot (0.3) + f_4(700) \cdot (0.4)}\}$$

and in general, in week n:

(23–28)

$$f_n(X_n) = \text{Min}\{\underset{Act}{X_n;} \quad \underset{Wait}{f_{n+1}(500) \cdot (0.3) + f_{n+1}(600) \cdot (0.3) + f_{n+1}(700) \cdot (0.4)}\}$$

$$n = 1, 2, \ldots, 4$$

Equations (23–24) and (23–28) may be solved recursively, starting with equation (23–24) and working backward. At week 5 the material must be purchased if it has not been purchased earlier. At week 4, equation (23–25) holds. To perform the minimization involved in equation (23–25) we set the values of the two alternatives ("act" versus "wait") equal to each other and solve for the break-even value of X_4, represented by X_{4b}:

(23–29)
$$\begin{aligned} X_{4b} &= 500(0.3) + 600(0.3) + 700(0.4) \\ &= 150 + 180 + 280 = 610 \end{aligned}$$

If the price in week 4 is below \$610, the purchase should immediately be made; whereas if the price is above \$610, the purchase should be delayed. It is necessary to record the minimum expected cost at week 4:

$$(23\text{-}30) \qquad f_4(X_4) = \begin{cases} 500 \text{ if } X_4 = 500 \\ 600 \text{ if } X_4 = 600 \\ 610 \text{ otherwise} \end{cases}$$

Equation (23–30) states that the minimum expected cost as of week 4 is \$500 if the price is \$500, \$600 if the price is \$600, or \$610 if the price is \$700. The value of \$610 represents the expected price in week 5.

Now, consider week 3:

(23–31)

$$\overset{Act}{} \qquad\qquad \overset{Wait}{}$$

$$f_3(X_3) = \text{Min}\{X_3; \quad f_4(500)(0.3) + f_4(600)(0.3) + f_4(700)(0.4)\}$$

Substituting equation (23–30) into equation (23–31):

$$\overset{Act}{} \qquad\qquad \overset{Wait}{}$$

$$(23\text{-}32) \quad f_3(X_3) = \text{Min}\{X_3; \quad 500(0.3) + 600(0.3) + 610(0.4)\}$$

Again, we find the break-even value for X_3, represented as X_{3b}, at which the two alternatives have equal value:

$$(23\text{-}33) \qquad \begin{aligned} X_{3b} &= 500(0.3) + 600(0.3) + 610(0.4) \\ &= 150 + 180 + 244 = 574 \end{aligned}$$

If the price in week 3 is below \$574, the purchase should immediately be made; but if the price is above \$574, the purchase should be delayed. The minimum expected cost at week 3 is recorded as follows:

$$(23\text{-}34) \qquad\qquad f_3(X_3) = \begin{cases} 500 \text{ if } X_3 = 500 \\ 574 \text{ otherwise} \end{cases}$$

At week 2:

$$\overset{Act}{} \qquad\qquad \overset{Wait}{}$$

$$(23\text{-}35) \quad f_2(X_2) = \text{Min}\{X_2; \quad 500(0.3) + 574(0.3) + 574(0.4)\}$$

Thus:

$$(23\text{-}36) \qquad \begin{aligned} X_{2b} &= 500(0.3) + 574(0.3) + 574(0.4) \\ &= 150 + 172.2 + 229.6 = 551.8 \end{aligned}$$

and

$$(23\text{-}37) \qquad\qquad f_2(X_2) = \begin{cases} 500 \text{ if } X_2 = 500 \\ 551.8 \text{ otherwise} \end{cases}$$

Finally, in week 1:

$$\overset{Act}{} \qquad\qquad \overset{Wait}{}$$

$$(23\text{-}38) \quad f_1(X_1) = \text{Min}\{X_1; \quad 500(0.3) + 551.8(0.3) + 551.8(0.4)\}$$

Thus:

$$(23\text{--}39) \qquad \begin{aligned} X_{1b} &= 500(0.3) + 551.8(0.3) + 551.8(0.4) \\ &= 150 + 166.54 + 220.72 = 536.26 \end{aligned}$$

and

$$(23\text{--}40) \qquad f_1(X_1) = \begin{cases} 500 \text{ if } X_1 = 500 \\ 536.26 \text{ otherwise} \end{cases}$$

The optimal policy for the purchasing manager may be summarized as follows: If the price in weeks 1, 2, or 3 is $500, make the purchase immediately; otherwise, wait. If the price in week 4 is either $500 or $600, make the purchase immediately; otherwise, wait. If no purchase has been made by week 5, the purchase must be made at the price prevailing in week 5. If the optimal policy is followed, equation (23–40) indicates that the minimum expected cost is $500 if X_1 equals $500, and $536.26 if X_1 is greater than $500. Prior to knowing X_1, the minimum expected cost is $500(0.3) + 536.26 \ (0.7) = \$525.38$.

CONCLUSION

The basic concepts behind the technique of dynamic programming have been presented through the use of examples. The technique is applicable when a problem can be broken down into a number of subproblems. The general method must be adapted for particular problems, since the characteristics of each potential type of recurrence relation determine the easiest methods of solution. In addition, the technique may be applicable for problems under uncertainty (i.e., problems containing random variables).

APPENDIX. THE USE OF DYNAMIC PROGRAMMING IN MARKOV PROCESSES[5]

It is possible to use the technique of dynamic programming to study the short-run, transient behavior of a Markov process. The following example illustrates the use of dynamic programming to solve a Markov process model where the solution depends on the initial state. In this type of problem the short-run behavior is relevant to the decision.

Example

Consider the machine described in Example 1 of Chapter 22 (p. 420). Suppose the machine moves from state 1 (in adjustment) to state 2 (out

---

[5] Chapter 22 on Markov processes should be read before this Appendix is studied.

of adjustment), and vice versa, with the probabilities of change as given in Table 23–11:

TABLE 23–11

From \ To	In adjustment (state 1)	Out of adjustment (state 2)
In adjustment (state 1)	0.9	0.1
Out of adjustment (state 2)	0.7	0.3

Assume that when the machine is in state 1 for a day, a profit of $200 is gained; whereas if the machine is in state 2 for a day, a loss of $600 is incurred. If the decision maker is concerned with the long run, he would proceed as before and calculate the steady-state probabilities as follows:

(23–41)
$$P\left(\begin{array}{c}\text{state 1}\\\text{on day } n\end{array}\middle|\begin{array}{c}\text{state 1}\\\text{on day 1}\end{array}\right) = (0.9)P\left(\begin{array}{c}\text{state 1}\\\text{on day } n\end{array}\middle|\begin{array}{c}\text{state 1}\\\text{on day 1}\end{array}\right)$$
$$+ (0.7)\left\{1 - P\left(\begin{array}{c}\text{state 1}\\\text{on day } n\end{array}\middle|\begin{array}{c}\text{state 1}\\\text{on day 1}\end{array}\right)\right\}$$

so that:

(23–42)
$$P\left(\begin{array}{c}\text{state 1}\\\text{on day } n\end{array}\middle|\begin{array}{c}\text{state 1}\\\text{on day 1}\end{array}\right) = \frac{0.7}{1 - 0.9 + 0.7} = \frac{0.7}{0.8} = \frac{7}{8} \text{ as } n \to \infty$$

The expected daily profit in the long run would be:

$$EP = (7/8)\$200 + (1/8)(-\$600) = \$100$$

Now, suppose that the decision maker is concerned with the short-run or transient behavior of the process. If the machine is in state 1 on day 1, he may wish to know the expected profit over the next five days. This expected profit may be calculated by evaluating all branches of the probability tree in Figure 23–4. However, instead of calculating the short-run expected profit by working through the probability tree in Figure 23–4, we shall use dynamic programming to make the calculation.

FIGURE 23–4

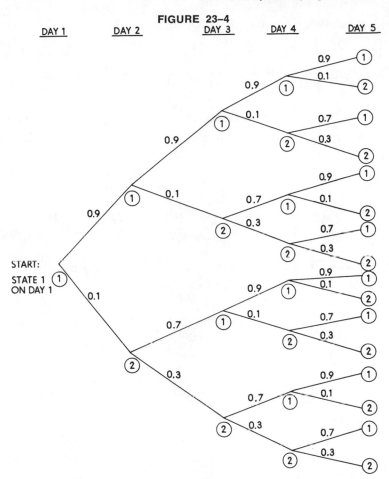

DAY 1   DAY 2   DAY 3   DAY 4   DAY 5

Dynamic programming formulation

Let:

n = day number; $n = 1, 2, \ldots , 5$ (the stage number)

X_n = state variable indicating the state of the process (1 or 2) on day n

$f_n(X_n)$ = maximum profit earned from day n to day 5 when the process is in state X_n on day n and optimal decisions are made from day n to day 5 (the return function)

In the process under consideration, there are no decisions to make; later on, we will add the possibility of making decisions along the way. Starting at the end of the process (day 5), we write:

$$(23\text{–}43) \qquad f_5(X_5) = \begin{cases} +200 \text{ if } X_5 = 1 \\ -600 \text{ if } X_5 = 2 \end{cases}$$

Working backward, on day 4 we write:

(23–44)
$$f_4(X_4) = \begin{cases} +200 \text{ if } X_4 = 1 \\ -600 \text{ if } X_4 = 2 \end{cases} + p_1(X_4)f_5(1) + [(1 - p_1(X_4)]f_5(2)$$

where $p_1(X_4)$ is the probability of changing from state X_4 to state 1. And in general, we write the following recurrence relation between $f_n(X_n)$ and $f_{n+1}(\cdot)$:

$$(23\text{–}45) \quad f_n(X_n) = \begin{cases} 200 \text{ if } X_n = 1 \\ -600 \text{ if } X_n = 2 \end{cases} + p_1(X_n)f_{n+1}(1)$$
$$+ [1 - p_1(X_n)]f_{n+1}(2)$$
$$n = 1, 2, \ldots, 4$$

Now the set of equations (23–45) may be solved recursively, starting with equation (23–43) and working backward. As each equation is solved, we substitute its value back into the next equation; eventually, we obtain the value for $f_1(1)$, the maximum expected profit to be earned from day 1 to day 5 when the process starts out in state 1 (in adjustment). The calculations are performed as follows:

$$(23\text{–}46) \quad \begin{aligned} f_5(1) &= \quad 200 \\ f_5(2) &= -600 \end{aligned}$$

$$(23\text{–}47) \quad \begin{aligned} f_4(1) &= \quad 200 + (0.9)(200) + [1 - 0.9](-600) = \quad 320 \\ f_4(2) &= -600 + (0.7)(200) + [1 - 0.7](-600) = -640 \end{aligned}$$

$$(23\text{–}48) \quad \begin{aligned} f_3(1) &= \quad 200 + (0.9)(320) + [1 - 0.9](-640) = \quad 424 \\ f_3(2) &= -600 + (0.7)(320) + [1 - 0.7](-640) = -568 \end{aligned}$$

$$(23\text{–}49) \quad \begin{aligned} f_2(1) &= \quad 200 + (0.9)(424) + [1 - 0.9](-568) = \quad 524.8 \\ f_2(2) &= -600 + (0.7)(424) + [1 - 0.7](-568) = -473.6 \end{aligned}$$

$$\begin{aligned} f_1(1) &= \quad 200 + (0.9)(524.8) + [1 - 0.9](-473.6) \\ (23\text{–}50) \qquad &= \quad 624.96 \\ f_1(2) &= -600 + (0.7)(524.8) + [1 - 0.7](-473.6) \\ &= -374.72 \end{aligned}$$

The expected profit in the next five days, given that the machine starts off in state 1 (in adjustment), is $624.96, or an average daily profit of $124.99, as compared to the steady-state profit of $100 in the long run. On the other hand, if the machine starts off in state 2 (out of adjustment), the expected profit over the next five days would be −$374.72, or an expected daily loss of $74.94.

Up to this point, the technique of dynamic programming has simply been an alternative way of performing the calculations for the probability tree in Figure 23–4. Now the problem is complicated by including an option to repair the machine each day.

Extension of example: Repair decision

Now, you have the option to hire a repairman to repair the machine when it is observed in state 2 (out of adjustment). You observe the machine at the beginning of the day, and the repairman performs his repairs very quickly, so that a full day's operation in state 1 is completed after his repair. Assume the state transitions occur at the end of the working day. The cost of having the machine repaired each time is $850. Should the repairman be hired?

In order to solve this decision problem, we must calculate the incremental value of being in state 1 versus being in state 2. This problem cannot be solved by using the steady-state probabilities, for it refers to the initial state of a system which will run into the future. Also, one must take into account the fact that the incremental value of being in state 1 versus state 2 will be affected by future decisions to repair or not to repair. In this type of problem, dynamic programming often provides an answer.

Consider the five-day problem discussed above. If our decision maker were concerned only with the following five days, then he would use a similar dynamic programming formulation, but this time there would be an explicit decision or action to be taken (or not taken) each time the system was in state 2 (out of adjustment). We proceed as follows. At day 5:

$$f_5(1) = 200$$

(23–51)
$$
\begin{array}{cc}
 & Repair \quad Do\ not\ repair \\
f_5(2) = \mathrm{Max}\{-850 + 200, & -600\} \\
- \mathrm{Max}\{-650, & -600\} \\
= -600
\end{array}
$$

Let us record the optimal decision rule as a function of the state variable and let the optimal decision on day n be represented by $Y_n{}^*(X_n)$. If one represents "repair" and zero represents "do not repair," then:

(23–52) $Y_5{}^*(1) = 0$ and $Y_5{}^*(2) = 0$

That is, we do not repair on day 5, whether the machine is in state 1 or state 2. Working backward, on day 4 we write:

$$f_4(1) = 200 + (0.9)(200) + [1 - 0.9](-600) = 320$$

(23–53)   *Repair*   *Do not repair*

$$f_4(2) = \text{Max} \left\{ \begin{array}{ll} -850 + 200 + 0.9(200) & -600 + (0.7)(200) \\ \quad + [1 - 0.9](-600), & \quad + [1 - 0.7](-600) \end{array} \right\}$$
$$= \text{Max}\{-530, \qquad\qquad -640\}$$
$$= -530$$

Recording the optimal decision rule as a function of the state variable, we write:

(23–54) $Y_4{}^*(1) = 0$ and $Y_4{}^*(2) = 1$

The decision to repair when the machine is out of adjustment was undesirable on day 5 but is desirable on day 4. On day 3:

$$f_3(1) = 200 + (0.9)(320 + [1 - 0.9](-530) = 435$$

(23–55)   *Repair*   *Do not repair*

$$f_3(2) = \text{Max} \left\{ \begin{array}{ll} -850 + 200 + (0.9)(320) & -600 + (0.7)(320) \\ \quad +[1 - 0.9](-530), & \quad + [1 - 0.7](-530) \end{array} \right\}$$
$$= \text{Max}\{-415, \qquad\qquad -535\}$$
$$= -415$$

and

(23–56) $Y_3{}^*(1) = 0$ and $Y_3{}^*(2) = 1$

On day 2:

$$f_2(1) = 200 + (0.9)(435) + [1 - 0.9](-415) = 550$$

(23–57)   *Repair*   *Do not repair*

$$f_2(2) = \text{Max} \left\{ \begin{array}{ll} -850 + 200 + (0.9)(435) & -600 + (0.7)(435) \\ \quad + [1 - 0.9](-415), & \quad + [1 - 0.7](-415) \end{array} \right\}$$
$$= \text{Max}\{-300, \qquad\qquad -420\}$$
$$= -300$$

and

(23–58) $Y_2{}^*(1) = 0$ and $Y_2{}^*(2) = 1$

Finally, on day 1:

$$f_1(1) = 200 + (0.9)(550) + [1 - 0.9](-300) = 665$$

(23–59)   *Repair*   *Do not repair*

$$f_1(2) = \text{Max} \left\{ \begin{array}{ll} -850 + 200 + (0.9)(550) & -600 + (0.7)(550) \\ \quad + [1 - 0.9](-300), & \quad + [1 - 0.7](-300) \end{array} \right\}$$
$$= \text{Max}\{-185, \qquad\qquad -305\}$$
$$= -185$$

and

(23–60) $Y_1{}^*(1) = 0$ and $Y_1{}^*(2) = 1$

The set of optimal decision rules $Y_1^*(X_1), Y_2^*(X_2), \ldots, Y_5^*(X_5)$ constitutes an optimal policy with respect to the repair decision for a five-day horizon. Note that on day 5 it is not optimal to repair if the machine is out of adjustment, whereas on days 1 through 4 it is optimal to repair if the machine is out of adjustment. This situation occurs because the gain from repairing the machine has two components. First, the day's production is valued at \$200 instead of $-\$600$. Second, the machine is in state 1 at the end of the day rather than state 2, and future probabilities are more heavily weighted in favor of state 1. On day 5 the process stops, and the future value of ending day 5 in state 1 is worthless. On day 4, however, the future value of ending the day in state 1 has some value. A naïve comparison of one-day benefits of \$800 versus one-day costs of \$850 would lead one to reject the repair alternative, whereas the dynamic programming analysis indicates precisely when the repair option should be taken.

Note that under the optimal repair policy, the expected profit for five days if the machine starts off in state 1 is \$665 [see equation (23–59)], as compared to \$624.96 without the repair option. Thus the optimal use of the repair option adds \$40.04 to the expected profit if the machine starts off in adjustment.

If the actual problem does not involve a finite horizon such as five days, there are two ways to modify our procedure. One way is to continue to work backward from some general day n to day $n - k$, and maximize the average daily return over the $k + 1$ days of operation. As we continue to work backward, eventually the maximum average daily return will approach a constant value, and the decision rule for the first day would be the appropriate one to use.

An alternative way to handle the infinite-horizon problem is to add discounting to the process. If the time value of money is taken into account, then each term representing future gains is discounted. As we work backward from n to day $n - k$, eventually the maximum present value of all returns will approach a constant value. Then the decision rule for the first day would be the appropriate one to use in the infinite-horizon case.

It should be noted that the first of these methods maximizes average daily return, and the second maximizes the present value of all future returns. If the discount factor α is substantially less than one, the two methods may produce different results, and the decision maker must decide which objective is appropriate.

BIBLIOGRAPHY

BELLMAN, R. E. *Adaptive Control Processes: A Guided Tour.* Princeton: Princeton University Press, 1961.

————. *Dynamic Programming*. Princeton: Princeton University Press, 1957.

————, and DREYFUS, S. E. *Applied Dynamic Programming*. Princeton: Princeton University Press, 1962.

HADLEY, G. *Nonlinear and Dynamic Programming*. Reading, Mass.: Addison-Wesley Publishing Co., Inc., 1964.

HOWARD, R. A. *Dynamic Programming and Markov Processes*. Cambridge: M.I.T. Press, 1960.

NEMHAUSER, GEORGE L. *Introduction to Dynamic Programming*. New York: John Wiley & Sons, Inc., 1966.

WAGNER, H. M. *Principles of Operations Research*. Englewood Cliffs, N.J.: Prentice-Hall, Inc., 1969.

WHITE, D. J. *Dynamic Programming*. San Francisco: Holden-Day, Inc., 1969.

PROBLEMS

23–1. A manager must decide on a pricing policy for a new product over the next four years. He is considering five different price levels: $12, $14, $16, $18, and $20 per unit. After evaluating potential price moves by his competitors, he has constructed the following payoff table which relates his price in a given year to the present value of the profit expected that year:

Payoff table

Price \ Year	1	2	3	4
$12	3	9	3	7
$14	2	1	2	2
$16	7	4	8	1
$18	9	2	6	4
$20	5	5	3	1

a) If there are no restrictions on price changes from year to year, state the optimal pricing strategy and compute the maximum expected profitability.

b) Now suppose the manager wishes to avoid making price changes of more than $2 from one year to the next. Find the optimal policy and compute the maximum expected profitability.

23–2. A cattle breeder has a herd of 400 cattle in 1973. He plans to sell his entire herd at the beginning of 1974 at $150 per head. He may sell cattle in 1973 at a price per head which is dependent on the number of cattle he chooses to sell. If Y represents the number he sells in 1973, then the price he obtains per head will be:

$$P = 200 - 0.2Y, \qquad 0 \le Y \le 1{,}000$$

Alternatively, any cattle not sold are bred at a cost of $30 per head, and the breeding ratio is 1.4 cattle resulting per head bred.

a) Compute the cattle breeder's profit if he sells all of his herd in 1973.
b) Compute his profit if he sells none of his herd in 1973.
c) Write down a general expression for his profit if he sells Y cattle in 1973 and breeds the remainder $(400 - Y)$. Simplify your expression as much as you can.
d) Substitute into your profit expression in (c) above the value $Y = 50$, and compute expected profit when 50 cattle are sold in 1973.
e) Now take the derivative of your expression in (c) above with respect to Y and set it equal to zero. Verify that the optimal number of cattle to sell in 1973 is 50.
f) This problem is a two-year version of the 10-year cattle-breeding problem discussed in this chapter. Equation (23–16) represents maximum expected profit when there is one year left, as in our case:

(23–16) $f_9(X_9) = 180X_9 + 500$

where X_9 represents the size of the herd.

Substitute the herd size of 400 into equation (23–16), and compute the maximum expected profit for our problem. Your answer should be identical to the answer to part (d) above.

g) Use equation (23–16) to calculate the maximum expected profit of a herd of 200 in 1973.

23–3. Suppose the cattle breeder in Problem 23–2 had an opportunity to invest money obtained from selling cattle in 1973 at an interest rate of 10 percent per year.

a) Calculate the present value of his profit if he sells none of his herd in 1973. Assume his breeding costs are incurred immediately, whereas his profits from selling his entire herd next year are obtained one year hence.
b) Rewrite your general expression in part (c) of Problem 23–2 to

include the effect of the time value of money. Simplify your expression.

c) Now take the derivative of your expression in (*b*) above with respect to Y and set it equal to zero. Verify that when the time value of money is added to the analysis, the optimal number of cattle to sell in 1973 increases.

23–4. A cattle breeder may either breed his cattle or sell his cattle in the market. The breeder starts with a herd of 100 cattle and plans to sell his entire herd at the beginning of five years from now at $300 per head. If he sells cattle in the market, the price P is given as follows:

$$P = 500 - 0.1Y, \qquad 0 \leq Y \leq 5{,}000$$

where Y represents the number of cattle sold in a given year. If he breeds cattle, the cost is $50 per head, and the breeding ratio is approximately 1.8.

a) Write down the expression for the return function $f_n(X_n)$ for year 5.

b) Write down an expression for the return function in year 4, $f_4(X_4)$, using Y_4 to represent the number of cattle sold in the market in year 4. Simplify your equation by substituting in the expression for $f_5(X_5)$ obtained in (*a*) above.

c) Perform the maximization required in the equation in (*b*) above by taking a derivative and setting it equal to zero.

d) Using the optimal decision at year 4 as obtained in (*c*) above, rewrite the value of the return function $f_4(X_4)$ in terms of X_4 alone.

e) Now consider year 3, and write the return function $f_3(X_3)$. Simplify your equation by substituting in the expression for $f_4(X_4)$ obtained in (*d*) above.

Note that your sequence of steps (*c*) and (*d*) may be repeated for each prior year; in this manner, the complete problem may be solved.

23–5. Consider an inventory problem like that of Example 2 on page 452. Suppose that the demand is as follows:

Month	Demand
January	4
February	5
March	3
April	2

The setup cost is $5, the variable production cost is $1, and the inventory holding cost is $1 per month. Further suppose that the beginning inventory on January 1 is one unit. What is the optimum production schedule for this problem?

23–6. A manager must hire a secretary in 5 days. The manager uses a testing procedure which results in each applicant being given a numerical rating. Assume that the best rating he observes each day varies according to the probabilities in the table below:

Best rating	Probability
10..............	0.2
9..............	0.4
8..............	0.4

If a potential secretary is not offered the job the day she applies, she accepts employment elsewhere. If the manager has not hired a secretary before day 5, he must hire the best secretary who applies on day 5. His objective is to maximize the expected rating of the secretary he hires.

a) Consider the situation on day 4, one day from the end. Compute the expected rating which will be obtained if the manager does not hire a secretary on day 4, but chooses to delay until day 5.

b) Use your result to state the optimal decision rule for day 4. For example, under what conditions should the manager delay choosing a secretary, and under what conditions should he act immediately, assuming he knows the best rating obtained on day 4?

c) Now consider the situation on day 3. Compute the expected rating which will be obtained if the manager does not hire a secretary on day 3 but chooses to delay his decision. Remember that the manager need not necessarily hire the best secretary applying on day 4. He should delay his choice further if the best rating on day 4 is low, as found in part (b) above.

d) Use your result in part (c) above to state the optimal decision rule for day 3.

23–7. Redo Problem 23–6, using the following notation:

$$n = \text{day number; } n = 1, 2, \ldots , 5 \text{ (the stage number)}$$
$$X_n = \text{best rating observed on day } n \text{ (the state variable)}$$
$$f_n(X_n) = \text{maximum expected rating if best rating observed on}$$
day n is X_n and an optimal policy is followed from day n to the end of the process (the return function)

a) Consider the last day (day 5), and write an equation for $f_5(X_5)$.

b) Consider the next-to-last day (day 4), and write an equation for $f_4(X_4)$. Note that $f_4(X_4)$ equals the larger of the expected ratings under the two alternatives—"act" and "wait."

c) Set the two expected outcomes in part (b) equal to find the break-even value of X_4, represented as X_{4b}. Then state the optimal decision rule at day 4. Verify that your rule is the same as the one obtained in part (b) of Problem 23–6.

d) Using the optimal decision rule for day 4, write an equation for $f_3(X_3)$.

e) Now perform parts (c) and (d) alternatively to obtain $f_2(X_2)$ and $f_1(X_1)$. If the best rating on day 1 is 9, what action should the manager follow on day 1, and what is his maximum expected rating?

f) Suppose the personnel department says that it is able to guarantee a secretary with a "9" rating if it is given three days to do so. Decide whether the offer is helpful to the manager or not.

23–8. This problem requires an understanding of Markov processes (see Chapter 22).

Assume a machine moves from state 1 (in adjustment) to state 2 (out of adjustment), and vice versa, with the following probabilities of change:

From \ To	In adjustment (state 1)	Out of adjustment (state 2)
In adjustment (state 1)	0.5	0.5
Out of adjustment (state 2)	0.4	0.6

Assume that when the machine is in state 1 for a day, a profit of $100 is gained; and if the machine is in state 2 for a day, a loss of $50 is incurred.

a) Compute the steady-state probabilities and the expected daily profit rate.

b) Now suppose the machine may be repaired at a cost of $200. You observe the machine at the beginning of the day, and the repairman performs his repairs very quickly, so a full day's operation in state 1 occurs after repairing. Assume the state transitions occur at the end of the working day. If the manager is interested in only the next 5 days of operation, use dynamic programming to compute the optimal decision rules concerning the repair decision. What is the expected value of starting the five-day period with the machine in state 1?

23–9. An investor has $10 million to invest sometime in the next five months. Each month a new investment opportunity arises; the return each investment promises is a random variable distributed according to the probabilities in the table below:

Return on investment	Probability
20%.	0.6
30	0.3
100	0.1

At the beginning of each month, an investment opportunity is presented, with some actual return based on the probabilities in the table. The investor must either take that opportunity or reject it. Once rejected, the opportunity is withdrawn. If the investor has not invested his money by the fifth month, he must invest it at the return available in the fifth month.

Let:

X_n = return available in month n

$f_n(X_n)$ = maximum expected return if return of X_n is available in month n and optimal decisions are made from month n to month 5

a) Write an equation for the return in the fifth month, $f_5(X_5)$.
b) Now consider the situation in month 4. Write an equation for $f_4(X_4)$. Note that $f_4(X_4)$ equals the larger of the expected returns under the two alternatives—"act" and "wait."
c) Set the two expected profits in part (b) above equal to find the break-even value of X_4, represented as X_{4b}. Then state the optimal decision rule at month 4.
d) Using the optimal decision rule for month 4, write an equation for $f_3(X_3)$.
e) Now perform parts (c) and (d) alternatively to obtain $f_2(X_2)$ and $f_1(X_1)$. If the return available in month 1 is 30 percent, should the investor make his investment in month 1, or should he delay? What is his expected return if he makes the optimal decision?

23–10. A winemaker has produced his last barrel of wine before retirement. He must decide how many years to age the wine before bottling and selling it. The price he obtains for the wine increases as the age of the wine increases, according to the table below:

Age of wine (in years)	Price of wine
1.	$56
2.	59
3.	67
4.	75
5.	82
6.	84

The winemaker will not age his wine more than six years. Let:

n = year number (the stage number)

X_n = age of wine in years (the state variable)

$f_n(X_n)$ = maximum discounted revenue available when wine of age X_n exists at year n and optimal decisions are followed from year n to year 6 (the return function)

Assume the discount rate is 10 percent per year.

Note that $X_n = n$ in this particular problem.

a) Write an equation for $f_6(X_6)$.

b) Write an equation for $f_5(X_5)$. Note that $f_5(X_5)$ equals the larger of the present values of the two alternatives—"sell" or "wait."

c) Find the optimal decision rule in year 5.

d) Write an equation for $f_4(X_4)$.

e) Now perform parts (c) and (d) alternatively to obtain $f_3(X_3)$, $f_2(X_2)$, and $f_1(X_1)$. How long should the winemaker age his wine, and what will the present value (in year 0) of his revenue be?

23–11. A ship's cargo capacity is 20 tons. There are three different types of cargo which may be carried in the ship—type 1, type 2, and type 3. The profit obtained from carrying a unit of each type of cargo is contained in the table below. The weight of a unit of each type is also included in the table.

Cargo type	Value/unit	Weight/unit (tons)
1.....	$ 40	5
2.....	220	10
3.....	360	15

a) By trial and error, find the cargo combination which maximizes profits and which satisfies the weight constraint of 20 tons.

b) Now, let:

X_n = available tons when the first n types of cargo are being considered (the state variable)

$f_n(X_n)$ = maximum profit available when available capacity is X_n, n types of cargo are being considered, and optimal decisions are made

Y_i = number of units of type i (i = 1, 2, and 3) included in the cargo combination (the decision variable)

Write an equation for $f_1(X_1)$. Note that $f_1(X_1)$ represents the maximum profit available when available capacity is X_1 and when only type 1 is considered for cargo. (*Hint:* Use the symbol [ ] to represent "greatest integer in.")

c) Now write an equation for $f_2(X_2)$ which uses the symbol Y_2 to indicate the number of units of type 2 to include. Note that $f_2(X_2)$ is the maximum profit which can be obtained when available capacity is X_2 and the first two types of cargo are considered.

d) Now write an equation for $f_3(X_3)$.

23–12. An investor is considering buying into each of three ventures that have been proposed to him. He estimates the return on his investment in each. The projects have minimum investments of $60,000, $80,000, and $50,000, respectively. A fourth alternative of investment in government bonds is available for any amount invested, returning annually $4 per $100 invested.

Project No. 1 (shopping center development)		Project No. 2 (housing development)		Project No. 3 (industrial firm)	
Investment amount (000)	Annual return (000)	Investment amount (000)	Annual return (000)	Investment amount (000)	Annual return (000)
$ 60	$ 6.0	$ 80	$ 6.0	$ 50	$4.0
70	8.0	90	8.0	60	4.8
80	9.0	100	10.0	70	5.6
90	10.0	110	12.0	80	6.4
100	11.0	120	13.0	90	7.2
110	11.5	130	13.8	100	8.0
120 (maximum investment)	12.0	140	14.2	110	8.8
		150 (maximum investment)	14.5	120 (maximum investment)	9.6

If the investor has $200,000 available, how should he invest it to maximize his annual return? If he has $150,000? If he has $250,000? What is the annual return in each case?

23–13. You are considering your transportation costs over the next five years. The characteristics of the automobile you buy are listed in the table below. In no case would you keep an automobile longer than four years.

Year	Operating costs during year	Sale value at end of year
1	$ 450	$1,400
2	600	1,100
3	800	900
4	1,100	800

Purchase cost new is $2,000.

a) Suppose you consider buying only new cars. How often should you buy a new car if you wish to minimize transportation costs (purchase costs plus operating costs less sale value)?

b) Suppose you would consider buying a used car at the prices listed in the last column of the table (excluding, of course, the possibility of buying a four-year-old model). Does this change your optimal policy?

23–14. Refer to the stewardess problem, Problem 13–6 (p. 221). Formulate this as a dynamic programming problem and solve.

23–15. Refer to the warehousing problem described on pages 209–211. Formulate this as a dynamic programming problem and solve. (*Hint:* There are really only two possibilities—either a full or an empty warehouse at the end of each period.)

23–16. Reformulate Problem 23–11 above (the cargo-loading problem) by letting X represent the number of tons available and letting $f(X)$ represent the maximum profit obtainable from all three types of cargo when optimal decisions are made. If we define $f(0) = 0$ and $f(X) = 0$ for all $X < 0$, verify that the following functional equation holds:

$$f(X + 1) = \text{Max}\{f(X) + f(1); \; 40 + f(X - 4);$$
$$220 + f(X - 9); \; 360 + f(X - 14)\}$$

Compute $f(1)$ through $f(20)$.

23–17. You are moving and can make at most three house-hunting trips, eight weeks apart, to find a house. You have decided that the probability of finding an "acceptable" house is as follows:

Price	Probability of finding acceptable house at this exact price	Cumulative probability of finding an acceptable house at this price or lower
$30,000.	0.5	0.5
40,000.	0.3	0.8
60,000.	0.2	1.0
	Sum = 1.0	

You must buy a house before you move. You have estimated the cost of one house-hunting trip at $2,000 (not reimbursed by your employer). You feel that in eight weeks' time there is enough turnover so that the three trips will be probabilistically independent in their outcomes.

Use the concepts of dynamic programming to obtain a *complete* optimal strategy which would tell you what to do after each visit to minimize your *expected cost* of finding and acquiring an acceptable house. Then apply your optimal strategy to the case in which you have just completed your first visit and have found an acceptable house at $40,000. Should you buy it or look further?

23–18. A drug firm is trying to develop a cure for a particular ailment. Five possible compounds are under consideration. Each is considered to have a 1/10 chance to be effective as a cure (i.e., a 1/10 chance of success). To test each compound will take one month and cost $10 (hundreds of dollars). The drug firm has three months in which to test the five compounds.

The problem is to develop a testing strategy. A strategy involves determining how many compounds to test in each month. For example, one strategy is: try one compound in month 1; if not successful, try a second in month 2; if still not successful, try the remaining three in month 3. Note that testing the compounds sequentially reduces the expected cost since it reduces the probability that all five compounds will have to be tested before a success is found.

Assume that the probabilities are independent. Note that if k compounds are tried in any month, the probability of at least one success is $[1 - (0.9)^k]$.

a) Formulate a general dynamic recursion for N periods and M compounds to be tested. The objective is to minimize the cost of finding a success.

b) Apply your recursion to the data in the case above ($M = 5$ compounds, $N = 3$ months).

23–19. A firm uses a digger to mine coal in a certain mine. The mine has a life of 10 years. The company currently is using a digger that is two years old. A new digger costs $150,000. Maintenance, downtime, and other costs vary with the age of a machine as shown:

Age of machine at beginning of year	Costs of maintenance, etc., during year	Age of machine at beginning of year	Costs of maintenance, etc., during year
New	$ 0	5 years	$ 70,000
1 year	10,000	6	90,000
2	20,000	7	120,000
3	30,000	8	150,000
4	50,000	9	180,000

At any time a machine may be rebuilt. This makes the machine equivalent to a two-year-old machine in terms of maintenance costs, etc. The cost of a rebuild is $60,000. The firm wishes to find an optimum policy (one that minimizes maintenance and equipment costs) for equipment replacement and rebuild over the 10-year period. Assume equipment has no value at end of the 10 years. Note that in any year the firm has three choices: (1) keep the current digger another year; (2) rebuild the digger; (3) replace the digger with a new one.

a)   Formulate the dynamic recursion for this problem.
b)   Solve the problem.

24

Branch and bound

The term "combinatorial problem" refers to a problem in which there is a very large number of feasible solutions, and in which each decision variable is either 0 or 1 (representing on or off, present or absent, yes or no, or some similar binary choice). Examples of combinatorial problems in business include many scheduling problems such as scheduling airline crews to flights and the scheduling of orders through a job-shop manufacturing facility. In this chapter we present a technique recently evolved to deal with combinatorial problems; it is called *branch and bound*. Consider the following example.

Example: An assignment problem[1]

A firm has four plants and four warehouses. Each plant must be uniquely assigned to one warehouse (and vice versa). The pairing (or assignment) of plants to warehouses will affect total shipping costs, and the goal is to obtain an assignment with the smallest total shipping cost. Table 24–1 contains annual shipping costs for each possible matching of a plant to a warehouse.

This problem is a combinatorial problem because there is a number of possible solutions, each one of which involves a yes or no answer to the question, "Is plant i assigned to warehouse j?" There are four possible ways in which plant A can be assigned; given an assignment for A, there are three possible ways in which plant B can be assigned; then two ways for C, and finally, D is paired with the remaining warehouse.

---

[1] We use an assignment problem to present the branch-and-bound technique even though more specialized and efficient procedures exist to deal with this particular combinatorial problem.

485

TABLE 24-1
Annual shipping costs ($000's)

Plant \ Warehouse	1	2	3	4
A	10	33	41	20
B	24	17	50	60
C	39	32	62	29
D	22	27	39	37

Thus the total number of possible assignments is $N = (4)(3)(2)(1) = 4! = 24$. While 24 is not too large a number, the same problem with 10 plants and 10 warehouses would contain $10! = 3,628,800$ possible solutions. This is the fundamental characteristic of a combinatorial problem; even a relatively small problem (10 plants and 10 warehouses) has a very large number of possible solutions.

In our example with 24 possible solutions, we could evaluate each feasible solution to find the one with minimum cost; this approach is called *complete enumeration*. However, in the 10×10 case, even on a computer, the enumeration and evaluation of all possible solutions would take an excessive period of time. Thus the strategy of complete enumeration cannot generally be applied, and we seek some strategy involving only *partial enumeration*.

The simplex method of linear programming (Chapter 14) is an example of one partial-enumeration procedure. We know that the optimal solution to a linear programming problem is at a corner-point of the feasible region, but the simplex method does not evaluate all feasible corner-points. It moves from one corner-point to an adjacent one producing greater benefit, continuing until no further benefits can be obtained. This approach typically evaluates only a small fraction of all feasible corner-points and is therefore quite efficient.

When a problem is solved by intuitive, *ad hoc* procedures we frequently eliminate from consideration large classes or categories of possible solutions, by deciding that the optimal solution would never (or rarely) be in any of those categories. This approach again uses the concept of partial rather than complete enumeration. The branch-and-bound technique formalizes this type of *ad hoc* procedure.

THE BRANCH-AND-BOUND TECHNIQUE

The branch-and-bound technique for a cost minimization problem proceeds in several steps as follows:

1. *Branch.* Consider the category or set of all possible solutions to the problem (typically, a large number). Then divide that total category into two or more separate subcategories on the basis of some partial solution (such as plant A is assigned to warehouse 1, or plant A is *not* assigned to warehoue 1).

2. *Bound.*

a)   *A lower bound.* Next, find some way of placing a *lower bound* or lower limit on the cost of any solution in each of the subcategories created in step 1. Any lower bound will, by definition, be less than or equal to the cost of any solution in the subcategory.

b)   *The upper bound.* The upper bound is determined by the cost of the best feasible solution to the problem that has been obtained thus far. To start, an arbitrary feasible solution may be selected. Thereafter, when a new solution is found that is better, its cost becomes the upper bound, or the *best solution obtained thus far.*

3. *Cut.* Consider the lower bounds on the subcategories created in step 1. We may discard completely any subcategories for which the cost of the lower bound is greater than the best solution obtained thus far. Since the lower bound represents the most optimistic estimate for any possible solution in the subcategory, finding that the lower bound exceeds the cost of a known feasible solution indicates that the optimum cannot be in that subcategory, and the whole subcategory can safely be discarded. This is how we avoid enumerating all possible solutions.

4. *Go back to step 1.* Select a subcategory to study further. Repeat the branch-and-bound steps, discarding categories of solutions until there are no more categories to examine. The best solution obtained thus far becomes the optimal solution to the problem. The example given at the beginning of the chapter will illustrate the steps in the technique.

The first branch

Consider the example with cost data in Table 24–1. There are 24 possible solutions. Suppose we arbitrarily focus on the tentative assignment of plant A to warehouse 1 (or *not* that assignment). Then our total set of 24 solutions is divided into two categories; those solutions with $(A, 1)$ paired; and those solutions which do not match plant A with warehouse 1, denoted by $(\overline{A, 1})$. This is our first "branch"; the process is depicted in Figure 24–1.

FIGURE 24–1
First branch of example

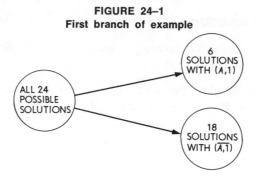

Lower bounds

We now need a way to bound each category; i.e., we need a way to calculate a lower limit on costs for the solutions in each category. Consider the category associated with the assignment $(A, 1)$. The cost of this assignment is $10 plus the cost associated with the remaining plant-warehouse assignments. To find a bound on this, suppose we cross out the first row of Table 24–1 (since plant A is assigned) and the first column (since warehouse 1 is assigned). The new cost table is reproduced in Table 24–2.

TABLE 24–2
Remaining shipping cost, given (A, 1)

Plant \ Warehouse	2	3	4
B	17	50	60
C	32	62	29
D	27	39	37

Now we want to compute a lower bound on the assignment of the remaining plants B, C, D to the remaining warehouses 2, 3, 4. One way to obtain a lower bound is to select the minimum numbers in each row in Table 24–2 and add them. We reason as follows: each of the remaining plants (B, C, and D) must have some warehouse paired with them. If we assume that for each plant the lowest cost warehouse is assigned, then the sum of these numbers is a *lower bound* on the cost of the best feasible assignment. In our example, the calculations are as follows:

Row	Minimum in row
B	17
C	29
D	27

Sum = 73 (infeasible)

Note that this way of producing a lower bound will not always represent a feasible assignment. In this case, the minimums of the rows in Table 24–2 represent the assignments $(B, 2)$, $(C, 4)$, and $(D, 2)$. This is not a feasible assignment since warehouse 2 is assigned twice and warehouse 3 is not assigned at all. Nevertheless, the sum of these minimums, 73, is a lower bound; the minimum cost of assigning the remaining three plants and warehouses must be at least as large as 73.

An alternative way of obtaining a lower bound on the remaining assignment of three plants to three warehouses is to consider each warehouse being assigned to the lowest cost plant; i.e., the *column* minimums in Table 24–2. The column minimums are:

Column	Minimum in column
2	17
3	39
4	29

Sum = 85 (feasible)

Again, choosing the minimum-cost plant for each remaining warehouse will not always produce a feasible assignment. In this particular instance, however, the assignment indicated by the column minimums is $(B, 2)$, $(D, 4)$, $(C, 3)$, which is in fact a feasible assignment of the remaining plants and warehouses.

Since we plan to use the lower bound to exclude categories of solutions from consideration, the *highest* lower bound is of maximum use. In other words, we have obtained two lower bounds on the remaining assignment of three plants and three warehouses: 73 and 85. We will use the larger of these (85) as our lower bound.[2] Now, adding 85 to the actual cost of the $(A, 1)$ matching initially assumed, we have $85 + 10 = 95$ as a lower bound on any solution in the "Solutions with $(A, 1)$" category.

Best solution obtained so far. After the branch-and-bound process is used, we will record and save the *best feasible solution obtained so far* as an upper bound on the actual minimum-cost solution. Initially, however, we may choose an arbitrary feasible assignment such as $(A, 1)$,

---

[2] The lower bound of 73 implies that there are no feasible solutions with cost below 73. The lower bound of 85 implies that there are no feasible solutions below 85. The bound of 85 *dominates* the bound of 73; if there are no solutions below 85, there can be none below 73. Thus we retain only the largest lower bound for further calculations.

$(B, 2)$, $(C, 3)$, $(D, 4)$ and record the cost: $10 + 17 + 62 + 37 = 126$. Thus 126 is our initial "best solution obtained so far." However, after our first branch on $(A, 1)$ or $(\overline{A, 1})$ and subsequent lower bounding of $(A, 1)$, we have a better feasible solution than 126.

Recall that the row minimums of Table 24–2 producing a lower bound for three plants and warehouses of 73 did *not* represent a feasible assignment. However, the *column* minimums, with a sum of 85, *did* represent a feasible assignment. The (feasible) assignment of $(A, 1)$ and column minimums has a cost of $10 + 85 = 95$, and since this value is lower than 126, we replace 126 by 95 as our best solution obtained so far. Thus an *upper bound* (or limit) on the minimum-cost solution is 95; the best minimum-cost solution must be less than or equal to 95.

Another lower bound. Now consider the other end of the first branch (see Figure 24–1). The category of solutions with $(\overline{A, 1})$ (i.e., *not* containing the pairing of A to 1) must be studied to obtain a lower bound. Considering Table 24–1, we reason as follows: If A is not assigned to 1, then the "10" entry corresponding to $(A, 1)$ is not allowed. Thus, A must be assigned to one of the other warehouses, and similarly, warehouse 1 must be paired with one of the remaining plants B, C, D. We can repeat the column minimum analysis and the row minimum analysis, this time with all four rows and columns, except that the entry "10" must be deleted. Then we obtain:

Row	Row minimum	Column	Column minimum
A	20*	1	22*
B	17	2	17
C	29	3	39
D	22	4	20
	Sum = 88 (infeasible)		Sum = 98 (infeasible)

* This would have been 10, but that entry has been disallowed.

Neither of the assignments associated with row or column minimums is feasible, but the number 98 still represents a lower bound on the best solution in the $(\overline{A, 1})$ category.

Cut

We now have the category $(A, 1)$ with lower bound 95 and category $(\overline{A, 1})$ with lower bound 98, and the best solution obtained thus far (upper bound) is 95. We now compare the lower bound of the $(\overline{A, 1})$ category (98) with the best solution obtained thus far (95). Since the lower bound is above the best solution, we can eliminate from further consideration the complete set of possible solutions in the category $(\overline{A,1})$. This elimination removes 18 of the 24 allowable solutions.[3]

The second branch

For the second branch we select a category not yet eliminated and again "branch" on some arbitrary matching of a plant and warehouse. Thus we consider the category $(A, 1)$ in Figure 24–1 and branch on the pairing "$(B, 2)$." Figure 24–2 indicates the current situation (we have added lower bounds and the best solution so far to the figure).

FIGURE 24–2
Second branch of Example*

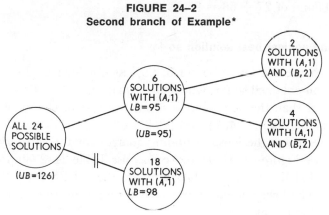

* Note: LB = lower bound; UB = upper bound (best solution so far).

Lower bounds

Consider the category $[(A, 1), (B, 2)]$. The actual cost of the stated assignment is $10 + 17 = 27$. We now eliminate rows A and B and columns 1 and 2 from the original Table 24–1, producing Table 24–3:

TABLE 24–3
Remaining shipping costs, given (A, 1) and (B, 2)

Plant \ Warehouse	3	4
C	62	29
D	39	37

---

[3] In general we will rarely be so fortunate as to be able to eliminate three fourths of all potential solutions after just one branch and bound.

From Table 24–3, the row and column minimums are:

Row	Row minimum	Column	Column minimum
C	29	3	39
D	37	4	29
	Sum = 66 (infeasible)		Sum = 68 (feasible)

We add the larger of these (68) to the 27 already incurred to produce a lower bound of $27 + 68 = 95$.

Comparing against best solution so far

We compare the lower bound of 95 just obtained to the cost of the best solution obtained so far, which also equals 95. Since the lower bound is not larger than the best solution so far, we cannot eliminate this category of solutions with $(A, 1)$ and $(B, 2)$.

Now we repeat the lower bounding analysis for the category $[(A, 1), (\overline{B, 2})]$ (see Figure 24–2). Here we may use Table 24–2 [shipping costs, given $(A, 1)$] but we must also eliminate the $(B, 2)$ entry "17" from the table. The lower bound is obtained through the row minimum and column minimum analysis:

Row	Row minimum	Column	Column minimum
B	50*	2	27*
C	29	3	39
D	27	4	29
	Sum = 106 (feasible)		Sum = 95 (infeasible)

* This would have been 17, but that entry has been disallowed.

The lower bound is thus the cost of the $(A, 1)$ assignment (10) plus 106; $10 + 106 = 116$.

Comparing 116 against the best solution obtained so far (95), we can eliminate all solutions in the category $[(A, 1)\ (\overline{B, 2})]$ from further consideration, since the lower limit on their costs is 116, while we already have a feasible solution which costs only 95. This elimination removes four more possible solutions from contention; with the 18 removed at the first branch, we have eliminated $18 + 4 = 22$ out of the 24 possible solutions.

The third branch

The category $[(A, 1), (B, 2)]$ is the only category not eliminated, so we will branch from it. We again branch on an arbitrary assignment, $(C, 3)$ versus $(\overline{C, 3})$ as in Figure 24–3; note that here $(\overline{C, 3})$ implies the assignment $(C, 4)$, since $(A, 1)$ and $(B, 2)$ have already been assigned.

FIGURE 24–3
Third branch of example*

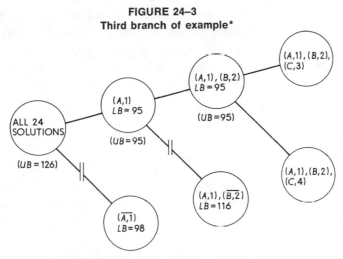

* Note: LB = lower bound; UB = upper bound (best solution so far).

Consider the category $[(A, 1), (B, 2), (C, 3)]$. These three assignments require that plant D be assigned to warehouse 4, and the cost of this assignment is $10 + 17 + 62 + 37 = 126$ (feasible). Since 126 is larger than the best solution so far (95), we eliminate this solution from consideration.

Now consider the other category $[A, 1), (B, 2), (C, 4)]$. This assignment requires that plant D be paired with warehouse 3, and the cost of this assignment is $10 + 17 + 39 + 29 = 95$ (feasible).

At this point all categories except $[(A, 1), (B, 2), (C, 4)]$ have been eliminated because their lower bounds were above the cost of the best solution obtained so far. Moreover, the category just considered contains only one assignment: $(A, 1), (B, 2), (C, 4), (D, 3)$, with cost equal to 95. Thus we are finished, and this assignment is the minimum-cost assignment.

Amount of partial enumeration

Our example had 24 possible assignments. Figure 24–3 shows that our branch-and-bound analysis only made six evaluations, although the evaluations involved finding row and column minimums and comparing lower bounds against the latest upper bound for each category. The example was carefully designed so that the branch-and-bound procedure would work quite effectively (i.e., the initial assignments chosen to branch on, $(A, 1)$ and $(B, 2)$, were optimal assignments *and* ones to which the solution was quite sensitive, so that the alternative categories containing $(\overline{A, 1})$ and $(\overline{B, 2})$ could be quickly eliminated). This is not always the case, and one could conceive of a pathological case in which the branch-and-bound analysis would require consideration of all 24 possible solutions. However, in the usual case the branch-and-bound analysis will only need to consider a fraction of the total number of possible solutions, and this is where its computational power and importance arises.

When to stop

A general stopping rule for the branch-and-bound technique is as follows: Whenever a feasible solution is obtained whose actual cost is equal to or less than the lower bound for all categories not yet eliminated, that feasible solution is an optimal one (there may be more than one optimal solution). Thus in Figure 24–3, as soon as the first branch was made and the lower bound of 95 was achieved through column minimums, we had a feasible solution of 95, while the lower bounds of the (two) categories were 95 and 98 (eliminated by the upper bound of 95). Right then we could have stopped and produced the (feasible) solution obtained through column minimums as an optimal solution. In fact, carrying out the branching and bounding as we did, we actually explored whether or not there were any alternative optimal solutions (there were not).

STEPS OF BRANCH-AND-BOUND METHOD

The branch-and-bound method to minimize[4] may be summarized as follows:

1. Make a branch.
2. Compute a lower bound for each category produced.

---

[4] The method may be used to maximize by changing the direction of all the inequalities; i.e., lower to upper, greater than to less than, etc.

3. Compare each lower bound with the best solution obtained so far;

    a) If the lower bound is larger than the best solution so far, eliminate the category from further consideration.

    b) If (*a*) is not true, then ask whether the lower bound represents a *feasible* solution. If it does, then replace the best solution so far with this new (lower) solution value.

4. If at any time the best feasible solution so far is less than or equal to the lower bound of each category not yet eliminated, you have an optimal solution and may stop.

5. Otherwise, consider the category with the smallest lower bound, and go to step 1 above.

In general, a "branch" may produce more than two new categories. For example, in our assignment problem we could have made an initial set of branches by, in turn, assigning plant *A* to each of the separate warehouses 1, 2, 3, and 4 (see Figure 24–4).

FIGURE 24–4
Alternative first branch for example

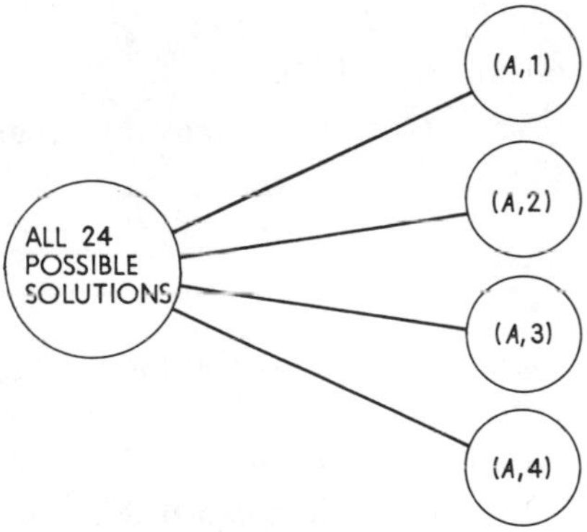

One must use the information about the actual problem at hand before deciding how to branch and bound; the specific problem to be solved will dictate how the branching and bounding will be accomplished.

OTHER APPLICATIONS OF BRANCH-AND-BOUND METHOD

The technique described here is quite general; it is easily programmed on a computer, and in principle it can be applied to any problem of a combinatorial nature, such as plant location problems, the so-called traveling salesman problem (where a group of cities must be visited just once, in the sequence which minimizes distance traveled), or determining minimum-cost production changeover sequences. The branch-and-bound technique is not a panacea for these problems; large combinatorial problems could still require excessively large amounts of computer time. However, it enlarges the size of combinatorial problems which can be solved, and if it is applied to a really large problem it will at least be able to provide the best solution up to a given point of analysis. This is an important characteristic; one may terminate the branch-and-bound procedure at any point and obtain a feasible solution which is the best one found up to that point.

BIBLIOGRAPHY

HILLIER, F. S., and LIEBERMAN, G. J. *Introduction to Operations Research.* San Francisco: Holden-Day, Inc., 1967.

LAWLER, E. L., and WOODS, D. E. "Branch-and-Bound Methods: A Survey." *Operations Research,* vol. 14, no. 4 (1966), pp. 699–719.

LITTLE, J. D. C.; MURTY, K. G.; SWEENEY, D. W.; and KAREL, C. "An Algorithm for the Traveling Salesman Problem." *Operations Research,* vol. 11, (1963), pp. 972–89.

PLANE, D. R., and McMILLAN, C., JR. *Discrete Optimization.* Englewood Cliffs, N.J.: Prentice-Hall, Inc., 1971.

WAGNER, H. M. *Principles of Operations Research.* Englewood Cliffs, N.J.: Prentice-Hall, Inc., 1969.

PROBLEMS

24–1. In Table 24–1, alter the shipping cost for the $(A, 1)$ assignment from 10 to 15 and use the branch-and-bound method shown in the chapter to obtain the new optimal solution.

24–2. The traveling salesman problem can be described as an assignment problem in which no item can be assigned to itself and subtours are not allowed. For example, suppose the distance between pairs of cities were as follows:

From \ To	A	B	C	D
A	0	13	41	20
B	24	0	50	60
C	39	32	0	29
D	22	27	39	0

The traveling salesman problem requires a specified route which visits each of the cities once and only once, at minimum total distance traveled.

Use the branch-and-bound method to obtain the optimum solution to this traveling salesman problem.

24–3. List four problems arising in business which can be characterized (as a first approximation) as assignment problems.

24–4. List a business problem which can be characterized (as a first approximation) as a traveling salesman problem.

Appendix of tables

TABLE A
The standardized normal distribution function,* $F(Z)$

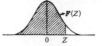

Z	0.00	0.01	0.02	0.03	0.04	0.05	0.06	0.07	0.08	0.09
0.0	0.5000	0.5040	0.5080	0.5120	0.5160	0.5199	0.5239	0.5279	0.5319	0.5359
0.1	0.5398	0.5438	0.5478	0.5517	0.5557	0.5596	0.5636	0.5675	0.5714	0.5753
0.2	0.5793	0.5832	0.5871	0.5910	0.5948	0.5987	0.6026	0.6064	0.6103	0.6141
0.3	0.6179	0.6217	0.6255	0.6293	0.6331	0.6368	0.6406	0.6443	0.6480	0.6517
0.4	0.6554	0.6591	0.6628	0.6664	0.6700	0.6736	0.6772	0.6808	0.6844	0.6879
0.5	0.6915	0.6950	0.6985	0.7019	0.7054	0.7088	0.7123	0.7157	0.7190	0.7224
0.6	0.7257	0.7291	0.7324	0.7357	0.7389	0.7422	0.7454	0.7486	0.7517	0.7549
0.7	0.7580	0.7611	0.7642	0.7673	0.7703	0.7734	0.7764	0.7794	0.7823	0.7852
0.8	0.7881	0.7910	0.7939	0.7967	0.7995	0.8023	0.8051	0.8078	0.8106	0.8133
0.9	0.8159	0.8186	0.8212	0.8238	0.8264	0.8289	0.8315	0.8340	0.8365	0.8389
1.0	0.8413	0.8438	0.8461	0.8485	0.8508	0.8531	0.8554	0.8577	0.8599	0.8621
1.1	0.8643	0.8665	0.8686	0.8708	0.8729	0.8749	0.8770	0.8790	0.8810	0.8830
1.2	0.8849	0.8869	0.8888	0.8907	0.8925	0.8944	0.8962	0.8980	0.8997	0.90147
1.3	0.90320	0.90490	0.90658	0.90824	0.90988	0.91149	0.91309	0.91466	0.91621	0.91774
1.4	0.91924	0.92073	0.92220	0.92364	0.92507	0.92647	0.92785	0.92922	0.93056	0.93189
1.5	0.93319	0.93448	0.93574	0.93699	0.93822	0.93943	0.94062	0.94179	0.94295	0.94408
1.6	0.94520	0.94630	0.94738	0.94845	0.94950	0.95053	0.95154	0.95254	0.95352	0.95449
1.7	0.95543	0.95637	0.95728	0.95818	0.95907	0.95994	0.96080	0.96164	0.96246	0.96327
1.8	0.96407	0.96485	0.96562	0.96638	0.96712	0.96784	0.96856	0.96926	0.96995	0.97062
1.9	0.97128	0.97193	0.97257	0.97320	0.97381	0.97441	0.97500	0.97558	0.97615	0.97670
2.0	0.97725	0.97778	0.97831	0.97882	0.97932	0.97982	0.98030	0.98077	0.98124	0.98169
2.1	0.98214	0.98257	0.98300	0.98341	0.98382	0.98422	0.98461	0.98500	0.98537	0.98574
2.2	0.98610	0.98645	0.98679	0.98713	0.98745	0.98778	0.98809	0.98840	0.98870	0.98899
2.3	0.98928	0.98956	0.98983	$0.9^2 0097$	$0.9^2 0358$	$0.9^2 0613$	$0.9^2 0863$	$0.9^2 1106$	$0.9^2 1344$	$0.9^2 1576$
2.4	$0.9^2 1802$	$0.9^2 2024$	$0.9^2 2240$	$0.9^2 2451$	$0.9^2 2656$	$0.9^2 2857$	$0.9^2 3053$	$0.9^2 3244$	$0.9^2 3431$	$0.9^2 3613$
2.5	$0.9^2 3790$	$0.9^2 3963$	$0.9^2 4132$	$0.9^2 4297$	$0.9^2 4457$	$0.9^2 4614$	$0.9^2 4766$	$0.9^2 4915$	$0.9^2 5060$	$0.9^2 5201$
3.0	$0.9^2 8650$	$0.9^2 8694$	$0.9^2 8736$	$0.9^2 8777$	$0.9^2 8817$	$0.9^2 8856$	$0.9^2 8893$	$0.9^2 8930$	$0.9^2 8965$	$0.9^2 8999$
3.5	$0.9^3 7674$	$0.9^3 7759$	$0.9^3 7842$	$0.9^3 7922$	$0.9^3 7999$	$0.9^3 8074$	$0.9^3 8146$	$0.9^3 8215$	$0.9^3 8282$	$0.9^3 8347$
4.0	$0.9^4 6833$	$0.9^4 6964$	$0.9^4 7090$	$0.9^4 7211$	$0.9^4 7327$	$0.9^4 7439$	$0.9^4 7546$	$0.9^4 7649$	$0.9^4 7748$	$0.9^4 7843$

For example: $F(2.41) = .9^2 2024 = .992024$.

* From A. Hald, *Statistical Tables and Formulas* (New York: John Wiley & Sons, Inc., 1952); reproduced by permission of Professor A. Hald and the publishers.

TABLE B
$N(D)$—loss function*

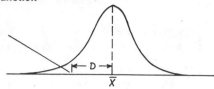

D	.00	.01	.02	.03	.04	.05	.06	.07	.08	.09
.0	.3989	.3940	.3890	.3841	.3793	.3744	.3697	.3649	.3602	.3556
.1	.3509	.3464	.3418	.3373	.3328	.3284	.3240	.3197	.3154	.3111
.2	.3069	.3027	.2986	.2944	.2904	.2863	.2824	.2784	.2745	.2706
.3	.2668	.2630	.2592	.2555	.2518	.2481	.2445	.2409	.2374	.2339
.4	.2304	.2270	.2236	.2203	.2169	.2137	.2104	.2072	.2040	.2009
.5	.1978	.1947	.1917	.1887	.1857	.1828	.1799	.1771	.1742	.1714
.6	.1687	.1659	.1633	.1606	.1580	.1554	.1528	.1503	.1478	.1453
.7	.1429	.1405	.1381	.1358	.1334	.1312	.1289	.1267	.1245	.1223
.8	.1202	.1181	.1160	.1140	.1120	.1100	.1080	.1061	.1042	.1023
.9	.1004	.09860	.09680	.09503	.09328	.09156	.08986	.08819	.08654	.08491
1.0	.08332	.08174	.08019	.07866	.07716	.07568	.07422	.07279	.07138	.06999
1.1	.06862	.06727	.06595	.06465	.06336	.06210	.06086	.05964	.05844	.05726
1.2	.05610	.05496	.05384	.05274	.05165	.05059	.04954	.04851	.04750	.04650
1.3	.04553	.04457	.04363	.04270	.04179	.04090	.04002	.03916	.03831	.03748
1.4	.03667	.03587	.03508	.03431	.03356	.03281	.03208	.03137	.03067	.02998
1.5	.02931	.02865	.02800	.02736	.02674	.02612	.02552	.02494	.02436	.02380
1.6	.02324	.02270	.02217	.02165	.02114	.02064	.02015	.01967	.01920	.01874
1.7	.01829	.01785	.01742	.01699	.01658	.01617	.01578	.01539	.01501	.01464
1.8	.01428	.01392	.01357	.01323	.01290	.01257	.01226	.01195	.01164	.01134
1.9	.01105	.01077	.01049	.01022	$.0^2 9957$	$.0^2 9698$	$.0^2 9445$	$.0^2 9198$	$.0^2 8957$	$.0^2 8721$
2.0	$.0^2 8491$	$.0^2 8266$	$.0^2 8046$	$.0^2 7832$	$.0^2 7623$	$.0^2 7418$	$.0^2 7219$	$.0^2 7024$	$.0^2 6835$	$.0^2 6649$
2.1	$.0^2 6468$	$.0^2 6292$	$.0^2 6120$	$.0^2 5952$	$.0^2 5788$	$.0^2 5628$	$.0^2 5472$	$.0^2 5320$	$.0^2 5172$	$.0^2 5028$
2.2	$.0^2 4887$	$.0^2 4750$	$.0^2 4616$	$.0^2 4486$	$.0^2 4358$	$.0^2 4235$	$.0^2 4114$	$.0^2 3996$	$.0^2 3882$	$.0^2 3770$
2.3	$.0^2 3662$	$.0^2 3556$	$.0^2 3453$	$.0^2 3352$	$.0^2 3255$	$.0^2 3159$	$.0^2 3067$	$.0^2 2977$	$.0^2 2889$	$.0^2 2804$
2.4	$.0^2 2720$	$.0^2 2640$	$.0^2 2561$	$.0^2 2484$	$.0^2 2410$	$.0^2 2337$	$.0^2 2267$	$.0^2 2199$	$.0^2 2132$	$.0^2 2067$
2.5	$.0^2 2005$	$.0^2 1943$	$.0^2 1883$	$.0^2 1826$	$.0^2 1769$	$.0^2 1715$	$.0^2 1662$	$.0^2 1610$	$.0^2 1560$	$.0^2 1511$
3.0	$.0^3 3822$	$.0^3 3689$	$.0^3 3560$	$.0^3 3436$	$.0^3 3316$	$.0^3 3199$	$.0^3 3087$	$.0^3 2978$	$.0^3 2873$	$.0^3 2771$
3.5	$.0^4 5848$	$.0^4 5620$	$.0^4 5400$	$.0^4 5188$	$.0^4 4984$	$.0^4 4788$	$.0^4 4599$	$.0^4 4417$	$.0^4 4242$	$.0^4 4073$
4.0	$.0^5 7145$	$.0^5 6835$	$.0^5 6538$	$.0^5 6253$	$.0^5 5980$	$.0^5 5718$	$.0^5 5468$	$.0^5 5227$	$.0^5 4997$	$.0^5 4777$

$N(D)$ is defined as follows:

$$N(D) = \int_{-\infty}^{-D} (-D - X)f^*(X)dX = \int_{D}^{\infty} (X - D)f^*(X)dX$$

where $f^*(X)$ is the standardized normal density function and D is positive.

* By permission from R. Schlaifer, *Probability and Statistics for Business Decisions* (New York: McGraw-Hill Book Co., 1959).

TABLE C
Cumulative binomial distribution* $P(R \geq r|n, p)$
n = 1

p r	01	02	03	04	05	06	07	08	09	10
1	0100	0200	0300	0400	0500	0600	0700	0800	0900	1000

p r	11	12	13	14	15	16	17	18	19	20
1	1100	1200	1300	1400	1500	1600	1700	1800	1900	2000

p r	21	22	23	24	25	26	27	28	29	30
1	2100	2200	2300	2400	2500	2600	2700	2800	2900	3000

p r	31	32	33	34	35	36	37	38	39	40
1	3100	3200	3300	3400	3500	3600	3700	3800	3900	4000

p r	41	42	43	44	45	46	47	48	49	50
1	4100	4200	4300	4400	4500	4600	4700	4800	4900	5000

n = 2

p r	01	02	03	04	05	06	07	08	09	10
1	0199	0396	0591	0784	0975	1164	1351	1536	1719	1900
2	0001	0004	0009	0016	0025	0036	0049	0064	0081	0100

p r	11	12	13	14	15	16	17	18	19	20
1	2079	2256	2431	2604	2775	2944	3111	3276	3439	3600
2	0121	0144	0169	0196	0225	0256	0289	0324	0361	0400

p r	21	22	23	24	25	26	27	28	29	30
1	3759	3916	4071	4224	4375	4524	4671	4816	4959	5100
2	0441	0484	0529	0576	0625	0676	0729	0784	0841	0900

p r	31	32	33	34	35	36	37	38	39	40
1	5239	5376	5511	5644	5775	5904	6031	6156	6279	6400
2	0961	1024	1089	1156	1225	1296	1369	1444	1521	1600

p r	41	42	43	44	45	46	47	48	49	50
1	6519	6636	6751	6864	6975	7084	7191	7296	7399	7500
2	1681	1764	1849	1936	2025	2116	2209	2304	2401	2500

n = 3

p r	01	02	03	04	05	06	07	08	09	10
1	0297	0588	0873	1153	1426	1694	1956	2213	2464	2710
2	0003	0012	0026	0047	0073	0104	0140	0182	0228	0280
3				0001	0001	0002	0003	0005	0007	0010

p r	11	12	13	14	15	16	17	18	19	20
1	2950	3185	3415	3639	3859	4073	4282	4486	4686	4880
2	0336	0397	0463	0533	0608	0686	0769	0855	0946	1040
3	0013	0017	0022	0027	0034	0041	0049	0058	0069	0080

p r	21	22	23	24	25	26	27	28	29	30
1	5070	5254	5435	5610	5781	5948	6110	6268	6421	6570
2	1138	1239	1344	1452	1563	1676	1793	1913	2035	2160
3	0093	0106	0122	0138	0156	0176	0197	0220	0244	0270

* By permission from R. Schlaifer, *Probability and Statistics for Business Decisions* (New York: McGraw-Hill Book Co., 1959).

TABLE C—Continued

P	31	32	33	34	35	36	37	38	39	40
r										
1	6715	6856	6992	7125	7254	7379	7500	7617	7730	7840
2	2287	2417	2548	2682	2818	2955	3094	3235	3377	3520
3	0298	0328	0359	0393	0429	0467	0507	0549	0593	0640

P	41	42	43	44	45	46	47	48	49	50
r										
1	7946	8049	8148	8244	8336	8425	8511	8594	8673	8750
2	3665	3810	3957	4104	4253	4401	4551	4700	4850	5000
3	0689	0741	0795	0852	0911	0973	1038	1106	1176	1250

$n = 4$

P	01	02	03	04	05	06	07	08	09	10
r										
1	0394	0776	1147	1507	1855	2193	2519	2836	3143	3439
2	0006	0023	0052	0091	0140	0199	0267	0344	0430	0523
3			0001	0002	0005	0008	0013	0019	0027	0037
4									0001	0001

P	11	12	13	14	15	16	17	18	19	20
r										
1	3726	4003	4271	4530	4780	5021	5254	5479	5695	5904
2	0624	0732	0847	0968	1095	1228	1366	1509	1656	1808
3	0049	0063	0079	0098	0120	0144	0171	0202	0235	0272
4	0001	0002	0003	0004	0005	0007	0008	0010	0013	0016

P	21	22	23	24	25	26	27	28	29	30
r										
1	6105	6298	6485	6664	6836	7001	7160	7313	7459	7599
2	1963	2122	2285	2450	2617	2787	2959	3132	3307	3483
3	0312	0356	0403	0453	0508	0566	0628	0694	0763	0837
4	0019	0023	0028	0033	0039	0046	0053	0061	0071	0081

P	31	32	33	34	35	36	37	38	39	40
r										
1	7733	7862	7985	8103	8215	8322	8425	8522	8615	8704
2	3660	3837	4015	4193	4370	4547	4724	4900	5075	5248
3	0915	0996	1082	1171	1265	1362	1464	1569	1679	1792
4	0092	0105	0119	0134	0150	0168	0187	0209	0231	0256

P	41	42	43	44	45	46	47	48	49	50
r										
1	8788	8868	8944	9017	9085	9150	9211	9269	9323	9375
2	5420	5590	5759	5926	6090	6252	6412	6569	6724	6875
3	1909	2030	2155	2283	2415	2550	2689	2831	2977	3125
4	0283	0311	0342	0375	0410	0448	0488	0531	0576	0625

$n = 5$

P	01	02	03	04	05	06	07	08	09	10
1	0490	0961	1413	1846	2262	2661	3043	3409	3760	4095
2	0010	0038	0085	0148	0226	0319	0425	0544	0674	0815
3		0001	0003	0006	0012	0020	0031	0045	0063	0086
4						0001	0001	0002	0003	0005

P	11	12	13	14	15	16	17	18	19	20
r										
1	4416	4723	5016	5296	5563	5818	6061	6293	6513	6723
2	0965	1125	1292	1467	1648	1835	2027	2224	2424	2627
3	0112	0143	0179	0220	0266	0318	0375	0437	0505	0579
4	0007	0009	0013	0017	0022	0029	0036	0045	0055	0067
5				0001	0001	0001	0001	0002	0002	0003

P	21	22	23	24	25	26	27	28	29	30
r										
1	6923	7113	7293	7464	7627	7781	7927	8065	8196	8319
2	2833	3041	3251	3461	3672	3883	4093	4303	4511	4718
3	0659	0744	0836	0933	1035	1143	1257	1376	1501	1631
4	0081	0097	0114	0134	0156	0181	0208	0238	0272	0308
5	0004	0005	0006	0008	0010	0012	0014	0017	0021	0024

TABLE C—Continued

P	31	32	33	34	35	36	37	38	39	40
r										
1	8436	8546	8650	8748	8840	8926	9008	9084	9155	9222
2	4923	5125	5325	5522	5716	5906	6093	6276	6455	6630
3	1766	1905	2050	2199	2352	2509	2670	2835	3003	3174
4	0347	0390	0436	0486	0540	0598	0660	0726	0796	0870
5	0029	0034	0039	0045	0053	0060	0069	0079	0090	0102

P	41	42	43	44	45	46	47	48	49	50
r										
1	9285	9344	9398	9449	9497	9541	9582	9620	9655	9688
2	6801	6967	7129	7286	7438	7585	7728	7865	7998	8125
3	3349	3525	3705	3886	4069	4253	4439	4625	4813	5000
4	0949	1033	1121	1214	1312	1415	1522	1635	1753	1875
5	0116	0131	0147	0165	0185	0206	0229	0255	0282	0313

$n = 6$

P	01	02	03	04	05	06	07	08	09	10
r										
1	0585	1142	1670	2172	2649	3101	3530	3936	4321	4686
2	0015	0057	0125	0216	0328	0459	0608	0773	0952	1143
3		0002	0005	0012	0022	0038	0058	0085	0118	0159
4				0001	0002	0003	0005	0008	0013
5										0001

P	11	12	13	14	15	16	17	18	19	20
r										
1	5030	5356	5664	5954	6229	6487	6731	6960	7176	7379
2	1345	1556	1776	2003	2235	2472	2713	2956	3201	3446
3	0206	0261	0324	0395	0473	0560	0655	0759	0870	0989
4	0018	0025	0034	0045	0059	0075	0094	0116	0141	0170
5	0001	0001	0002	0003	0004	0005	0007	0010	0013	0016
6										0001

P	21	22	23	24	25	26	27	28	29	30
r										
1	7569	7748	7916	8073	8220	8358	8487	8607	8719	8824
2	3692	3937	4180	4422	4661	4896	5128	5356	5580	5798
3	1115	1250	1391	1539	1694	1856	2023	2196	2374	2557
4	0202	0239	0280	0326	0376	0431	0492	0557	0628	0705
5	0020	0025	0031	0038	0046	0056	0067	0079	0093	0109
6	0001	0001	0001	0002	0002	0003	0004	0005	0006	0007

P	31	32	33	34	35	36	37	38	39	40
r										
1	8921	9011	9095	9173	9246	9313	9375	9432	9485	9533
2	6012	6220	6422	6619	6809	6994	7172	7343	7508	7667
3	2744	2936	3130	3328	3529	3732	3937	4143	4350	4557
4	0787	0875	0969	1069	1174	1286	1404	1527	1657	1792
5	0127	0148	0170	0195	0223	0254	0288	0325	0365	0410
6	0009	0011	0013	0015	0018	0022	0026	0030	0035	0041

P	41	42	43	44	45	46	47	48	49	50
r										
1	9578	9619	9657	9692	9723	9752	9778	9802	9824	9844
2	7819	7965	8105	8238	8364	8485	8599	8707	8810	8906
3	4764	4971	5177	5382	5585	5786	5985	6180	6373	6563
4	1933	2080	2232	2390	2553	2721	2893	3070	3252	3438
5	0458	0510	0566	0627	0692	0762	0837	0917	1003	1094
6	0048	0055	0063	0073	0083	0095	0108	0122	0138	0156

$n = 7$

P	01	02	03	04	05	06	07	08	09	10
r										
1	0679	1319	1920	2486	3017	3515	3983	4422	4832	5217
2	0020	0079	0171	0294	0444	0618	0813	1026	1255	1497
3		0003	0009	0020	0038	0063	0097	0140	0193	0257
4				0001	0002	0004	0007	0012	0018	0027
5								0001	0001	0002

TABLE C—Continued

P	11	12	13	14	15	16	17	18	19	20
f										
1	5577	5913	6227	6521	6794	7049	7286	7507	7712	7903
2	1750	2012	2281	2556	2834	3115	3396	3677	3956	4233
3	0331	0416	0513	0620	0738	0866	1005	1154	1313	1480
4	0039	0054	0072	0094	0121	0153	0189	0231	0279	0333
5	0003	0004	0006	0009	0012	0017	0022	0029	0037	0047
6					0001	0001	0001	0002	0003	0004

P	21	22	23	24	25	26	27	28	29	30
f										
1	8080	8243	8395	8535	8665	8785	8895	8997	9090	9176
2	4506	4775	5040	5298	5551	5796	6035	6266	6490	6706
3	1657	1841	2033	2231	2436	2646	2861	3081	3304	3529
4	0394	0461	0536	0617	0706	0802	0905	1016	1134	1260
5	0058	0072	0088	0107	0129	0153	0181	0213	0248	0288
6	0005	0006	0008	0011	0013	0017	0021	0026	0031	0038
7					0001	0001	0001	0001	0002	0002

P	31	32	33	34	35	36	37	38	39	40
f										
1	9255	9328	9394	9454	9510	9560	9606	9648	9686	9720
2	6914	7113	7304	7487	7662	7828	7987	8137	8279	8414
3	3757	3987	4217	4447	4677	4906	5134	5359	5581	5801
4	1394	1534	1682	1837	1998	2167	2341	2521	2707	2898
5	0332	0380	0434	0492	0556	0625	0701	0782	0869	0963
6	0046	0055	0065	0077	0090	0105	0123	0142	0164	0188
7	0003	0003	0004	0005	0006	0008	0009	0011	0014	0016

P	41	42	43	44	45	46	47	48	49	50
f										
1	9751	9779	9805	9827	9848	9866	9883	9897	9910	9922
2	8541	8660	8772	8877	8976	9068	9153	9233	9307	9375
3	6017	6229	6436	6638	6836	7027	7213	7393	7567	7734
4	3094	3294	3498	3706	3917	4131	4346	4563	4781	5000
5	1063	1169	1282	1402	1529	1663	1803	1951	2105	2266
6	0216	0246	0279	0316	0357	0402	0451	0504	0562	0625
7	0019	0023	0027	0032	0037	0044	0051	0059	0068	0078

$n = 8$

P	01	02	03	04	05	06	07	08	09	10
f										
1	0773	1492	2163	2786	3366	3904	4404	4868	5297	5695
2	0027	0103	0223	0381	0572	0792	1035	1298	1577	1869
3	0001	0004	0013	0031	0058	0096	0147	0211	0289	0381
4			0001	0002	0004	0007	0013	0022	0034	0050
5							0001	0001	0003	0004

P	11	12	13	14	15	16	17	18	19	20
f										
1	6063	6404	6718	7008	7275	7521	7748	7956	8147	8322
2	2171	2480	2794	3111	3428	3744	4057	4366	4670	4967
3	0487	0608	0743	0891	1052	1226	1412	1608	1815	2031
4	0071	0097	0129	0168	0214	0267	0328	0397	0476	0563
5	0007	0010	0015	0021	0029	0038	0050	0065	0083	0104
6		0001	0001	0002	0002	0003	0005	0007	0009	0012
7									0001	0001

P	21	22	23	24	25	26	27	28	29	30
f										
1	8483	8630	8764	8887	8999	9101	9194	9278	9354	9424
2	5257	5538	5811	6075	6329	6573	6807	7031	7244	7447
3	2255	2486	2724	2967	3215	3465	3718	3973	4228	4482
4	0659	0765	0880	1004	1138	1281	1433	1594	1763	1941
5	0129	0158	0191	0230	0273	0322	0377	0438	0505	0580
6	0016	0021	0027	0034	0042	0052	0064	0078	0094	0113
7	0001	0002	0002	0003	0004	0005	0006	0008	0010	0013
8									0001	0001

TABLE C—Continued

P	31	32	33	34	35	36	37	38	39	40
r										
1	9486	9543	9594	9640	9681	9719	9752	9782	9808	9832
2	7640	7822	7994	8156	8309	8452	8586	8711	8828	8936
3	4736	4987	5236	5481	5722	5958	6189	6415	6634	6846
4	2126	2319	2519	2724	2936	3153	3374	3599	3828	4059
5	0661	0750	0846	0949	1061	1180	1307	1443	1586	1737
6	0134	0159	0187	0218	0253	0293	0336	0385	0439	0498
7	0016	0020	0024	0030	0036	0043	0051	0061	0072	0085
8	0001	0001	0001	0002	0002	0003	0004	0004	0005	0007

P	41	42	43	44	45	46	47	48	49	50
r										
1	9853	9872	9889	9903	9916	9928	9938	9947	9954	9961
2	9037	9130	9216	9295	9368	9435	9496	9552	9602	9648
3	7052	7250	7440	7624	7799	7966	8125	8276	8419	8555
4	4292	4527	4762	4996	5230	5463	5694	5922	6146	6367
5	1895	2062	2235	2416	2604	2798	2999	3205	3416	3633
6	0563	0634	0711	0794	0885	0982	1086	1198	1318	1445
7	0100	0117	0136	0157	0181	0208	0239	0272	0310	0352
8	0008	0010	0012	0014	0017	0020	0024	0028	0033	0039

n = 9

P	01	02	03	04	05	06	07	08	09	10
r										
1	0865	1663	2398	3075	3698	4270	4796	5278	5721	6126
2	0034	0131	0282	0478	0712	0978	1271	1583	1912	2252
3	0001	0006	0020	0045	0084	0138	0209	0298	0405	0530
4			0001	0003	0006	0013	0023	0037	0057	0083
5						0001	0002	0003	0005	0009
6										0001

P	11	12	13	14	15	16	17	18	19	20
r										
1	6496	6835	7145	7427	7684	7918	8131	8324	8499	8658
2	2599	2951	3304	3657	4005	4348	4685	5012	5330	5638
3	0672	0833	1009	1202	1409	1629	1861	2105	2357	2618
4	0117	0158	0209	0269	0339	0420	0512	0615	0730	0856
5	0014	0021	0030	0041	0056	0075	0098	0125	0158	0196
6	0001	0002	0003	0004	0006	0009	0013	0017	0023	0031
7						0001	0001	0002	0002	0003

P	21	22	23	24	25	26	27	28	29	30
r										
1	8801	8931	9048	9154	9249	9335	9411	9480	9542	9596
2	5934	6218	6491	6750	6997	7230	7452	7660	7856	8040
3	2885	3158	3434	3713	3993	4273	4552	4829	5102	5372
4	0994	1144	1304	1475	1657	1849	2050	2260	2478	2703
5	0240	0291	0350	0416	0489	0571	0662	0762	0870	0988
6	0040	0051	0065	0081	0100	0122	0149	0179	0213	0253
7	0004	0006	0008	0010	0013	0017	0022	0028	0035	0043
8			0001	0001	0001	0001	0002	0003	0003	0004

P	31	32	33	34	35	36	37	38	39	40
r										
1	9645	9689	9728	9762	9793	9820	9844	9865	9883	9899
2	8212	8372	8522	8661	8789	8908	9017	9118	9210	9295
3	5636	5894	6146	6390	6627	6856	7076	7287	7489	7682
4	2935	3173	3415	3662	3911	4163	4416	4669	4922	5174
5	1115	1252	1398	1553	1717	1890	2072	2262	2460	2666
6	0298	0348	0404	0467	0536	0612	0696	0787	0886	0994
7	0053	0064	0078	0094	0112	0133	0157	0184	0215	0250
8	0006	0007	0009	0011	0014	0017	0021	0026	0031	0036
9				0001	0001	0001	0001	0002	0002	0003

P	41	42	43	44	45	46	47	48	49	50
r										
1	9913	9926	9936	9946	9954	9961	9967	9972	9977	9980
2	9372	9442	9505	9563	9615	9662	9704	9741	9775	9805
3	7866	8039	8204	8359	8505	8642	8769	8889	8999	9102
4	5424	5670	5913	6152	6386	6614	6836	7052	7260	7461
5	2878	3097	3322	3551	3786	4024	4265	4509	4754	5000
6	1109	1233	1366	1508	1658	1817	1985	2161	2346	2539
7	0290	0334	0383	0437	0498	0564	0637	0717	0804	0898
8	0046	0055	0065	0077	0091	0107	0125	0145	0169	0195
9	0003	0004	0005	0006	0008	0009	0011	0014	0016	0020

TABLE C—Continued
$n = 10$

P / r	01	02	03	04	05	06	07	08	09	10
1	0956	1829	2626	3352	4013	4614	5160	5656	6106	6513
2	0043	0162	0345	0582	0861	1176	1517	1879	2254	2639
3	0001	0009	0028	0062	0115	0188	0283	0401	0540	0702
4			0001	0004	0010	0020	0036	0058	0088	0128
5					0001	0002	0003	0006	0010	0016
6									0001	0001

P / r	11	12	13	14	15	16	17	18	19	20
1	6882	7215	7516	7787	8031	8251	8448	8626	8784	8926
2	3028	3417	3804	4184	4557	4920	5270	5608	5932	6242
3	0884	1087	1308	1545	1798	2064	2341	2628	2922	3222
4	0178	0239	0313	0400	0500	0614	0741	0883	1039	1209
5	0025	0037	0053	0073	0099	0130	0168	0213	0266	0328
6	0003	0004	0006	0010	0014	0020	0027	0037	0049	0064
7			0001	0001	0001	0002	0003	0004	0006	0009
8									0001	0001

P / r	21	22	23	24	25	26	27	28	29	30
1	9053	9166	9267	9357	9437	9508	9570	9626	9674	9718
2	6536	6815	7079	7327	7560	7778	7981	8170	8345	8507
3	3526	3831	4137	4442	4744	5042	5335	5622	5901	6172
4	1391	1587	1794	2012	2241	2479	2726	2979	3239	3504
5	0399	0479	0569	0670	0781	0904	1037	1181	1337	1503
6	0082	0104	0130	0161	0197	0239	0287	0342	0404	0473
7	0012	0016	0021	0027	0035	0045	0056	0070	0087	0106
8	0001	0002	0002	0003	0004	0006	0007	0010	0012	0016
9							0001	0001	0001	0001

P / r	31	32	33	34	35	36	37	38	39	40
1	9755	9789	9818	9843	9865	9885	9902	9916	9929	9940
2	8656	8794	8920	9035	9140	9236	9323	9402	9473	9536
3	6434	6687	6930	7162	7384	7595	7794	7983	8160	8327
4	3772	4044	4316	4589	4862	5132	5400	5664	5923	6177
5	1679	1867	2064	2270	2485	2708	2939	3177	3420	3669
6	0551	0637	0732	0836	0949	1072	1205	1348	1500	1662
7	0129	0155	0185	0220	0260	0305	0356	0413	0477	0548
8	0020	0025	0032	0039	0048	0059	0071	0086	0103	0123
9	0002	0003	0003	0004	0005	0007	0009	0011	0014	0017
10								0001	0001	0001

P / r	41	42	43	44	45	46	47	48	49	50
1	9949	9957	9964	9970	9975	9979	9983	9986	9988	9990
2	9594	9645	9691	9731	9767	9799	9827	9852	9874	9893
3	8483	8628	8764	8889	9004	9111	9209	9298	9379	9453
4	6425	6665	6898	7123	7340	7547	7745	7933	8112	8281
5	3922	4178	4436	4696	4956	5216	5474	5730	5982	6230
6	1834	2016	2207	2407	2616	2832	3057	3288	3526	3770
7	0626	0712	0806	0908	1020	1141	1271	1410	1560	1719
8	0146	0172	0202	0236	0274	0317	0366	0420	0480	0547
9	0021	0025	0031	0037	0045	0054	0065	0077	0091	0107
10	0001	0002	0002	0003	0003	0004	0005	0006	0008	0010

$n = 11$

P / r	01	02	03	04	05	06	07	08	09	10
1	1047	1993	2847	3618	4312	4937	5499	6004	6456	6862
2	0052	0195	0413	0692	1017	1382	1772	2181	2601	3026
3	0002	0012	0037	0083	0152	0248	0370	0519	0695	0896
4			0002	0007	0016	0030	0053	0085	0132	0185
5					0001	0003	0005	0010	0017	0028
6								0001	0002	0003

TABLE C—Continued

P r	11	12	13	14	15	16	17	18	19	20
1	7225	7549	7839	8097	8327	8531	8712	8873	9015	9141
2	3452	3873	4286	4689	5078	5453	5811	6151	6474	6779
3	1120	1366	1632	1915	2212	2521	2839	3164	3494	3826
4	0256	0341	0442	0560	0694	0846	1013	1197	1397	1611
5	0042	0061	0087	0119	0159	0207	0266	0334	0413	0504
6	0005	0008	0012	0018	0027	0037	0051	0068	0090	0117
7		0001	0001	0002	0003	0005	0007	0010	0014	0020
8							0001	0001	0002	0002

P r	21	22	23	24	25	26	27	28	29	30
1	9252	9350	9436	9511	9578	9636	9686	9730	9769	9802
2	7065	7333	7582	7814	8029	8227	8410	8577	8730	8870
3	4158	4488	4814	5134	5448	5753	6049	6335	6610	6873
4	1840	2081	2333	2596	2867	3146	3430	3719	4011	4304
5	0607	0723	0851	0992	1146	1313	1493	1685	1888	2103
6	0148	0186	0231	0283	0343	0412	0490	0577	0674	0782
7	0027	0035	0046	0059	0076	0095	0119	0146	0179	0216
8	0003	0005	0007	0009	0012	0016	0021	0027	0034	0043
9			0001	0001	0001	0002	0002	0003	0004	0006

P r	31	32	33	34	35	36	37	38	39	40
1	9831	9856	9878	9896	9912	9926	9938	9948	9956	9964
2	8997	9112	9216	9310	9394	9470	9537	9597	9650	9698
3	7183	7361	7587	7799	7999	8186	8360	8522	8672	8811
4	4598	4890	5179	5464	5744	6019	6286	6545	6796	7037
5	2328	2563	2807	3059	3317	3581	3850	4122	4397	4672
6	0901	1031	1171	1324	1487	1661	1847	2043	2249	2465
7	0260	0309	0366	0430	0501	0581	0670	0768	0876	0994
8	0054	0067	0082	0101	0122	0148	0177	0210	0249	0293
9	0008	0010	0013	0016	0020	0026	0032	0039	0048	0059
10	0001	0001	0001	0002	0002	0003	0004	0005	0006	0007

P r	41	42	43	44	45	46	47	48	49	50
1	9970	9975	9979	9983	9986	9989	9991	9992	9994	9995
2	9739	9776	9808	9836	9861	9882	9900	9916	9930	9941
3	8938	9055	9162	9260	9348	9428	9499	9564	9622	9673
4	7269	7490	7700	7900	8089	8266	8433	8588	8733	8867
5	4948	5223	5495	5764	6029	6288	6541	6787	7026	7256
6	2690	2924	3166	3414	3669	3929	4193	4460	4739	5000
7	1121	1260	1408	1568	1738	1919	2110	2312	2523	2744
8	0343	0399	0461	0532	0610	0696	0791	0895	1009	1133
9	0072	0087	0104	0125	0148	0175	0206	0241	0282	0327
10	0009	0012	0014	0018	0022	0027	0033	0040	0049	0059
11	0001	0001	0001	0001	0002	0002	0002	0003	0004	0005

$$n = 12$$

P r	01	02	03	04	05	06	07	08	09	10
1	1136	2153	3062	3873	4596	5241	5814	6323	6775	7176
2	0062	0231	0486	0809	1184	1595	2033	2487	2948	3410
3	0002	0015	0048	0107	0196	0316	0468	0652	0866	1109
4		0001	0003	0010	0022	0043	0075	0120	0180	0256
5				0001	0002	0004	0009	0016	0027	0043
6							0001	0002	0003	0005
7										0001

P r	11	12	13	14	15	16	17	18	19	20
1	7530	7843	8120	8363	8578	8766	8931	9076	9202	9313
2	3867	4314	4748	5166	5565	5945	6304	6641	6957	7251
3	1377	1667	1977	2303	2642	2990	3344	3702	4060	4417
4	0351	0464	0597	0750	0922	1114	1324	1552	1795	2054
5	0065	0095	0133	0181	0239	0310	0393	0489	0600	0726
6	0009	0014	0022	0033	0046	0065	0088	0116	0151	0194
7	0001	0002	0003	0004	0007	0010	0015	0021	0029	0039
8					0001	0001	0002	0003	0004	0006
9										0001

TABLE C—Continued

p	21	22	23	24	25	26	27	28	29	30
r										
1	9409	9493	9566	9629	9683	9730	9771	9806	9836	9862
2	7524	7776	8009	8222	8416	8594	8755	8900	9032	9150
3	4768	5114	5450	5778	6093	6397	6687	6963	7225	7472
4	2326	2610	2904	3205	3512	3824	4137	4452	4765	5075
5	0866	1021	1192	1377	1576	1790	2016	2254	2504	2763
6	0245	0304	0374	0453	0544	0646	0760	0887	1026	1178
7	0052	0068	0089	0113	0143	0178	0219	0267	0322	0386
8	0008	0011	0016	0021	0028	0036	0047	0060	0076	0095
9	0001	0001	0002	0003	0004	0005	0007	0010	0013	0017
10						0001	0001	0001	0002	0002

p	31	32	33	34	35	36	37	38	39	40
r										
1	9884	9902	9918	9932	9943	9953	9961	9968	9973	9978
2	9256	9350	9435	9509	9576	9634	9685	9730	9770	9804
3	7704	7922	8124	8313	8487	8648	8795	8931	9054	9166
4	5381	5681	5973	6258	6533	6799	7053	7296	7528	7747
5	3032	3308	3590	3876	4167	4459	4751	5043	5332	5618
6	1343	1521	1711	1913	2127	2352	2588	2833	3087	3348
7	0458	0540	0632	0734	0846	0970	1106	1253	1411	1582
8	0118	0144	0176	0213	0255	0304	0359	0422	0493	0573
9	0022	0028	0036	0045	0056	0070	0086	0104	0127	0153
10	0003	0004	0005	0007	0008	0011	0014	0018	0022	0028
11				0001	0001	0001	0001	0002	0002	0003

p	41	42	43	44	45	46	47	48	49	50
r										
1	9982	9986	9988	9990	9992	9994	9995	9996	9997	9998
2	9834	9860	9882	9901	9917	9931	9943	9953	9961	9968
3	9267	9358	9440	9513	9579	9637	9688	9733	9773	9807
4	7953	8147	8329	8498	8655	8801	8934	9057	9168	9270
5	5899	6175	6443	6704	6956	7198	7430	7652	7862	8062
6	3616	3889	4167	4448	4731	5014	5297	5577	5855	6128
7	1765	1959	2164	2380	2607	2843	3089	3343	3604	3872
8	0662	0760	0869	0988	1117	1258	1411	1575	1751	1938
9	0183	0218	0258	0304	0356	0415	0481	0555	0638	0730
10	0035	0043	0053	0065	0079	0095	0114	0137	0163	0193
11	0004	0005	0007	0009	0011	0014	0017	0021	0026	0032
12				0001	0001	0001	0001	0001	0002	0002

$$n = 13$$

p	01	02	03	04	05	06	07	08	09	10
r										
1	1225	2310	3270	4118	4867	5526	6107	6617	7065	7458
2	0072	0270	0564	0932	1354	1814	2298	2794	3293	3787
3	0003	0020	0062	0135	0245	0392	0578	0799	1054	1339
4		0001	0005	0014	0031	0060	0103	0163	0242	0342
5				0001	0003	0007	0013	0024	0041	0065
6						0001	0001	0003	0005	0009
7									0001	0001

p	11	12	13	14	15	16	17	18	19	20
r										
1	7802	8102	8364	8592	8791	8963	9113	9242	9354	9450
2	4270	4738	5186	5614	6017	6396	6751	7080	7384	7664
3	1651	1985	2337	2704	3080	3463	3848	4231	4611	4983
4	0464	0609	0776	0967	1180	1414	1667	1939	2226	2527
5	0097	0139	0193	0260	0342	0438	0551	0681	0827	0991
6	0015	0024	0036	0053	0075	0104	0139	0183	0237	0300
7	0002	0003	0005	0008	0013	0019	0027	0038	0052	0070
8			0001	0001	0002	0003	0004	0006	0009	0012
9								0001	0001	0002

TABLE C—Continued

P	21	22	23	24	25	26	27	28	29	30
r										
1	9533	9604	9666	9718	9762	9800	9833	9860	9883	9903
2	7920	8154	8367	8559	8733	8889	9029	9154	9265	9363
3	5347	5699	6039	6364	6674	6968	7245	7505	7749	7975
4	2839	3161	3489	3822	4157	4493	4826	5155	5478	5794
5	1173	1371	1585	1816	2060	2319	2589	2870	3160	3457
6	0375	0462	0562	0675	0802	0944	1099	1270	1455	1654
7	0093	0120	0154	0195	0243	0299	0365	0440	0527	0624
8	0017	0024	0032	0043	0056	0073	0093	0118	0147	0182
9	0002	0004	0005	0007	0010	0013	0018	0024	0031	0040
10			0001	0001	0001	0002	0003	0004	0005	0007
11									0001	0001

P	31	32	33	34	35	36	37	38	39	40
r										
1	9920	9934	9945	9955	9963	9970	9975	9980	9984	9987
2	9450	9527	9594	9653	9704	9749	9787	9821	9849	9874
3	8185	8379	8557	8720	8868	9003	9125	9235	9333	9421
4	6101	6398	6683	6957	7217	7464	7698	7917	8123	8314
5	3760	4067	4376	4686	4995	5301	5603	5899	6188	6470
6	1867	2093	2331	2581	2841	3111	3388	3673	3962	4256
7	0733	0854	0988	1135	1295	1468	1654	1853	2065	2288
8	0223	0271	0326	0390	0462	0544	0635	0738	0851	0977
9	0052	0065	0082	0102	0126	0154	0187	0225	0270	0321
10	0009	0012	0015	0020	0025	0032	0040	0051	0063	0078
11	0001	0001	0002	0003	0003	0005	0006	0008	0010	0013
12							0001	0001	0001	0001

P	41	42	43	44	45	46	47	48	49	50
r										
1	9990	9992	9993	9995	9996	9997	9997	9998	9998	9999
2	9895	9912	9928	9940	9951	9960	9967	9974	9979	9983
3	9499	9569	9630	9684	9731	9772	9808	9838	9865	9888
4	8492	8656	8807	8945	9071	9185	9288	9381	9464	9539
5	6742	7003	7254	7493	7721	7935	8137	8326	8502	8666
6	4552	4849	5146	5441	5732	6019	6299	6573	6838	7095
7	2524	2770	3025	3290	3563	3842	4127	4415	4707	5000
8	1114	1264	1426	1600	1788	1988	2200	2424	2659	2905
9	0379	0446	0520	0605	0698	0803	0918	1045	1183	1334
10	0096	0117	0141	0170	0203	0242	0287	0338	0396	0461
11	0017	0021	0027	0033	0041	0051	0063	0077	0093	0112
12	0002	0002	0003	0004	0005	0007	0009	0011	0014	0017
13							0001	0001	0001	0001

$$n = 14$$

P	01	02	03	04	05	06	07	08	09	10
r										
1	1313	2464	3472	4353	5123	5795	6380	6888	7330	7712
2	0084	0310	0645	1059	1530	2037	2564	3100	3632	4154
3	0003	0025	0077	0167	0301	0478	0698	0958	1255	1584
4		0001	0006	0019	0042	0080	0136	0214	0315	0441
5				0002	0004	0010	0020	0035	0059	0092
6						0001	0002	0004	0008	0015
7									0001	0002

P	11	12	13	14	15	16	17	18	19	20
r										
1	8044	8330	8577	8789	8972	9129	9264	9379	9477	9560
2	4658	5141	5599	6031	6433	6807	7152	7469	7758	8021
3	1939	2315	2708	3111	3521	3932	4341	4744	5138	5519
4	0594	0774	0979	1210	1465	1742	2038	2351	2679	3018
5	0137	0196	0269	0359	0467	0594	0741	0907	1093	1298
6	0024	0038	0057	0082	0115	0157	0209	0273	0349	0439
7	0003	0006	0009	0015	0022	0032	0046	0064	0087	0116
8		0001	0001	0002	0003	0005	0008	0012	0017	0024
9						0001	0001	0002	0003	0004

TABLE C—Continued

p	21	22	23	24	25	26	27	28	29	30
r										
1	9631	9691	9742	9786	9822	9852	9878	9899	9917	9932
2	8259	8473	8665	8837	8990	9126	9246	9352	9444	9525
3	5887	6239	6574	6891	7189	7467	7727	7967	8188	8392
4	3366	3719	4076	4432	4787	5136	5479	5813	6137	6448
5	1523	1765	2023	2297	2585	2884	3193	3509	3832	4158
6	0543	0662	0797	0949	1117	1301	1502	1718	1949	2195
7	0152	0196	0248	0310	0383	0467	0563	0673	0796	0933
8	0033	0045	0060	0079	0103	0132	0167	0208	0257	0315
9	0006	0008	0011	0016	0022	0029	0038	0050	0065	0083
10	0001	0001	0002	0002	0003	0005	0007	0009	0012	0017
11						0001	0001	0001	0002	0002

p	31	32	33	34	35	36	37	38	39	40
r										
1	9945	9955	9963	9970	9976	9981	9984	9988	9990	9992
2	9596	9657	9710	9756	9795	9828	9857	9881	9902	9919
3	8577	8746	8899	9037	9161	9271	9370	9457	9534	9602
4	6747	7032	7301	7556	7795	8018	8226	8418	8595	8757
5	4486	4813	5138	5458	5773	6080	6378	6666	6943	7207
6	2454	2724	3006	3297	3595	3899	4208	4519	4831	5141
7	1084	1250	1431	1626	1836	2059	2296	2545	2805	3075
8	0381	0458	0545	0643	0753	0876	1012	1162	1325	1501
9	0105	0131	0163	0200	0243	0294	0353	0420	0497	0583
10	0022	0029	0037	0048	0060	0076	0095	0117	0144	0175
11	0003	0005	0006	0008	0011	0014	0019	0024	0031	0039
12		0001	0001	0001	0001	0002	0003	0003	0005	0006
13										0001

p	41	42	43	44	45	46	47	48	49	50
r										
1	9994	9995	9996	9997	9998	9998	9999	9999	9999	9999
2	9934	9946	9956	9964	9971	9977	9981	9985	9988	9991
3	9661	9713	9758	9797	9830	9858	9883	9903	9921	9935
4	8905	9039	9161	9270	9368	9455	9532	9601	9661	9713
5	7459	7697	7922	8132	8328	8510	8678	8833	8974	9102
6	5450	5754	6052	6344	6627	6900	7163	7415	7654	7880
7	3355	3643	3937	4236	4539	4843	5148	5451	5751	6047
8	1692	1896	2113	2344	2586	2840	3105	3380	3663	3953
9	0680	0789	0910	1043	1189	1348	1520	1707	1906	2120
10	0212	0255	0304	0361	0426	0500	0583	0677	0782	0898
11	0049	0061	0076	0093	0114	0139	0168	0202	0241	0287
12	0008	0010	0013	0017	0022	0027	0034	0042	0053	0065
13	0001	0001	0001	0002	0003	0003	0004	0006	0007	0009
14										0001

n = 15

p	01	02	03	04	05	06	07	08	09	10
r										
1	1399	2614	3667	4579	5367	6047	6633	7137	7570	7941
2	0096	0353	0730	1191	1710	2262	2832	3403	3965	4510
3	0004	0030	0094	0203	0362	0571	0829	1130	1469	1841
4		0002	0008	0024	0055	0104	0175	0273	0399	0556
5			0001	0002	0006	0014	0028	0050	0082	0127
6					0001	0001	0003	0007	0013	0022
7								0001	0002	0003

p	11	12	13	14	15	16	17	18	19	20
r										
1	8259	8530	8762	8959	9126	9269	9389	9490	9576	9648
2	5031	5524	5987	6417	6814	7179	7511	7813	8085	8329
3	2238	2654	3084	3520	3958	4392	4819	5234	5635	6020
4	0742	0959	1204	1476	1773	2092	2429	2782	3146	3518
5	0187	0265	0361	0478	0617	0778	0961	1167	1394	1642
6	0037	0057	0084	0121	0168	0227	0300	0387	0490	0611
7	0006	0010	0015	0024	0036	0052	0074	0102	0137	0181
8	0001	0001	0002	0004	0006	0010	0014	0021	0030	0042
9					0001	0001	0002	0003	0005	0008
10									0001	0001

TABLE C—Continued

P r	21	22	23	24	25	26	27	28	29	30
1	9709	9759	9802	9837	9866	9891	9911	9928	9941	9953
2	8547	8741	8913	9065	9198	9315	9417	9505	9581	9647
3	6385	6731	7055	7358	7639	7899	8137	8355	8553	8732
4	3895	4274	4650	5022	5387	5742	6086	6416	6732	7031
5	1910	2195	2495	2810	3135	3469	3810	4154	4500	4845
6	0748	0905	1079	1272	1484	1713	1958	2220	2495	2784
7	0234	0298	0374	0463	0566	0684	0817	0965	1130	1311
8	0058	0078	0104	0135	0173	0219	0274	0338	0413	0500
9	0011	0016	0023	0031	0042	0056	0073	0094	0121	0152
10	0002	0003	0004	0006	0008	0011	0015	0021	0028	0037
11			0001	0001	0001	0002	0002	0003	0005	0007
12									0001	0001

P r	31	32	33	34	35	36	37	38	39	40
1	9962	9969	9975	9980	9984	9988	9990	9992	9994	9995
2	9704	9752	9794	9829	9858	9883	9904	9922	9936	9948
3	8893	9038	9167	9281	9383	9472	9550	9618	9678	9729
4	7314	7580	7829	8060	8273	8469	8649	8813	8961	9095
5	5187	5523	5852	6171	6481	6778	7062	7332	7587	7827
6	3084	3393	3709	4032	4357	4684	5011	5335	5654	5968
7	1509	1722	1951	2194	2452	2722	3003	3295	3595	3902
8	0599	0711	0837	0977	1132	1302	1487	1687	1902	2131
9	0190	0236	0289	0351	0422	0504	0597	0702	0820	0950
10	0048	0062	0079	0099	0124	0154	0190	0232	0281	0338
11	0009	0012	0016	0022	0028	0037	0047	0059	0075	0093
12	0001	0002	0003	0004	0005	0006	0009	0011	0015	0019
13					0001	0001	0001	0002	0002	0003

P r	41	42	43	44	45	46	47	48	49	50
1	9996	9997	9998	9998	9999	9999	9999	9999	10000	10000
2	9958	9966	9973	9979	9983	9987	9990	9992	9994	9995
3	9773	9811	9843	9870	9893	9913	9929	9943	9954	9963
4	9215	9322	9417	9502	9576	9641	9697	9746	9788	9824
5	8052	8261	8454	8633	8796	8945	9080	9201	9310	9408
6	6274	6570	6856	7131	7392	7641	7875	8095	8301	8491
7	4214	4530	4847	5164	5478	5789	6095	6394	6684	6964
8	2374	2630	2898	3176	3465	3762	4065	4374	4686	5000
9	1095	1254	1427	1615	1818	2034	2265	2510	2767	3036
10	0404	0479	0565	0661	0769	0890	1024	1171	1333	1509
11	0116	0143	0174	0211	0255	0305	0363	0430	0506	0592
12	0025	0032	0040	0051	0063	0079	0097	0119	0145	0176
13	0004	0005	0007	0009	0011	0014	0018	0023	0029	0037
14			0001	0001	0001	0002	0002	0003	0004	0005

$n = 16$

P r	01	02	03	04	05	06	07	08	09	10
1	1485	2762	3857	4796	5599	6284	6869	7366	7789	8147
2	0109	0399	0818	1327	1892	2489	3098	3701	4289	4853
3	0005	0037	0113	0242	0429	0673	0969	1311	1694	2108
4		0002	0011	0032	0070	0132	0221	0342	0496	0684
5			0001	0003	0009	0019	0038	0068	0111	0170
6					0001	0002	0005	0010	0019	0033
7							0001	0001	0003	0005
8										0001

P r	11	12	13	14	15	16	17	18	19	20
1	8450	8707	8923	9105	9257	9386	9493	9582	9657	9719
2	5386	5885	6347	6773	7161	7513	7830	8115	8368	8593
3	2545	2999	3461	3926	4386	4838	5277	5698	6101	6482
4	0907	1162	1448	1763	2101	2460	2836	3223	3619	4019
5	0248	0348	0471	0618	0791	0988	1211	1458	1727	2018
6	0053	0082	0120	0171	0235	0315	0412	0527	0662	0817
7	0009	0015	0024	0038	0056	0080	0112	0153	0204	0267
8	0001	0002	0004	0007	0011	0016	0024	0036	0051	0070
9			0001	0001	0002	0003	0004	0007	0010	0015
10							0001	0001	0002	0002

TABLE C—Continued

P	21	22	23	24	25	26	27	28	29	30
r										
1	9770	9812	9847	9876	9900	9919	9935	9948	9958	9967
2	8791	8965	9117	9250	9365	9465	9550	9623	9686	9739
3	6839	7173	7483	7768	8029	8267	8482	8677	8851	9006
4	4418	4814	5203	5583	5950	6303	6640	6959	7260	7541
5	2327	2652	2991	3341	3698	4060	4425	4788	5147	5501
6	0992	1188	1405	1641	1897	2169	2458	2761	3077	3402
7	0342	0432	0536	0657	0796	0951	1125	1317	1526	1753
8	0095	0127	0166	0214	0271	0340	0420	0514	0621	0744
9	0021	0030	0041	0056	0075	0098	0127	0163	0206	0257
10	0004	0006	0008	0012	0016	0023	0031	0041	0055	0071
11	0001	0001	0001	0002	0003	0004	0006	0008	0011	0016
12						0001	0001	0001	0002	0003

P	31	32	33	34	35	36	37	38	39	40
r										
1	9974	9979	9984	9987	9990	9992	9994	9995	9996	9997
2	9784	9822	9854	9880	9902	9921	9936	9948	9959	9967
3	9144	9266	9374	9467	9549	9620	9681	9734	9778	9817
4	7804	8047	8270	8475	8661	8830	8983	9119	9241	9349
5	5846	6181	6504	6813	7108	7387	7649	7895	8123	8334
6	3736	4074	4416	4759	5100	5438	5770	6094	6408	6712
7	1997	2257	2531	2819	3119	3428	3746	4070	4398	4728
8	0881	1035	1205	1391	1594	1813	2048	2298	2562	2839
9	0317	0388	0470	0564	0671	0791	0926	1076	1242	1423
10	0092	0117	0148	0185	0229	0289	0341	0411	0491	0583
11	0021	0028	0037	0048	0062	0079	0100	0125	0155	0191
12	0004	0005	0007	0010	0013	0017	0023	0030	0038	0049
13		0001	0001	0001	0002	0003	0004	0005	0007	0009
14								0001	0001	0001

P	41	42	43	44	45	46	47	48	49	50
r										
1	9998	9998	9999	9999	9999	9999	10000	10000	10000	10000
2	9974	9979	9984	9987	9990	9992	9994	9995	9997	9997
3	9849	9876	9899	9918	9934	9947	9958	9966	9973	9979
4	9444	9527	9600	9664	9719	9766	9806	9840	9869	9894
5	8529	8707	8869	9015	9147	9265	9370	9463	9544	9616
6	7003	7280	7543	7792	8024	8241	8441	8626	8795	8949
7	5058	5387	5711	6029	6340	6641	6932	7210	7476	7728
8	3128	3428	3736	4051	4371	4694	5019	5343	5665	5982
9	1619	1832	2060	2302	2559	2829	3111	3405	3707	4018
10	0687	0805	0936	1081	1241	1416	1607	1814	2036	2272
11	0234	0284	0342	0409	0486	0574	0674	0786	0911	1051
12	0062	0078	0098	0121	0149	0183	0222	0268	0322	0384
13	0012	0016	0021	0027	0035	0044	0055	0069	0086	0106
14	0002	0002	0003	0004	0006	0007	0010	0013	0016	0021
15					0001	0001	0001	0001	0002	0003

$$n = 17$$

P	01	02	03	04	05	06	07	08	09	10
r										
1	1571	2907	4042	5004	5819	6507	7088	7577	7988	8332
2	0123	0446	0909	1465	2078	2717	3362	3995	4604	5182
3	0006	0044	0134	0286	0503	0782	1118	1503	1927	2382
4		0003	0014	0040	0088	0164	0273	0419	0603	0826
5			0001	0004	0012	0026	0051	0089	0145	0221
6					0001	0003	0007	0015	0027	0047
7						0001	0002	0004	0008	
8										0001

P	11	12	13	14	15	16	17	18	19	20
r										
1	8621	8862	9063	9230	9369	9484	9579	9657	9722	9775
2	5723	6223	6682	7099	7475	7813	8113	8379	8613	8818
3	2858	3345	3836	4324	4802	5266	5711	6133	6532	6904
4	1087	1383	1710	2065	2444	2841	3251	3669	4091	4511
5	0321	0446	0598	0778	0987	1224	1487	1775	2087	2418
6	0075	0114	0166	0234	0319	0423	0548	0695	0864	1057
7	0014	0023	0037	0056	0083	0118	0163	0220	0291	0377
8	0002	0004	0007	0011	0017	0027	0039	0057	0080	0109
9		0001	0001	0002	0003	0005	0008	0012	0018	0026
10						0001	0001	0002	0003	0005
11										0001

TABLE C—Continued

P \ r	21	22	23	24	25	26	27	28	29	30
1	9818	9854	9882	9906	9925	9940	9953	9962	9970	9977
2	8996	9152	9285	9400	9499	9583	9654	9714	9765	9807
3	7249	7567	7859	8123	8363	8578	8771	8942	9093	9226
4	4927	5333	5728	6107	6470	6814	7137	7440	7721	7981
5	2766	3128	3500	3879	4261	4643	5023	5396	5760	6113
6	1273	1510	1770	2049	2347	2661	2989	3329	3677	4032
7	0479	0598	0736	0894	1071	1268	1485	1721	1976	2248
8	0147	0194	0251	0320	0402	0499	0611	0739	0884	1046
9	0037	0051	0070	0094	0124	0161	0206	0261	0326	0403
10	0007	0011	0016	0022	0031	0042	0057	0075	0098	0127
11	0001	0002	0003	0004	0006	0009	0013	0018	0024	0032
12				0001	0001	0002	0002	0003	0005	0007
13									0001	0001

P \ r	31	32	33	34	35	36	37	38	39	40
1	9982	9986	9989	9991	9993	9995	9996	9997	9998	9998
2	9843	9872	9896	9917	9933	9946	9957	9966	9973	9979
3	9343	9444	9532	9608	9673	9728	9775	9815	9849	9877
4	8219	8437	8634	8812	8972	9115	9241	9353	9450	9536
5	6453	6778	7087	7378	7652	7906	8142	8360	8559	8740
6	4390	4749	5105	5458	5803	6139	6465	6778	7077	7361
7	2536	2838	3153	3479	3812	4152	4495	4839	5182	5522
8	1287	1426	1642	1877	2128	2395	2676	2971	3278	3595
9	0498	0595	0712	0845	0994	1159	1341	1541	1757	1989
10	0162	0204	0254	0314	0383	0464	0557	0664	0784	0919
11	0043	0057	0074	0095	0120	0151	0189	0234	0286	0348
12	0009	0013	0017	0023	0030	0040	0051	0066	0084	0106
13	0002	0002	0003	0004	0006	0008	0011	0015	0019	0025
14				0001	0001	0001	0002	0002	0003	0005
15										0001

P \ r	41	42	43	44	45	46	47	48	49	50
1	9999	9999	9999	9999	10000	10000	10000	10000	10000	10000
2	9984	9987	9990	9992	9994	9996	9997	9998	9998	9999
3	9900	9920	9935	9948	9959	9968	9975	9980	9985	9988
4	9610	9674	9729	9776	9816	9849	9877	9901	9920	9936
5	8904	9051	9183	9301	9404	9495	9575	9644	9704	9755
6	7628	7879	8113	8330	8529	8712	8878	9028	9162	9283
7	5856	6182	6499	6805	7098	7377	7641	7890	8122	8338
8	3920	4250	4585	4921	5257	5590	5918	6239	6552	6855
9	2238	2502	2780	3072	3374	3687	4008	4335	4667	5000
10	1070	1236	1419	1618	1834	2066	2314	2577	2855	3145
11	0480	0503	0597	0705	0826	0962	1112	1279	1462	1662
12	0133	0165	0203	0248	0301	0363	0434	0517	0611	0717
13	0033	0042	0054	0069	0086	0108	0134	0165	0202	0245
14	0006	0008	0011	0014	0019	0024	0031	0040	0050	0064
15	0001	0001	0002	0002	0003	0004	0005	0007	0009	0012
16							0001	0001	0001	0001

$n = 18$

P \ r	01	02	03	04	05	06	07	08	09	10
1	1655	3049	4220	5204	6028	6717	7292	7771	8169	8499
2	0138	0495	1003	1607	2265	2945	3622	4281	4909	5497
3	0007	0052	0157	0333	0581	0898	1275	1702	2168	2662
4		0004	0018	0050	0109	0201	0333	0506	0723	0982
5			0002	0006	0015	0034	0067	0116	0186	0282
6				0001	0002	0005	0010	0021	0038	0064
7							0001	0003	0006	0012
8									0001	0002

P \ r	11	12	13	14	15	16	17	18	19	20
1	8773	8998	9185	9338	9464	9566	9651	9719	9775	9820
2	6042	6540	6992	7398	7759	8080	8362	8609	8824	9009
3	3173	3690	4206	4713	5203	5673	6119	6538	6927	7287
4	1282	1618	1986	2382	2798	3229	3669	4112	4554	4990
5	0405	0558	0743	0959	1206	1482	1787	2116	2467	2836

TABLE C—Continued

r	11	12	13	14	15	16	17	18	19	20
6	0102	0154	0222	0310	0419	0551	0708	0889	1097	1329
7	0021	0034	0054	0081	0118	0167	0229	0306	0400	0513
8	0003	0006	0011	0017	0027	0041	0060	0086	0120	0163
9		0001	0002	0003	0005	0008	0013	0020	0029	0043
10					0001	0001	0002	0004	0006	0009
11								0001	0001	0002

r	21	22	23	24	25	26	27	28	29	30
1	9856	9886	9909	9928	9944	9956	9965	9973	9979	9984
2	9169	9306	9423	9522	9605	9676	9735	9784	9824	9858
3	7616	7916	8187	8430	8647	8839	9009	9158	9288	9400
4	5414	5825	6218	6591	6943	7272	7578	7860	8119	8354
5	3220	3613	4012	4414	4813	5208	5594	5968	6329	6673
6	1586	1866	2168	2488	2825	3176	3538	3907	4281	4656
7	0645	0799	0974	1171	1390	1630	1891	2171	2469	2783
8	0217	0283	0363	0458	0569	0699	0847	1014	1200	1407
9	0060	0083	0112	0148	0193	0249	0316	0395	0488	0596
10	0014	0020	0028	0039	0054	0073	0097	0127	0164	0210
11	0003	0004	0006	0009	0012	0018	0025	0034	0046	0061
12		0001	0001	0002	0002	0003	0005	0007	0010	0014
13						0001	0001	0001	0002	0003

r	31	32	33	34	35	36	37	38	39	40
1	9987	9990	9993	9994	9996	9997	9998	9998	9999	9999
2	9886	9908	9927	9942	9954	9964	9972	9978	9983	9987
3	9498	9581	9652	9713	9764	9807	9843	9873	9897	9918
4	8568	8759	8931	9083	9217	9335	9439	9528	9606	9672
5	7001	7309	7598	7866	8114	8341	8549	8737	8907	9058
6	5029	5398	5759	6111	6450	6776	7086	7379	7655	7912
7	3111	3450	3797	4151	4509	4867	5224	5576	5921	6257
8	1633	1878	2141	2421	2717	3027	3349	3681	4021	4366
9	0720	0861	1019	1196	1391	1604	1835	2084	2350	2632
10	0264	0329	0405	0494	0597	0714	0847	0997	1163	1347
11	0080	0104	0133	0169	0212	0264	0325	0397	0480	0576
12	0020	0027	0036	0047	0062	0080	0102	0130	0163	0203
13	0004	0005	0008	0011	0014	0019	0026	0034	0044	0058
14	0001	0001	0001	0002	0003	0004	0005	0007	0010	0013
15						0001	0001	0001	0002	0002

r	41	42	43	44	45	46	47	48	49	50
1	9999	9999	10000	10000	10000	10000	10000	10000	10000	10000
2	9990	9992	9994	9996	9997	9998	9998	9999	9999	9999
3	9934	9948	9959	9968	9975	9981	9985	9989	9991	9993
4	9729	9777	9818	9852	9880	9904	9923	9939	9952	9962
5	9193	9313	9418	9510	9589	9658	9717	9767	9810	9846
6	8151	8372	8573	8757	8923	9072	9205	9324	9428	9519
7	6582	6895	7193	7476	7742	7991	8222	8436	8632	8811
8	4713	5062	5408	5750	6085	6412	6728	7032	7322	7597
9	2928	3236	3556	3885	4222	4562	4906	5249	5591	5927
10	1549	1768	2004	2258	2527	2812	3110	3421	3742	4073
11	0686	0811	0951	1107	1280	1470	1677	1902	2144	2403
12	0250	0307	0372	0449	0537	0658	0753	0883	1028	1189
13	0074	0094	0118	0147	0183	0225	0275	0334	0402	0461
14	0017	0022	0029	0038	0049	0063	0079	0100	0125	0154
15	0003	0004	0006	0007	0010	0013	0017	0023	0029	0038
16		0001	0001	0001	0001	0002	0003	0004	0005	0007
17									0001	0001

n = 19

r	01	02	03	04	05	06	07	08	09	10
1	1738	3188	4394	5396	6226	6914	7481	7949	8334	8649
2	0153	0546	1100	1751	2453	3171	3879	4560	5202	5797
3	0009	0061	0183	0384	0665	1021	1439	1908	2415	2946
4		0005	0022	0061	0132	0243	0398	0602	0953	1150
5			0002	0007	0020	0044	0085	0147	0235	0352
6				0001	0002	0006	0014	0029	0051	0086
7						0001	0002	0004	0009	0017
8								0001	0001	0003

TABLE C—Continued

p / r	11	12	13	14	15	16	17	18	19	20
1	8908	9119	9291	9431	9544	9636	9710	9770	9818	9856
2	6342	6835	7277	7669	8015	8318	8581	8809	9004	9171
3	3488	4032	4568	5089	5587	6059	6500	6910	7287	7631
4	1490	1867	2275	2708	3159	3620	4085	4549	5005	5449
5	0502	0685	0904	1158	1444	1762	2107	2476	2864	3267
6	0135	0202	0290	0401	0537	0700	0891	1110	1357	1631
7	0030	0048	0076	0113	0163	0228	0310	0411	0532	0676
8	0005	0009	0016	0026	0041	0061	0089	0126	0173	0233
9	0001	0002	0003	0005	0008	0014	0021	0032	0047	0067
10				0001	0001	0002	0004	0007	0010	0016
11							0001	0001	0002	0003

p / r	21	22	23	24	25	26	27	28	29	30
1	9887	9911	9930	9946	9958	9967	9975	9981	9985	9989
2	9313	9434	9535	9619	9690	9749	9797	9837	9869	9896
3	7942	8222	8471	8692	8887	9057	9205	9333	9443	9538
4	5877	6285	6671	7032	7369	7680	7965	8224	8458	8668
5	3681	4100	4520	4936	5346	5744	6129	6498	6848	7178
6	1929	2251	2592	2950	3322	3705	4093	4484	4875	5261
7	0843	1034	1248	1487	1749	2032	2336	2657	2995	3345
8	0307	0396	0503	0629	0775	0941	1129	1338	1568	1820
9	0093	0127	0169	0222	0287	0366	0459	0568	0694	0839
10	0023	0034	0047	0066	0089	0119	0156	0202	0258	0326
11	0005	0007	0011	0016	0023	0032	0044	0060	0080	0105
12	0001	0001	0002	0003	0005	0007	0010	0015	0021	0028
13				0001	0001	0001	0002	0003	0004	0006
14									0001	0001

p / r	31	32	33	34	35	36	37	38	39	40
1	9991	9993	9995	9996	9997	9998	9998	9999	9999	9999
2	9917	9935	9949	9960	9969	9976	9981	9986	9989	9992
3	9618	9686	9743	9791	9830	9863	9890	9913	9931	9945
4	8856	9028	9169	9297	9409	9505	9588	9659	9719	9770
5	7486	7773	8037	8280	8500	8699	8878	9038	9179	9304
6	5641	6010	6366	6707	7032	7339	7627	7895	8143	8371
7	3705	4073	4445	4818	5188	5554	5913	6261	6597	6919
8	2091	2381	2688	3010	3344	3690	4043	4401	4762	5122
9	1003	1186	1389	1612	1855	2116	2395	2691	3002	3325
10	0405	0499	0608	0733	0875	1035	1213	1410	1626	1861
11	0137	0176	0223	0280	0347	0426	0518	0625	0747	0885
12	0038	0051	0068	0089	0114	0146	0185	0231	0287	0352
13	0009	0012	0017	0023	0031	0041	0054	0070	0091	0116
14	0002	0002	0003	0005	0007	0009	0013	0017	0023	0031
15			0001	0001	0001	0002	0002	0003	0005	0006
16									0001	0001

p / r	41	42	43	44	45	46	47	48	49	50
1	10000	10000	10000	10000	10000	10000	10000	10000	10000	10000
2	9994	9995	9996	9997	9998	9999	9999	9999	10000	10000
3	9957	9967	9974	9980	9985	9988	9991	9993	9995	9996
4	9813	9849	9878	9903	9923	9939	9952	9963	9971	9978
5	9413	9508	9590	9660	9720	9771	9814	9850	9879	9904
6	8579	8767	8937	9088	9223	9342	9446	9537	9615	9682
7	7226	7515	7787	8039	8273	8488	8684	8862	9022	9165
8	5480	5832	6176	6509	6831	7138	7430	7706	7964	8204
9	3660	4003	4353	4706	5060	5413	5762	6105	6439	6762
10	2114	2385	2672	2974	3290	3617	3954	4299	4648	5000
11	1040	1213	1404	1613	1841	2087	2351	2631	2928	3238
12	0429	0518	0621	0738	0871	1021	1187	1372	1575	1796
13	0146	0183	0227	0280	0342	0415	0500	0597	0709	0835
14	0040	0052	0067	0086	0109	0137	0171	0212	0261	0318
15	0009	0012	0016	0021	0028	0036	0046	0060	0076	0096
16	0001	0002	0003	0004	0005	0007	0010	0013	0017	0022
17				0001	0001	0001	0001	0002	0003	0004

TABLE C—Continued
n = 20

P\r	01	02	03	04	05	06	07	08	09	10
1	1821	3324	4562	5580	6415	7099	7658	8113	8484	8784
2	0169	0599	1198	1897	2642	3395	4131	4831	5484	6083
3	0010	0071	0210	0439	0755	1150	1610	2121	2666	3231
4		0006	0027	0074	0159	0290	0471	0706	0993	1330
5			0003	0010	0026	0056	0107	0183	0290	0432
6				0001	0003	0009	0019	0038	0068	0113
7						0001	0003	0006	0013	0024
8								0001	0002	0004
9										0001

P\r	11	12	13	14	15	16	17	18	19	20
1	9028	9224	9383	9510	9612	9694	9759	9811	9852	9885
2	6624	7109	7539	7916	8244	8529	8773	8982	9159	9308
3	3802	4369	4920	5450	5951	6420	6854	7252	7614	7939
4	1710	2127	2573	3041	3523	4010	4496	4974	5439	5886
5	0610	0827	1083	1375	1702	2059	2443	2849	3271	3704
6	0175	0260	0370	0507	0673	0870	1098	1356	1643	1958
7	0041	0067	0103	0153	0219	0304	0409	0537	0689	0867
8	0008	0014	0024	0038	0059	0088	0127	0177	0241	0321
9	0001	0002	0005	0008	0013	0021	0033	0049	0071	0100
10			0001	0001	0002	0004	0007	0011	0017	0026
11						0001	0001	0002	0004	0006
12									0001	0001

P\r	21	22	23	24	25	26	27	28	29	30
1	9910	9931	9946	9959	9968	9976	9982	9986	9989	9992
2	9434	9539	9626	9698	9757	9805	9845	9877	9903	9924
3	8230	8488	8716	8915	9087	9237	9365	9474	9567	9645
4	6310	6711	7085	7431	7748	8038	8300	8534	8744	8929
5	4142	4580	5014	5439	5852	6248	6625	6981	7315	7625
6	2297	2657	3035	3427	3828	4235	4643	5048	5447	5836
7	1071	1301	1557	1838	2142	2467	2810	3169	3540	3920
8	0419	0536	0675	0835	1018	1225	1455	1707	1982	2277
9	0138	0186	0246	0320	0409	0515	0640	0784	0948	1133
10	0038	0054	0075	0103	0139	0183	0238	0305	0385	0480
11	0009	0013	0019	0028	0039	0055	0074	0100	0132	0171
12	0002	0003	0004	0006	0009	0014	0019	0027	0038	0051
13			0001	0001	0002	0003	0004	0006	0009	0013
14							0001	0001	0002	0003

P\r	31	32	33	34	35	36	37	38	39	40
1	9994	9996	9997	9998	9998	9999	9999	9999	9999	10000
2	9940	9953	9964	9972	9979	9984	9988	9991	9993	9995
3	9711	9765	9811	9848	9879	9904	9924	9940	9953	9964
4	9092	9235	9358	9465	9556	9634	9700	9755	9802	9840
5	7911	8173	8411	8626	8818	8989	9141	9274	9390	9490
6	6213	6574	6917	7242	7546	7829	8090	8329	8547	8744
7	4305	4693	5079	5460	5834	6197	6547	6882	7200	7500
8	2591	2922	3268	3624	3990	4361	4735	5108	5478	5841
9	1340	1568	1818	2087	2376	2683	3005	3341	3688	4044
10	0591	0719	0866	1032	1218	1424	1650	1897	2163	2447
11	0220	0275	0350	0434	0532	0645	0775	0923	1090	1275
12	0069	0091	0119	0154	0196	0247	0308	0381	0466	0565
13	0018	0025	0034	0045	0060	0079	0102	0132	0167	0210
14	0004	0006	0008	0011	0015	0021	0028	0037	0049	0065
15	0001	0001	0001	0002	0003	0004	0006	0009	0012	0016
16						0001	0001	0002	0002	0003

P\r	41	42	43	44	45	46	47	48	49	50
1	10000	10000	10000	10000	10000	10000	10000	10000	10000	10000
2	9996	9997	9998	9998	9999	9999	9999	10000	10000	10000
3	9972	9979	9984	9988	9991	9993	9995	9996	9997	9998
4	9872	9898	9920	9937	9951	9962	9971	9977	9983	9987
5	9577	9651	9714	9767	9811	9848	9879	9904	9924	9941

TABLE C—Concluded

P r	41	42	43	44	45	46	47	48	49	50
6	8921	9078	9217	9340	9447	9539	9619	9687	9745	9793
7	7780	8041	8281	8501	8701	8881	9042	9186	9312	9423
8	6196	6539	6868	7183	7480	7759	8020	8261	8482	8684
9	4406	4771	5136	5499	5857	6207	6546	6873	7186	7483
10	2748	3064	3394	3736	4086	4443	4804	5166	5525	5881
11	1480	1705	1949	2212	2493	2791	3104	3432	3771	4119
12	0679	0810	0958	1123	1308	1511	1734	1977	2238	2517
13	0262	0324	0397	0482	0580	0694	0823	0969	1133	1316
14	0084	0107	0136	0172	0214	0265	0326	0397	0480	0577
15	0022	0029	0038	0050	0064	0083	0105	0133	0166	0207
16	0004	0006	0008	0011	0015	0020	0027	0035	0046	0059
17	0001	0001	0001	0002	0003	0004	0005	0007	0010	0013
18						0001	0001	0001	0001	0002

Index

*This book has been set in 11 and 10 point
Baskerville, leaded 2 points. Chapter numbers
are 24 point Helvetica and chapter titles are
16 point Helvetica. The size of the type page
is 27 by 46 picas.*